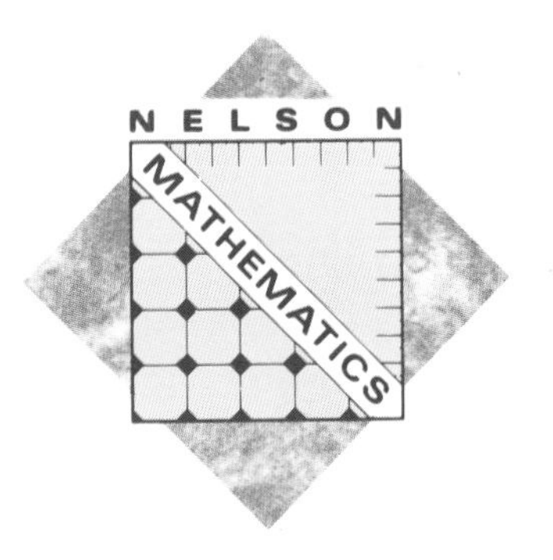

Task MATHS 5

BARBARA BALL & DEREK BALL

Nelson

CONTENTS

14 TABLE GAMES 1

15 COLOURINGS 14

16 EVERY PICTURE TELLS A STORY 25

17 MANAGING THE FUTURE 49

18 EQUABLE SHAPES 63

19 DISSECTING CUBES 80

REVIEW EXERCISES C 93

27 Fractions and decimals 93
28 Probability 95
29 Networks and flow charts 100
30 Combinatorics 103
31 Properties of shapes 107
32 Algebraic manipulation 112
33 Money (2) 115
34 Ratio 116
35 Rate and proportion 118
36 Indices and exponential growth 123
37 Equations (2) 125
38 Polynomial equations 128
39 Rearranging formulae 132
40 Nets and polyhedra 137
41 Pythagoras' theorem and trigonometry in three dimensions 141

20 REPEATING PATTERNS 145

21 HOW DO YOU DECIDE? 160

22 KNOWING WHERE YOU ARE 179

23 WHAT DO YOU BELIEVE? 195

24 TELLING THE COMPUTER WHAT TO DRAW 215

25 GETTING THE MOST OUT OF LIFE 232

REVIEW EXERCISES D 244

42 Everyday graphs 244
43 Graphs of functions 249
44 Bearings and loci 253
45 Statistics (2) 257
46 Properties of circles 261
47 Enlargement and similarity 262
48 Inequalities and linear programming 265
49 Transformations and matrices 268
50 Trigonometry and triangles 272
51 Co-ordinates and vectors 274
52 Algebraic fractions and dimensional analysis 277

INFORMATION 280

1 Units: abbreviations, equivalence 280
2 Triangles, quadrilaterals and the circle 280
3 Three-dimensional shapes 282
4 Approximating 283

A NOTE TO STUDENTS

This book is organised into themes, not into mathematical topics as most mathematics books are. In any one theme you might meet a number of different mathematical topics.

Each of the chapters of this book begins with a task which introduces the theme for that chapter. This is followed by some questions, arranged in sections, which broaden the theme. These questions help you to develop your knowledge, skills and understanding of mathematics, and to use and apply your mathematics to the theme. Sometimes there are information boxes to explain mathematical words, ideas or techniques.

Some of the questions are marked with ▬. These are somewhat harder than the unmarked questions. Some are marked with 〓. These are difficult questions.

At the end of each chapter there are a number of Further Coursework Tasks. Each of these tasks extends the task in some way. You are unlikely to want to tackle more than one of the Further Coursework Tasks in a chapter.

Throughout this book it is assumed that you have a calculator available whenever you need it. On many pages there is also a red picture of a computer. This indicates that a computer, or sometimes a graphical or programmable calculator, would be very useful for working on a particular question or coursework task.

There are two sections of Review Exercises in the book. These exercises contain questions of the type set in GCSE examination papers, and enable you to consolidate particular mathematical topics.

At the end of the book there is an Information section. You might need to refer to this when you are answering some of the questions or when you are tackling some of the Further Coursework Tasks.

14 TABLE GAMES

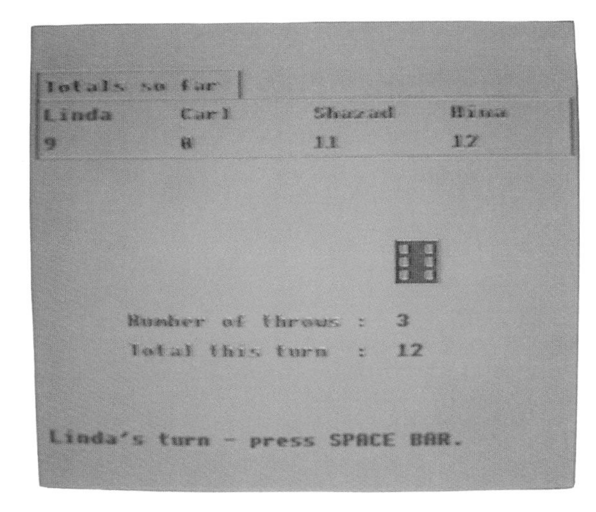

Digame is a dice game for two or more players.
To play Digame you need one die.
Here are the rules.

1 You take turns.

2 When it is your turn, you throw the die as many times as you like.

3 When you decide to stop, the total for your turn is added to your score.

4 If you throw a one before you decide to stop, then your turn is over and you score zero for your turn.

5 The first player to reach 100 is the winner. You do not have to get exactly 100 to win.

- Play Digame.

- Write about the strategy you used when playing. How did you decide when to end each turn? Was your strategy successful?

SECTION A

1 (*a*) What is the worst score you can get during one turn in Digame?

(*b*) What is the second worst score?

(*c*) In how many ways can you score 5 during one turn at Digame?

(*d*) In how many ways can you score 3?

(*e*) Is it possible to win Digame by having just one turn? If so, what is the smallest number of times you would have to throw the die?

2 The following are pieces of advice about playing Digame. Some pieces of advice might be better than others.

Say which pieces of advice are helpful and which are unhelpful. You need only write down letters to show which advice is good or bad.

A Never throw the die more than four times in any turn.

B Always stop after you throw a six, because a one usually follows a six.

C Always stop when you reach 14, because that score is too good to lose.

D If you have thrown two big numbers (above three) stop because the next number is bound to be small and might be one.

E If you are a long way behind be very careful. Never throw the die more than three times in a turn.

F If you are a long way behind take risks. Be rather more daring than you would normally.

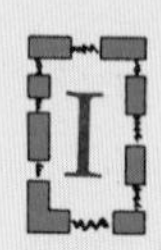

If you throw a die once, what are your chances of throwing a six?

The answer is 1 in 6. Here are some different ways of saying this:

chances are 1 in 6
it will happen 1 out of 6
odds are 5 to 1 against
the probability is $\frac{1}{6}$

Which way of saying it means most to you? In mathematics most people use the last method, and say that the probability of throwing a six is $\frac{1}{6}$.

This means that, on average, a six would be obtained on $\frac{1}{6}$ of the throws.

Probabilities are always numbers between 0 and 1.

A probability of 0 means that something can **never** happen. For example, when throwing a die, the probability of throwing a seven is 0.

A probability of 1 means that something is bound to happen. For example, when throwing a die, the probability of throwing a number less than seven is 1.

3 (*a*) What is the probability of throwing a one?

(*b*) What is the probability of not throwing a one?

(*c*) What is the probability of throwing an even number?

(*d*) What is the probability of throwing a number greater than zero?

(*e*) What is the probability of throwing a number greater than ten?

(*f*) If 60 people are playing Digame how many of them would you expect to throw a one on their first throw?

4 Suppose you throw an unbiased die twice.

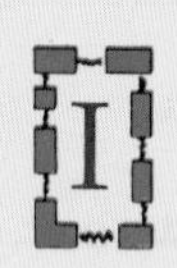

You might throw a three first, followed by a four. This could be written (3,4).

Or you might throw a five first, followed by another five. This could be written (5,5).

Or you might throw a four first, followed by a three. This could be written (4,3).

(*a*) (3,4), (5,5) and (4,3) are three possible outcomes of throwing a die twice. Write down all the possible outcomes.

Include outcomes for which the first number thrown is one.

(*b*) In how many outcomes is a one thrown either the first time or the second time or both?

(*c*) What is the probability of obtaining a one on at least one of the throws?

(*d*) What is the probability of not throwing a one on either of the throws?

(*e*) 72 people are playing Digame. For their first turn they all decide to throw their die exactly twice. Approximately how many of them would you expect to score zero on their first turn?

5 Give a reason for disagreeing with each of the following statements.

(*a*) If 90 people are playing Digame exactly 15 of them will throw a one on their first throw.

(*b*) Always stop after five throws of the die, because the sixth throw is bound to be a one.

(*c*) It is very unlikely that you will throw a die ten times without getting a one. So if you have already thrown it nine times you ought to stop.

(*d*) Never look at your opponent's score when deciding whether to throw the die again.

6 A Digame player is foolish enough to go on throwing the die until a one is thrown.

Do an experiment to find the average score that is likely to be obtained immediately before the one is thrown.

For this experiment you can use a die.

Keep throwing the die until you throw a one.

Add up all the numbers you throw before throwing a one. Do not add the one.

After you have thrown the one, record your total carefully.

Do this as many times as you can.

Try to get some results from other people as well.

Find the average (mean) of all the results you can get.

Use the result of this experiment to provide advice for Digame players.

7 Your score at Digame is 94 and it is your turn. You decide to keep going until either you win or throw a one.

(*a*) How many ways are there of winning after just one throw of the die? What is the probability that you will win after one throw of the die?

(*b*) What is the probability that you will win after two throws of the die?

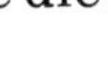

(*c*) What is the probability that you will win after three throws of the die?

(*d*) What is the probability that you will win after four throws of the die?

(*e*) What is the probability that you will not win this turn?

8 A reckless player tries to win Digame in one turn. Estimate the probability of success.

SECTION B

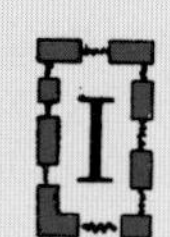

A domino is a rectangle made up of two squares. Each square has a number on it (usually represented by dots).

This is a (3,2) domino.

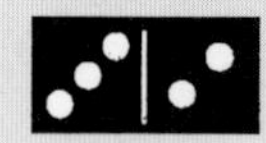

There are ten different dominoes which can be made using the numbers 0, 1, 2 and 3. These are shown below.

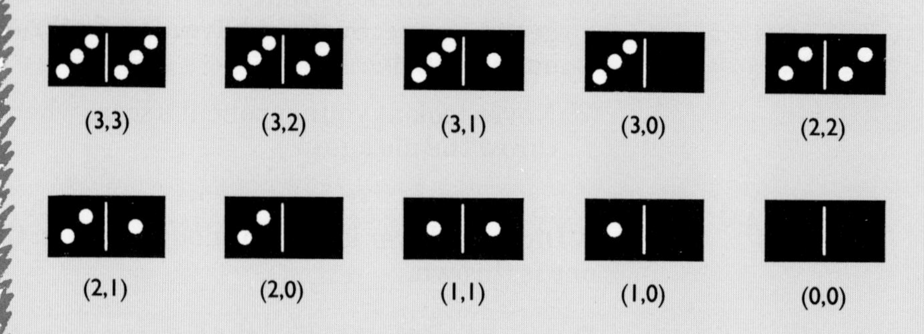

1 (*a*) The standard set of dominoes uses the numbers 0, 1, 2, 3, 4, 5 and 6. List all the dominoes that can be made using these numbers. You can describe the dominoes as (3,2), (5,5) and so on. You need not draw pictures.

(*b*) A domino with the same number in each square is called a **double**.

How many doubles are there in the standard set of dominoes?

(*c*) How many dominoes are there in the standard set with a six on?

(*d*) How many dominoes are there with either a five or a six on or both?

2 A set of dominoes is shuffled and the dominoes are placed face down on a table, so that their numbers cannot be seen. One domino is picked.

(*a*) What is the probability that it is a double?

(*b*) What is the probability that it has a 6 on it?

(*c*) What is the probability that there are 2 spots on it altogether?

(*d*) What is the probability that there are 8 spots on it altogether?

(*e*) What is the probability that there are 13 spots on it altogether?

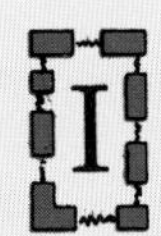

In the domino game of Follow On the dominoes are placed face down on the table. Each player picks up 7 dominoes and looks at them but does not let the other player or players see.

At the start of the game one player chooses a domino to start the chain and places it face upwards on the table. The next player can place a domino next to the first domino. It can be placed at either end of the first domino, as long as it matches.

3 (*a*) Some people say you have to start the game of Follow On with a 'double'. Suppose the first player starts the game with the domino (6,6).

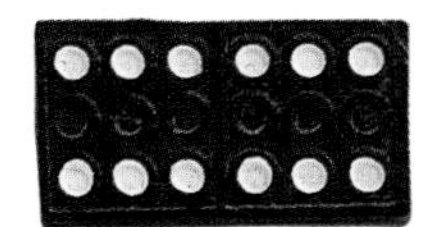

How many different dominoes could the second player use?

(*b*) Some people say you do not have to start Follow On with a double. Suppose the first player starts the game with the domino (5,3).

How many dominoes could the second player use?

(*c*) Suppose the game has reached the stage shown below.

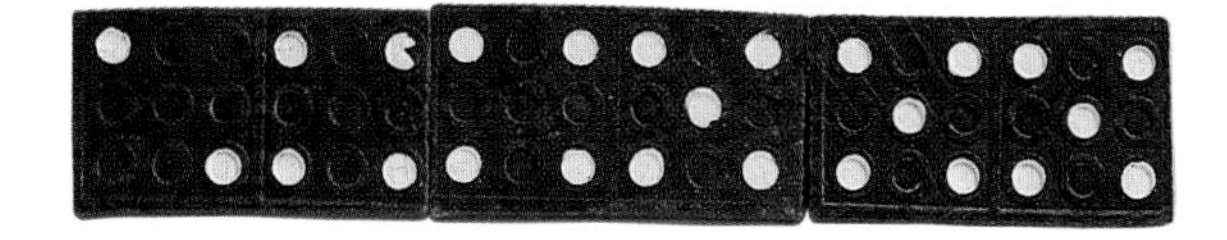

How many different dominoes is it possible to play next?

(*d*) Suppose the game has reached this stage.

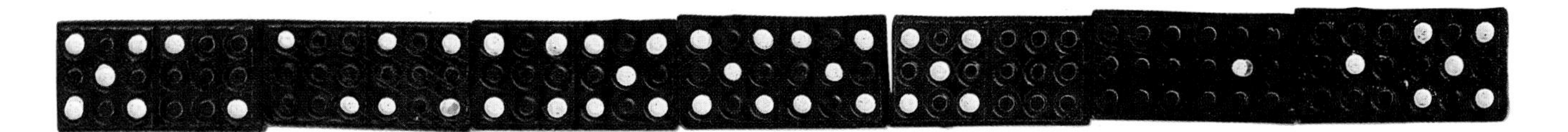

How many different dominoes is it possible to play next?

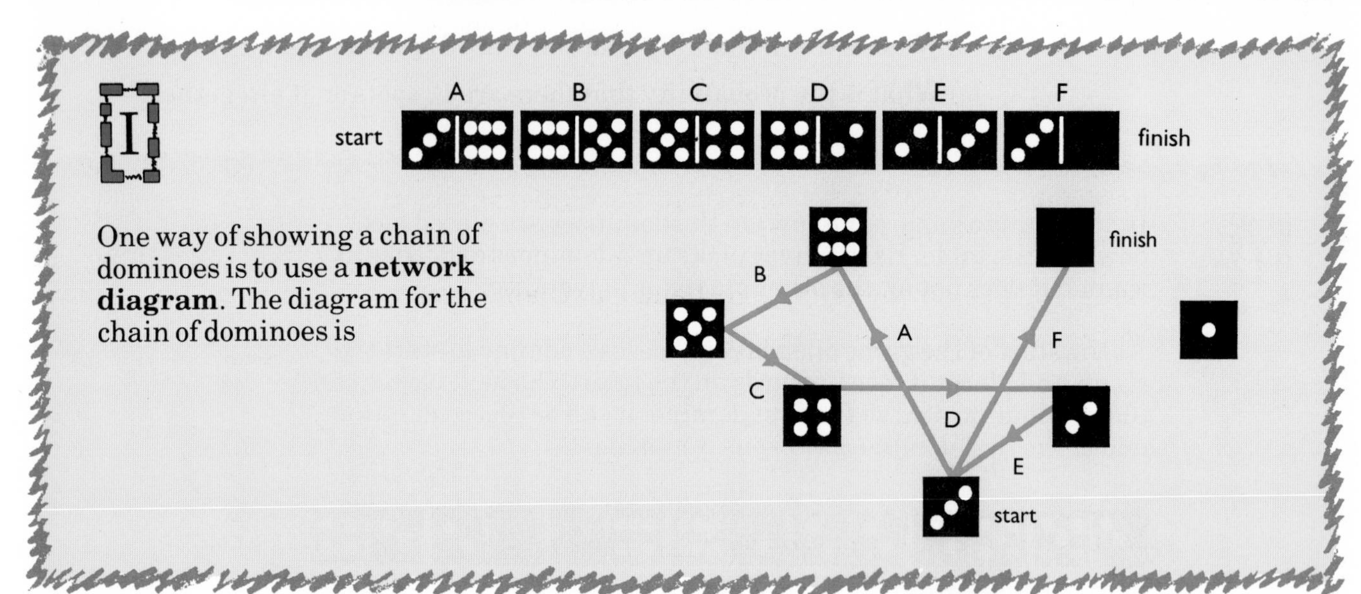

One way of showing a chain of dominoes is to use a **network diagram**. The diagram for the chain of dominoes is

4 (*a*) Draw the network diagram for the chain shown below.

(*b*) Someone decides to use all the dominoes which do **not** have a blank or a six on them.

(i) How many dominoes will be used?
(ii) Draw a network diagram to show how a chain can be formed from all these dominoes.

(*c*) 'Forming a chain from a set of dominoes is like drawing a network diagram without taking your pen off the paper and without drawing any line more than once.'

Explain this statement.

(*d*) Someone decides to use all the dominoes which do **not** have a one, a three or a five on them.

Can a chain be formed using all these dominoes? Explain your answer.

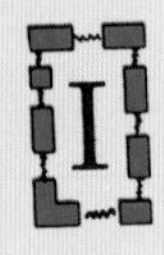

Threes and Fives is another domino game. You play it in exactly the same way that you play Follow On. The only difference is that you have the opportunity to score points every time you play a domino.

On every turn you see whether you score by adding together the numbers at the ends of the chain. If the sum is a multiple of three or a multiple of five you score. If the sum of the numbers at the ends of the chain is **not** a multiple of 3 or 5 you score nothing.

For example, look at the following chain.

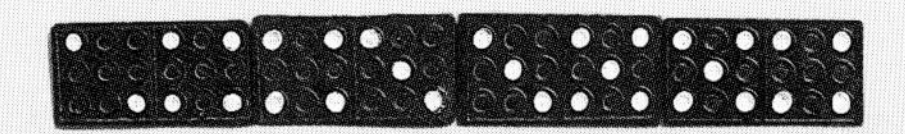

The numbers at the two ends of the chain are two and four. The total is 6. 6 is a multiple of 3. In fact, it is 2×3. So the person who last played a domino would score 2.

The picture below shows another chain. This chain scores 1 because the numbers at the ends add up to 5 (or 1×5).

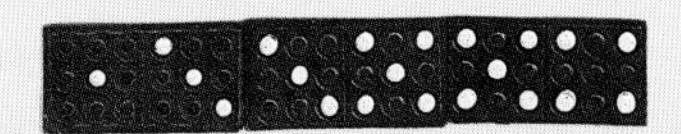

When playing Threes and Fives you always lay down 'doubles' across the chain instead of along it.

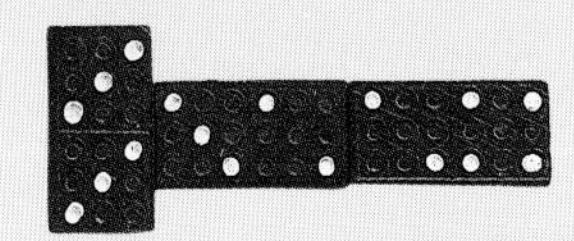

If there is a double at the end of the chain you count both of the numbers on the double when finding the total of the ends. The chain shown above has a total of $3 + 3 + 4 = 10$. So it scores 2.

You start a game of Threes and Fives as follows.

Each player picks up *seven* dominoes and looks at them but does not let the other player see them. The fourteen remaining dominoes are left face down, so that neither player knows what they are.

If you are the first player you start by choosing one of your dominoes to place face upwards on the table. This domino scores if the total number of spots on the domino is a multiple of 3 or 5. The domino does not have to be a double.

If you cannot play any of your dominoes you pick one up from the remaining dominoes.

The game is over either when one player has no dominoes left, or when there are no dominoes left to pick up and neither player can play.

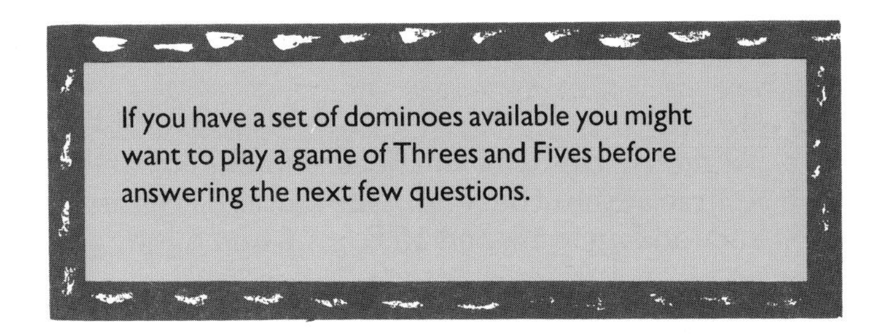

If you have a set of dominoes available you might want to play a game of Threes and Fives before answering the next few questions.

5 How much does each of the following chains score?

(*a*) 

(*b*) 

(*c*) 

(*d*) 

(*e*)

6 How much does each of the following chains score?

(*a*) 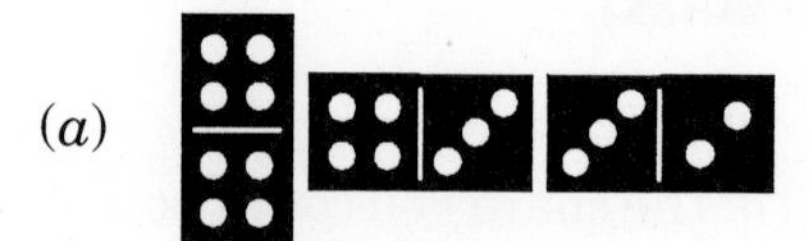

(*b*) 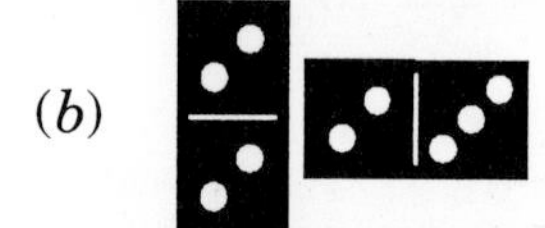

(*c*) 

(*d*) 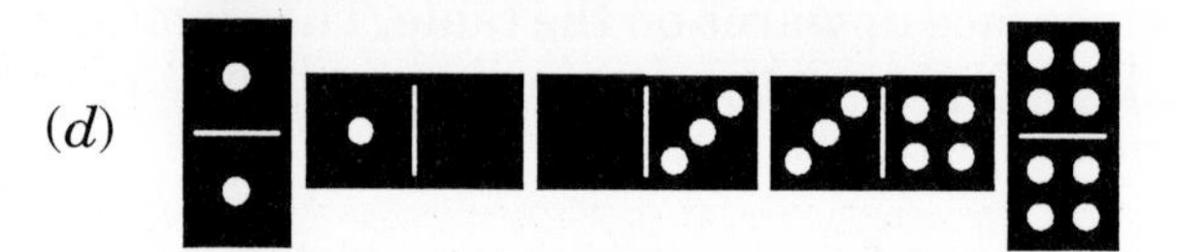

7 One way of scoring 8 is shown below.

To get 8 in this way you need a double-six at one end of the chain and a three at the other end. This scores 8 because the numbers at the ends add up to 15, and 15 is 3×5 *and* 5×3.

Describe a different way of scoring 8.

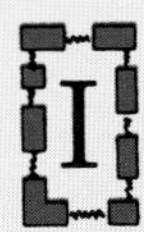

Suppose someone starts a game of Threes and Fives by playing (4,2).

That person would score 2. There are twelve different dominoes the second player could play. Some of these are shown below:

scores 1

scores 2

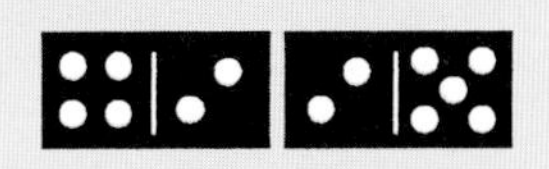

scores 3

scores 0

In fact, the highest score the second player can get from playing any of the twelve possible dominoes is 3.

8 Figure 1 shows what domino was played by the first player to start a game of Threes and Fives. In each case, say what the first player scored, and also what is the highest score the second player could get and how she could get that score.

(*a*)  (*b*)  (*c*)  (*d*) 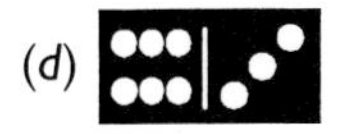 (*e*) 

Figure 1

9 (*a*) Why do you think (4,5) is considered to be a good domino to start with when playing Threes and Fives?

(*b*) Why do you think (6,3) is considered to be a dangerous domino to start with?

(*c*) Why does the first player sometimes know that (6,3) is a safe start?

(*d*) What is the probability that the person starting will be able to choose the (4,5) domino as the starting domino?

10 Here are two possible ways of scoring 2 in one go.

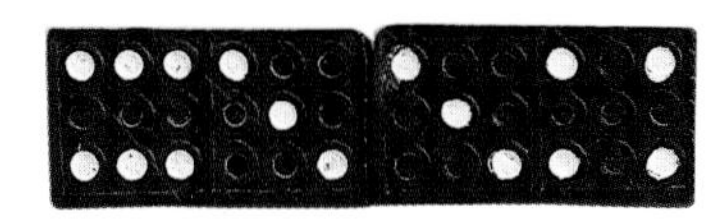

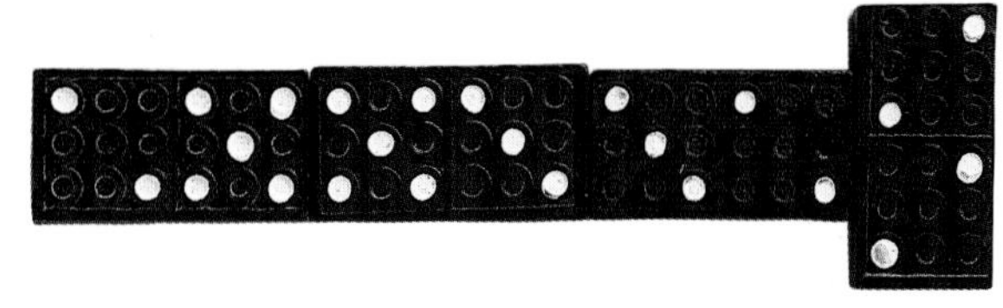

(*a*) Find three other ways of scoring 2 in one go.

(*b*) Find all possible ways of scoring 4 in one go. Check that you have found them all.

11 In the position shown below one player is holding three dominoes. The other player, whose turn it is to play is holding four dominoes. None of her four dominoes can be played. So she has to pick up a domino from the pack of 14 unused dominoes.

(*a*) How many dominoes are there which could be played on the chain shown?

(*b*) Of course, the player whose turn it is does not know what dominoes her opponent has. What is the probability that the domino she picks up can be played?

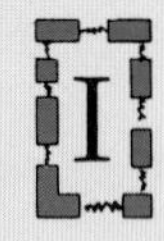

'A die is thrown twice. What is the probability that a six is obtained on exactly one of the two throws?

One way of answering this question is to use a **tree diagram.**

First throw	Second throw	Result	Probability
six ($\frac{1}{6}$)	six ($\frac{1}{6}$)	two sixes	$\frac{1}{6} \times \frac{1}{6} = \frac{1}{36}$
	not a six ($\frac{5}{6}$)	one six ✓	$\frac{1}{6} \times \frac{5}{6} = \frac{5}{36}$
not a six ($\frac{5}{6}$)	six ($\frac{1}{6}$)	one six ✓	$\frac{5}{6} \times \frac{1}{6} = \frac{5}{36}$
	not a six ($\frac{5}{6}$)	no sixes	$\frac{5}{6} \times \frac{5}{6} = \frac{25}{36}$

On the first throw the probability of throwing a six is $\frac{1}{6}$ and the probability of not throwing a six is $\frac{5}{6}$. These probabilities are marked on the branches of the tree. The same is done for the second throw.

To find the probability of each end point of the tree, multiply together the probabilities. This is shown on the diagram.

The results marked with a tick are the results we want. To find the probability of obtaining exactly one six, add up the probabilities ticked.

The probability of obtaining exactly one six is

$$\frac{5}{36} + \frac{5}{36} = \frac{10}{36} = \frac{5}{18}$$

12 'A coin is flipped twice. What is the probability of getting one head and one tail?'

Figure 2 is the start of a tree diagram for answering this question.

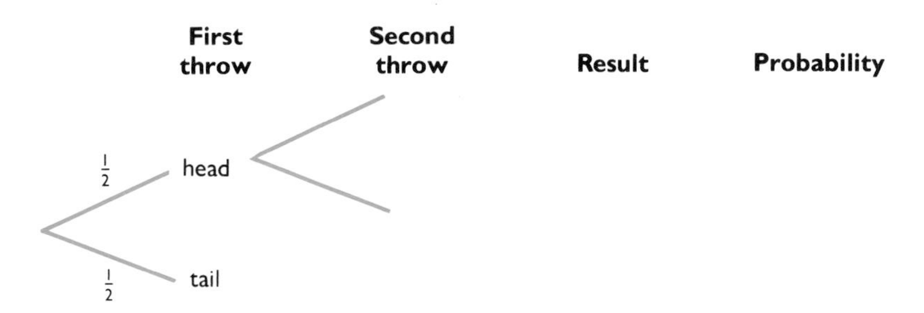

Figure 2

(a) Complete the diagram.

(b) What is the probability of getting one head and one tail?

13 A coin is flipped three times.

By drawing a tree diagram, find the probability that a head is obtained at least twice.

14 Someone who is playing Digame decides to throw the die exactly twice on her next turn (unless her first throw is a one so that she has to stop). Figure 3 is the start of a tree diagram to find the probability that she will score zero.

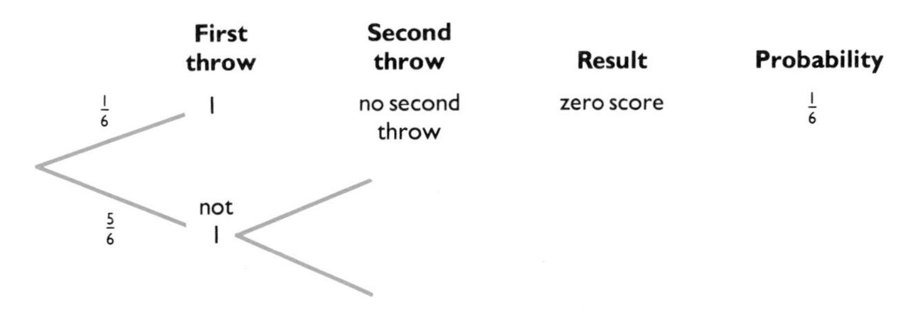

Figure 3

(a) Complete the tree diagram.

(b) What is the probability that she will score zero?

15 A set of dominoes is shuffled and placed face down on the table. Someone picks up two dominoes.

The tree diagram below enables you to find the probability that both the dominoes contain a six.

First domino	Second domino	Result	Probability
$\frac{7}{28}$ contains a six	$\frac{6}{27}$ contains a six	both contain a six	?
	$\frac{21}{27}$ does not contain a six	one contains a six	?
$\frac{21}{28}$ does not contain a six	$\frac{7}{27}$ contains a six	one contains a six	?
	$\frac{20}{27}$ does not contain a six	neither contain a six	?

(*a*) Make sure you understand the probabilities marked on the branches.

Copy the tree diagram and replace the question marks by the correct probabilities.

(*b*) What is the probability that both the dominoes contain a six?

(*c*) What is the probability that neither of the dominoes contains a six?

(*d*) Now suppose that three dominoes are picked instead of two. Extend the tree diagram to find the probability that none of the dominoes contains a six.

FURTHER COURSEWORK TASKS

1〉 Write about some aspects of darts. For example, write about possible finishing scores for a game of 501 Down. Or write about the way the numbers are arranged on a dartboard.

2〉 Design a board game.

You might want to get some ideas by looking at board games you know.

You might want to test your game by playing it. This might help you to think of improvements to your game.

3〉 Some sets of dominoes contain more dominoes than the standard sets in Britain. For example, one set has all possible dominoes from double-blank to double-nine.

Design a version of Threes and Fives which could be played with such a set.

4) This is how the numbers are arranged round a dartboard. Is this a good arrangement? How do you think they should be arranged?

The area in which you score 20 on a dartboard is the same size as the area in which you score 1. Some people think that it should be harder to score 20 on a dartboard than it is to score 1.

You might want to redesign a dartboard so that it is harder to score some numbers than others.

5) Figure 4 shows a ring of dominoes.

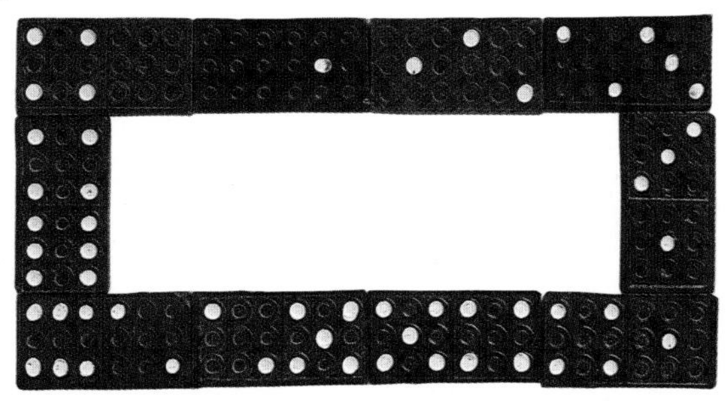

Figure 4

Can you form a ring using all the 28 dominoes in a standard set?

Can you form a ring using all the dominoes which do not have sixes on them?

Can you form a ring of all the dominoes with an even number of spots on them?

Can you form a ring of all the dominoes with an odd number of spots on them?

Make up and solve other problems of this type. Try to explain why some rings are possible and some are impossible.

You might find it helpful to use network diagrams, which were explained in the box before question 4 in Section B.

6) Choose a game. It could be a card game, such as Chase the Ace or Crib. It could be a dice game, such as Yahtzee. It could be a board game such as Monopoly or Sorry.

Write about some aspects of the game.

COLOURINGS

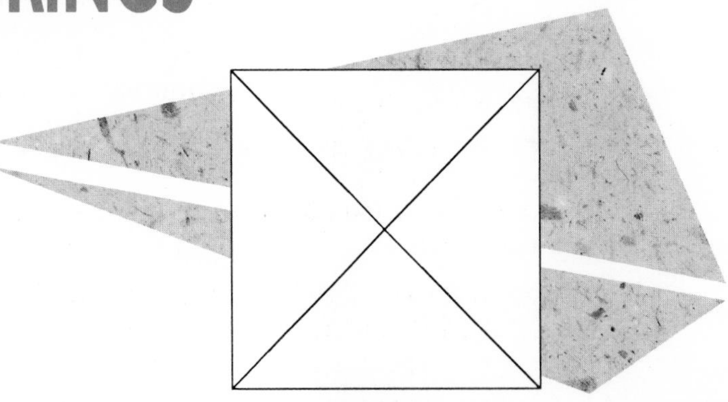

The drawing above shows the design for a tile. A tile is made by colouring this design using three colours: red, blue and yellow.

Here are three of the tiles that can be made.

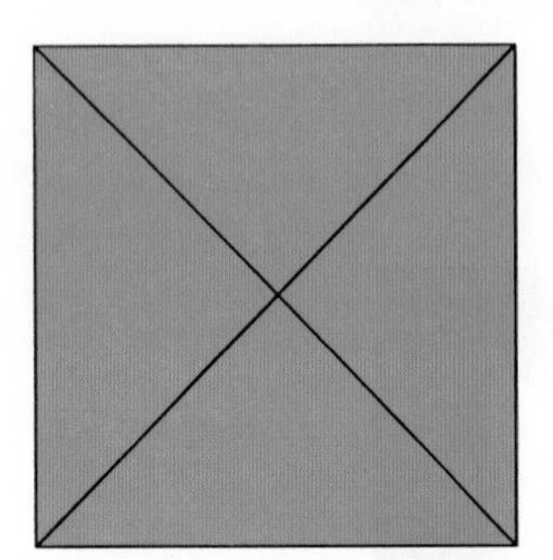

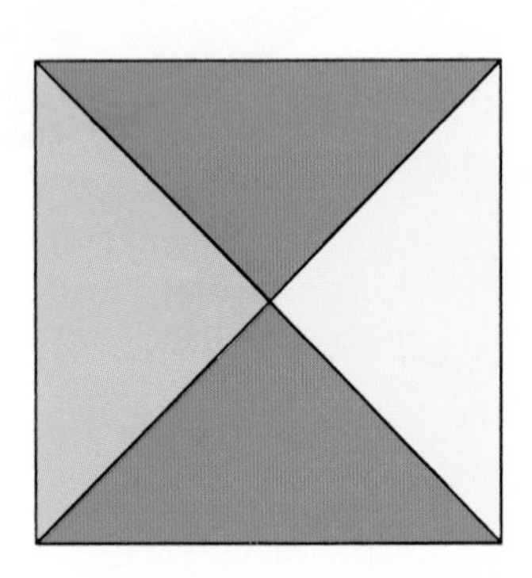

Get the resource sheet called *'Square tiles'*.

- How many different coloured tiles can you produce using the colours red, blue and yellow?

  Two tiles count as the same if one of them can be turned round to look exactly the same as the other.

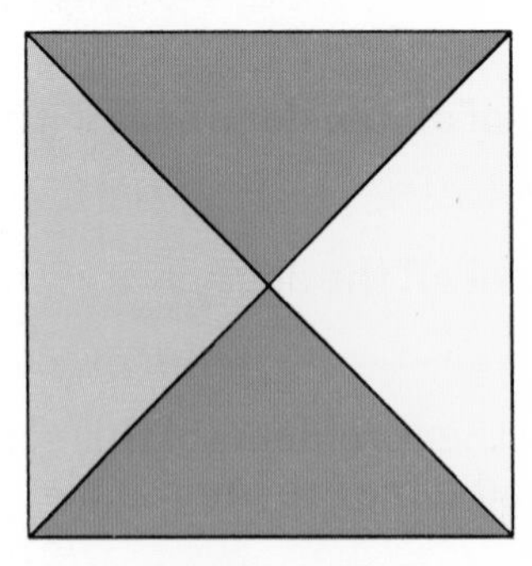

  Work systematically. This will help you to know that you have found all the tiles. One way of being systematic is to cut out the tiles and sort them into types.

  Do not lose the tiles you have cut out. You will find it useful to have a complete set of tiles for some of the questions in Section B.

- When you think you have found all possible tiles explain clearly how you know there are no others.

SECTION A

1 Look at the pair of tiles shown in figure 1.

Tile 1 *Tile 2*

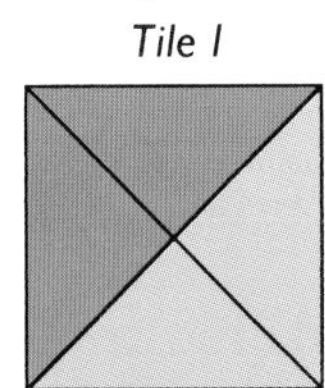
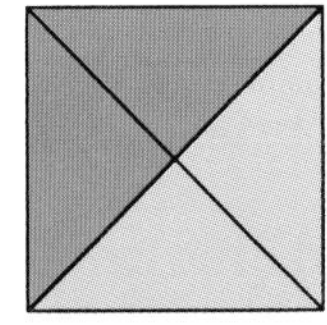
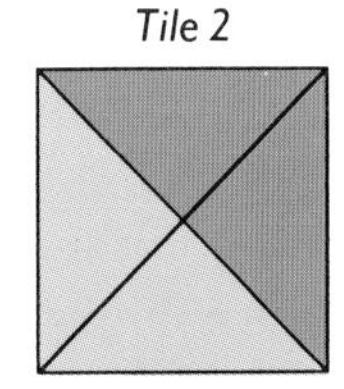

Figure 1

To make *Tile 1* look like *Tile 2*, *Tile 1* should be rotated clockwise through 90°.

For each of the following pairs state how to rotate *Tile 1* so that it looks like *Tile 2* (figure 2).

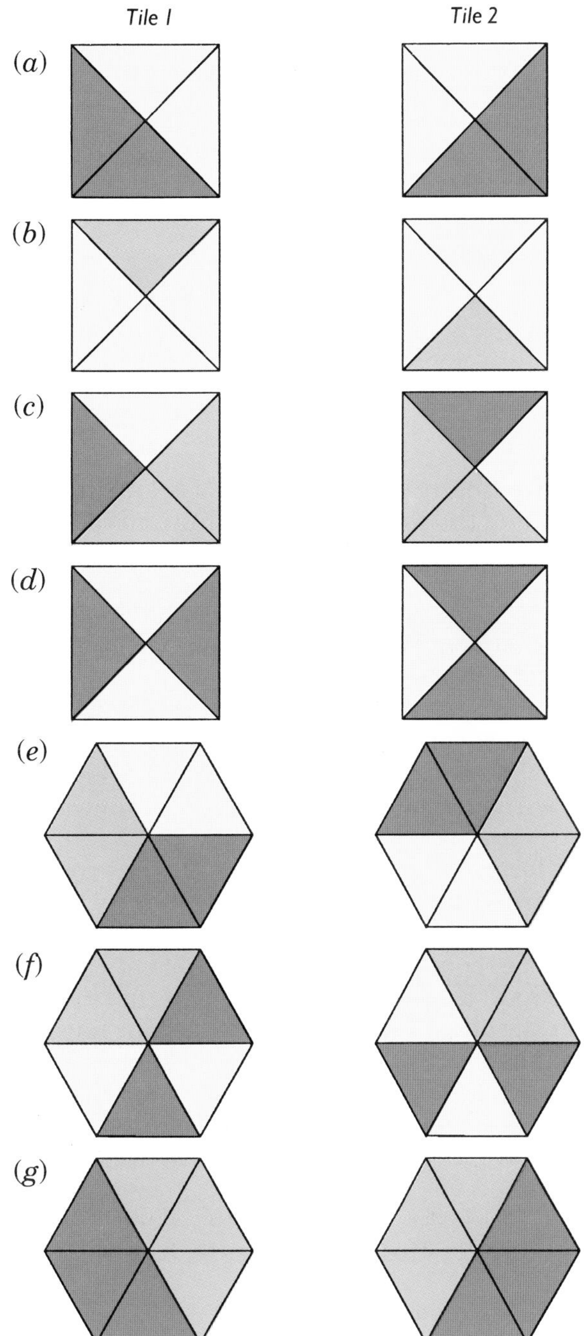

Figure 2

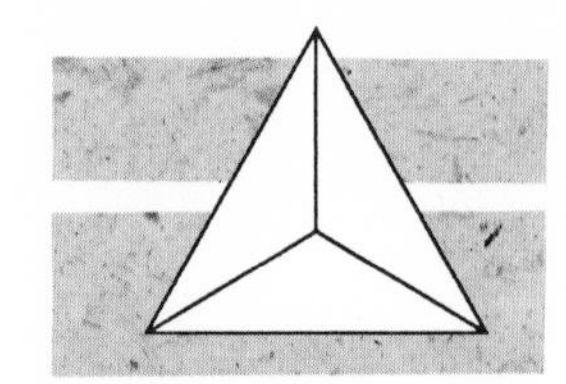
Figure 3

2 Get the resource sheet called *'Triangle tiles'*.

If the colours yellow, blue and red are used to colour the tile shown in figure 3, how many different tiles can be produced?

You do not have to use all three colours on every tile.

3 The colours red, yellow and blue are being used to colour tiles. Each of the tiles shown in figure 4 has been partly coloured. For each tile say how many different tiles can be made by finishing colouring the tile in different ways.

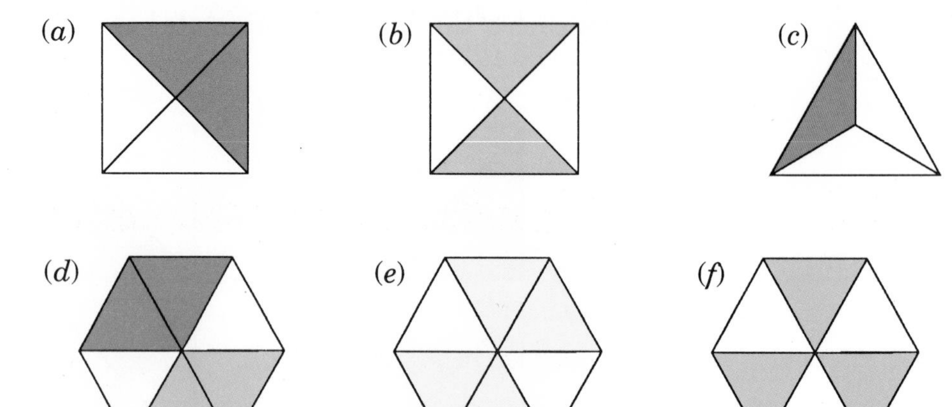

Figure 4

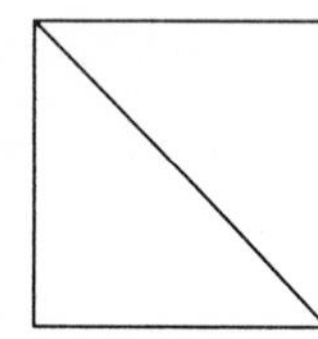
Figure 5

4 How many ways are there of colouring the tile shown in figure 5, using the colours yellow, blue and red?

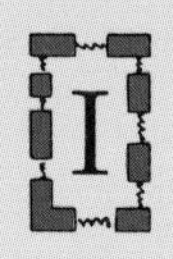

It is often useful to be able to know how many tiles there are without drawing them all.

Suppose you want to know how many ways there are of colouring the square tile shown in question 4, using four colours. You could work this out without drawing all the tiles as follows.

There are 4 different tiles which contain only one colour. This is because there are 4 colours to choose from.

There are also tiles containing two colours. There are 4 choices of colours for one half. For each of these choices there are 3 choices of colours left for the other half (because one colour has already been used). This makes $4 \times 3 = 12$ choices altogether. But there is no difference between a tile coloured red and then yellow, and a tile coloured yellow and then red. So we have counted all the tiles twice, and there are really only 6 different tiles containing two colours.

So altogether there are 10 different tiles that can be coloured using four colours.

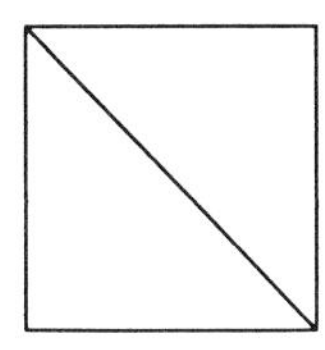

Figure 6

5 (*a*) How many ways are there of colouring the square tile, in figure 6, if five colours can be used?

(*b*) How many ways are there of colouring it if N colours can be used?

6 (*a*) How many ways are there of colouring the triangle tile, in figure 7, if 4 colours can be used?

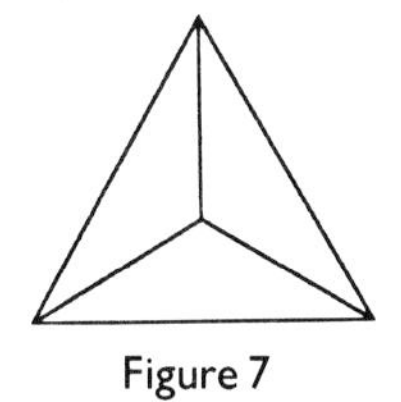

Figure 7

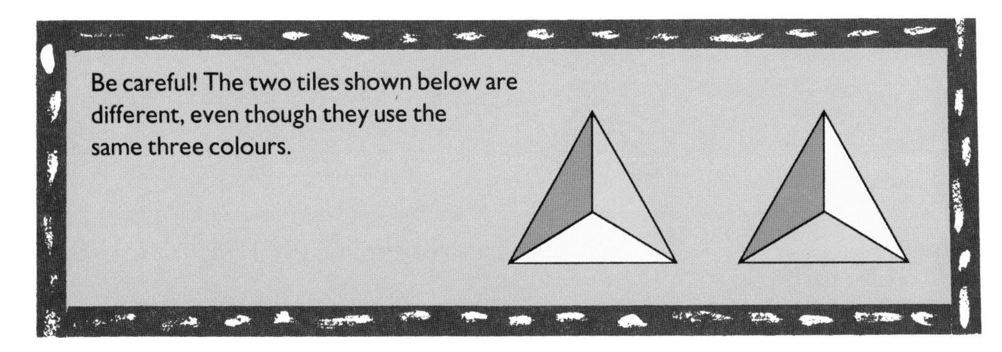

(*b*) How many ways are there of colouring it if five colours can be used?

(*c*) How many ways are there of colouring it if N colours can be used?

SECTION B

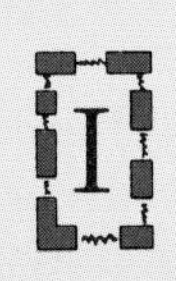

Two tiles are the same type if they are coloured in the same pattern, even if the colours used are different.

For example, the two tiles shown below are of the same type. They both have two colours and in each case one of the colours is used for three of the regions.

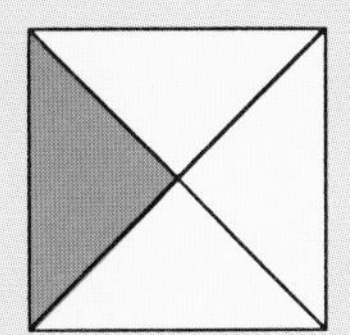

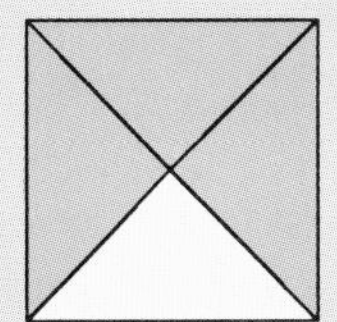

1 Write down which of the following tiles are the same **type**. How many different types of tiles are there among the 18 tiles shown?

(*a*)

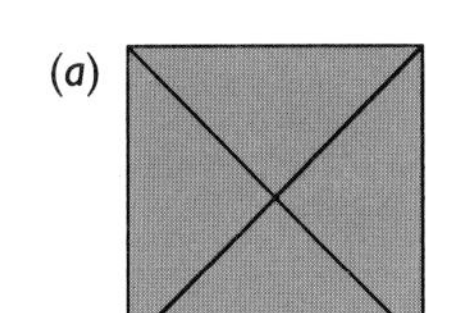

(*b*)

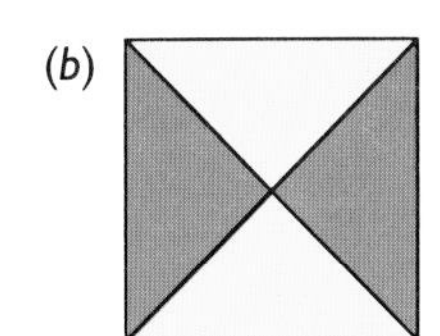

(*c*)

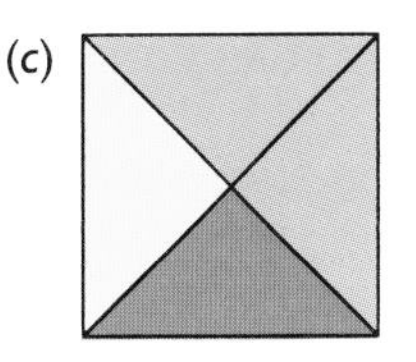

(*d*)

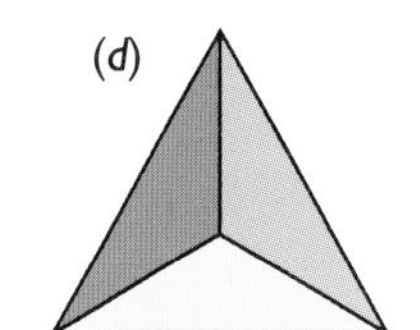

(*e*)

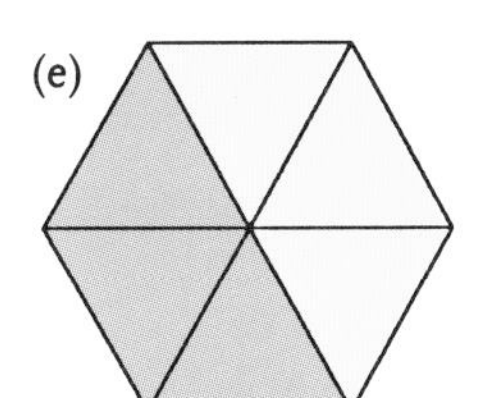

(*f*)

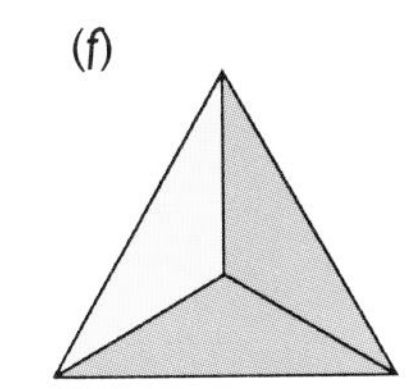

(*g*)

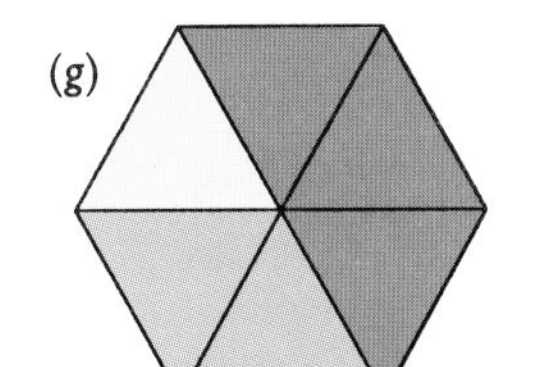

(*h*)

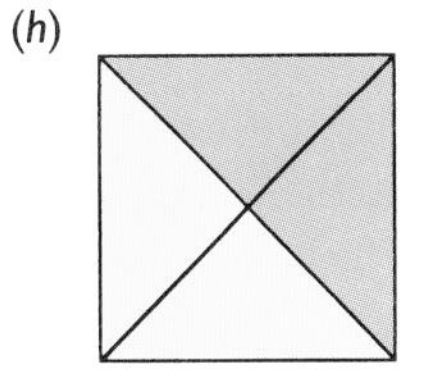

(*i*)

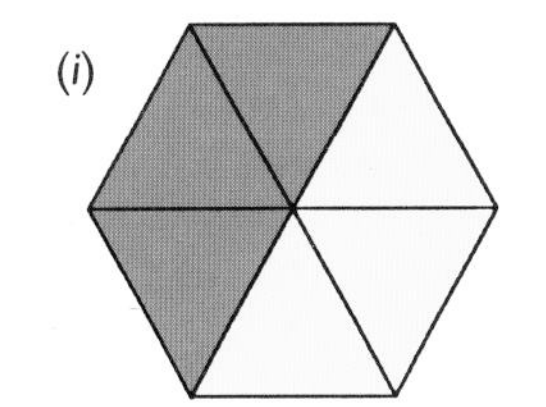

(*j*)

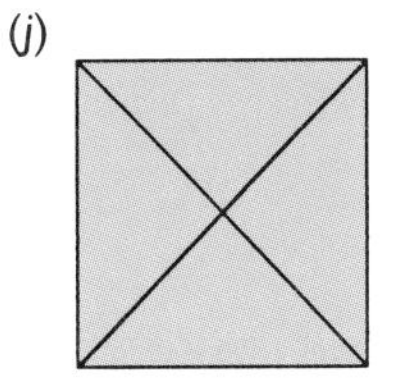

(k) 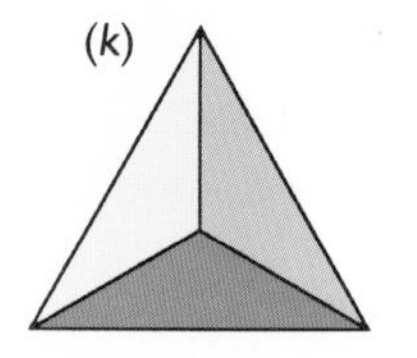

(l)  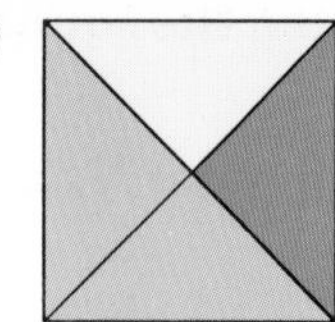

(m) 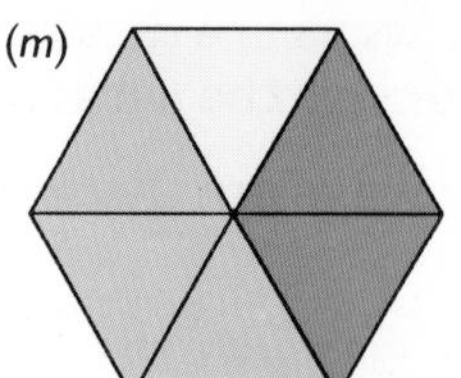

(n)

(o) 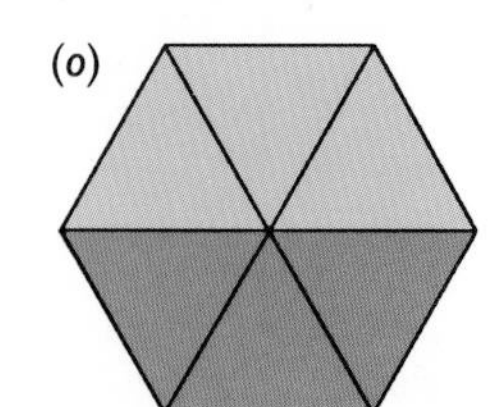

(p) 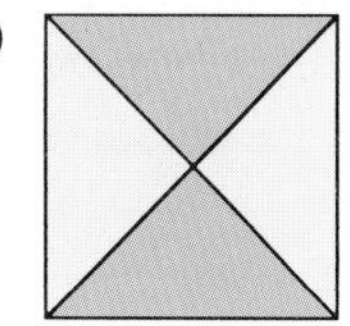

(q) 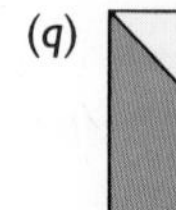 

(r) 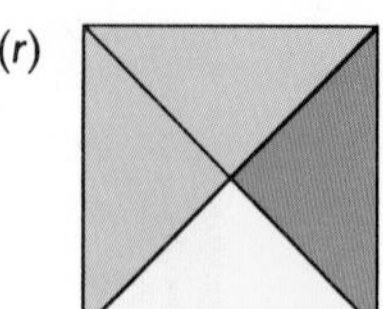

2 Get the resource sheet called *'Triangle tiles'*.

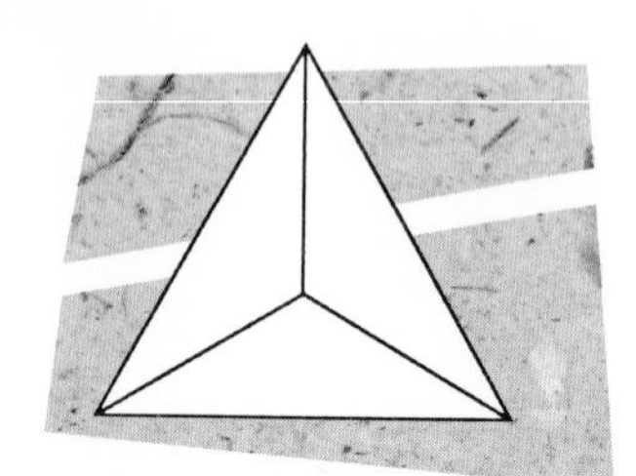

How many **types** of tile can be made by colouring this triangle tile? You can use as many different colours as you need.

3 Get the resource sheet called *'Hexagon tiles'*.

How many different **types** of tile can be made by colouring this tile? You can use as many different colours as you need.

4 The problem at the beginning of this chapter was about finding out how many different tiles can be made by colouring in the square design shown in figure 8.

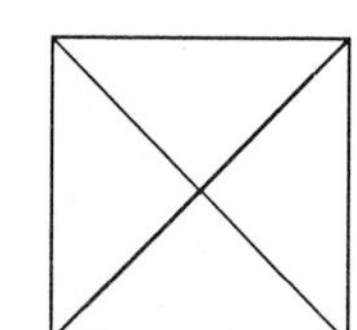

Figure 8

There are 24 different tiles.

(*a*) How many of these 24 tiles have only one colour on them?

(*b*) How many have exactly two colours on them?

(*c*) How many have three colours on them?

(*d*) How many have red on them?

(*e*) How many have red and yellow on them?

5 You might think the answer to question 4(*e*) is 4. Someone else might think the answer is 13.

Explain why both answers could be considered correct. You might find it helpful to use your set of tiles.

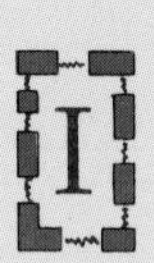

One way of being clearer about what you mean when you answer questions about the number of tiles with one, two or three colours is to draw a *Venn diagram*.

The Venn diagram on the right shows the number of the square tiles which are coloured red, blue and yellow.

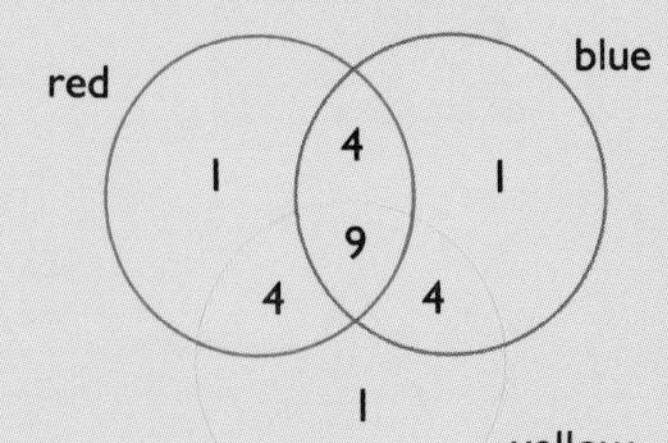

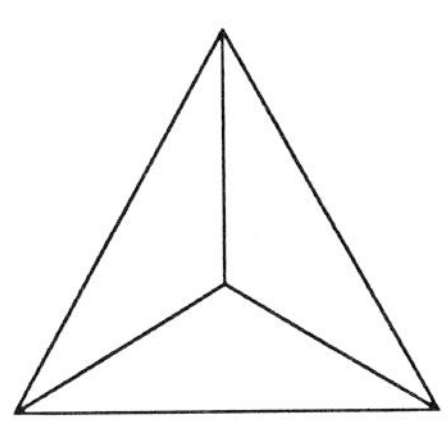
Figure 9

6 Question 2 in Section A was about colouring the tile shown in figure 9, using the colours red, yellow and blue.

There are 11 different tiles that can be produced.

Draw a Venn diagram to show how many of these tiles are coloured red, blue and yellow.

7 Use your answer to question 3 to find all the different colourings of the tile shown in figure 10, when the colours red, yellow and blue are used.

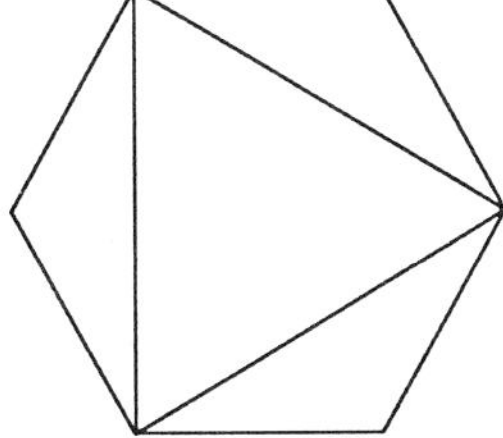
Figure 10

Draw a Venn diagram to show how many of these tiles are coloured red, yellow and blue.

8 A particular tile design is coloured in all possible different ways using the colours red, yellow and blue to produce N tiles.

Six of the tiles contain all three colours; twelve tiles contain red and blue; twelve tiles contain blue and yellow and twelve tiles contain yellow and red. Three of the tiles are coloured using only one colour.

(*a*) Draw a Venn diagram to show this information.

(*b*) What is the value of N?

9 Find a tile design which produces the results given in question 8.

SECTION C

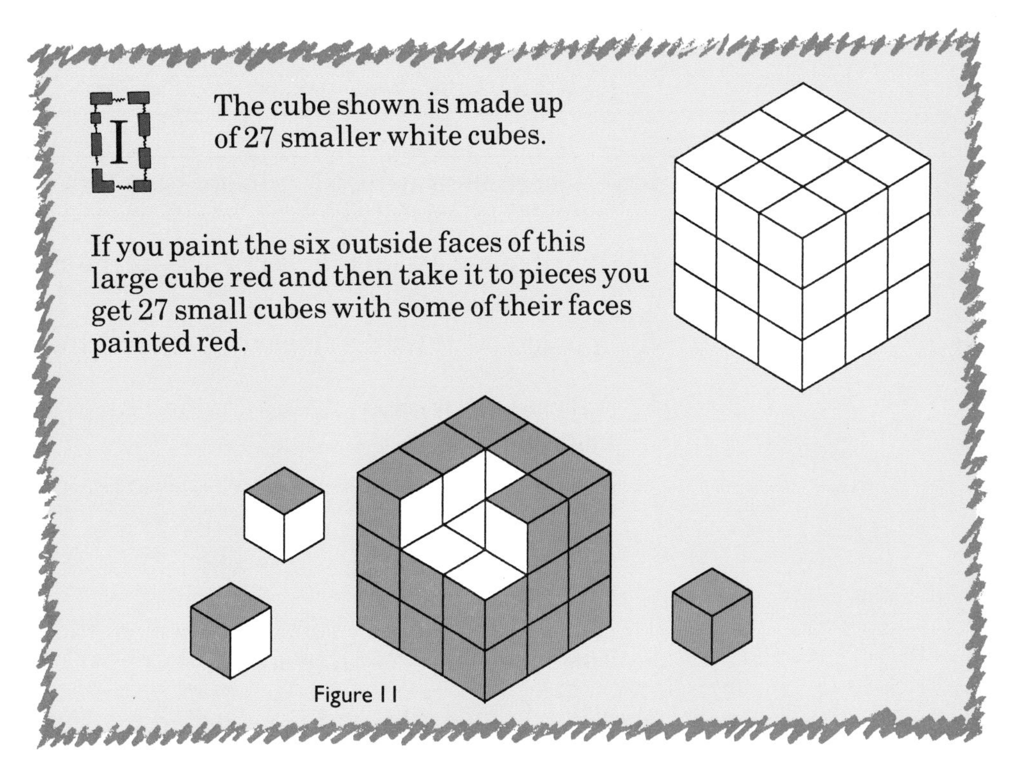

Figure 11

1 Look at figure 11. How many of the small cubes have

(*a* 3 faces painted red? (*b*) 2 faces painted red?

(*c*) 1 face painted red? (*d*) 0 faces painted red?

2 The results of question 1 can be entered in a table.

Size of large cube	Number of small cubes with this number of faces painted				Total number of small cubes
	0	1	2	3	
$2 \times 2 \times 2$					8
$3 \times 3 \times 3$					27
$4 \times 4 \times 4$					
$5 \times 5 \times 5$					
$6 \times 6 \times 6$					
$7 \times 7 \times 7$					
$8 \times 8 \times 8$					
$9 \times 9 \times 9$					
$10 \times 10 \times 10$					

(*a*) Copy the table. By considering a $2 \times 2 \times 2$ cube complete the first row of the table.

(*b*) Complete the other rows of the table.

3 (*a*) Can 1341 small cubes all be used to make a large cube? How do you know?

(*b*) Can 97 336 cubes all be used to make a large cube? How do you know?

(*c*) If 2000 cubes were used to make as large a cube as possible, how many of them would not be used?

4 27 small cubes are used, as in question 1, to make a large cube and the outside is painted.

(*a*) What is the total number of faces of the small cubes which are painted?

(*b*) What is the total number of faces which are not painted?

5 A large cube is made out of 125 small cubes and the outside is painted.

(*a*) What is the total number of faces of the small cubes which are painted?

(*b*) What is the total number which are not painted?

6 A large cube is made from 8 small cubes and the outside is painted. This means that 24 faces are painted.

(*a*) How many faces do the 8 small cubes have altogether?

(*b*) What percentage of these faces are painted?

7 The table below describes cube models made from small cubes and then painted on the outside.

Total number of cubes	Number of faces painted	Total number of faces	Fraction of faces painted	Percentage of faces painted
8	24			
27	54			
64		384		
125				

(*a*) Copy this table.

(*b*) Use your answers to question 6 to fill in one row of the table.

(*c*) Complete the table.

8 Look at the pattern of numbers in the table for question 7. Use this to decide how many cubes have been used if:

(*a*) 10% of the faces are painted,

(*b*) 2% of the faces are painted.

9 (*a*) Look again at question 2. The number of small cubes which have 2 painted faces depends on the length of an edge of the large cube. Complete the table below to show this.

Length of edge	2	3	4	5	6	7
No. of small cubes painted on 2 faces		12			48	

Using a horizontal scale of 2 cm for 1 unit of length of edge on the horizontal axis and 1 cm for 10 cubes on the vertical axis, draw a graph showing this relationship.

(*b*) On the same axes draw a similar graph showing the number of cubes painted on 1 face.

(*c*) On the same axes draw a similar graph showing the number of cubes painted on 3 faces.

10 A large cube is made from small cubes. The length of an edge of the large cube is N. The large cube is painted on the outside, as in questions 1 and 2.

(*a*) How many small cubes are painted on 3 faces? Justify your answer by thinking carefully about where these cubes are.

(*b*) How many small cubes are painted on 2 faces? Justify your answer by thinking carefully about where these cubes are.

(*c*) How many small cubes are painted on 1 face? Justify your answer by thinking carefully about where these cubes are.

(*d*) How many small cubes are painted on no faces? Justify your answer by thinking carefully about where these cubes are.

11 Use a graphical calculator or a graph-drawing program on a computer to produce graphs which are the same as the graphs you drew for question 9. Write down the equations you used to produce these three graphs.

12 Large cubes are made up of small cubes and painted as in questions 1 and 2.

(*a*) If the total number of painted faces is 1014, how many cubes have been used?

(*b*) If the number of small cubes painted on 1 side is equal to the number of small cubes painted on 2 sides, how many small cubes were used to make the large cube?

(*c*) If the number of small cubes painted on 1 side is 5 times the number painted on 2 sides, how many small cubes are unpainted?

(*d*) If the number of small cubes unpainted is 3 times the number painted on 1 side, how many cubes are painted on 2 sides?

(*e*) If the number of small cubes unpainted is 27 times the number painted on 2 sides, how many small cubes were used altogether?

(*f*) Is it possible for the number of small cubes unpainted to be exactly 299 568 times the number of cubes painted on 2 sides?

13 (*a*) Draw a graph showing how the number of *unpainted* faces of small cubes making up a large cube varies with the length of an edge of the large cube.

(*b*) Use a graphical calculator or a graph-drawing program on a computer to produce the same graph. What equation did you use to get this graph?

1⟩ Here are some tile designs.

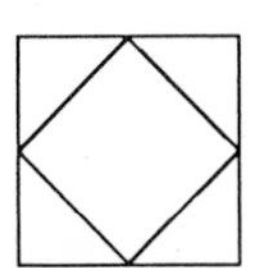

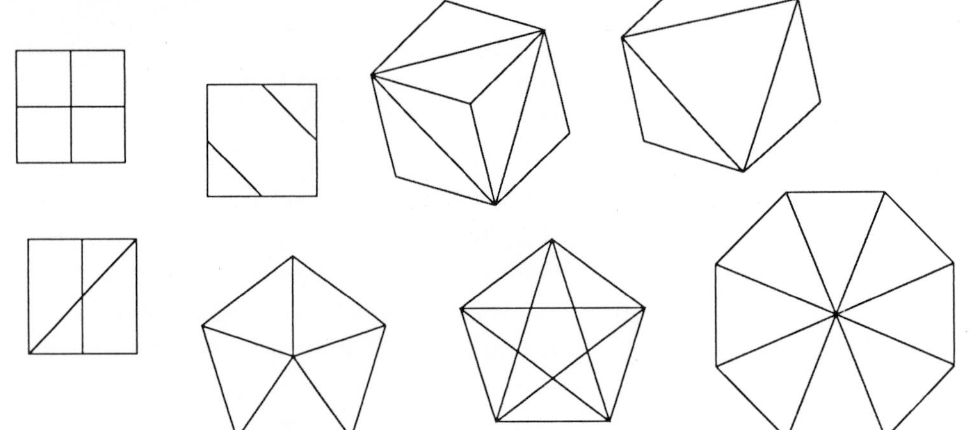

Choose one of these designs or make up a design of your own.

How many different tiles of your chosen design can you make using 3 colours?

How many tiles of your chosen design can you make using 4 colours?

You might want to discover how many you can make using N colours.

2) Find two different tile designs both of which produce the same number of tiles when three colours are used.

You might want to use the designs of Task 1, or to make up your own designs.

You can, of course, do the same task using a different number of colours.

3) Section C was about painting the outside of cubes made out of smaller cubes.

Figure 12 shows other sequences of models made out of cubes.

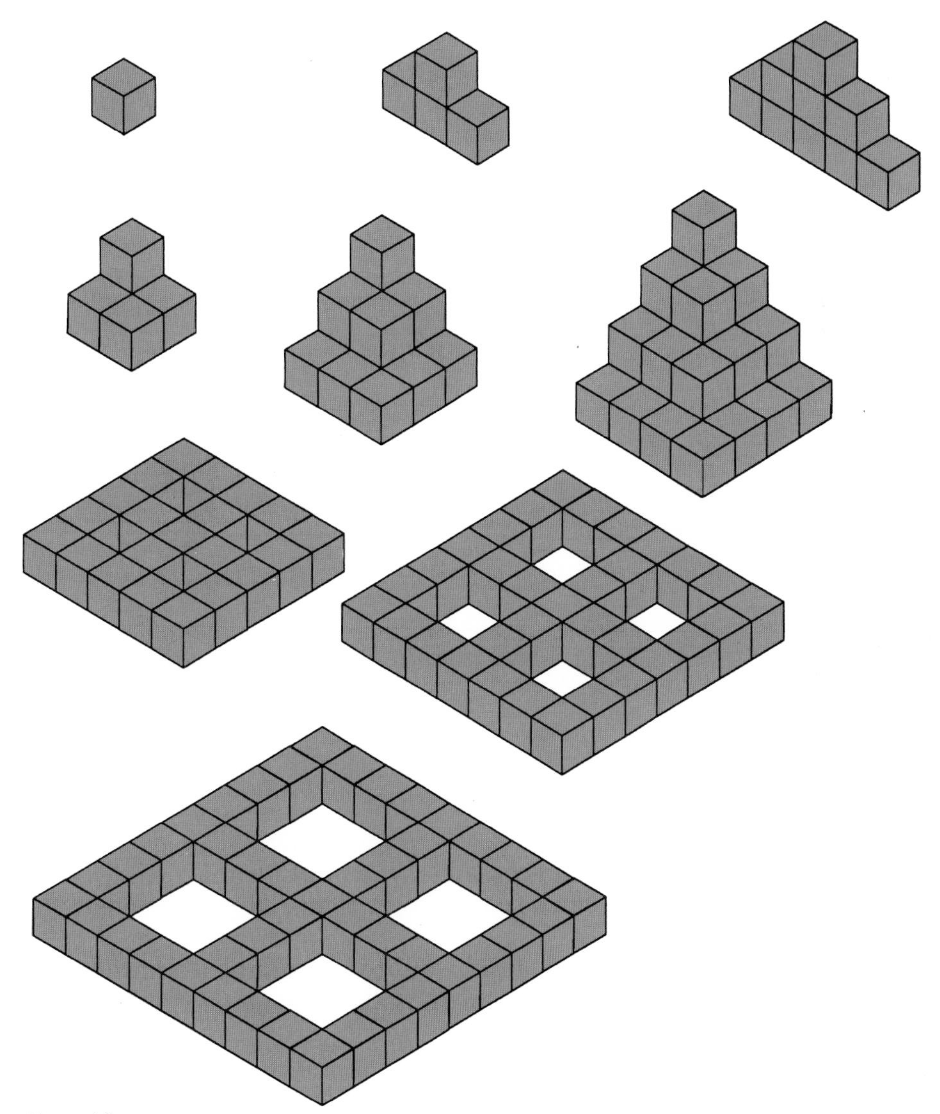

Figure 12

Choose one of these sequences or make up a sequence of your own. If the outsides of your sequence of models are painted red, how many of each of the small cubes of each model have no faces painted? 1 face painted? And so on.

You might want to find formulae which give the answers for the Nth model in your sequence.

4⟩

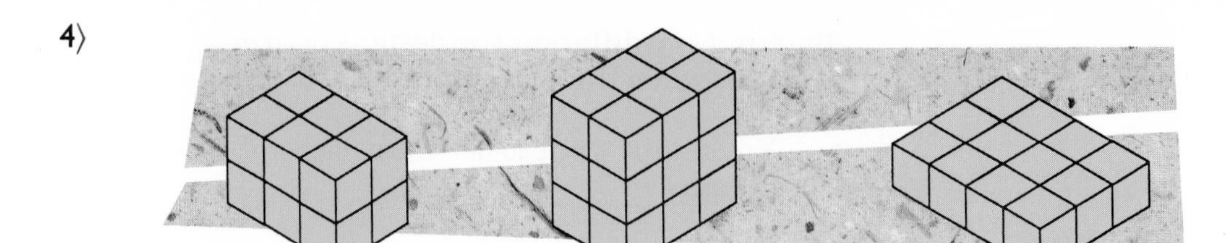

Investigate problems concerned with painting cuboids.

5⟩ 27 small cubes are put together to make a large cube as in question 1 of Section C. The outside is painted red. The cubes are then separated.

Is it possible to paint each of the other faces of the small cubes blue or yellow, in such a way that the cubes can be put together to show a completely blue large cube, and can also be put together to show a completely yellow large cube?

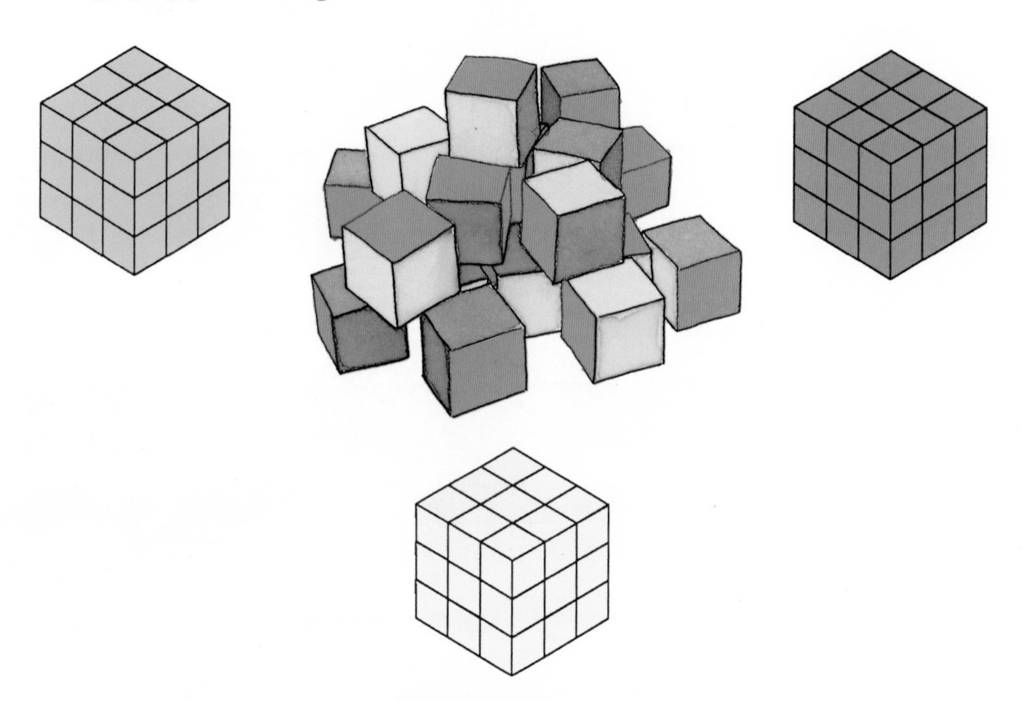

If it is possible, you might want to discover in how many different ways it can be done. You will need to decide what you mean by 'different'.

You might want to try solving a similar problem for a large cube which is made from 8 small cubes. Or 64 small cubes. Or 125 small cubes. Or N^3 small cubes.

16 EVERY PICTURE TELLS A STORY

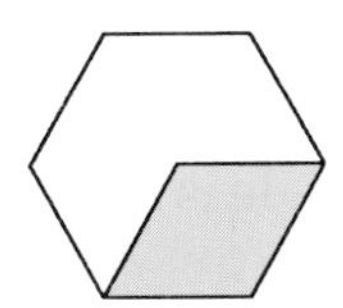

A picture is often said to be worth a thousand words. Pictures can often describe or explain mathematics which is hard to describe or explain by using words, or by using numbers or algebra.

- Look at the pictures below. Give an explanation of the connection between the pictures.
- Add some pictures of your own which could belong with the pictures shown.
- Now draw a new set of pictures which tell a slightly different story.

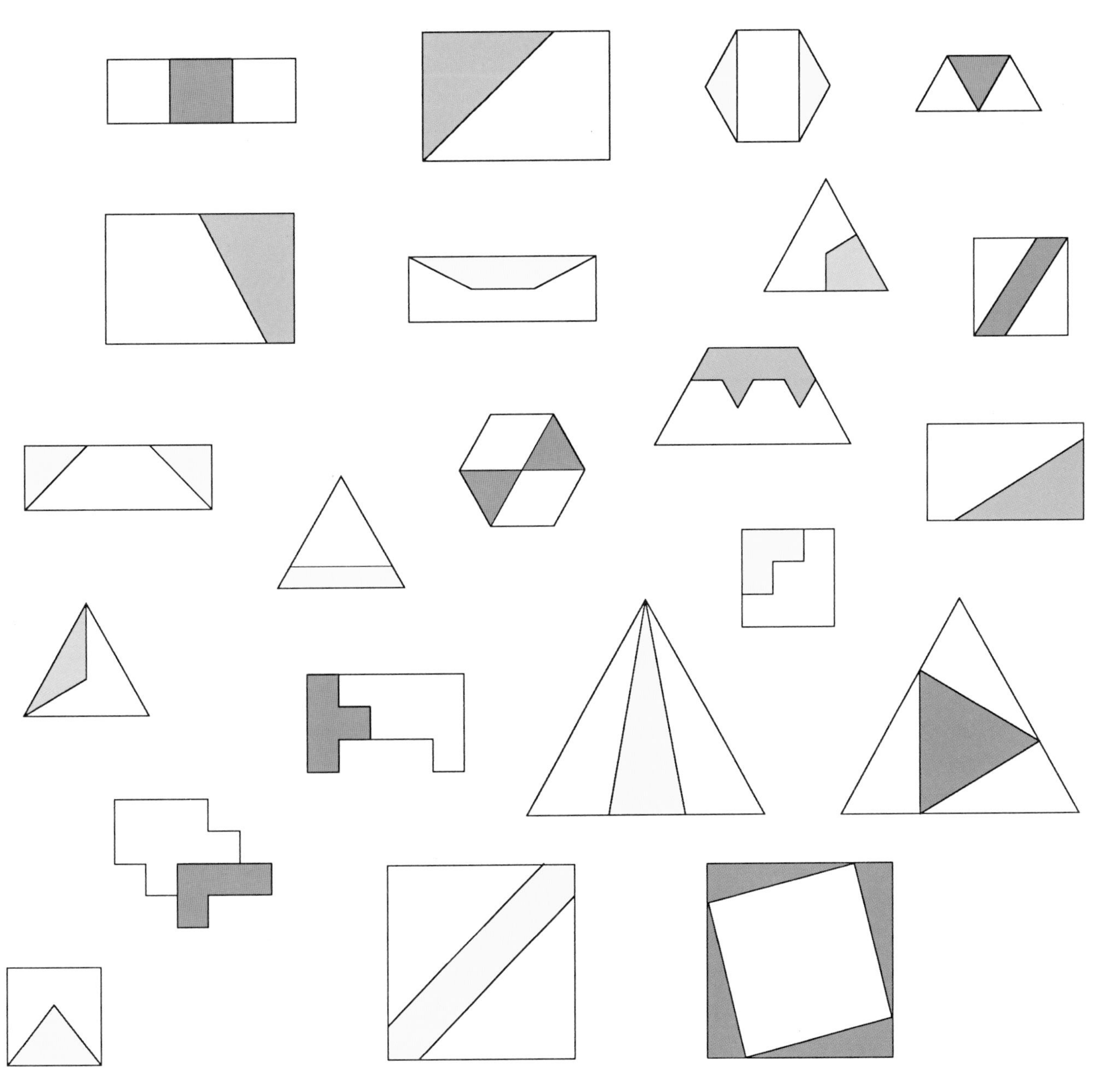

SECTION A

1 Look at the pictures shown in figure 1.

Figure 1

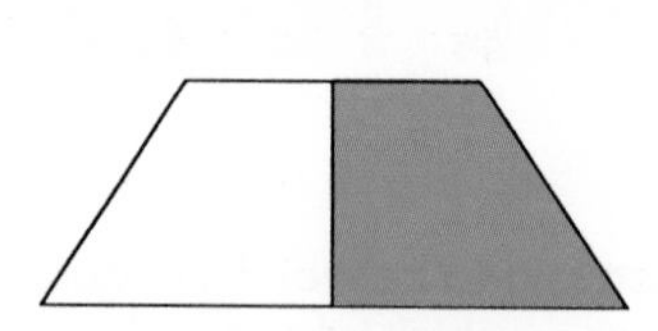

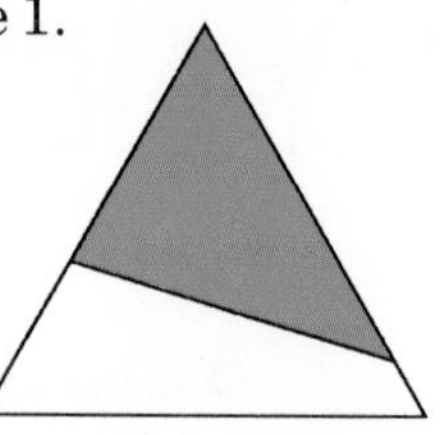

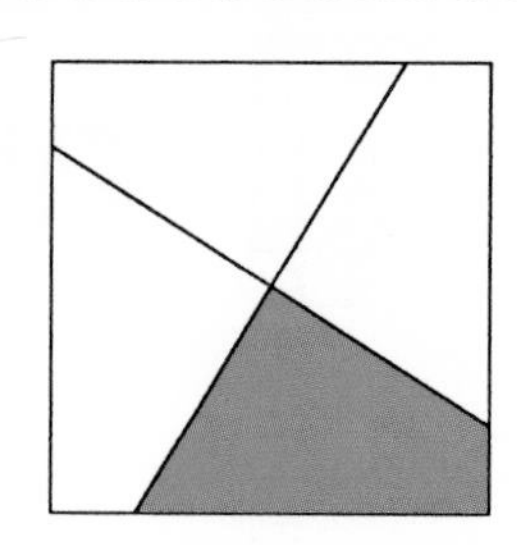

(*a*) What fraction of the area of the rectangle is red?

(*b*) What fraction of the area of the square is red?

(*c*) What fraction of the area of the trapezium is red?

(*d*) Why is it not so easy to know what fraction of the triangle is red?

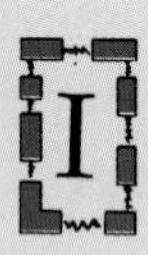

When two shapes in the drawing are the *same shape* and the *same size* they are called **congruent**. The white part of the rectangle in question 1 is congruent to the red part of the rectangle.

If two shapes are congruent, one of them would fit exactly on top of the other, although you might need to turn it over first.

2 Figure 2 shows a rectangle, part of which has been shaded blue.

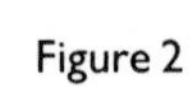

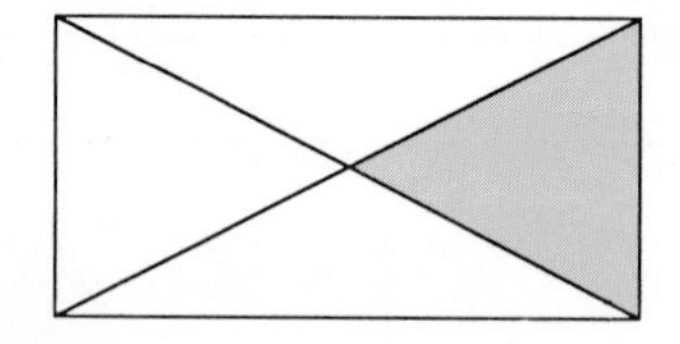

One way of finding out what fraction of the rectangle has been shaded is to do the following:

A Draw the picture of the rectangle, but without the shading.

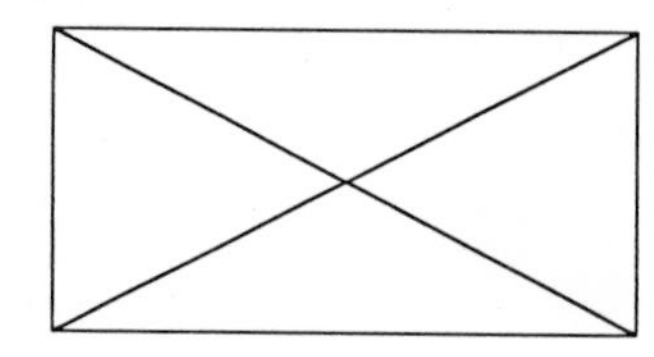

B Add extra lines to the picture so that all the pieces are congruent.

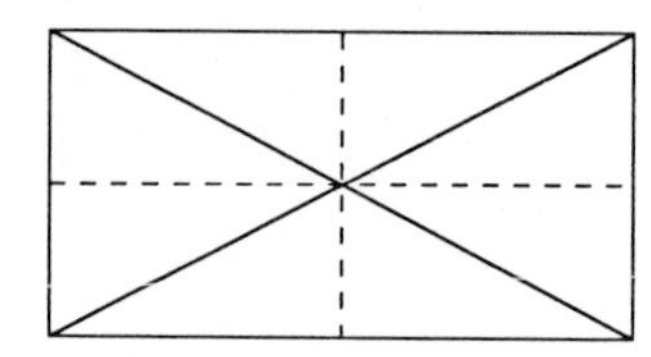

C Shade the new picture in the same way as the original rectangle.

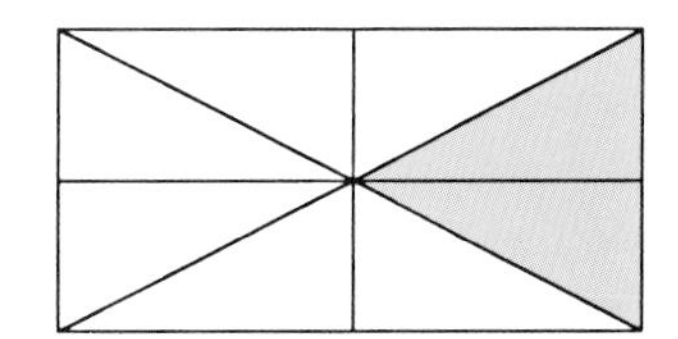

D Count the number of blue and white pieces to discover that the fraction shaded blue is $\frac{2}{8} = \frac{1}{4}$.

Do the same process (steps **A**, **B**, **C** and **D**) to find out what fraction of each of the following shapes is shaded green.

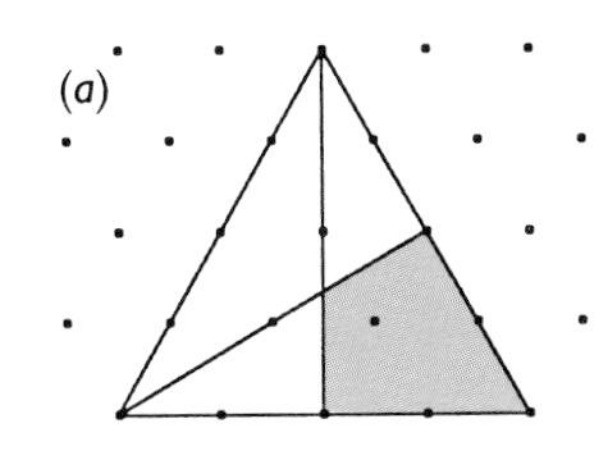

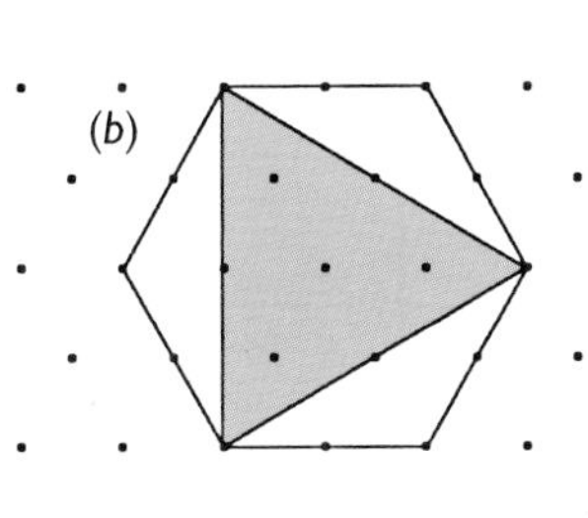

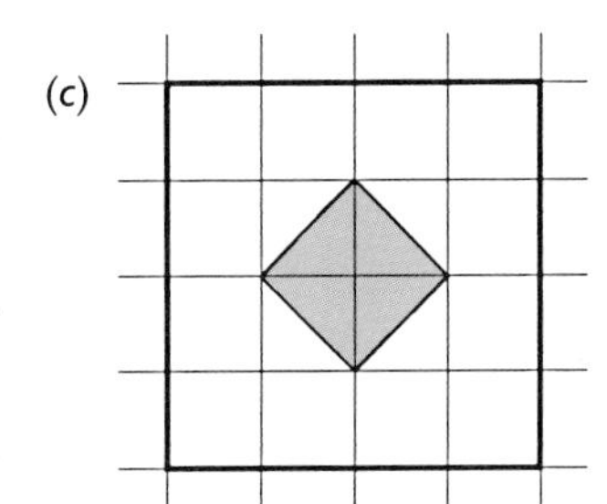

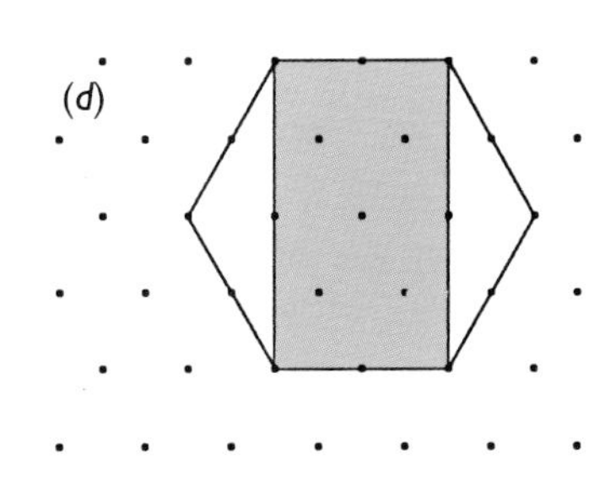

3 Figure 3 shows a triangle (shape 1) and a parallelogram (shape 2).

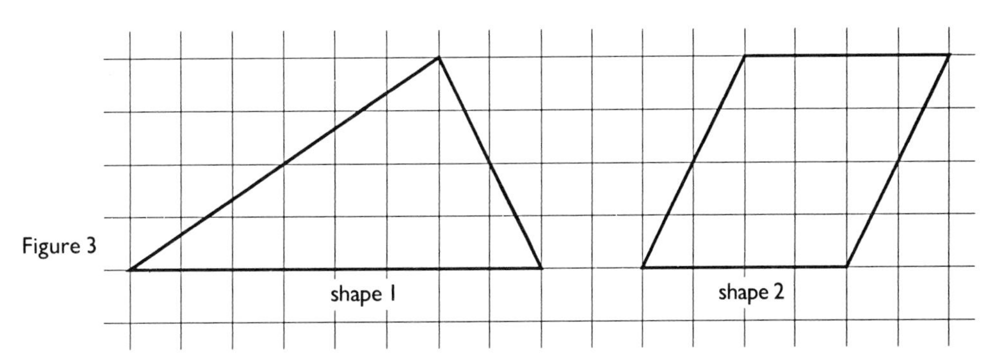

Figure 3

Figure 4 shows the same triangle and parallelogram. By looking at these pictures decide whether shape 1, or shape 2 has the larger area.

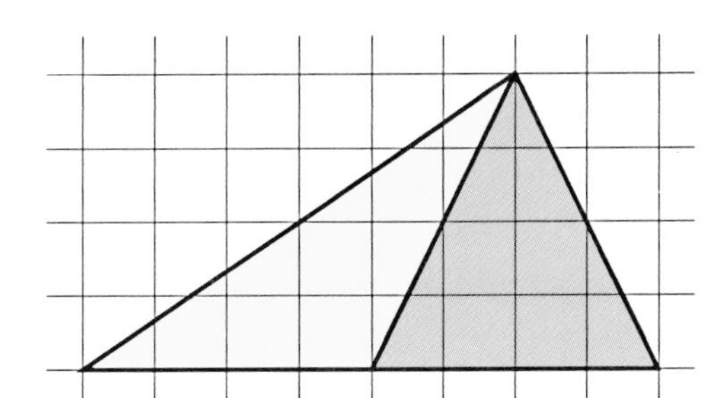

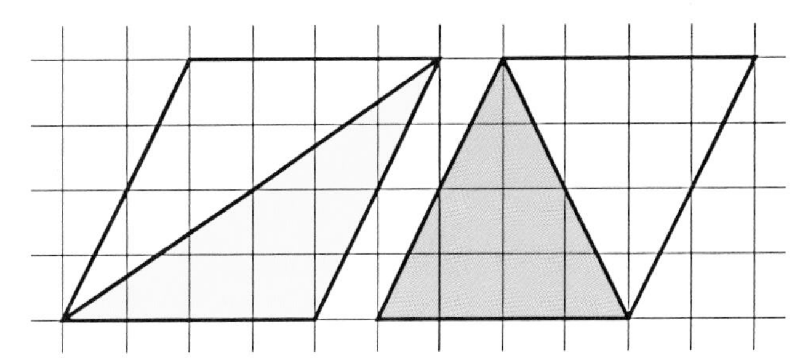

Figure 4

Explain your answer.

4 (*a*) Figure 5 shows a square with its midpoints joined. What fraction of the square is shaded pink?

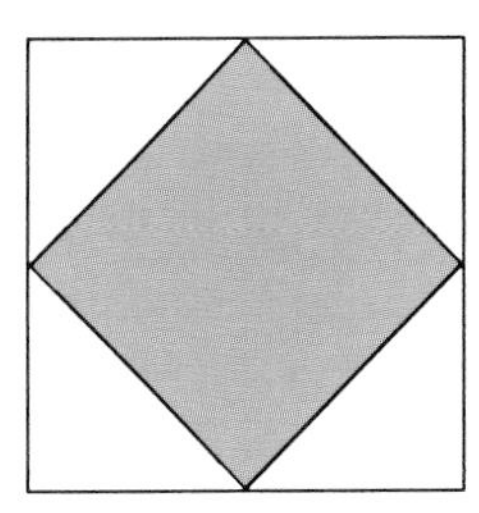

Figure 5

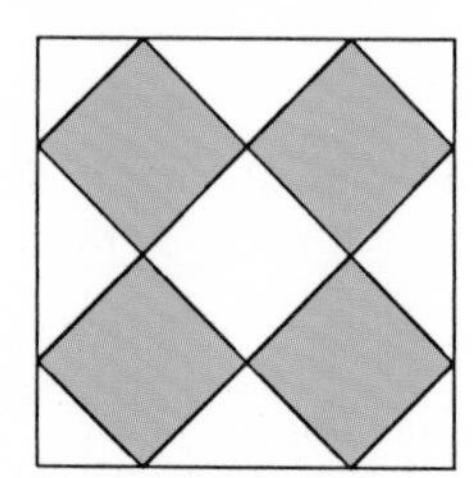
Figure 6

(*b*) What fraction of the square is shaded green in figure 6?

(*c*) What fraction of the square is shaded purple in figure 7?

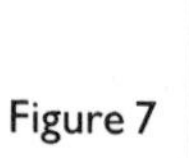
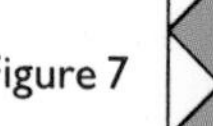
Figure 7

5 (*a*) A square ring is obtained by removing the centre from a square.

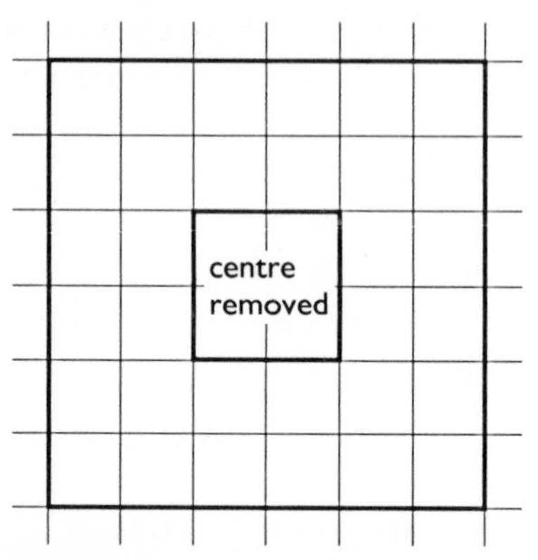

What fraction of the square is removed?

(*b*) What fraction of the square *ring* is shaded blue in figure 8? Explain your answer.

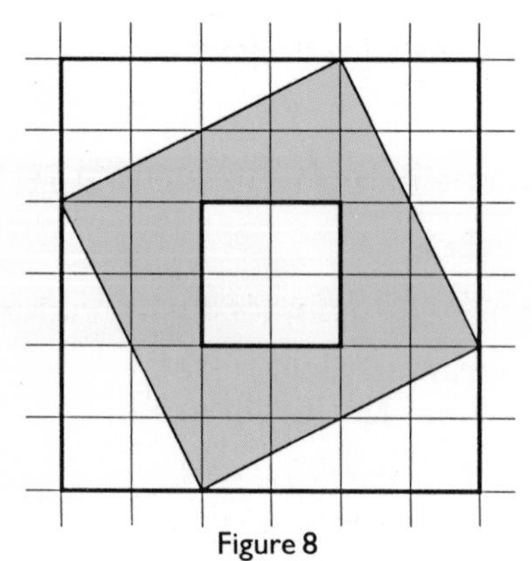
Figure 8

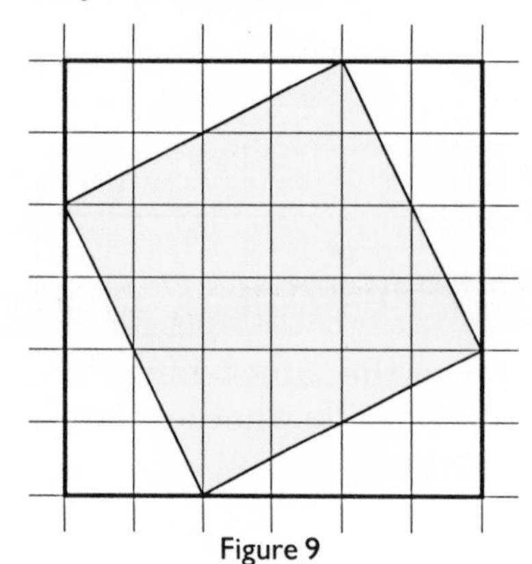
Figure 9

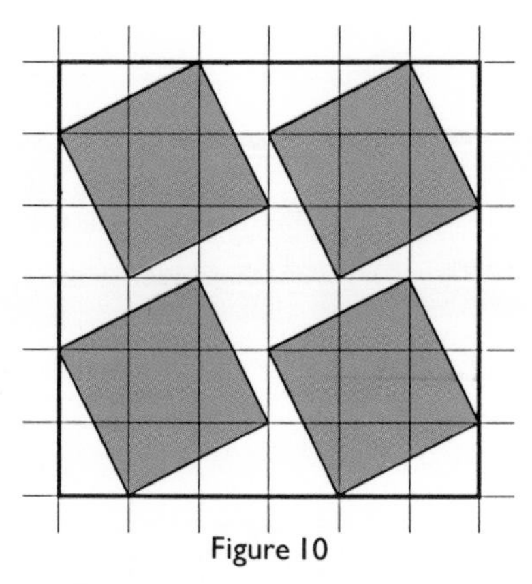
Figure 10

(*c*) Using the answers to parts (*a*) and (*b*), find the fraction of the square which is shaded yellow in figure 9. Explain your answer.

(*d*) What fraction of the square is shaded purple in figure 10?

6 (*a*) What fraction of the rectangle in figure 11 is shaded red?

(*b*) What fraction of the rectangle in figure 12 is shaded blue?

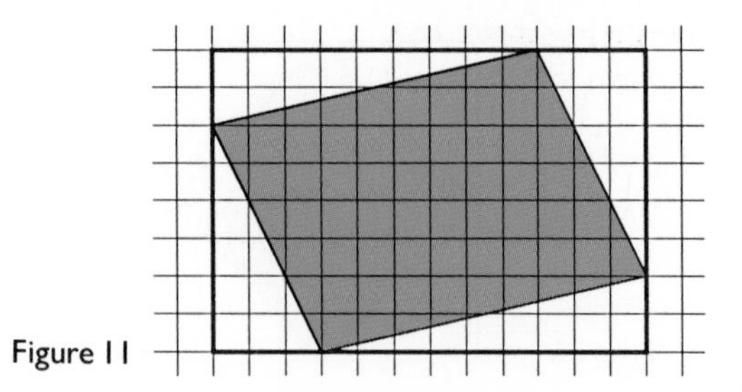
Figure 11

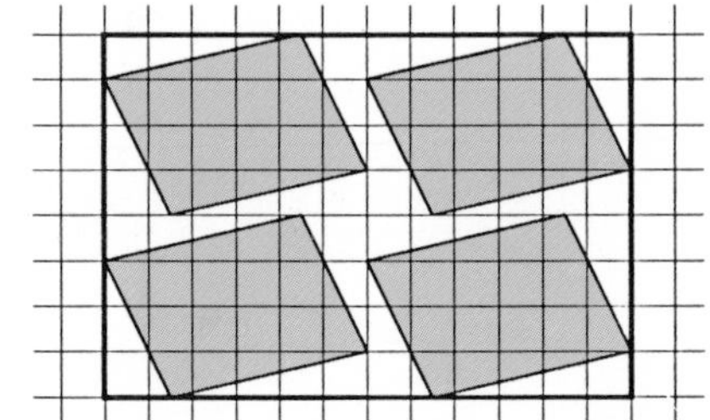
Figure 12

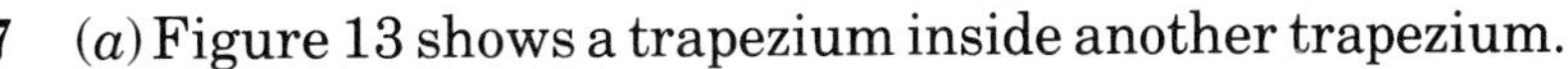

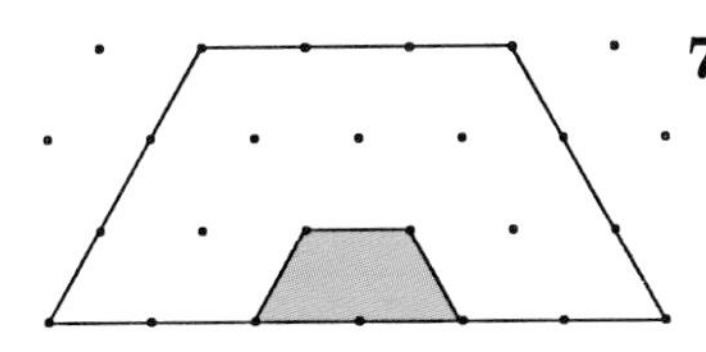
Figure 13

7 (*a*) Figure 13 shows a trapezium inside another trapezium.

By dividing the trapezium into congruent pieces, find the fraction of the trapezium which is shaded orange.

(*b*) Figure 14 shows a triangle inside another triangle of the same shape. Each triangle has an angle of 30°, an angle of 60° and an angle of 90°.

By dividing the larger triangle into congruent pieces, find the fraction which is shaded.

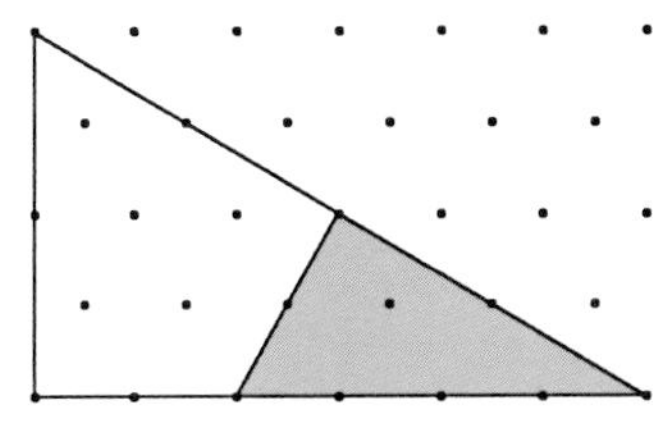
Figure 14

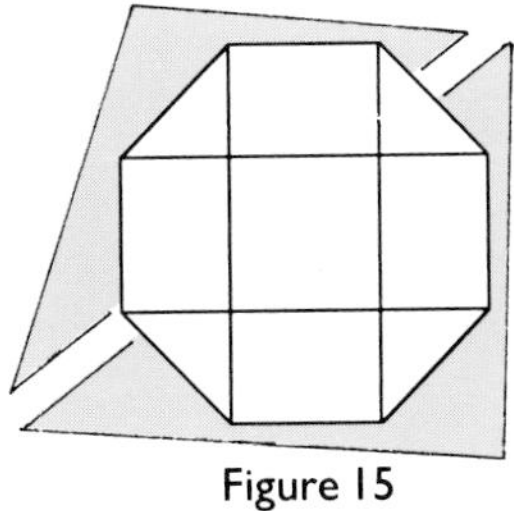
Figure 15

8 Figure 15 shows a regular octagon divided into pieces of three types: square, rectangle and triangle.

The same three types of pieces are used to make a larger shape, as shown below in figure 16.

(*a*) Explain why this larger shape is a regular octagon.

(*b*) What is the ratio of the area of the larger octagon to the area of the smaller octagon?
Explain your answer.

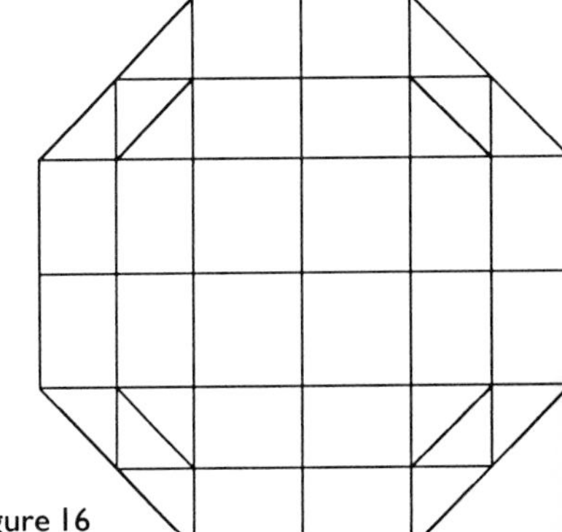
Figure 16

9 Two different shapes which have the same perimeter do not usually have the same area.

The equilateral triangle and the regular hexagon shown below have the same perimeter.

Find the ratio of the area of the hexagon to the area of the equilateral triangle.

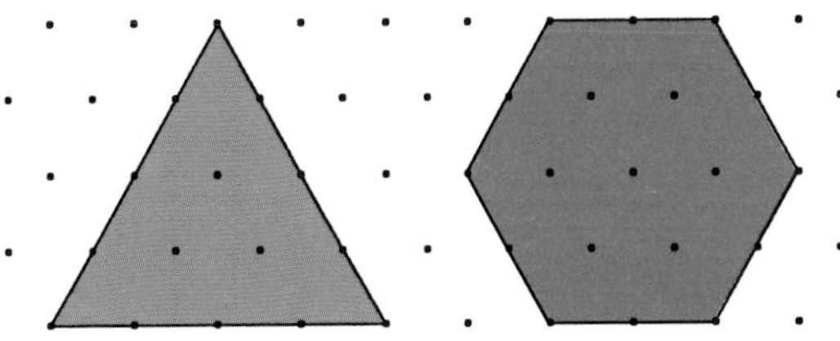

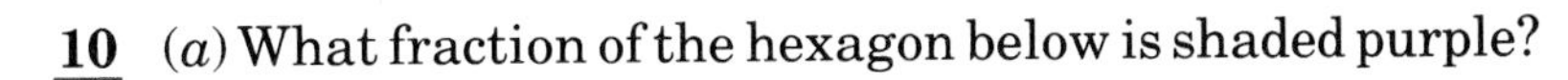

10 (*a*) What fraction of the hexagon below is shaded purple?

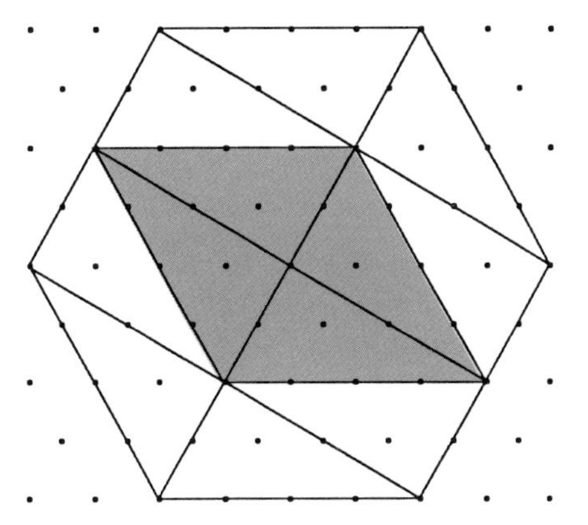

(*b*) What is the shape of the pink portion of the hexagon below? Explain your answer.

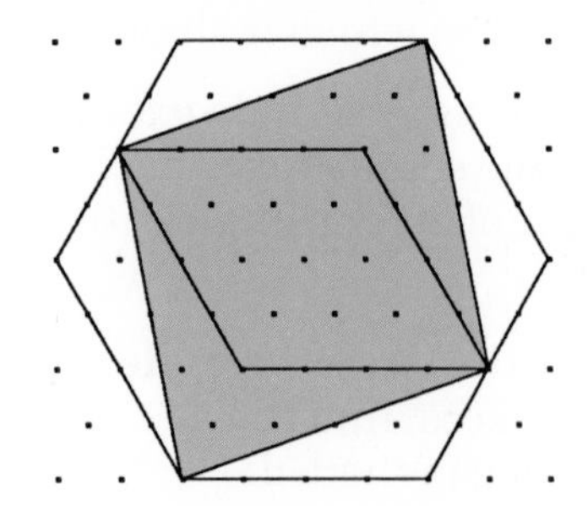

(*c*) What fraction of the hexagon above is shaded pink?

(*d*) What fraction of each of the hexagons shown below is shaded blue?

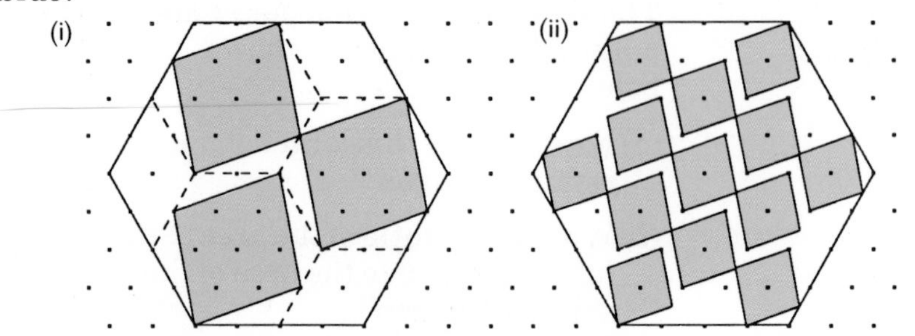

11 Approximately what percentage of each of the squares shown below is shaded orange?

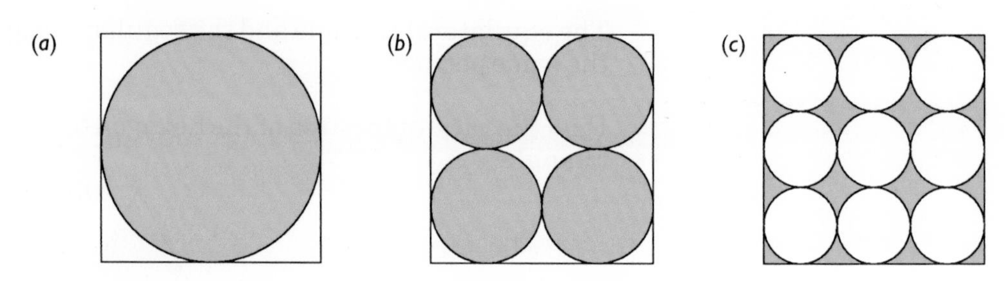

12 Approximately what percentage of each of the equilateral triangles shown below is shaded yellow?

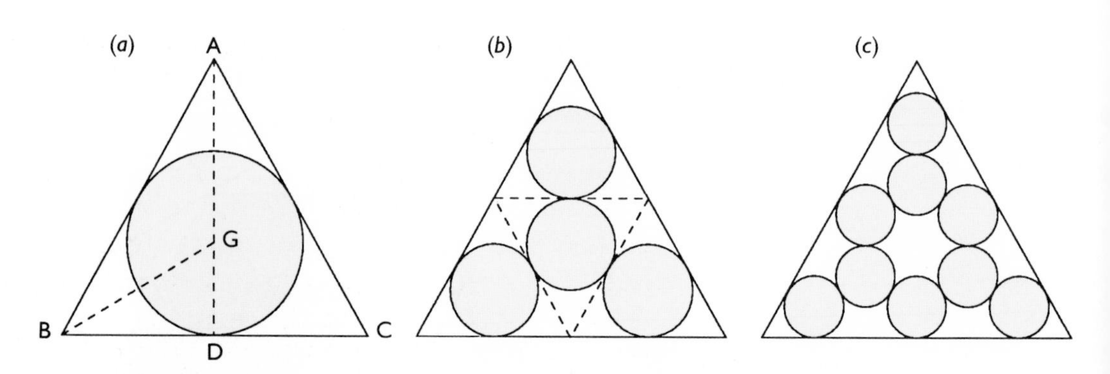

Hint: To do part (*a*), assume that the length of one side of the triangle is 2. Use trigonometry to calculate the length of the radius GD, and also to calculate the length of the line AD.

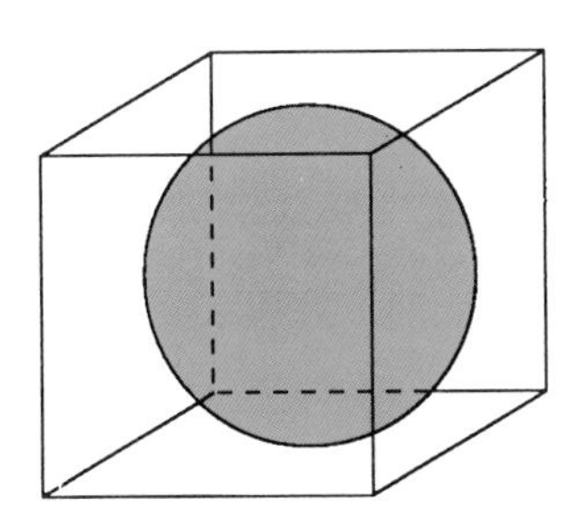

13 (*a*) A sphere just fits in a cube, as shown on the left.

What percentage of the cube does the sphere fill?

(*b*) Eight spheres just fit into a cube of the same size.

What percentage of the cube do these eight spheres fill?

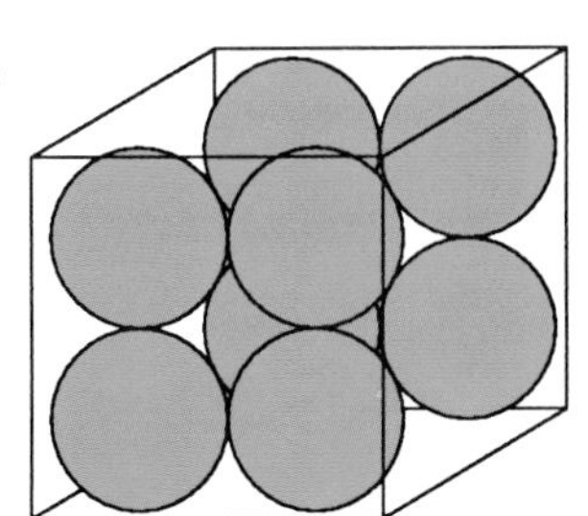

(*c*) If 27 spheres (three layers of nine spheres) just fitted into a cube of the same size, what percentage of the cube would they fill?

For questions 14, 15, 16 and 17 you need the resource sheet *'Circle pictures'*.

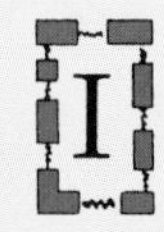

Look at the picture for question 14 on the *'Circle pictures'* resource sheet. The line in the picture meets the circle, but does not go inside it. A line like this is called a **tangent** to the circle.

14 (*a*) Draw the line of symmetry on the picture for question 14.

(*b*) What is the angle between the tangent to the circle and the line of symmetry? Explain your answer.

You will need Pythagoras' theorem for questions 15 and 16. You will find Pythagoras' theorem on page 281.

15 Look at the picture for question 15 on the *'Circle pictures'* resource sheet. The picture shows a circle and two tangents.

(*a*) Draw on the picture its line of symmetry.

(*b*) What does this tell you about the lengths PA and PB?

(*c*) Suppose the length PA is 12 cm and the radius of the circle is 5 cm. Find the distance of P from the centre of the circle.

16 Look at the picture for question 16 on the *'Circle pictures'* resource sheet. The picture shows a circle and one of its chords.

(*a*) Draw the line of symmetry of this picture.

(*b*) Where does the diameter of a circle, which is perpendicular to a chord, meet that chord?

(*c*) If the radius of the circle is 17 cm and the length of the chord is 30 cm, find the distance of the chord from the centre of the circle.

17 Look at the picture for question 17 on the *'Circle pictures'* resource sheet. The picture shows two intersecting circles with the same diameter.

(*a*) Draw the two lines of symmetry of the picture.

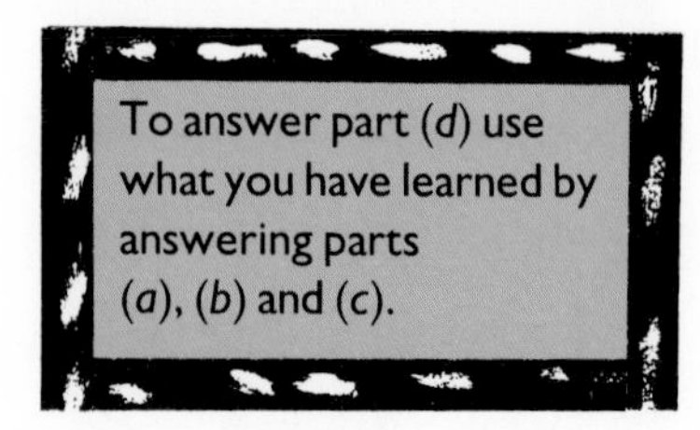

(*b*) What type of triangle is AHB?

(*c*) What can you say about the distances from A and B to the point where the two lines of symmetry meet?

(*d*) Use a compass to help you find the midpoint of the line PQ. You can also use a ruler for drawing a straight line, but do not use the ruler to measure.

(*e*) Suppose the circles in the picture grow, until the circle with centre A passes through the point B, and the circle with centre B passes through the point A.

What type of triangle is AHB now? Justify your answer.

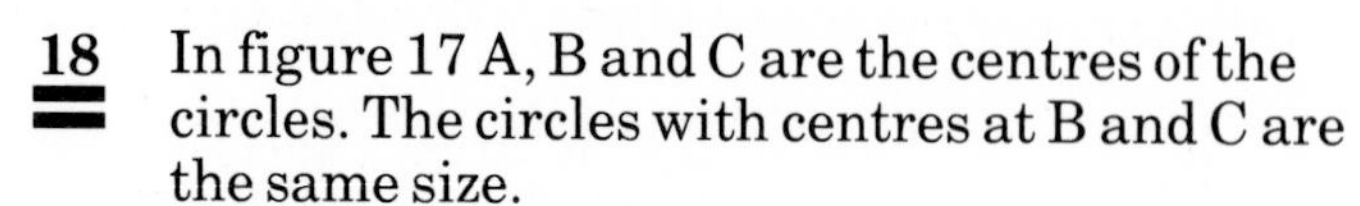

18 In figure 17 A, B and C are the centres of the circles. The circles with centres at B and C are the same size.

(*a*) What shape is ABCD?

(*b*) What is the line of symmetry of this picture?

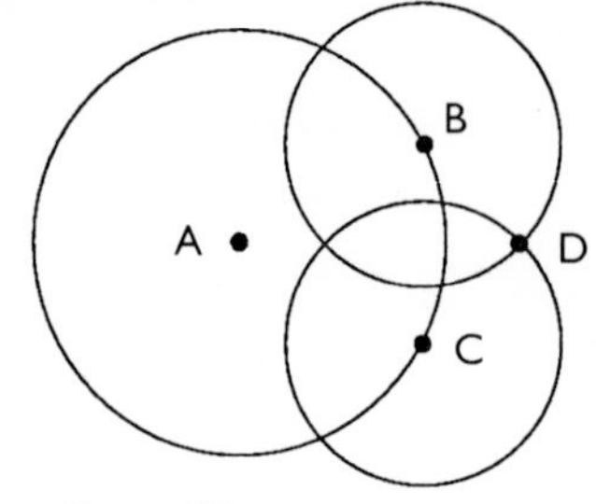

Figure 17

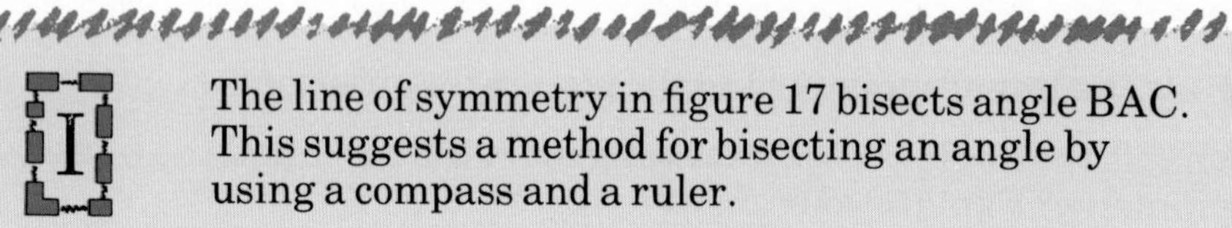

(*c*) The triangle XYZ, shown below, is not drawn to scale.

(i) Draw triangle XYZ accurately, using a compass and ruler.
(ii) Use a compass and ruler to bisect angle Y.

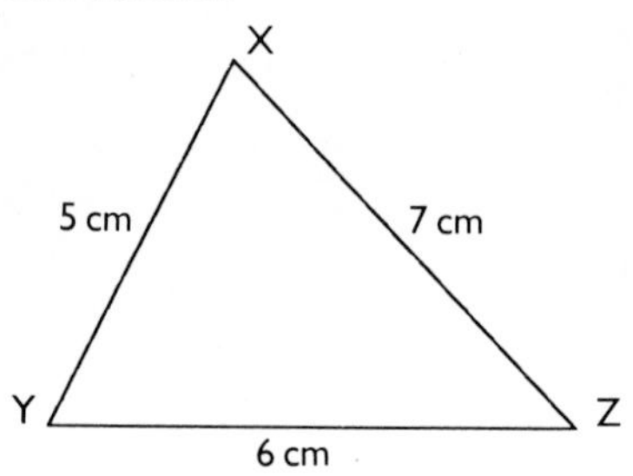

19 Figure 18 shows an equilateral triangle.

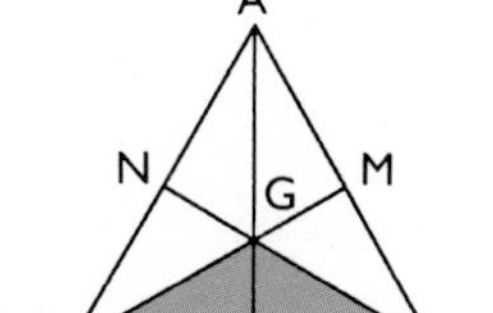

Figure 18

(*a*) (i) What fraction of the triangle is purple?
(ii) What does this tell you about the ratio of AG to GL?
(iii) What other ratios can you deduce from your answer to part (ii)?

(*b*) Figure 19 shows the result of shearing the equilateral triangle.

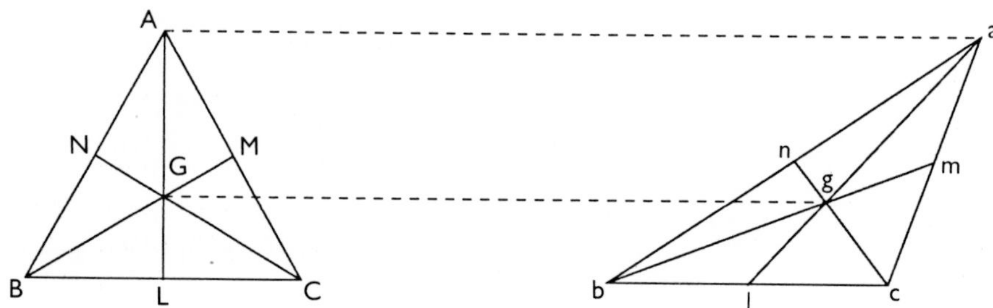

Figure 19

What is that ratio of ag to gl? Justify your answer.

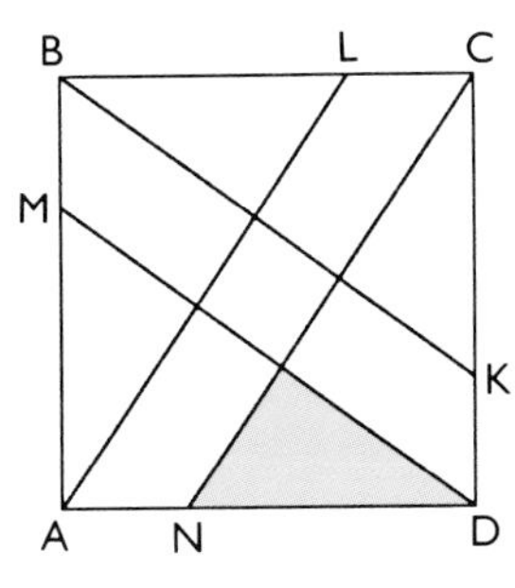

Figure 20

20 Figure 20 shows a dissection of a square.

AM:MB = 2:1, BL:LC = 2:1, CK:KD = 2:1, DN:NA = 2:1.

(*a*) What is the shape of the piece in the middle of the dissection? Justify your answer.

(*b*) Explain why the blue triangle is similar to triangle AMD.

(*c*) Assuming that the length of a side of the dissected square is 3, find the length of

(i) the hypotenuse of the shaded triangle,
(ii) the hypotenuse of triangle AMD.

(*d*) What is the ratio of the area of the blue triangle and triangle AMD?

Hint: The ratio of the areas of similar shapes is equal to the *square* of the ratio of corresponding lengths.

(*e*) What fraction of the area of the dissected square is the area of triangle AMD?

(*f*) What fraction of the area of the dissected square is the piece in the middle?

SECTION B

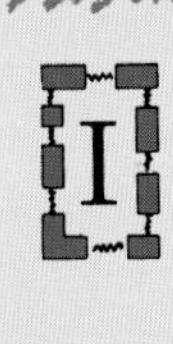

Whole numbers are either even numbers or odd numbers. One way of explaining the difference between an even number and an odd number is to draw a picture.

Figure 21 might help you to see why you get an *odd* number when you add an *even* number to an *odd* number.

Figure 21

1 Draw pictures to show why you get

(*a*) an *even* number when you add an *even* number to an *even* number.

(*b*) an *even* number when you add an *odd* number to an *odd* number.

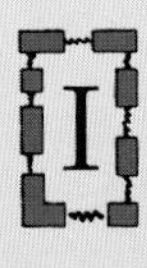

You can use a rectangular arrangement of dots to picture what happens when two numbers are multiplied.
The picture shows 8×5.

This is an even number because all the dots are paired off.

2 (*a*) Draw a picture to show that when you multiply an *even* number by an *even* number, the result is an *even number*.

(*b*) Draw a picture to show that when you multiply an *odd* number by an *odd* number the result is an *odd* number.

3 (*a*) Draw a picture to show that the square of an even number is a multiple of 4.

(*b*) Draw a picture to show that the square of an odd number is 1 more than a multiple of 4.

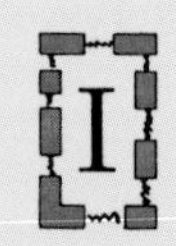

Earlier in this section, pictures for even and odd numbers were presented.

Figure 22 shows that an even number can be written as $2N$ and an odd number can be written as $2M+1$.

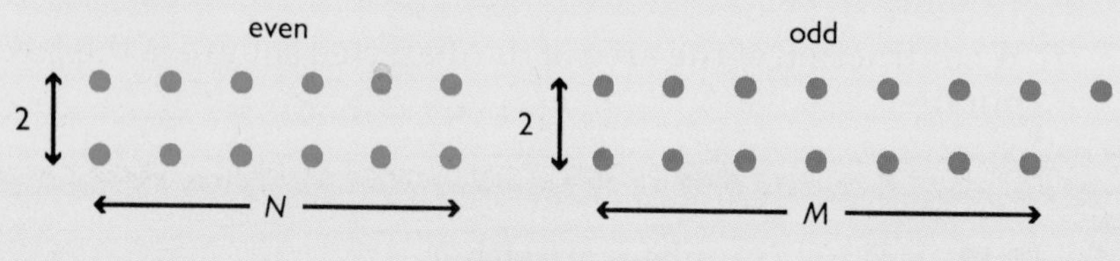

Figure 22

If you have two *different* even numbers to work with, you cannot call *both* of them $2N$. One can be $2N$ and one can be $2P$, for example.

A similar remark applies to two different odd numbers.

If you have an even number and an odd number to work with, do **not** call one of them $2N$ and the other $2N+1$, **unless** you know that the odd number is one more than the even number.

4 (*a*) Use algebra to show that the result of adding two odd numbers is an even number.

(*Hint:* Write one odd number as $2N+1$ and the other as $2P+1$. Show that when you add them the result is $2 \times$ something.)

(*b*) Use algebra to show that the result of adding an even number and an odd number is odd.

(*c*) Use algebra to show that the result of multiplying an even number by an odd number is even.

(*d*) Use algebra to show that the result of multiplying an odd number by an odd number is odd.

(*e*) Use algebra to show that the result of squaring an odd number is a number which is one more than a multiple of 4.

(*f*) Use algebra to show that the result of adding three consecutive numbers is a multiple of 3.

(*g*) Use algebra to show that the result of adding five consecutive numbers, the smallest of which is even, is a multiple of 10.

5 (*a*) Copy the table below.

X	−4	−3	−2	−1	0	1	2	3	4
−4									
−3									
−2									
−1									
0									
1								3	4
2						2	4	6	8
3							6	9	12
4							8	12	16

(*b*) Complete the last row by working from right to left and using the number sequence.

(*c*) Complete the rows in the bottom half of the table in the same way.

(*d*) Complete the right-hand column by working upwards and using the number sequence.

(*e*) Complete the right-hand half of the table in the same way.

(*f*) Complete the table by working from right to left along the rows.

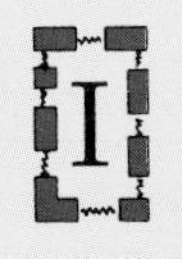

From the table you can see that the result of multiplying a **positive** number by a **negative** number is a **negative** number.

(*g*) What does the table tell you about the result of multiplying a **negative** number by a **negative** number?

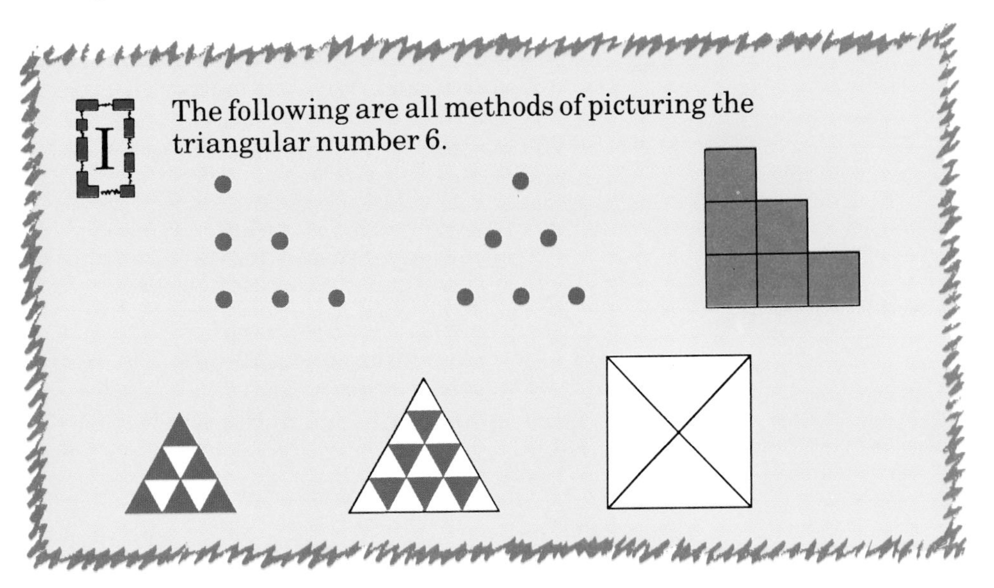

6 (*a*) 'If you add any two consecutive triangular numbers you get a square number. For example, $3 + 6 = 9 = 3^2$.'

(i) Show that the statement above works for the triangular numbers 10 and 15.
(ii) If you wanted to be sure that the statement above was true for *any* two consecutive triangular numbers you might draw a picture.

The box before this question gives several ways of picturing triangular numbers. Use one of these ways to illustrate the statement for the triangular numbers 10 and 15.

(*b*) 'If you double a triangular number, the number you get is the product of two consecutive numbers. For example, $6 \times 2 = 12 = 3 \times 4$.

Draw a picture that explains why this statement is true.

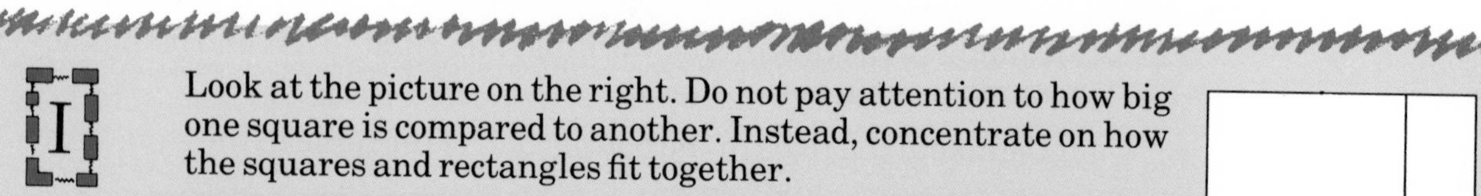

Look at the picture on the right. Do not pay attention to how big one square is compared to another. Instead, concentrate on how the squares and rectangles fit together.

The picture can be given many different meanings. Here are some of them.

A You can split a square into two squares of different sizes and two identical rectangles.

B If you multiply 11 by 11 you get 121.

C If you multiply out $(x + 1)(x + 1)$ you get $x^2 + 2x + 1$.

D If you multiply out $(a + b)(a + b)$ you get $a^2 + 2ab + b^2$.

E If you factorise $p^2 + 2pq + q^2$ you get $(p + q)(p + q)$.

F $6^2 + 6 + 7 = 7^2$.

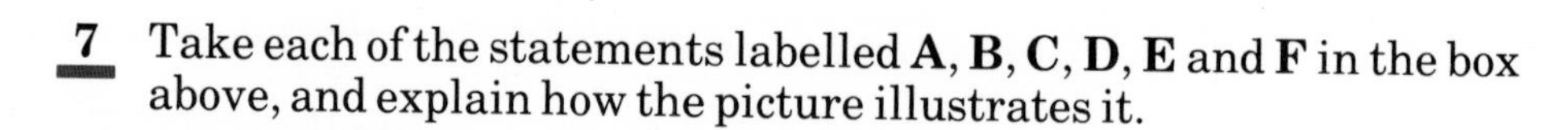

7 Take each of the statements labelled **A**, **B**, **C**, **D**, **E** and **F** in the box above, and explain how the picture illustrates it.

8 (*a*) Draw a single picture that illustrates both of the following statements.

A You can split a rectangle into: a square, two identical smaller squares and three identical rectangles.

B $12 \times 11 = 132$.

(*b*) Each of the following statements is incomplete. Each is illustrated by the picture you have drawn for part (*a*). Complete each statement. You might need to use the pictures to help you.

C $(a + 2)(a + 1) =$

D $e^2 + 3ef + 2f^2 = (\qquad)(\qquad)$

9 Each of the following statements needs its own *separate* picture. For each statement draw the picture and, where necessary, complete the statement.

(*a*) A square can be split into one large square, four identical smaller squares and four identical rectangles.

(*b*) $(a + 3)(a + 2) =$

(*c*) $x^2 + 5xy + 4y^2 =$

(*d*) $31 \times 31 =$

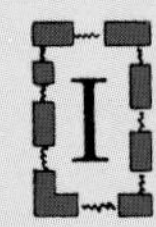

The picture below shows a square with a smaller square removed from its corner.

The orange piece is cut off and replaced in the position shown.

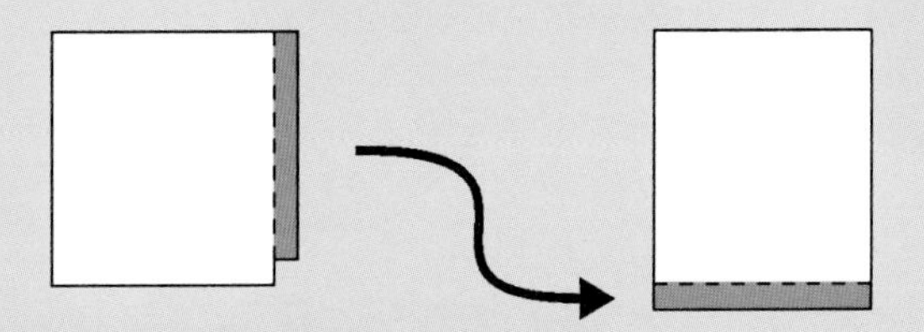

These pictures can be given many different meanings.

One is that $10^2 - 1 = 11 \times 9$.

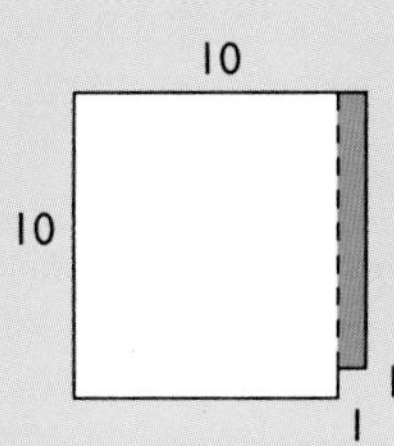

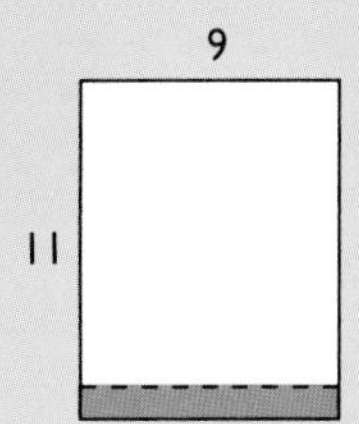

10 Each of the following statements is incomplete. Each is illustrated by the pictures in the box above.

Complete each statement.

(*a*) $20^2 - 1 =$ (*b*) $x^2 - 1 =$

(*c*) $a^2 - b^2 =$ (*d*) $30^2 - 9 =$

(*e*) $27 \times 23 =$ (*f*) $(p + 2q)(p - 2q) =$

(*g*) $7p^2 - 63 =$

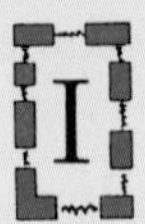

Here is one way of picturing $x^2 - 4x + 3$.

	x	-3
x	x^2	$-3x$
-1	$-x$	3

Notice that some of the lengths marked in the diagram above are negative. You might think that -1 and -3 are strange lengths for the sides of a rectangle, but the picture helps some people to multiply out and factorise expressions involving negative numbers.

The picture is a rectangle with sides of length $x - 3$ and $x - 1$.

So $x^2 - 4x + 3 = (x - 3)(x - 1)$.

11 Draw a picture to show each of the following, and complete each statement.

(*a*) $(p - 3)(p + 1) =$

(*b*) $a^2 - 3a + 2 =$

(*c*) $p^2 - p - 2 =$

(*d*) $x^2 + x - 6 =$

Here is one way of picturing $a^2 - ab - 6b^2$.

	a	$-3b$
a	a^2	$-3ab$
$2b$	$2ab$	$-6b^2$

Some of the rectangles in the diagram above again have negative lengths. The area of the whole rectangle is $a^2 + 2ab - 3ab - 6b^2$. Also, the whole rectangle has sides of length $a - 3b$ and $a + 2b$.

So $a^2 - ab - 6b^2 = (a - 3b)(a + 2b)$.

12 Draw a picture to show each of the following, and complete each statement.

(*a*) $(a + 3b)(a - 4b) =$

(*b*) $(p - 3q)(p - 2q) =$

(*c*) $x^2 + 2xy - 8y^2 =$

(*d*) $x^2 - 6xy + 8y^2 =$

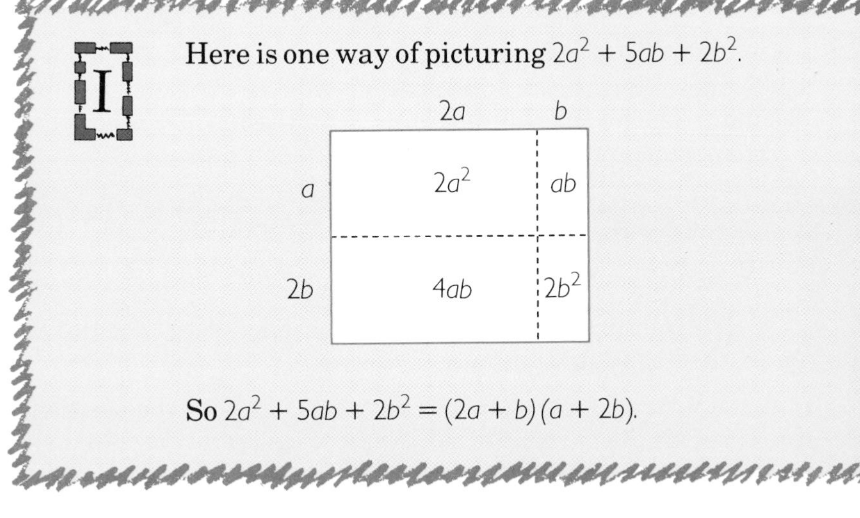

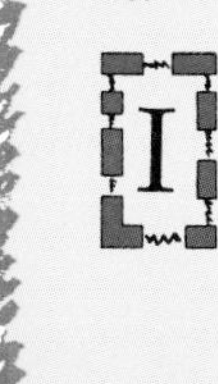

Here is one way of picturing $2a^2 + 5ab + 2b^2$.

So $2a^2 + 5ab + 2b^2 = (2a + b)(a + 2b)$.

13 Complete each of the following statements. (You can draw a picture to help you if you want to.)

(*a*) $2N^2 + 5N + 3 =$

(*b*) $(2p + 1)(p + 4) =$

(*c*) $3a^2 - 10ab + 3b^2 =$

(*d*) $3x^2 - 7x - 6 =$

14

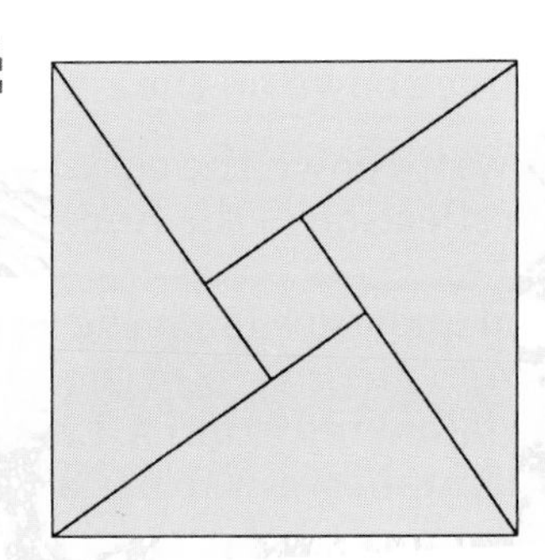

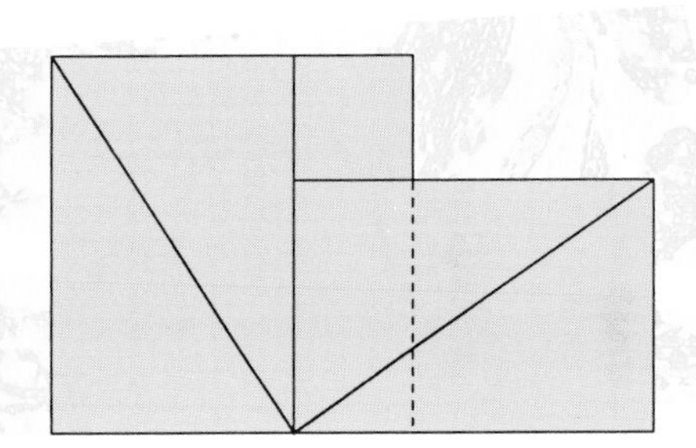

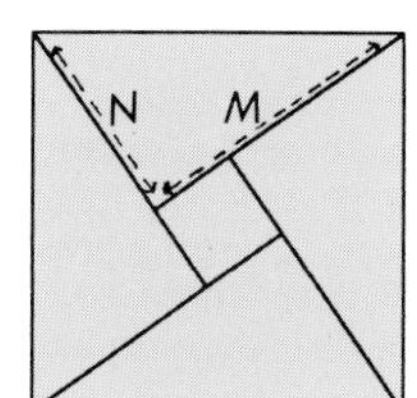

Figure 23

(*a*) Explain how the two drawings above demonstrate Pythagoras' theorem.

(*b*) Figure 23 is the same as one of the drawings above, but the lengths of two of the sides have been marked, using M and N.

(i) Use Pythagoras' theorem to find the area of the large square.
(ii) Find the area of the large square a different way, by adding together the areas of the five pieces into which it is dissected.
(iii) Explain how you can deduce from this that $(M - N)^2 = M^2 - 2MN + N^2$.

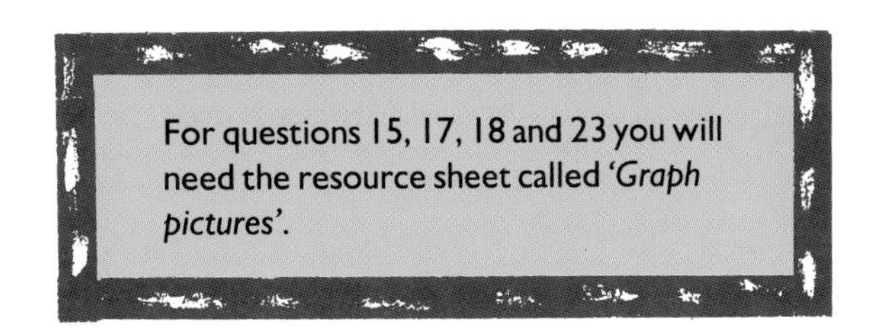

For questions 15, 17, 18 and 23 you will need the resource sheet called '*Graph pictures*'.

15 Several rectangles are such that the ratio of the lengths of adjacent sides is 2:1.

Suppose that the lengths of adjacent sides of such a rectangle are x and y. The picture for question 15 on the resource sheet called *'Graph pictures'* shows the relationship between x and y.

(*a*) One such rectangle is obtained when $x = 4$ and $y = 2$. Mark on the picture the point which represents this rectangle.

(*b*) Explain why the picture consists of *two* straight line graphs.

(*c*) The picture has two lines of symmetry. What are the equations of these lines of symmetry?

(*d*) What is the relationship between x and y if the perimeter of a rectangle is 10? Add the graph of this relationship to the picture.

(*e*) What is the meaning of the points at which the graph you have just drawn cuts the other graphs?

For questions 16 to 23 you will find it helpful to use a graphical calculator or a graph-drawing program on a computer.

16 The line in figure 24 is the graph of $y = 2x - 3$.

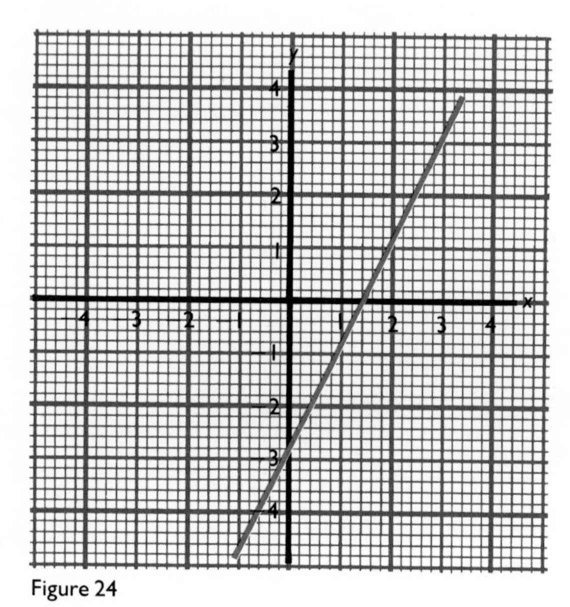

Figure 24

(*a*) Write down two equations which have graphs parallel to the line shown.

(*b*) Write down the equation of a line which meets the line shown on the y-axis.

(*c*) Write down the equation of a line which meets the line shown on the x-axis.

(*d*) Write down the equation of a line which is the reflection of the line shown in the y-axis.

17 Find question 17 on the resource sheet called *'Graph pictures'*. On the set of axes provided sketch the following graphs. Label each sketch graph clearly. You might want to use a graphical calculator to check your sketches.

(*a*) $y = x + 3$ (*b*) $y = x - 3$ (*c*) $y = -2x + 3$
(*d*) $y = -2x - 3$ (*e*) $y = \frac{x}{5}$ (*f*) $y = -5x$

18 Figure 25 shows the graphs of $y = x^2$ and $y = x^3$.

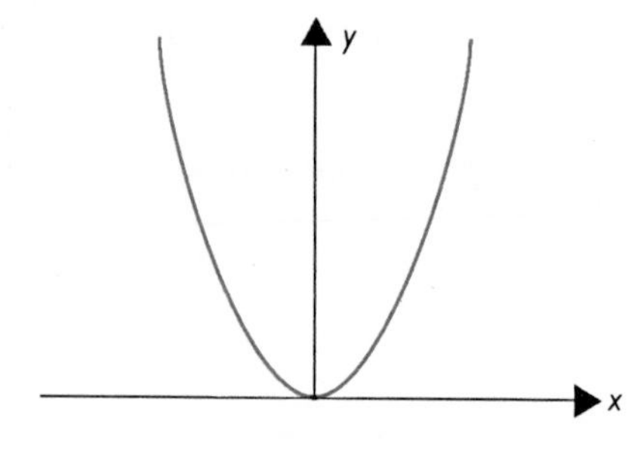

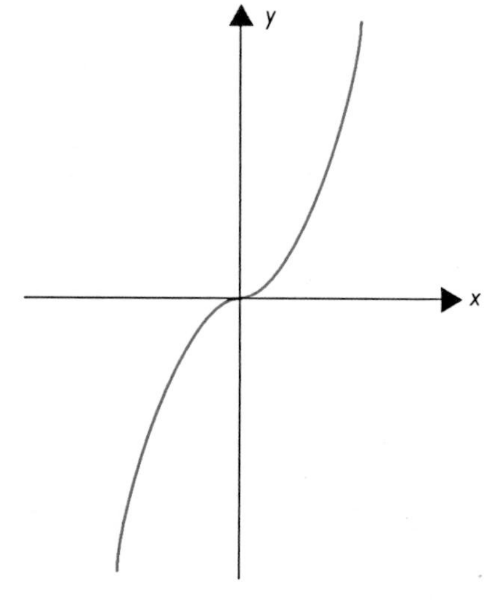

Figure 25

Two of the graphs in question 18 and one of the graphs in question 19 are the graphs of trigonometric functions (sine and cosine).

For a full explanation of the graphs of trigonometric functions see Chapter 20, pages 155 to 158.

(*a*) (i) What is the equation of the line of symmetry of the graph of $y = x^2$?
(ii) What is the centre of rotational symmetry, and the order of rotational symmetry, of the graph of $y = x^3$?

(*b*) Find question 18 on the resource sheet called *'Graph pictures'*. On each set of axes sketch the graphs of the equation given and describe the symmetry of the graph.

(i) $y = x^2 + 4$ (ii) $y = -x^2$ (iii) $y = 2x^2$
(iv) $y = -x^2 + 4$ (v) $y = x^3 - 4$ (vi) $y = -x^3 + 4$
(vii) $y = \frac{1}{x}$ (viii) $y = \frac{1}{x} - 4$ (ix) $y = \cos x + 1$
(x) $y = \sin x - 1$ (xi) $y = x^2 + 4x$ (xii) $y = x^3 - x$
(xiii) $y = \frac{1}{x-4}$

19 In each of the following say which of the three equations is represented by the sketch graph.

(*a*)

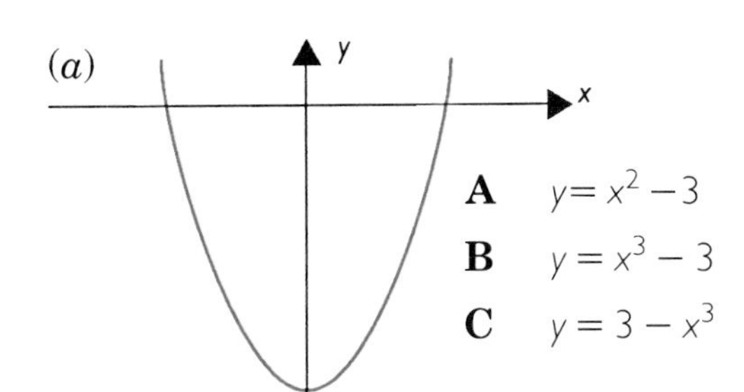

A $y = x^2 - 3$
B $y = x^3 - 3$
C $y = 3 - x^3$

(*b*) **A** $y = x^2 + 4$
B $y = x^3 + 4$
C $y = x^3 - 4$

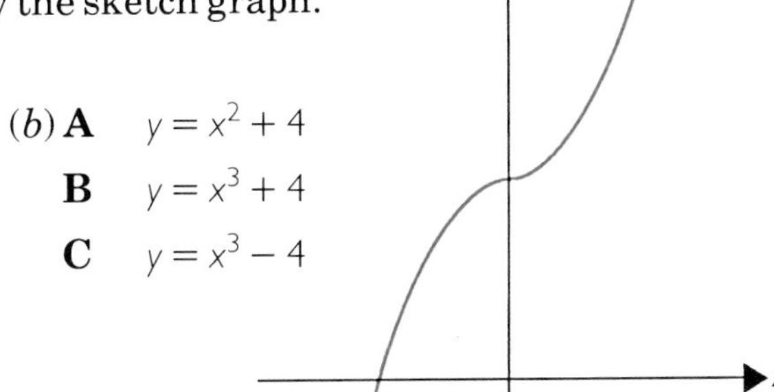

(*c*)

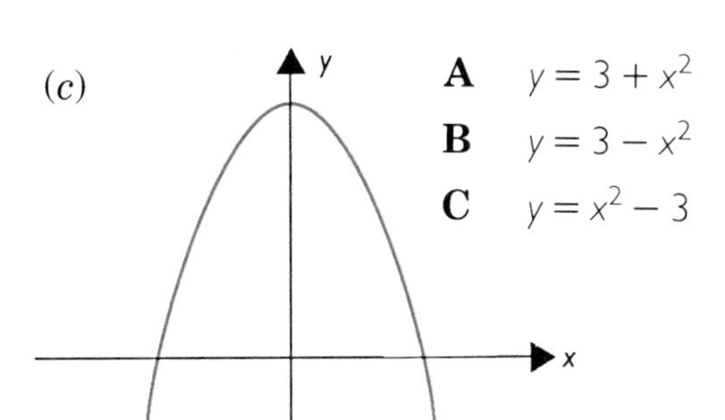

A $y = 3 + x^2$
B $y = 3 - x^2$
C $y = x^2 - 3$

(*d*) **A** $y = x^3 - 4$
B $y = x^3 - 4x$
C $y = 4x - x^3$

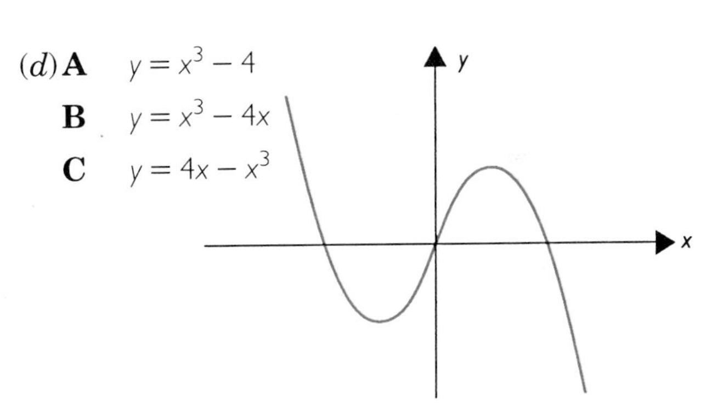

(*e*)

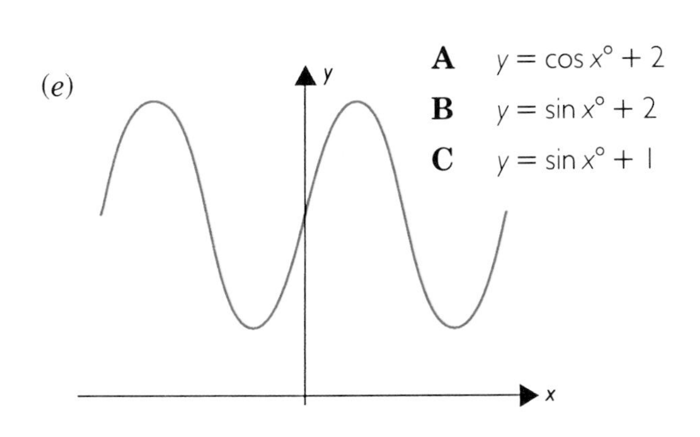

A $y = \cos x° + 2$
B $y = \sin x° + 2$
C $y = \sin x° + 1$

(*f*) **A** $y = \frac{1}{x}$
B $y = \frac{1}{x+3}$
C $y = \frac{1}{x} + 3$

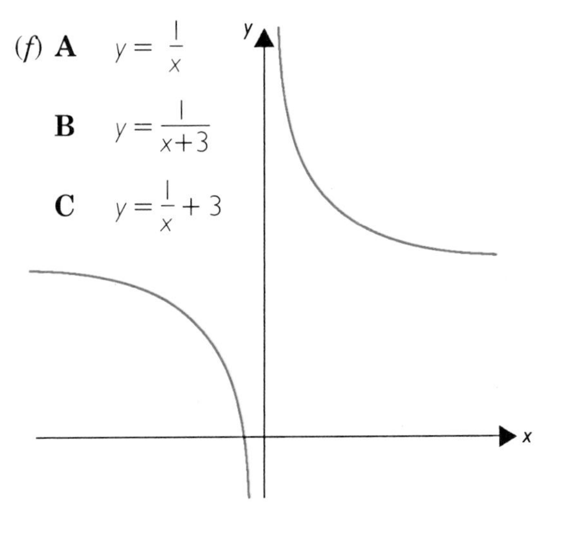

20 In each of the following pictures there is a labelled black graph and an unlabelled red graph.

For each picture suggest a possible equation for the graph drawn in red.

(a)

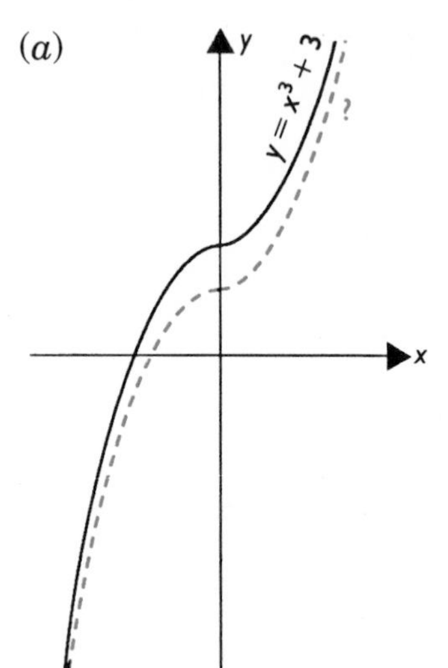

(b)

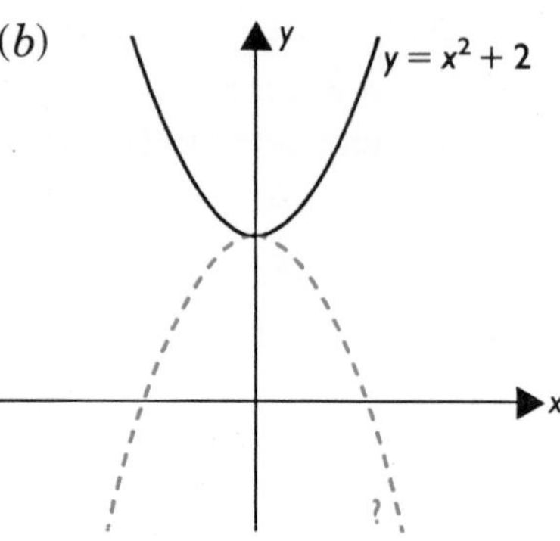

(c)

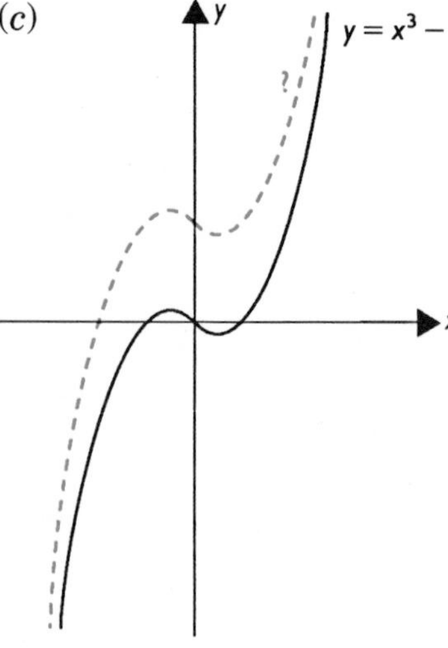

(d)

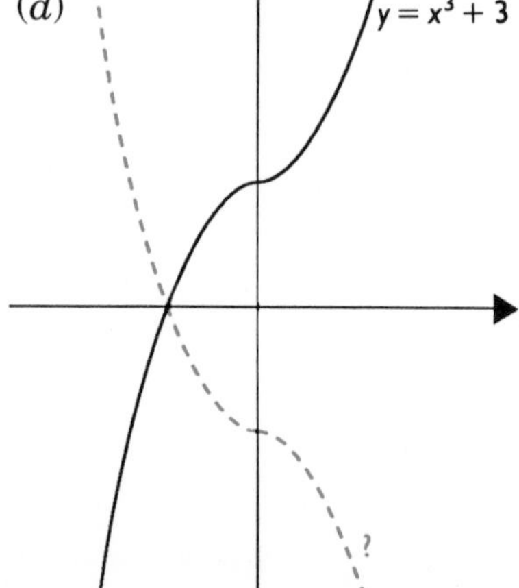

(e)

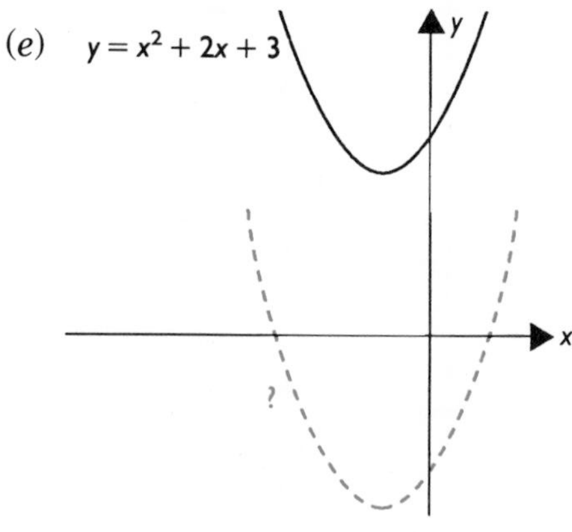

Figure 26

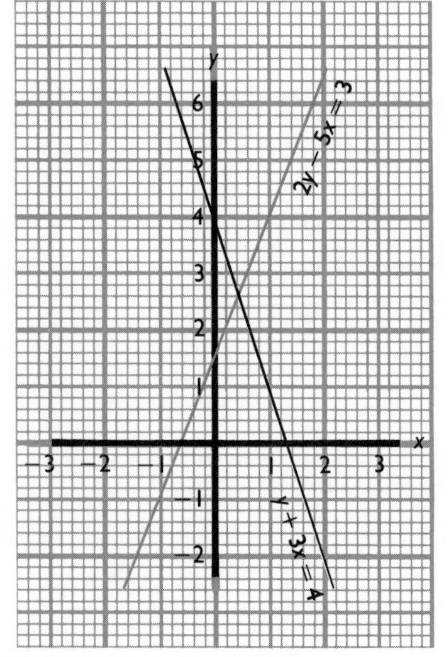

21 Figure 26 shows the graphs of $2y - 5x = 3$ and $y + 3x = 4$.

The simultaneous solution of the pair of equations

$$2y - 5x = 3$$
$$y + 3x = 4$$

can be found by looking at a particular point of the graph. Which point do you look at and what is the solution, correct to one decimal place?

22 Use a graphical calculator or a graph-plotting program on a computer to solve simultaneously the following pair of equations, correct to two decimal places.

$$x + 4y = 9$$
$$5x + 6y = 8$$

(*Hint:* It might be necessary, depending on which graph plotter you are using, to rearrange each equation in the form $y = ...$)

23 The picture for question 20 on the resource sheet called *'Graph pictures'* shows the graph of $y = x^2 + 2x - 3$.

(*a*) Use the graph to find the solutions of $x^2 + 2x - 3 = 0$.

(*b*) By drawing suitable lines on the same axes find the solutions of the following equations.

(i) $x^2 + 2x - 3 = 4$ (ii) $x^2 + 2x - 4 = 0$
(iii) $x^2 + 2x - 3 = -x$ (iv) $x^2 + x - 3 = 0$

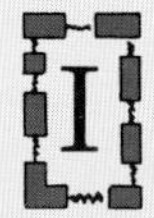

In Section D of Chapter 13 (in Book 4 of this series) a method was explained for finding the solutions of equations by trial and improvement.

Suppose you want to find a solution to the equation

$$x^2 - 3x - 6 = 0 \qquad \text{(A)}$$

This equation can be rearranged as follows:

$$x^2 = 3x + 6$$

Therefore $x = \dfrac{3x + 6}{x}$ (B)

Suppose you start by guessing that a solution to the equation is 3. You use equation (B) as a way of obtaining a new guess for the solution to the equation.

$$x_{new} = \frac{3x + 6}{x} \qquad \text{(C)}$$

So the new guess is $\dfrac{9 + 6}{3} = 5$

Now you can use 5 to get the next new guess as $\dfrac{15 + 6}{5} = 4.2$

Using a calculator you can soon obtain a solution of the equation (A) correct to two decimal places.

24 (*a*) For this question use the method explained in the box above. Taking 3 as your first guess, obtain a solution to the equation

$$x^2 - 3x - 6 = 0$$

(The solution you get should lie between 4 and 5).

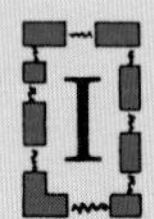

There is a second solution to the same equation as the graph shows.

But whatever you choose for your first guess, if you apply (C) in the box on page 43 you will never converge on this solution.

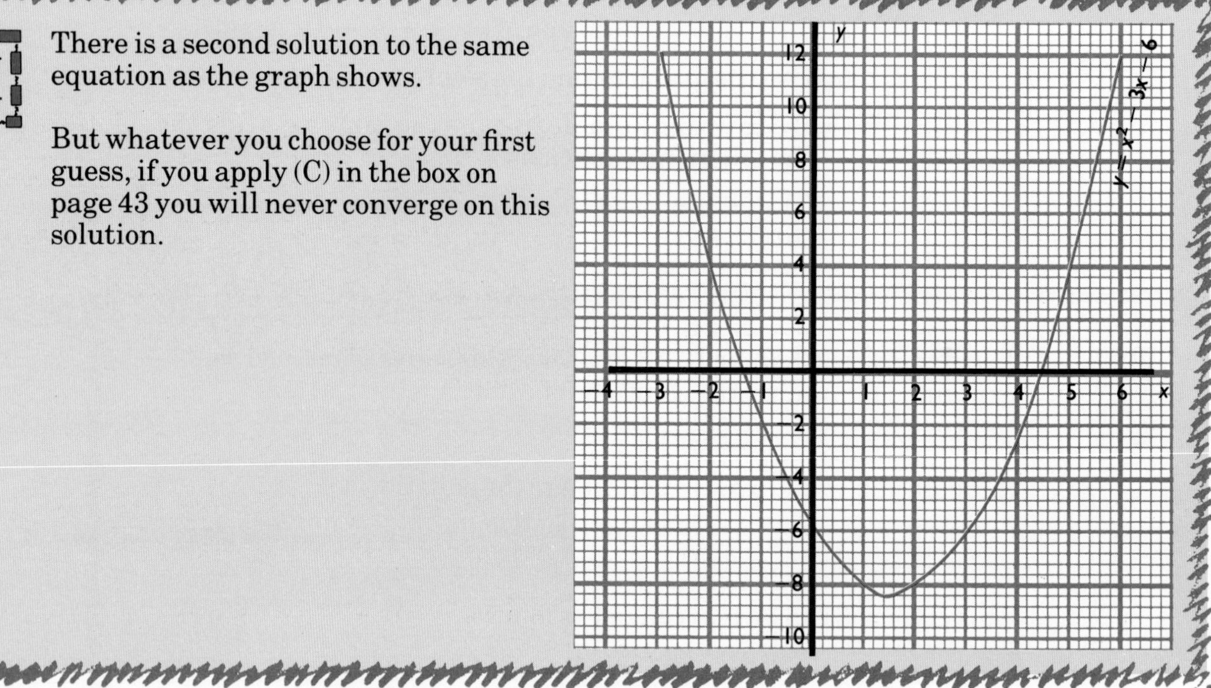

(*b*) According to the graph in the box above, there is a solution quite close to -1.4.

Repeat part (*a*), but this time take -1.4 as your first guess. What happens?

One way of getting the other solution of the equation is to use a different rearrangement. If you want to get both the solutions you will need to know two suitable arrangements. A way of doing this is explained in Review Exercise 38 on page 128.

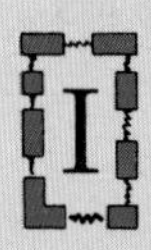

To explain why the rule $x_{new} = \frac{3x + 6}{x}$ always gives one of the solutions of equation $x^2 - 3x - 6 = 0$, but never the other solution the diagram below can be used. It is called a **cobweb diagram**. It shows the graphs of

$$y = \frac{3x + 6}{x} \text{ and } y = x$$

The two solutions of equation (A) are represented by the points where these two graphs intersect.

Suppose your first guess is 3 (the point **A**). To get the second guess you work out $\frac{3x + 6}{x}$ when x is 3. This takes you to point **B**.

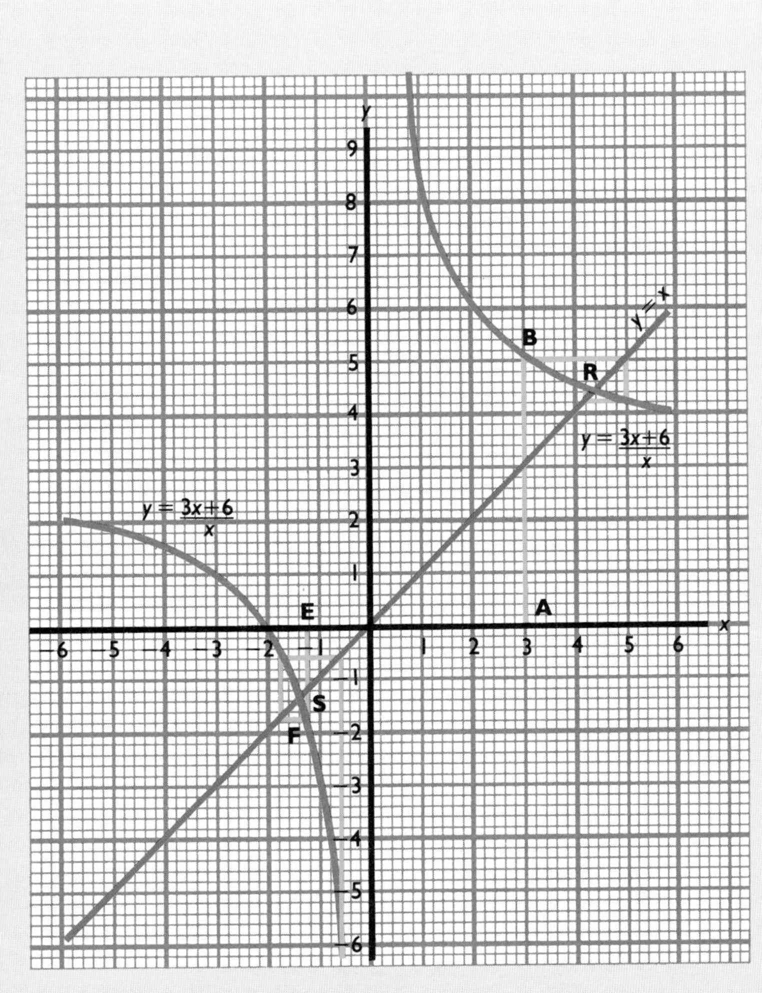

You keep repeating this and close in on the point **R**.

Suppose your first guess is -1.2 (the point **E**). To get the second guess you work out $\frac{3x+6}{x}$ when x is -1.2. This takes you to point **F**.

You keep repeating this and this takes you well away from point **S**.

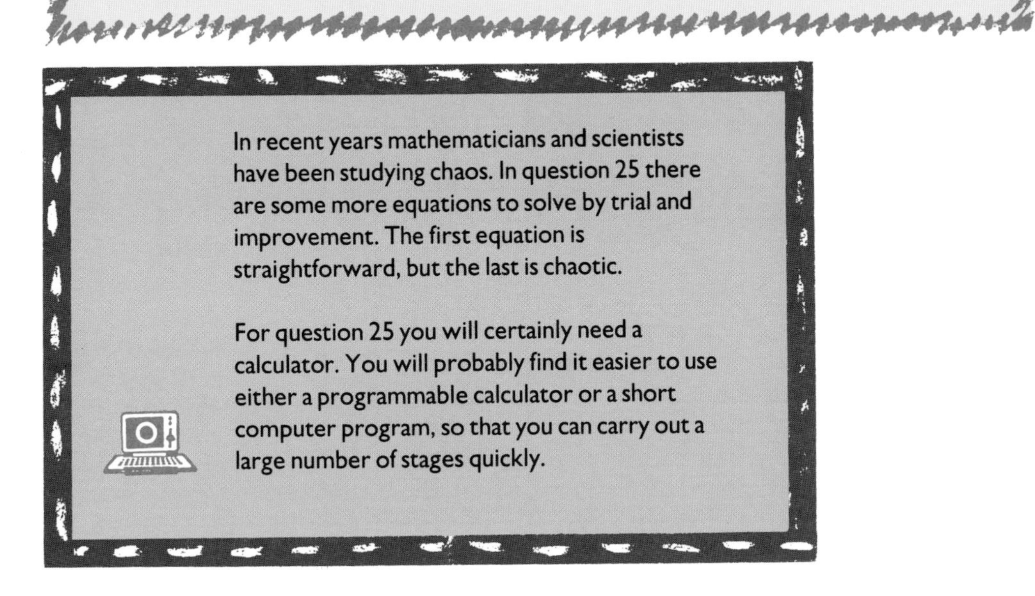

In recent years mathematicians and scientists have been studying chaos. In question 25 there are some more equations to solve by trial and improvement. The first equation is straightforward, but the last is chaotic.

For question 25 you will certainly need a calculator. You will probably find it easier to use either a programmable calculator or a short computer program, so that you can carry out a large number of stages quickly.

25 (*a*) Solve the equation

$$x = 2.8x(1 - x)$$

correct to 2 decimal places, by the same method as for question 24, using

$$x_{new} = 2.8x(1 - x)$$

The graph below shows a cobweb diagram for this equation.

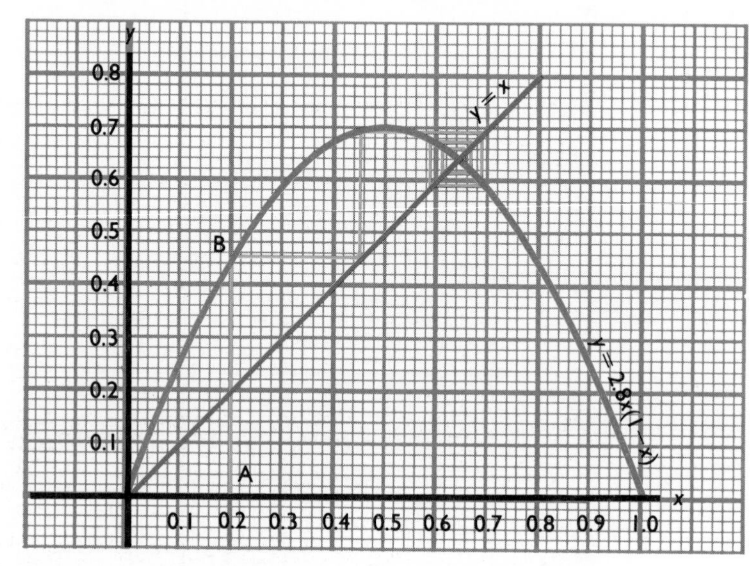

(*b*) Try to solve the equation

$$x = 3.2x(1 - x)$$

using

$$x_{new} = 3.2x(1 - x)$$

Explain what happens. The cobweb diagram below should help.

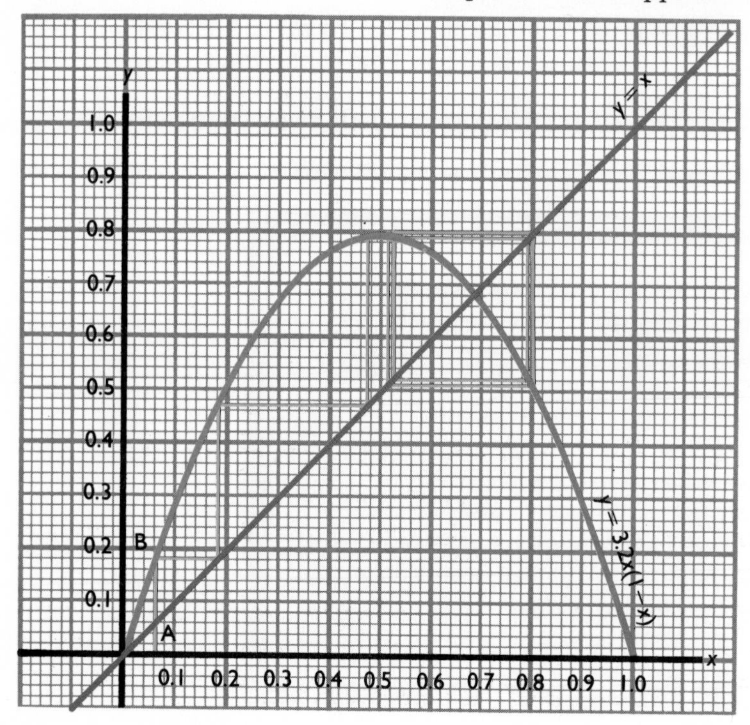

(*c*) Try to solve the equation

$$x = 3.5x(1 - x)$$

using

$$x_{new} = 3.5x(1 - x)$$

Explain what happens this time.

(*d*) Try to solve the equation

$$x = 3.6x(1 - x)$$

using

$$x_{new} = 3.6x(1 - x)$$

Explain what happens this time.

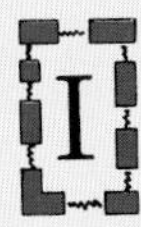

Question 25 illustrates how solving a particular type of equation by trial and improvement becomes more and more chaotic as the number at the beginning of the right-hand side is increased.

Figure 27 shows the 'solutions' obtained when equations of the form

$$x = kx(1 - x)$$

are solved by trial and improvement for different values of k.

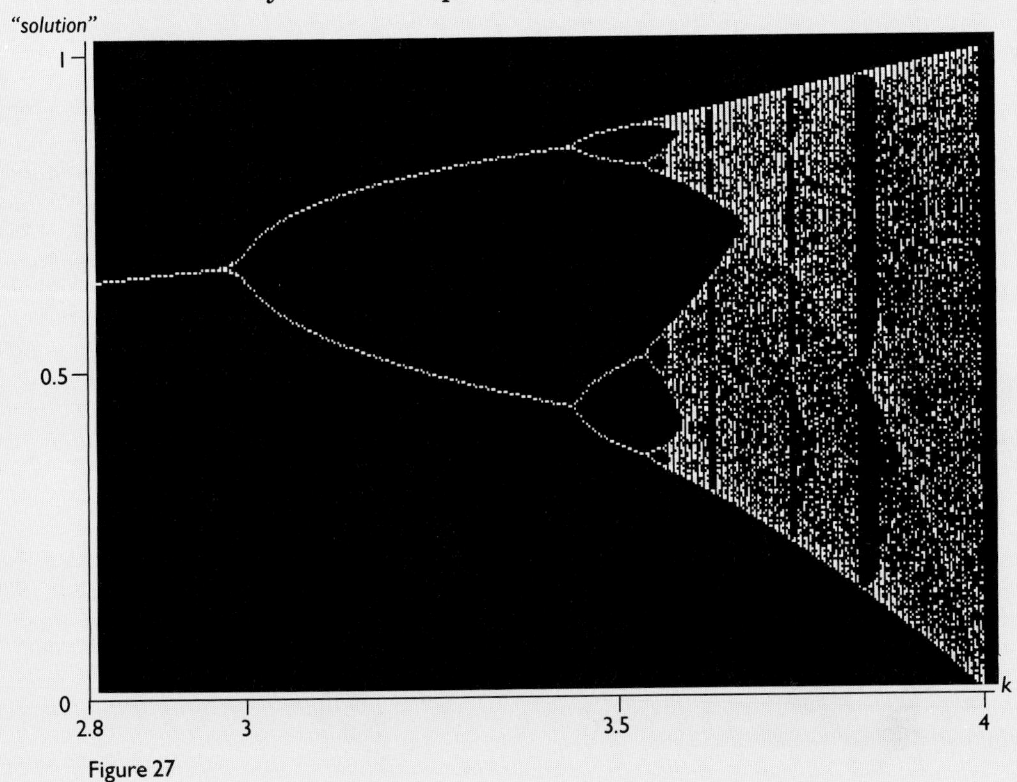

Figure 27

By the time $k = 3.6$ the process has become chaotic. But it seems from the picture that there are patterns in the chaos.

Make a poster to tell a story about some mathematics. Design the poster carefully so that it communicates its message clearly some ideas are provided on P48.
Write an account to go with your poster.

- Your account should clearly state the mathematical purpose of your poster.
- The account should explain the decisions you made when you designed your poster.
- Describe how you collected any information you needed to make your poster. If you obtained information from books, say which books. If you obtained information from talking to people, explain this.

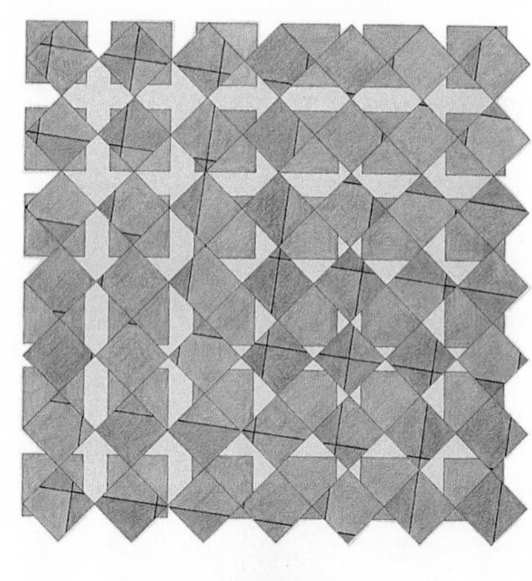

- The account should explain any geometrical constructions you needed to use.
- If you needed to calculate any lengths before you could draw your poster your account should explain your calculations.

There are several different posters you could choose to make.

1⟩ You could make an artistic poster.

Layers in shallow space (transformations) 1989
Susan Tebby

This picture is made by overlapping three square grids.

Rotating hexagons (permutation II) 1988
Susan Tebby

Rotating hexagons (permutation I) 1988
Susan Tebby

Rotating hexagons 1988
Susan Tebby

2⟩ You could make a poster which provides a puzzle for other people to solve.

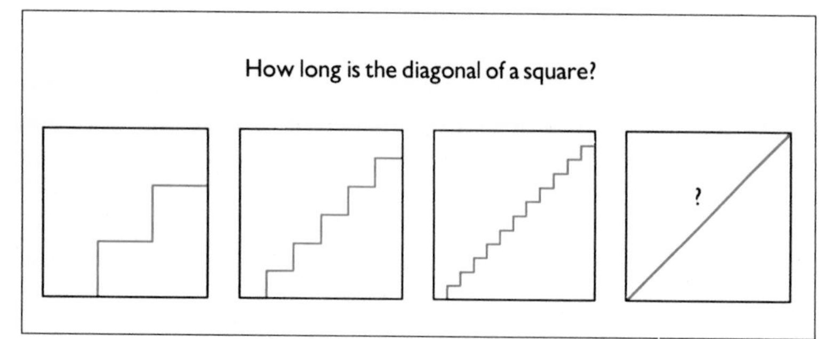

3⟩ You could make a poster which explains some mathematics.

Polygonal numbers

Triangular

Square

Pentagonal

Hexagonal

Triangular	1	3	6	10	15	21	28	36	45	55
Square	1	4	9	16	23	36	49	64	81	100
Pentagonal	1	5	12	22	35	51	70	92	117	145
Hexagonal	1	6	15	28	45	66	91	120	153	190
Heptagonal	1	7	18	34	55	81	112	148	189	235

MANAGING THE FUTURE

What will life be like for you in the year 2010?

Which of the following questions do you think you know accurate answers to? Which are you not sure about? Which do you have no idea about?

- How old will you be?
- How tall will you be?
- How much will you weigh?

- What will you be wearing?
- What will you be eating?
- What music will you be listening to?
- Where will you be living?

- What job will you be doing?
- How much will you be earning?
- How will you be travelling to work?

- How much will a pint of milk cost in 2010?
- Will there still be pints of milk?

- How many children will you have?
- What kind of schools will they go to?
- What will be the average family size in the year 2010?

- Who will be Prime Minister in the United Kingdom in the year 2010?
- Which party will be in power?
- Which party will you be supporting?
- Which countries will be poor in 2010?
- Which countries will be powerful?

- Will cars still be used as much as they are now?
- What other forms of transport will be popular?

- Will the world's climate have changed?
  If so, what effect will that have on your life?

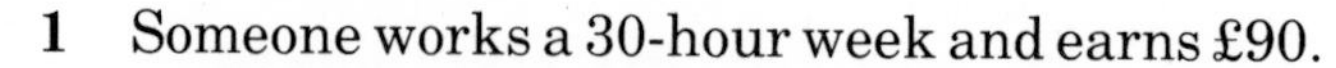

SECTION A

The theme of this section is earning money and budgeting how to spend it.

1 Someone works a 30-hour week and earns £90.

(*a*) If she was paid at the same rate for a 40-hour week, how much would she earn?

(*b*) How much would she earn for a 37-hour week?

2 In 1989 a licence for colour TV cost £62.50 per year. A house only needed one TV licence even if it had more than one TV.

(*a*) During 1989 a family of four rented a TV for £30 per calendar month.

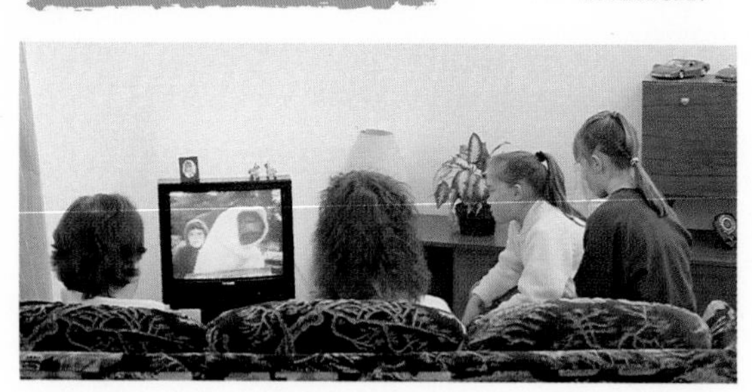

What was their total cost of TV viewing per person

(i) for that year?
(ii) per week?

(*b*) In a different family there were five people. This family rented two colour TVs at the same rental.

What was the total cost of TV watching per person per week for that family?

3 A colour TV costs £400 to buy. It costs £20 per month to rent the same TV and to have it maintained free of charge.

(*a*) After how many months will it be cheaper to buy the TV than to rent it?

(*b*) In answering part (*a*) there are several factors you have probably ignored. Here are two of them.

A The TV might go wrong and need repairing.

B Money can be put in a post office or building society and earn interest.

Consider each of these factors in turn. If you took it into account, would it make your answer to part (*a*) a longer time or a shorter time?

4 A boy decides to save some of the money he earns from his part-time job. He decides to save the same amount each week.

After 6 weeks he has saved £30.

(*a*) How much has he saved after 12 weeks?

(*b*) How much has he saved after 9 weeks?

(*c*) How much has he saved after 14 weeks?

5 A boy has a part-time job. He agrees to pay his parents a fixed proportion of what he earns each week for housekeeping.

When he earns £40 he pays his parents £15.

(*a*) How much will he pay his parents if he earns £60?

(*b*) How much will he pay if he earns £47?

(*c*) One week he pays his parents £21. How much does he earn that week?

6 A girl is left £150 by her granny. She puts it into a savings account which pays 12% interest per year.

(*a*) How much interest does she receive after one year?

(*b*) She leaves the £150 in the savings account for three years, but takes her interest out at the end of each year.

How much interest does she receive altogether for the three years?

7 If you want to save for the future you could invest £100 in a building society.

Suppose that the building society pays 9% interest per year on your money.

(*a*) How much interest would you receive at the end of one year?

(*b*) If you take out the interest you receive at the end of each year, how much interest would you receive after

(i) 3 years? (ii) 7 years? (iii) x years?

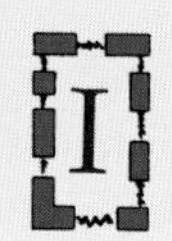

Instead of taking the interest out of your account you could leave it in the account. So, at the end of the first year, instead of having £100 in your account you would have £109. At the end of the second year the interest added to your account would be 9% of £109, which is £9.81. So you would then have £118.81. Interest added in this way is called **compound interest**.

Over the two years your money would have earned £18.81 interest. So £18.81 is the compound interest on £100 at 9% for 2 years.

(*c*) If you continued in the way described in the box above for a third year, how much money would be in your account after three years?

(*d*) What is the total interest earned on £100 invested at 9% compound interest for 4 years?

8 When a girl starts work she is paid £100 per week.

(*a*) At the end of both the first year and the second year she has an 8% pay rise.

How much does she earn after her second pay rise?

(*b*) At the end of the third year she has a 7% pay rise. How much does she earn after this pay rise?

9 A girl buys a car for £2000. In each of the first three years it loses 20% of its value it had at the start of the year.

How much is the car worth after she has owned it for three years?

10 A credit card company charges 2% interest per month on what the customer owes the credit card company at the end of the month.

(*a*) A customer owes the credit card company £200 at the beginning of June. No further credit is used and no money is paid during June. How much will the customer owe the company by the end of June?

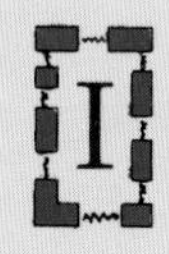

To find 2% of something you multiply it by 0.02. So to find out how much something is after 2% is added to it you can multiply by 1.02.

So one useful way of finding the answer to part (*a*) is to multiply by 1.02.

Check that this gives the answer you obtained for part (*a*).

You should find a similar method useful when answering the other parts of this question.

(*b*) In part (*a*) you found out how much the customer owed the credit card company by the end of June. Assuming that no further credit is used and no money is paid off, how much will the customer owe the credit card company

(i) by the end of July?
(ii) by the end of October?
(iii) by the end of the following May?

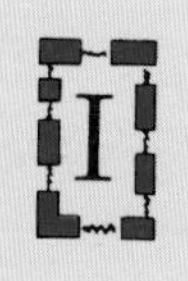

Credit card companies (and other people who lend money) have by law to state their interest as an APR. APR stands for Annual Percentage Rate. To find the APR charged by the credit card company in this question you calculate the interest paid over one year, assuming that no money is paid back during the year (even though credit card companies do not allow you to do this.)

(*c*) 'Compound interest of 2% per month is equivalent to an APR of 26.8% per annum.'

Use your answer to part (*b*)(iii) to help you explain what this statement means.

11 The barchart on page 53 shows average male and female earnings in 1989 for 16 groups of workers. Suppose someone wants to compare the earnings of male and female workers. For each group he calculates the average female earning as a percentage of the average male earning.

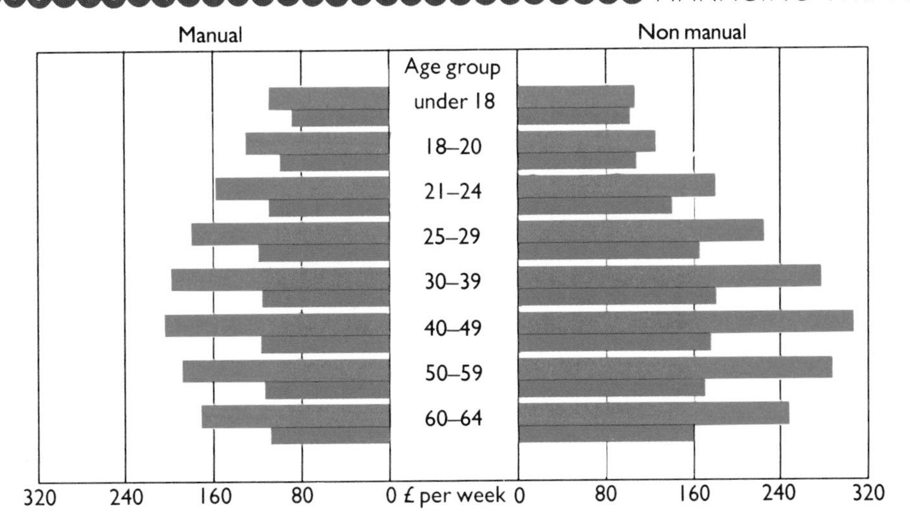

(*a*) By measuring the barchart find

(i) what this percentage is for full-time manual workers aged between 21 and 24.
(ii) for which group this percentage is highest.
(iii) for which group this percentage is lowest.

(*b*) On the basis of the information in this table do you think that the difference between average incomes for males and females is going to increase or decrease during the next ten years? Justify your answer.

12 The pie charts below shows the distribution of the world's population and income in 1960.

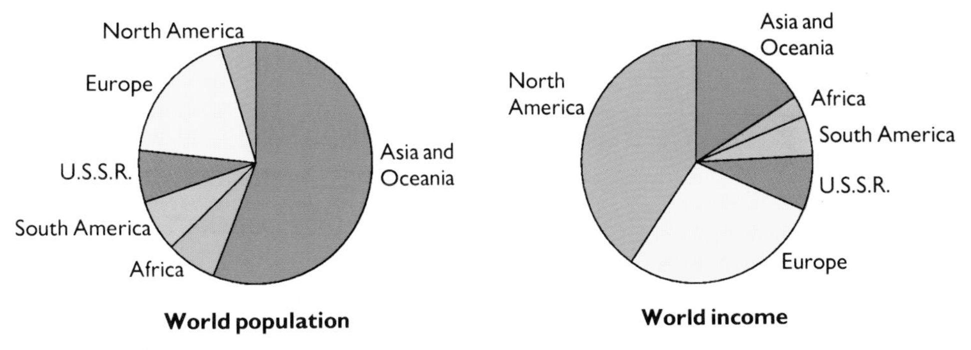

(*a*) In 1960 what percentage of the world's population lived in

(i) North America?
(ii) Asia?

(*b*) In 1960 what percentage of the world's income did

(i) North America have?
(ii) Asia have?

(*c*) It is clear from the pie charts that in 1960 the typical North American had a much higher income than the typical Asian.

Why would it not be true to say that in 1960 every North American was much better off than every Asian?

(*d*) Using your answer to parts (*a*) and (*b*), calculate how many times bigger the income of a typical North American was than the income of a typical Asian.

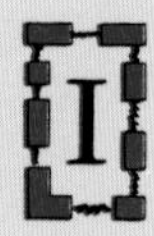

One estimate is that the population of North America is increasing by 10% every ten years, while the population of Asia is increasing by 16% every ten years.

13 (*a*) If the estimates in the box above are correct, what will be the ratio of the population of Asia to the population of North America by the year 2010?

(*b*) If the proportions of world income of North America and Asia do not change from 1960 to 2010, how many times better off will the typical North American be compared to the typical Asian by the year 2010?

SECTION B

The theme of this section is the resources needed by individuals, by families and by larger populations, and the ways in which the world population is changing.

1 (*a*) If a family of 4 between them eat 0.5 kg of potatoes on a typical day, what weight of potatoes will they eat in

(i) a week?
(ii) a year?

(*b*) What weight of potatoes would a family of 7 eat in a year, assuming that a typical person in this family eat potatoes at the same rate as a typical person in the other family?

(*c*) A city has 200 000 people. Assuming that they all consume potatoes at the same rate as people in the family of 4, approximately what weight of potatoes will the city eat in a year?

(*d*) Why does the assumption you made in (*c*) probably lead you to overestimate the potato consumption for the city?

2 In a typical week Jean treats herself to three Mars bars.

How many Mars bars is she likely to eat in

(*a*) 5 weeks? (*b*) 12 weeks? (*c*) a year?

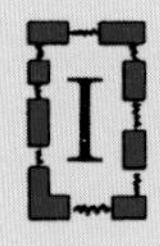

In question 2 the number of Mars bars is **directly proportional** to the number of weeks.

This means that if you double the number of weeks you double the number of Mars bars; if you have five times as many weeks you have five times as many Mars bars, and so on.

The graph shows the number of Mars bars plotted against the number of weeks.

When one quantity is *directly proportional* to another, the graph is a *straight line through the origin.*

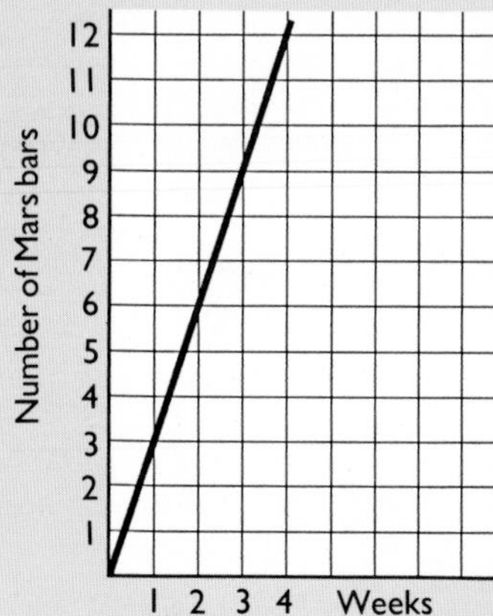

3 On a typical day a family drinks 2 pints of milk.

(*a*) How many pints of milk are drunk by the family in

(i) 3 days?
(ii) 4 days?
(iii) 6 days?

(*b*) Draw a graph to show the relationship between the number of pints of milk drunk and the number of days. Use 1 cm to represent 1 day on the horizontal axis and 1 cm to represent 1 pint on the vertical axis. Label the horizontal axis from 0 to 15 days.

(*c*) How many pints of milk are drunk by the family in

(i) 8 days?
(ii) 2 weeks?
(iii) a year?

(*d*) How long will it take the family to drink

(i) 10 pints?
(ii) 26 pints?
(iii) 14 gallons?
(1 gallon = 8 pints)

4 At present, the population of the world is increasing by about 80 million people per year.

(*a*) At this rate, by approximately how many people will it increase in

(i) 4 years?
(ii) $2\frac{1}{4}$ years?
(iii) one month?

(*b*) The figure of 80 million is obviously a rough estimate. Suppose this estimate is correct to the nearest 10 million.

(i) What is the smallest possible rate of increase per year?
(ii) What is the largest possible rate of increase per year?

(*c*) (i) What is the approximate increase in one day?
(ii) Using your answers to (*b*), give the largest and smallest possible values for the increase in one day.

5 'In the developed world the average person uses, directly or indirectly, about 120 kg of paper per year. In the Third World it is about 8 kg per person per year.'

(*a*) How much paper does the average person in the developed world use, directly or indirectly, in a day?

(*b*) What is meant by the phrase 'directly or indirectly'?

(*c*) Given that the population of the developed world is about 2 thousand million and the population of the Third World is about 3 thousand million, estimate, in tonnes, the weight of paper used throughout the world in a day. (1 tonne = 1000 kg)

(*d*) If this same amount of paper were used every day, but everyone in the world had a fair share, how much paper would each person use?

(*e*) If what is described in (*d*) were to happen, what would be the decrease in the amount each person in the developed world uses in a day?

(*f*) What would be the percentage decrease in paper use for each person in the developed world?

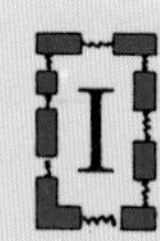

When two quantities are directly proportional both of them increase at the same rate. But sometimes two quantities are related so that one quantity *increases* while the other *decreases*.

Here is an example. Jason is raising money for Oxfam. He has decided he will raise £24 by asking several people to give the same amount.

The *more* people he asks, the *less* he will ask each of them to give.

If he asks 6 people, he will want them each to give £4. If he *increases* the number of people to 8, the amount he asks each of them to give will *decrease* to £3.

The graph on the right shows how the amount asked for is related to the number of people.

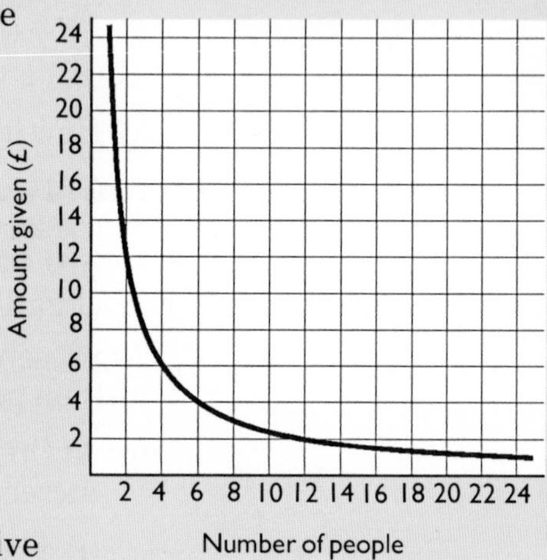

Two quantities related in this way are said to be **inversely proportional.** This means that they multiply together to give some fixed amount.

6 A sack of potatoes lasts a family of 4 people 60 days.

(*a*) If they ate potatoes at the same rate, how long would a sack of the same size last

(i) 8 people?
(ii) 6 people?
(iii) 1 person?
(iv) 15 people?

7 Someone planning a coach trip hires a coach with 49 seats. They have to pay a fixed amount for the coach.

If 20 people go on the coach trip each person must pay £6 to cover the cost of the coach.

(*a*) How much would each person need to pay if the number of people who go on the coach trip is

(i) 40?
(ii) 10?
(iii) 30?

(*b*) Draw a graph to show the relationship between the number of people on the coach trip and the cost per person. Take 1 cm on the horizontal axis to represent 10 people and 1 cm on the vertical axis to represent £1.

8 A car journey takes 6 hours, travelling at an average speed of 40 mph.

(*a*) How long is the journey?

(*b*) If the roads in ten years time are more congested and the average speed is reduced to 30 mph, how long will the journey take?

(*c*) How long would the journey take by train, if the average speed of the train is 100 mph?

(*d*) How long would the journey take by air, if the average speed of the plane is 250 mph?

(*e*) Why might the answer to (*d*) be misleading if compared to the answers to (*b*) or (*c*)?

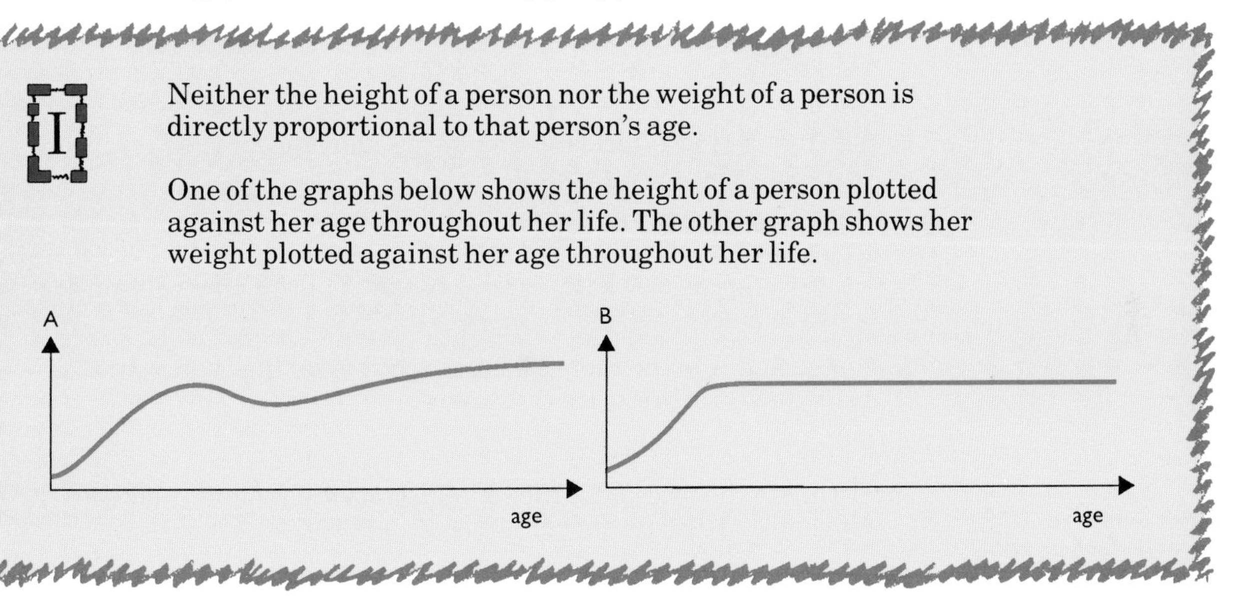

9 (*a*) In the box above which graph shows the height and which shows the weight of the person? Explain your answer.

(*b*) Approximately how long did this person live? Explain your answer.

10 The graph below shows the world record for the mile since 1923.

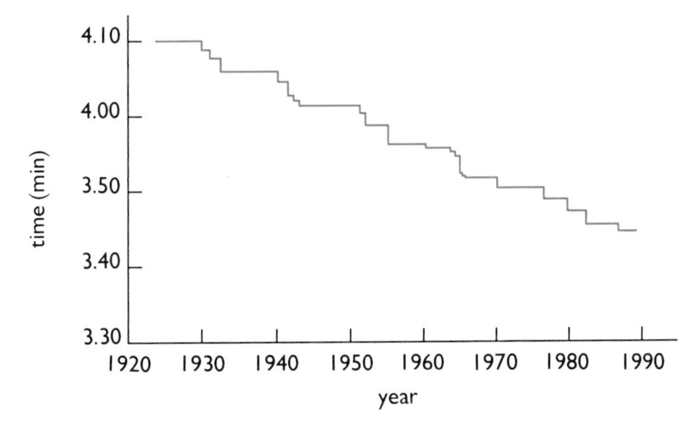

(*a*) Explain why the graph consists of a series of steps.

(*b*) Use the graph to estimate the world mile record in the year 2010.

11 The table below shows the prices of cars of the same make, but of different ages in November 1989.

Year	Price when new	Al price now
1984 A	5110	2700
1984 B	5110	2925
1985 B	5312	3125
1985 C	5420	3375
1986 C	5582	3600
1986 D	5750	3850
1987 D	6106	4100
1987 E	6228	4425
1988 E	6492	4775
1988 F	6752	5175
1989 F	7005	5950

(*a*) The figures in the 'price when new' column appear to be given correct to the nearest pound.

(i) How accurately do the figures in the 'A1 price now' appear to be given?
(ii) Why do you think the figures in the 'A1 price now' column are given less accurately?

(*b*) For each line of the table, calculate the percentage which the 'A1 price now' is of the 'price when new'.

(*c*) Comment on your answers to part (*b*).

(*d*) Estimate the price for a 1989 F registration car of this make in November 1993, if that car is in A1 condition.

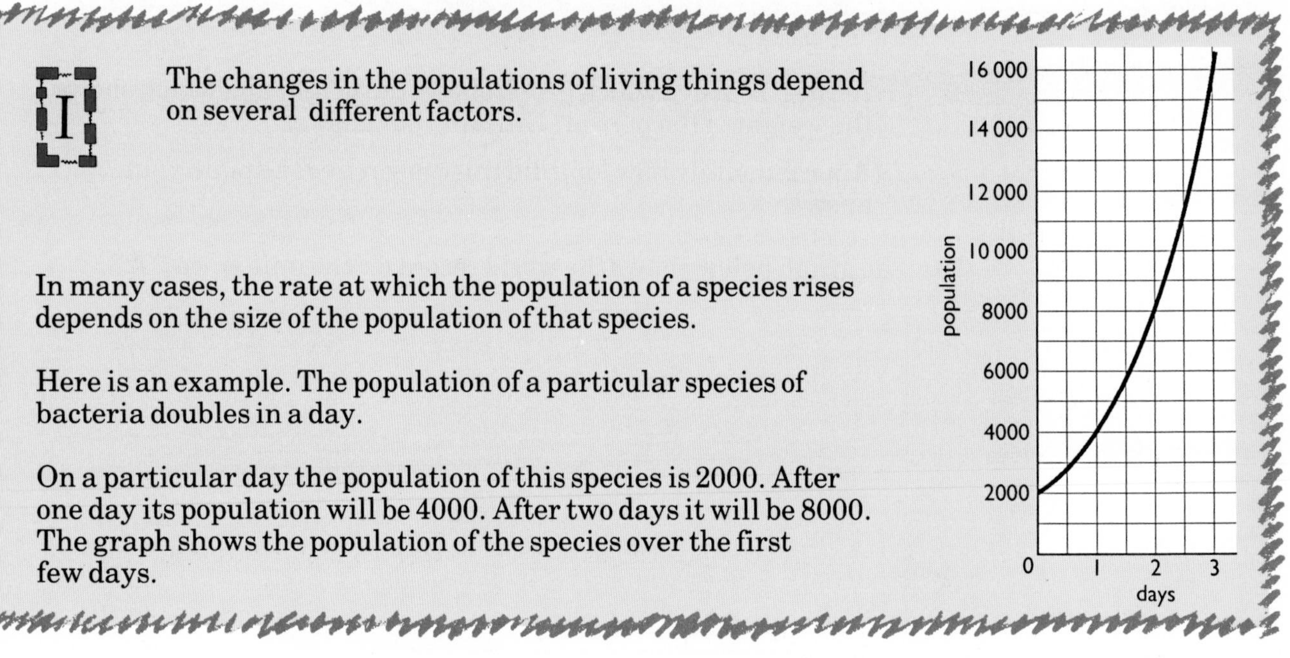

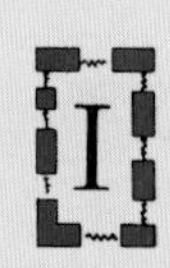

The changes in the populations of living things depend on several different factors.

In many cases, the rate at which the population of a species rises depends on the size of the population of that species.

Here is an example. The population of a particular species of bacteria doubles in a day.

On a particular day the population of this species is 2000. After one day its population will be 4000. After two days it will be 8000. The graph shows the population of the species over the first few days.

12 (*a*) What is the population of the species described in the box above after 6 days?

(*b*) After approximately how many days will the population reach 10 million?

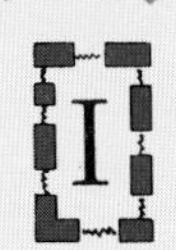

A different species of bacteria trebles its population every day.

Suppose that on a particular day its population is 1000.

After 1 day its population is 1000×3^1
After 2 days its population is 1000×3^2
After 3 days its population is 1000×3^3
After 4 days its population is 1000×3^4
After 5 days its population is 1000×3^5
After N days its population is 1000×3^N

13 Use the X^y button (or Y^x button) on your calculator to find the population of the bacteria described in the box above after

(i) 5 days
(ii) 28 days

(*b*) Use the X^y button (or Y^x button) on your calculator to find the population after $\frac{1}{2}$ day.

To find the answer to (*b*) you needed to multiply 1000 by $3^{\frac{1}{2}}$. To understand what $3^{\frac{1}{2}}$ means you can think what happens in the two halves of the first year.

During the first half of the year the population multiplies by $3^{\frac{1}{2}}$.
During the second half of the year it again multiplies by $3^{\frac{1}{2}}$.
During the whole year it multiplies by 3.

So $3^{\frac{1}{2}} \times 3^{\frac{1}{2}} = 3$. But $\sqrt{3} \times \sqrt{3} = 3$

In other words, $3^{\frac{1}{2}}$ is the square root of 3.

By thinking about what happens in a third of a year it can be seen that

$3^{\frac{1}{3}} \times 3^{\frac{1}{3}} \times 3^{\frac{1}{3}} = 3.$

So $3^{\frac{1}{3}}$ is the cube root of 3 ($\sqrt[3]{3}$).

14 (*a*) Use the  button (or Y^x button) on your calculator to find

(i) $\sqrt{7}$
(ii) $\sqrt{10}$
(iii) $\sqrt[3]{4}$
(iv) $\sqrt[4]{20}$

(*b*) (i) Find $(\sqrt{7})^5$.
(ii) Find $7^{2.5}$.
(iii) Comment on your answers to parts (i) and (ii). Explain.

15 Some experts estimate that the population of the human race is doubling every 40 years.

In 1990 the population was approximately 5 billion (or 5000 million).

(*a*) Estimate the population of the human race in

(i) 2030. (ii) 2070.

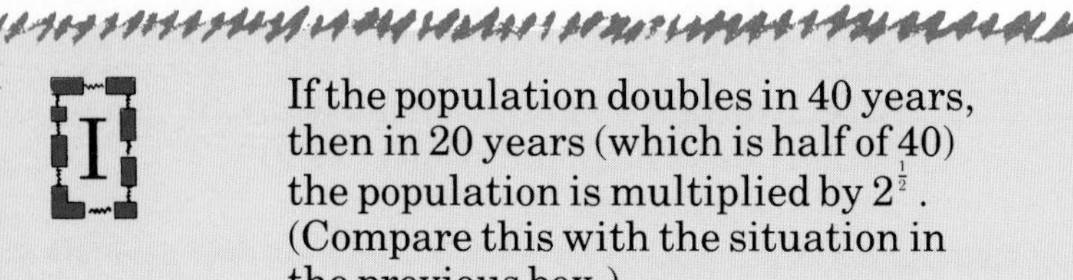

I

If the population doubles in 40 years, then in 20 years (which is half of 40) the population is multiplied by $2^{\frac{1}{2}}$. (Compare this with the situation in the previous box.)

(*b*) Estimate the population of the human race in

(i) 2010. (ii) 2050.

(*c*) Using the answers to (*a*) and (*b*), draw a graph of the population of the human race for the years 1990 to 2070. Take 1 cm to represent 10 years on the horizontal axis and 2 cm to represent 5 billion on the vertical axis.

(*d*) Use your graph to estimate the world population in the year 2040.

16 If compound interest is paid on a sum of money which has been invested, the graph showing how the money 'grows' is similar to the graphs for population growth.

Suppose £100 is invested at 10% per annum. After 1 year it will be worth £110 (its value will have been multiplied by 1.10).

(*a*) How much will it be worth after

(i) 2 years? (ii) 4 years? (iii) 6 years?
(iv) 8 years? (v) 10 years?

(*b*) Using the answers to (*a*), draw a graph showing how the amount of money changes during the first 10 years. Use 1 cm to represent 1 year on the horizontal axis and 4 cm to represent £100 on the vertical axis.

(*c*) If the person investing the money wishes to withdraw it after $6\frac{1}{2}$ years, how much money should she receive?

17 The pie chart below shows the way in which the world's energy is produced.

(*a*) By measuring the pie chart, find what percentage of energy comes from coal.

(*b*) What percentage of energy comes from hydro and nuclear power?

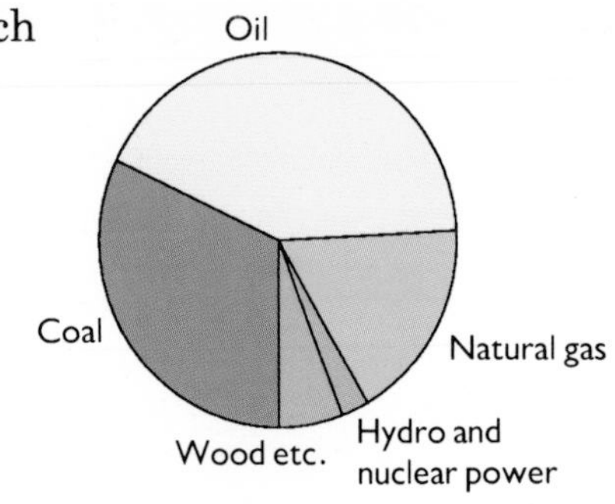

Some people think that the way of solving future energy shortage is to produce more nuclear power. Other people think this is a dangerous policy, not only because a nuclear power station might explode, as the one at Chernobyl did, but also because the waste products from nuclear reactors remain dangerous for a long period of time.

A radioactive substance produces energy by decaying into another substance. This new substance is often radioactive itself which is a large part of the waste problem.

A radioactive substance is a bit like a population of bacteria, except that it gets less rather than more as time goes on. The larger the quantity of the substance the faster it decays.

The rate at which a radioactive substance decays is usually measured in terms of half-life. The half-life is the length of time for half the substance to decay.

If there is 100 g of a substance with a half-life of 10 years, this means that after 10 years only 50 g of it will be left undecayed. After 20 years 25 g will be left, and so on.

18  (*a*) If a substance has a half-life of 10 years and there is 100 g of it to start with, how much is left after

(i) 30 years?
(ii) 40 years?

(*b*) Draw a graph to show the amount of the substance left against time. Use 1 cm to represent 10 years on the horizontal axis and 1 cm to represent 20 g on the vertical axis.

(*c*) Estimate the weight of substance left after 35 years.

(*d*) To speed up the calculation you can use the X^Y button (or Y^x button) on your calculator. The formula for the amount of substance left after N years is

$$100 \div 2^{N/10}$$

Use this formula to find

(i) how much is left after 200 years.
(ii) how much is left after 37 years.

19 The half-lives of four substances are given in the table below

Substance	Half-life
A	20 years
B	24 000 years
C	28 years
D	8 days

If there is 1 kg of each of these substances to start with, what weight of each will be left after 100 years?

1) How much interest is there in 'green' issues? Which 'green' issues interest or worry people the most?

Conduct a survey among students in your school. You might also want to ask parents, teachers, other adults or younger children.

2) How much does it cost you to live for a year?

Describe the budget you need to live for a year. Include your share of the cost of the home in which you live, for items such as heating and lighting. Include food, clothes, holidays and all your other expenses.

If you prefer you can work out how much it will cost you to live for a year after you have left home.

Remember to take account of *all* your expenses.

3) Is there equal opportunity for men and women, and/or for people from different ethnic groups, in terms of pay and employment prospects in the area where you live? Do people want there to be equal opportunities?

You can collect some evidence from within your school or from outside it. For example, you can find what jobs students in your school want to do, and whether they are optimistic about getting the jobs they want.

4) Look at some of the ways in which people are trying to protect the world's environment and explain how some of these ideas might work. Try to find some statistics to use with your explanation.

For example, you could find out what proportion of cars locally are using unleaded petrol. Or whether people are changing any of their living habits to be more 'environmentally friendly'.

5) How much energy does your family use at home during a year?

You might want to compare your use of energy with that of a typical family in Britain. On average, the amount of energy used by a family in one year is as follows.

Coal	600 kg	150 therms
Oil	150 litres	50 therms
Natural gas		390 therms
Electricity	4100 units	140 therms
Total		730 therms

(1 therm is approximately the same as 30 units of electricity. 1 unit is 1 kWh, the amount of electricity a 1 kW fire uses in an hour)

6) Houses increase in value. Cars decrease in value.

Find out about the way in which different possessions increase or decrease in value and look at the reasons why this happens.

EQUABLE SHAPES

Look at the two shapes below.

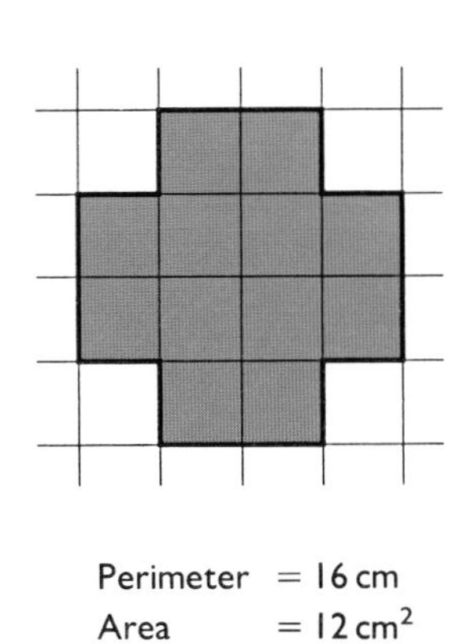

Perimeter = 16 cm
Area = 12 cm^2

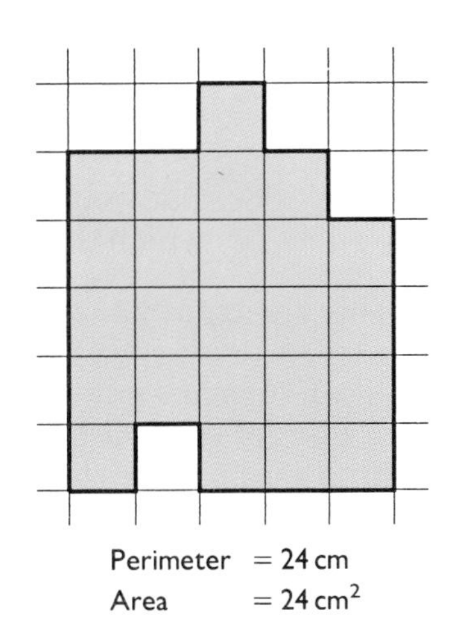

Perimeter = 24 cm
Area = 24 cm^2

The perimeters and areas of the shapes are shown. For the shape on the right, the perimeter is numerically equal to the area.

A shape for which the perimeter is numerically equal to the area can be called an **equable** shape. So the shape on the right above is an equable shape.

- Using squared paper, find some more shapes which are equable.
- Can you find an equable square or an equable rectangle?

SECTION A

1 (*a*) How many of the squares shown below are equable?

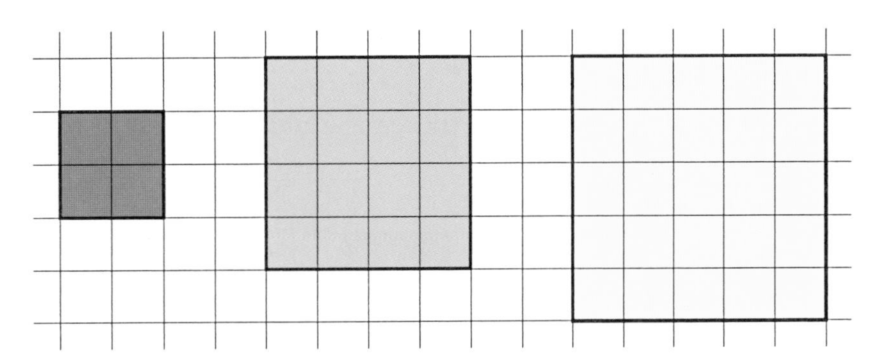

(*b*) How many of the rectangles shown below are equable?

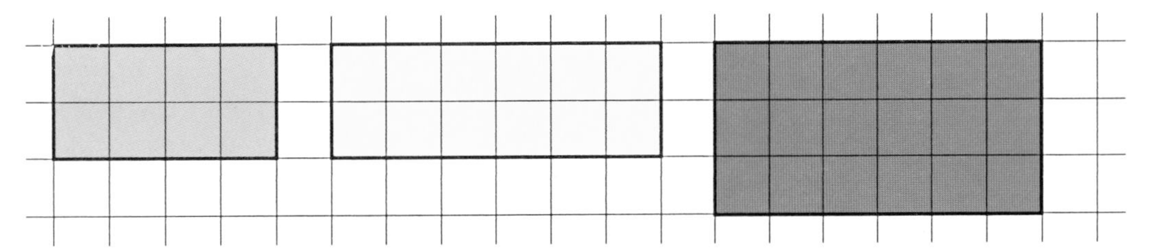

2 Many different rectangles can be drawn on squared paper using a whole number of squares. Obviously most of these rectangles will **not** be equable.

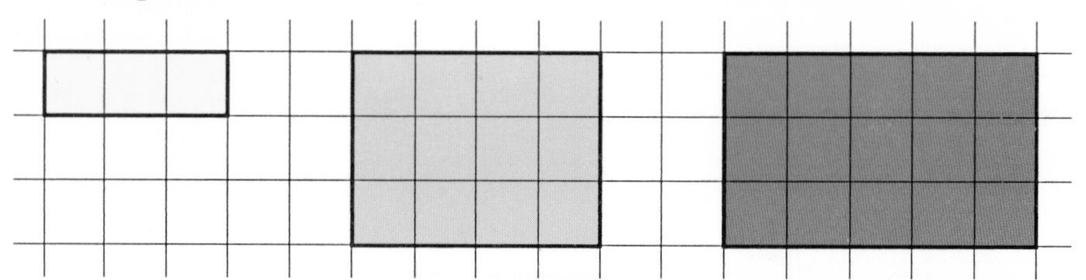

Can you find a rectangle made of a whole number of squares for which the perimeter is odd? Justify your answer.

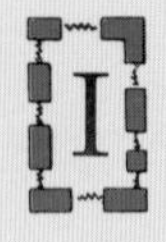

You can turn an equable shape into a larger equable shape by adding 'bumps' like this:

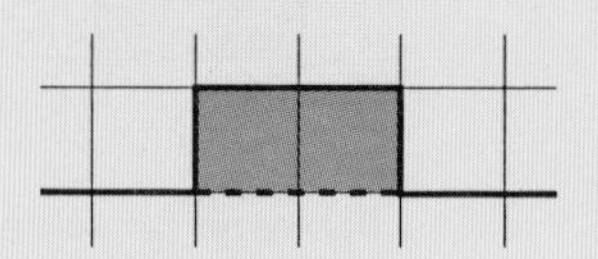

Picture **A** shows an equable shape. Its area and perimeter are both 20.

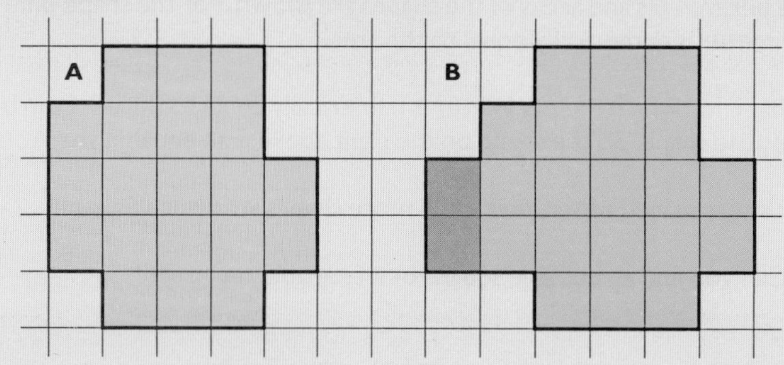

Picture **B** is made from picture **A** by adding the bump (shown shaded). The area and perimeter of the new shape are both 22, and so the new shape is equable.

More than one bump like this can be added to a shape to make a bigger equable shape.

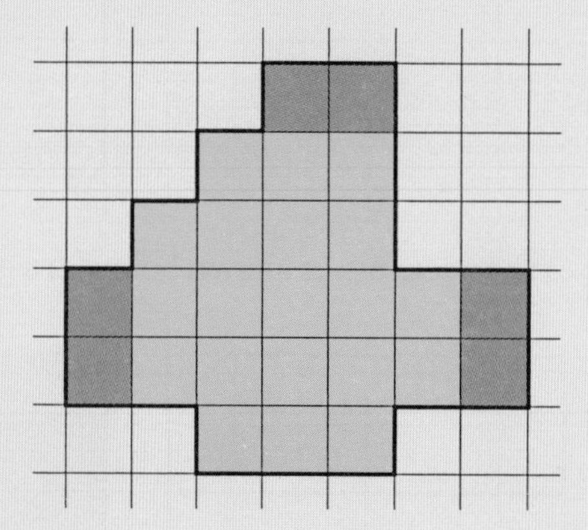

3 Choose one of the equable shapes you found at the start of this chapter.

Add three bumps to turn it into a bigger equable shape. After each bump is added, check that the new shape produced is still equable.

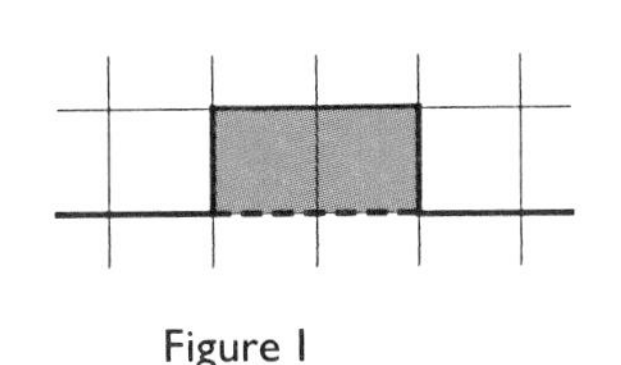

Figure 1

4 Figure 1 shows the bump you have been adding.

The dotted line is where the bump is joined to the original shape. When this bump is added the area of the shape increases by 2.

(*a*) Explain why the perimeter of the shape increases by 2 when this bump is added.

(*b*) Explain why an equable shape is still equable after a bump has been added.

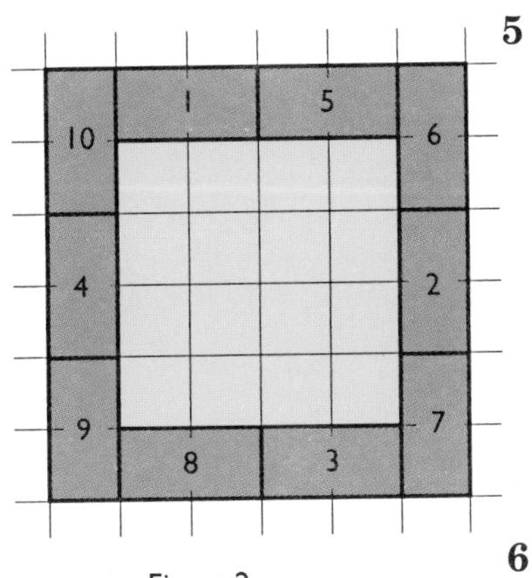

Figure 2

5 Somebody decides to add bumps to an equable square to make a bigger square. They start with a square of area 16. They know this square is equable.

10 bumps are added altogether. The bumps in figure 2 are numbered to show the order in which they are added.

(*a*) Is the bigger square produced by adding the 10 bumps equable?

(*b*) Explain why this method does not work. (You could do this by considering carefully what happens when bumps are added in the order given.)

6 Many different shapes can be made on squared paper using a whole number of squares. Most of them will **not** be equable.

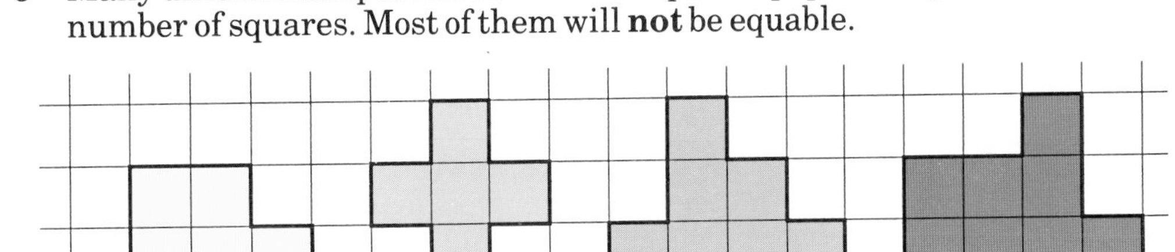

Can you find such a shape for which the perimeter is an odd number?

Justify your answer.

I

When a shape is not drawn on squared paper you can still find out if it is equable if you know the lengths of its sides.

Look at this rectangle.

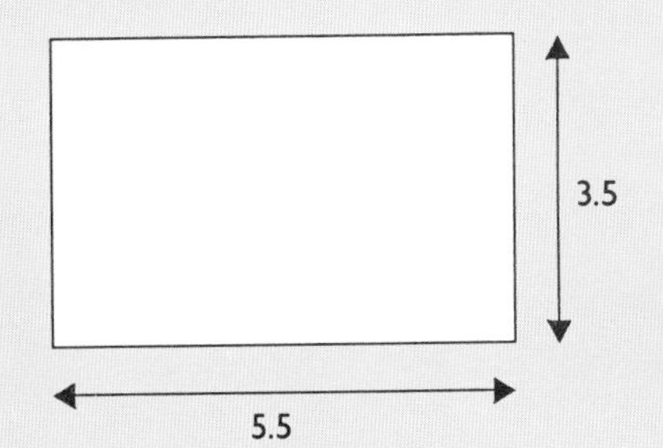

The perimeter of this shape is 18.

The area of this shape is 19.25.

So this shape is **not** equable.

7 How many of the following rectangles are equable?

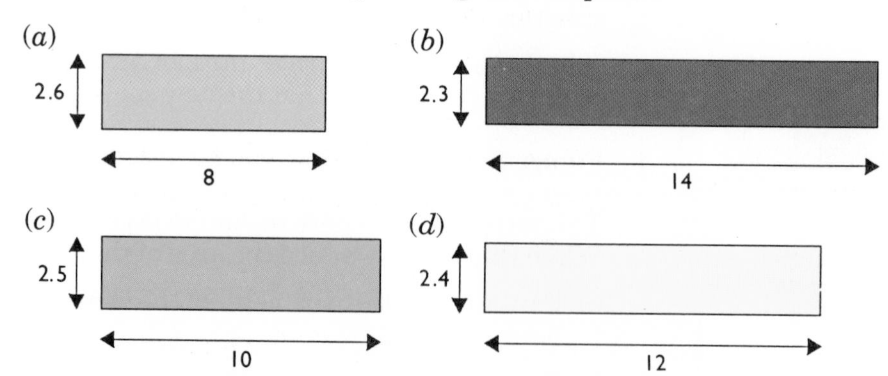

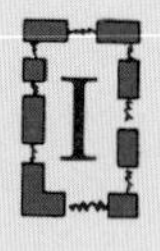

Suppose that the length of a rectangle is 5. What breadth makes the rectangle equable?

One way of doing this is by trial and improvement. Here is information about some rectangles of length 5.

Length	Breadth	Perimeter	Area
5	2	14	10
5	3	16	15
5	4	18	20
5	5	20	25

When the breadth is 3 the perimeter is *bigger* than the area.

When the breadth is 4 the perimeter is *smaller* than the area.

This means that somewhere between a breadth of 3 and a breadth of 4 the perimeter swaps over from being *bigger* to being *smaller*. In other words, the perimeter and area are *equal* somewhere between 3 and 4.

8 The length of an equable rectangle is 5. The box above explains how you can use a table of numbers to find out that its breadth is between 3 and 4.

You can extend the method to find a more accurate value for the breadth. Make another table. This time use 3.0, 3.1, 3.2, 3.3, 3.4, ... for the breadth.

Find the breadth of the equable rectangle as accurately as you can.

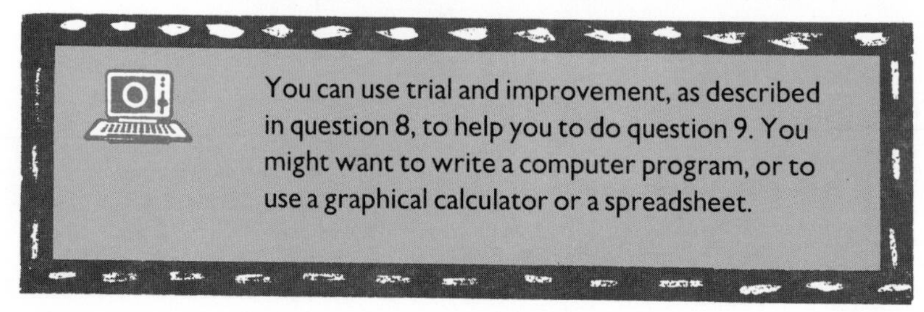

You can use trial and improvement, as described in question 8, to help you to do question 9. You might want to write a computer program, or to use a graphical calculator or a spreadsheet.

9 Find more rectangles which are equable. The lengths of the sides do not need to be whole numbers.

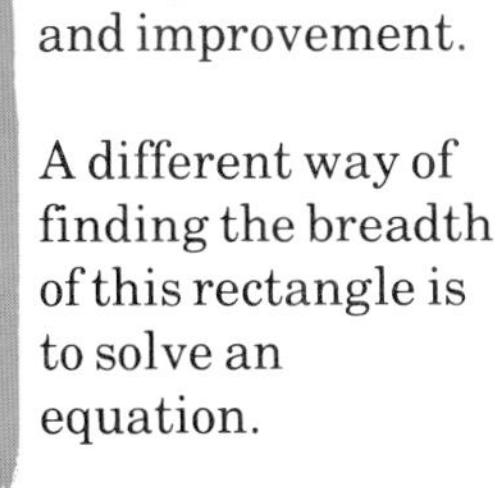

10 One side of an equable rectangle is of length 5 and the other side is of length a.

(*a*) What is the perimeter of the rectangle?

(*b*) What is the area of the rectangle?

(*c*) Explain why $5a = 10 + 2a$.

(*d*) Solve this equation to find the value of a.

(*e*) What is the area of this equable rectangle?

11 Use the method of question 10 to check your answers for question 9.

12 (*a*) Plot all your results about equable rectangles on a graph. Plot the length on the horizontal axis. Plot the breadth on the vertical axis. On both axes use 1 cm to represent 1 unit of length.

(*b*) Join up the points you have plotted with a smooth curve.

(*c*) Use your graph to find

(i) the breadth of an equable rectangle if its length is 3.5.
(ii) the length of a rectangle if its breadth is 5.5.

In the following question you will need to be able to rearrange an equation. If you want help with this look at the information box on page 132.

13 One side of an equable rectangle is x and the other side is y.

(*a*) Explain why $xy = 2x + 2y$

(*b*) Rearrange this equation to give a formula for y in terms of x.

(*c*) Use a graphical calculator or a computer graph plotter to draw the graph of y plotted against x.

(*d*) What happens to the graph where the length is 2?

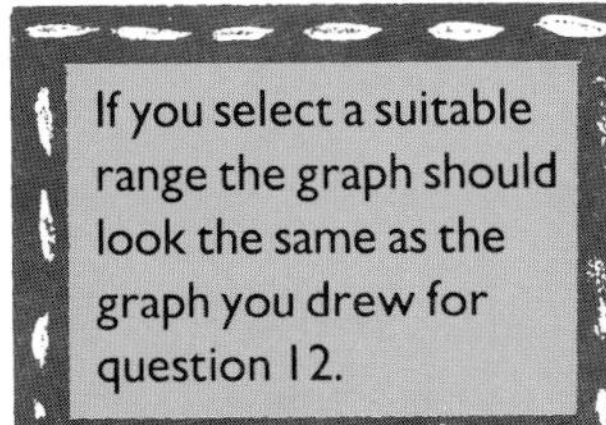

(*e*) For what values of length is it not possible to have an equable rectangle?

(*f*) What does the graph suggest to you about the breadth of an equable rectangle if the length is

(i) 2.1?
(ii) 2.01?
(iii) 2.001?

If you want more practice with rearranging equations you will find this in Review Exercise 39 on page 134.

SECTION B

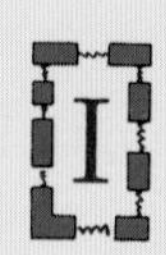

An equable shape is a shape for which the perimeter is **numerically** equal to the area. But the perimeter of a shape cannot *really* be equal to the area because perimeter is measured by length and not by area.

Before you can decide whether a real shape is to be called equable you have to agree what units to measure it in.

You might need to refer to the formulae given on page 281 for help with finding the circumference and area of a circle or the area of a triangle.

1 (*a*) Measure the diameter in centimetres of each of the circles shown below.

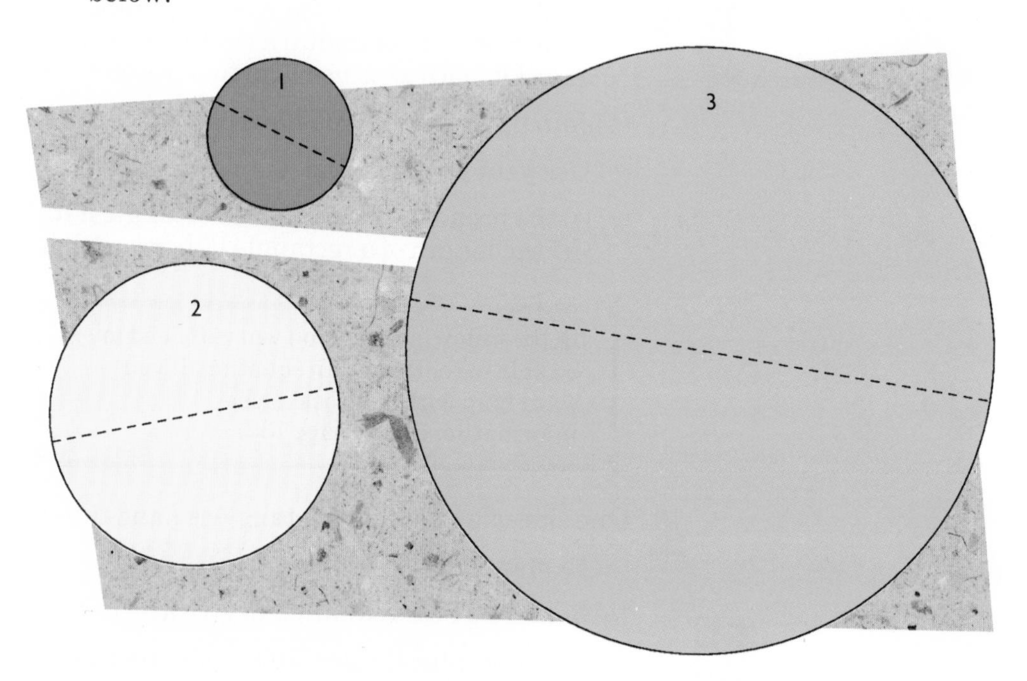

(*b*) Find the perimeter of each circle in centimetres. (The perimeter of a circle is usually called the circumference.)

(*c*) Find the area of each circle in square centimetres.

(*d*) Using these units, which of the circles is equable?

2 (*a*) What is the length and breadth of each of the rectangles shown below in centimetres?

(*b*) Find the perimeter of each of the rectangles in centimetres.

(*c*) Find the area of each of the rectangles in square centimetres.

(*d*) Using the units of centimetres and square centimetres, which of the rectangles are (approximately) equable?

For questions 3 and 4 you might find it helpful to use the resource sheet *'Measuring in decimals of an inch.'*

3 (*a*) What is the length and breadth of each of the rectangles shown in question 2 in inches?

(*b*) Find the perimeter of each of the rectangles in inches.

(*c*) Find the area of each of the rectangles in square inches.

(*d*) Using the units of inches and square inches, which of the rectangles are (approximately) equable?

4 (*a*) Make suitable measurements to find the perimeter and area of each of the shapes shown below in centimetres and square centimetres.

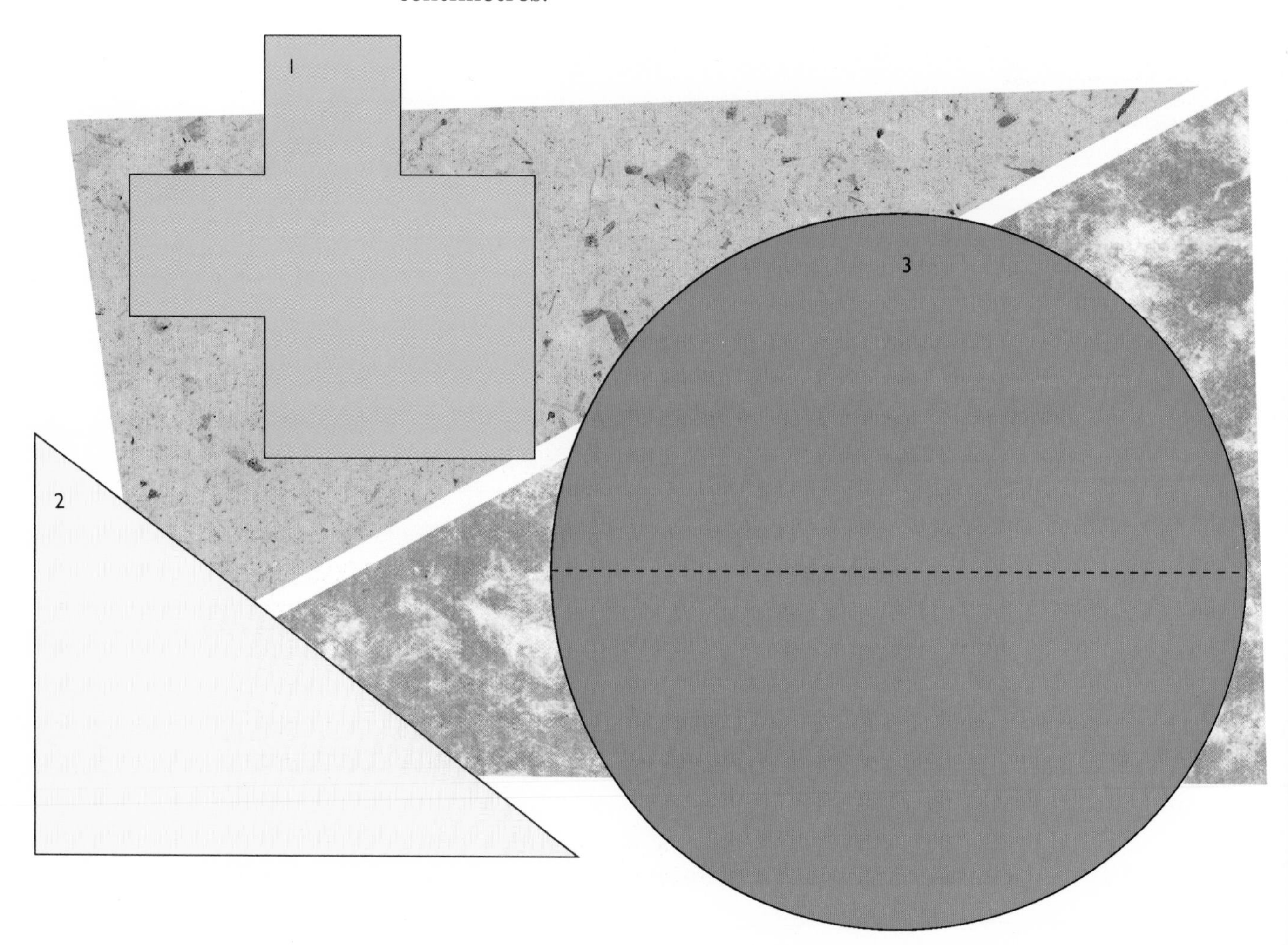

(*b*) Make suitable measurements to find the perimeter and area of each of the shapes in inches and square inches.

(*c*) Which shapes are equable when centimetres are used and which are equable when inches are used?

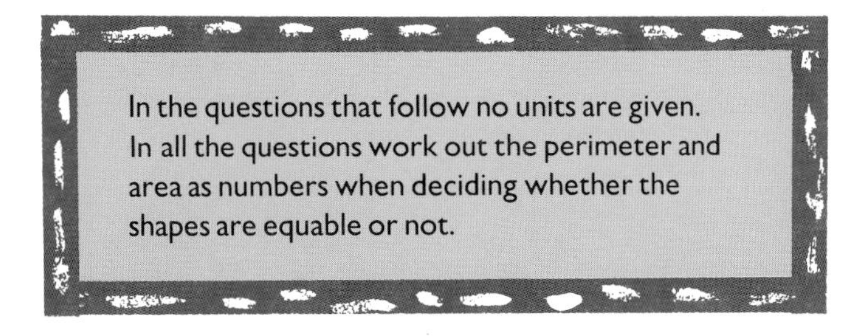

In the questions that follow no units are given.
In all the questions work out the perimeter and area as numbers when deciding whether the shapes are equable or not.

5 In each of the kites shown below two of the angles are right angles as indicated.

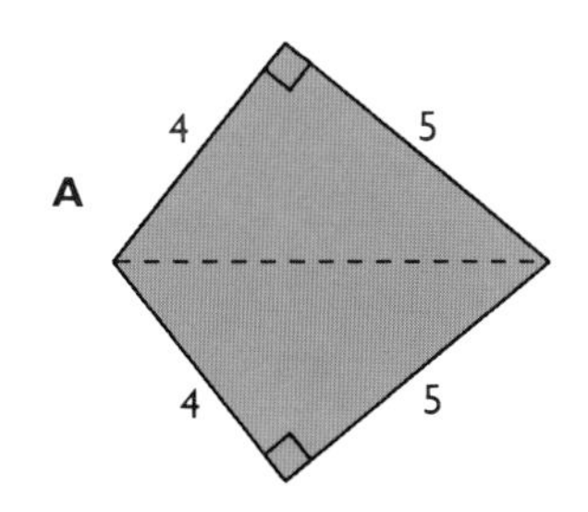

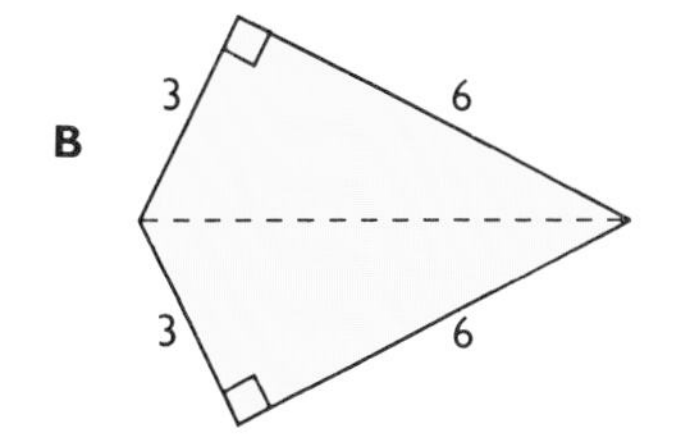

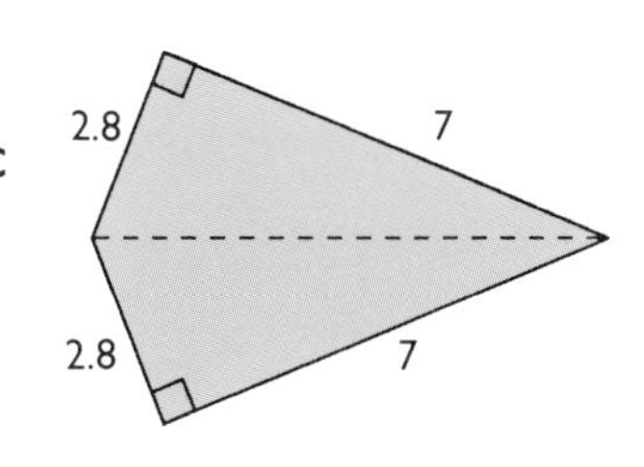

Which of the kites are equable?

For question 6 and some others you will need to use Pythagoras' theorem. This is on page 281.

6

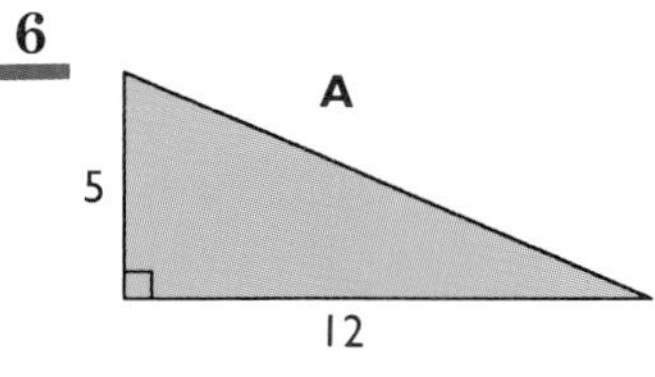

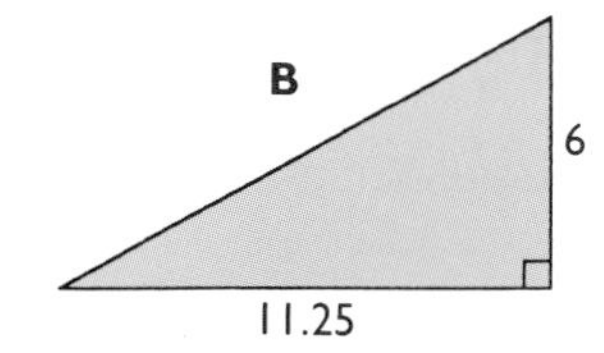

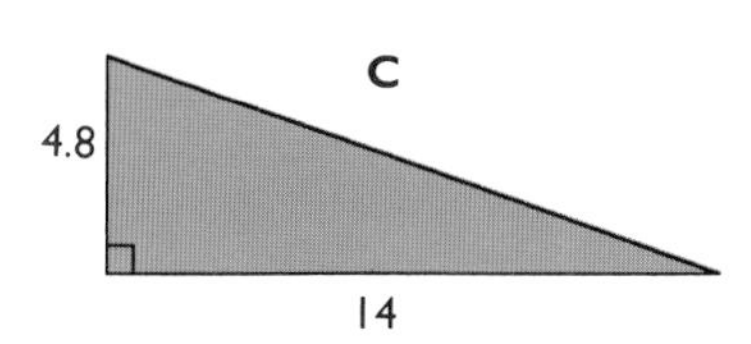

(*a*) Find the area of each of the right-angled triangles shown above.

(*b*) Find the perimeter of each triangle.

(*c*) Which triangles are equable?

7 Find the radius of the equable circle.

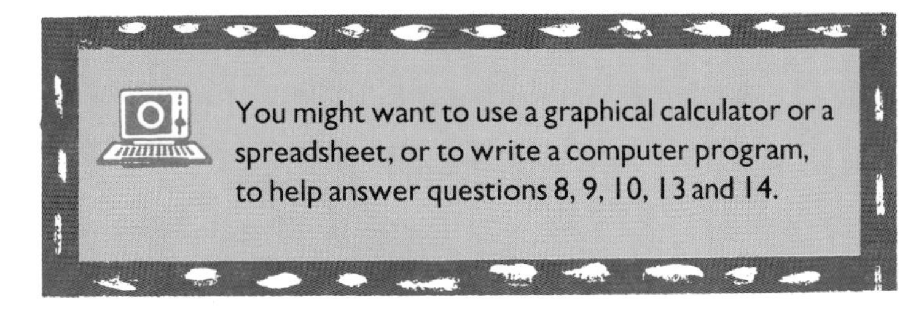

You might want to use a graphical calculator or a spreadsheet, or to write a computer program, to help answer questions 8, 9, 10, 13 and 14.

8 (*a*) What is the perimeter and area of a semicircle of radius 2?

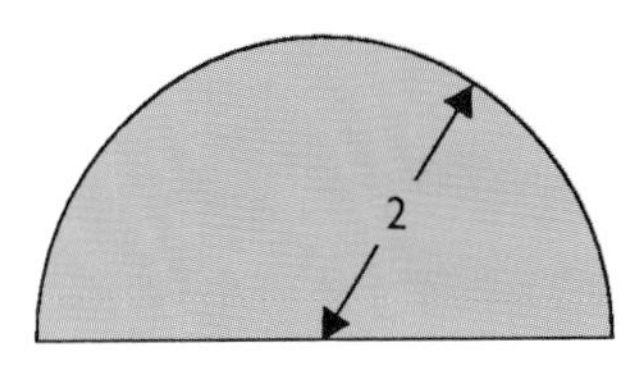

(*b*) Using trial and improvement find the approximate radius of an equable semicircle.

9 One of the sides of a right-angled triangle is 9.

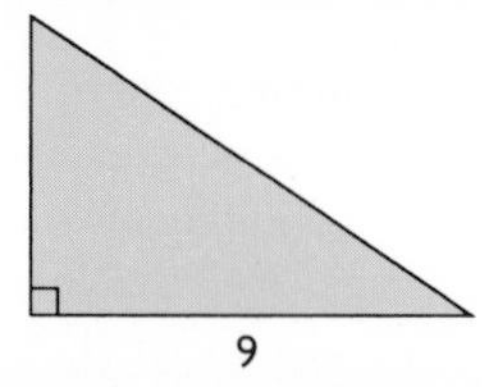

(*a*) What is the perimeter and area of the triangle if one of the other sides is 6?

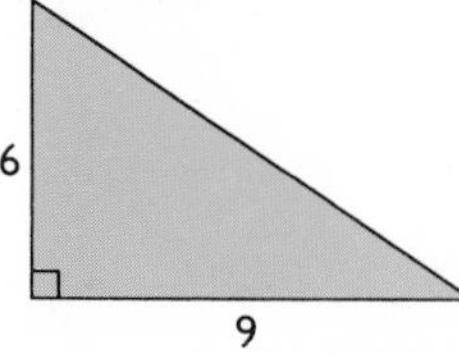

(*b*) What is the perimeter and area of the triangle if one of the other sides is 5?

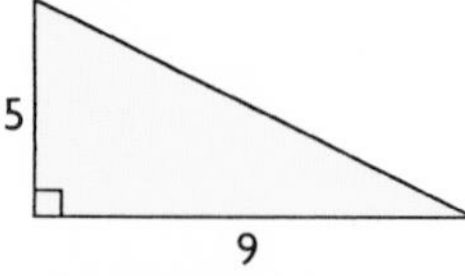

(*c*) Use trial and improvement to find an equable right-angled triangle one of whose sides is 9.

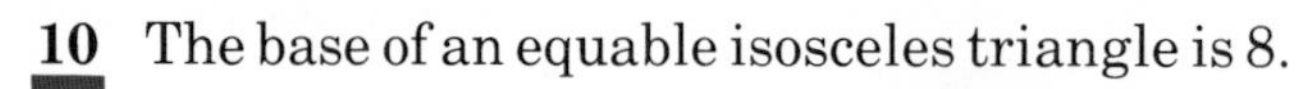

10 The base of an equable isosceles triangle is 8.

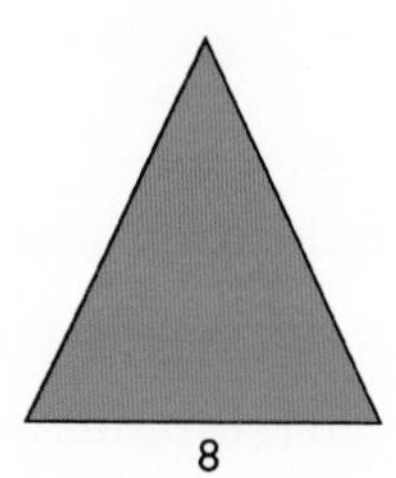

Use trial and improvement, or some other method, to find the lengths of the other two sides.

11 A rhombus has diagonals of lengths 8 and $2x$.

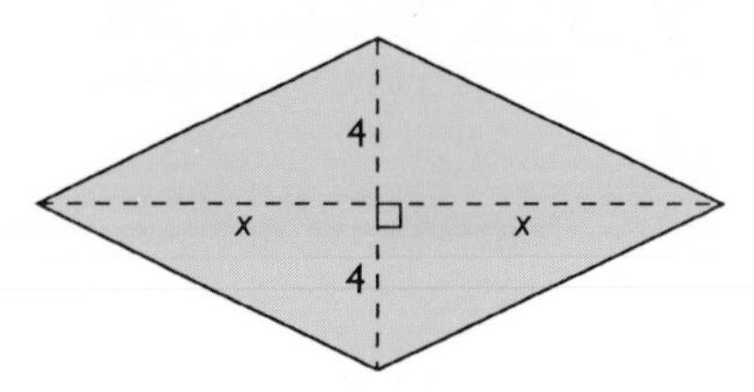

(*a*) Write down a formula for the perimeter and area of the rhombus in terms of x.

(*b*) If the rhombus is equable write down an equation for x.

(*c*) Solve the equation to find x. (One way of doing this is to square both sides of the equation. This will get rid of the square root.

(*d*) Find the area of the rhombus.

12

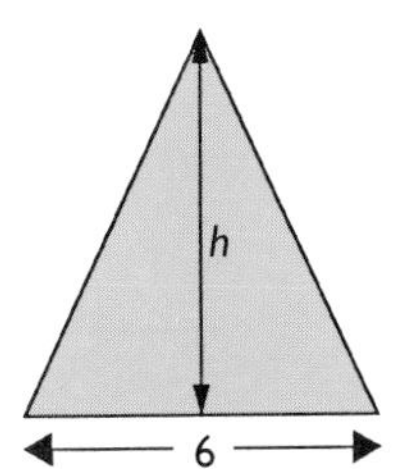

(*a*) Write down a formula for the area and the perimeter of the isosceles triangle shown above.

(*b*) If the triangle is equable write down an equation for h.

(*c*) Solve the equation to find h.

(*d*) Find the area of the equable triangle.

(*e*) Solve the same problem by a different method, by using x instead of h, where x is one of the equal sides of the triangle, as shown in the diagram.

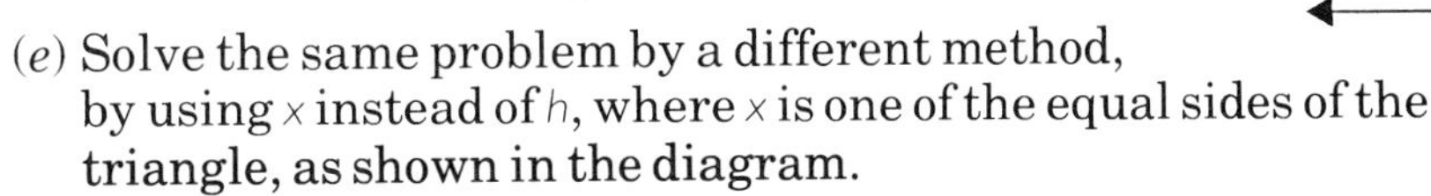

(*f*) Check that the two different methods give the same result.

I

Heron's formula gives the area of a triangle.

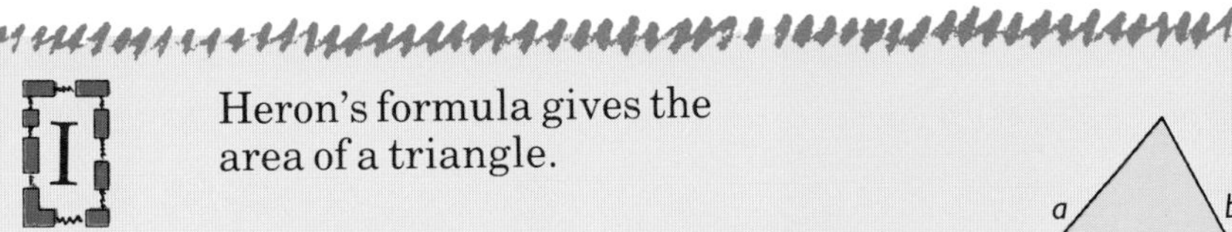

If the lengths of the sides of the triangle are a, b and c and if s is half the perimeter, then the area is

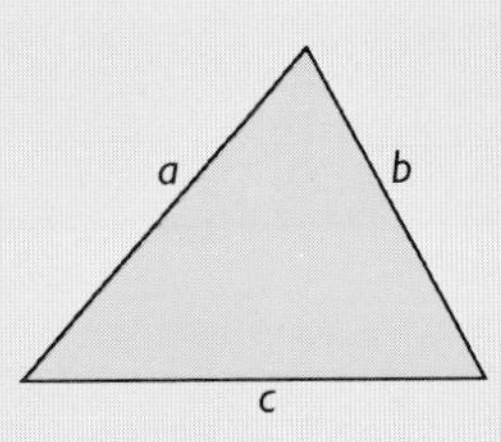

$$\sqrt{s(s-a)(s-b)(s-c)}$$

$$s = \tfrac{1}{2}(a+b+c)$$

13 (*a*) Which of the triangles shown below are equable?

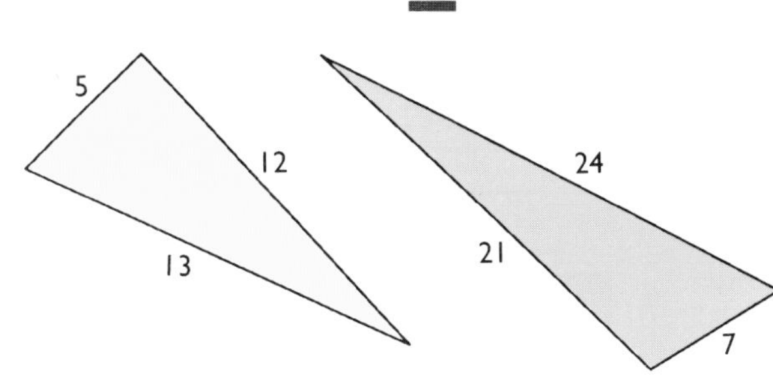

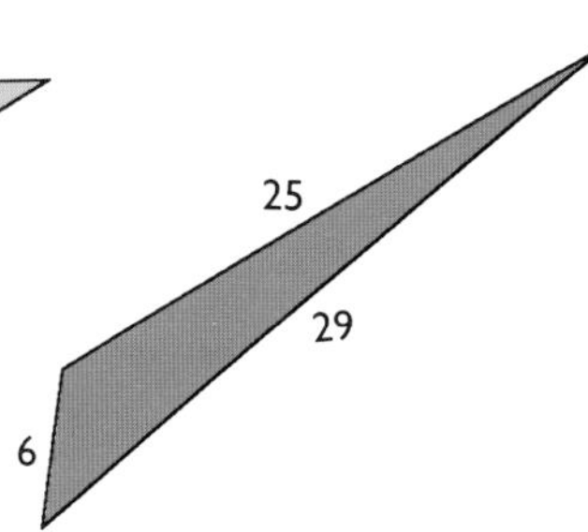

(*b*) There are two more equable triangles with integer sides. One of them has a side of length 20 and the other has a side of length 17.

Find the lengths of the other sides of these two triangles.

14 Two sides of an equable triangle have lengths 9 and 12.

Using Heron's formula, find the approximate length of the third side by trial and improvement.

SECTION C

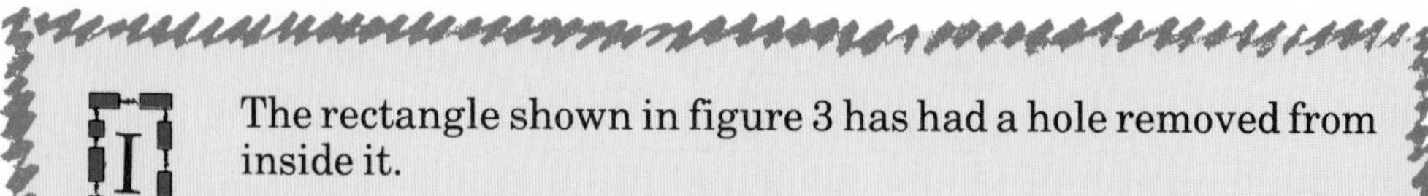

I

The rectangle shown in figure 3 has had a hole removed from inside it.

The shape remaining has an area of 32.

Some of its perimeter is outside and some is inside. Its total perimeter is 32.

So the shape is equable.

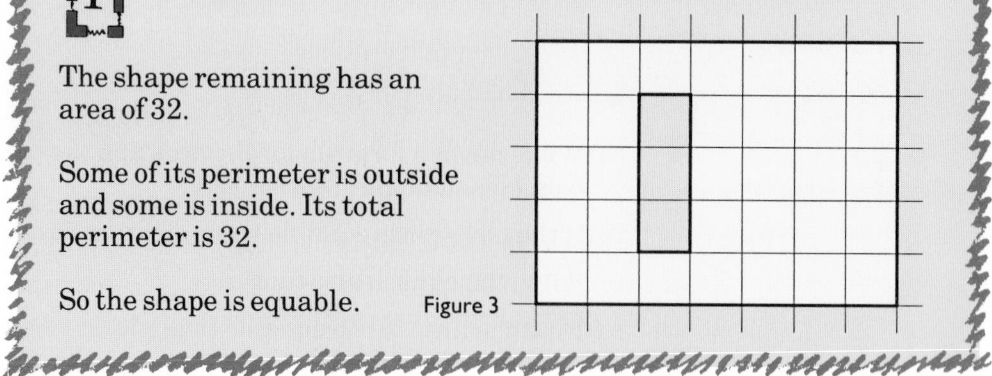

Figure 3

1 Which of the following shapes are equable?

(*a*)

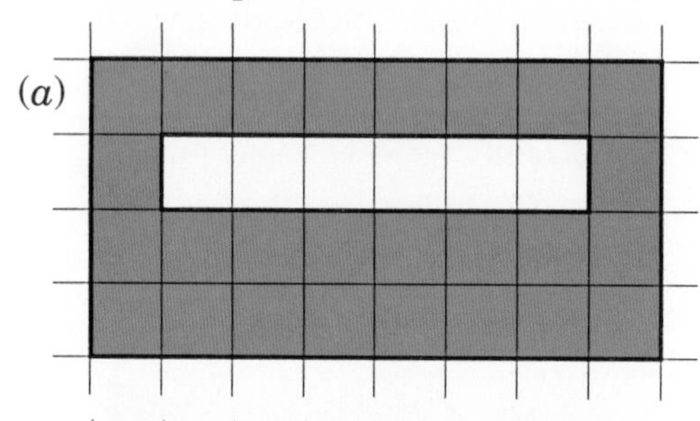

(*b*)

(*c*)

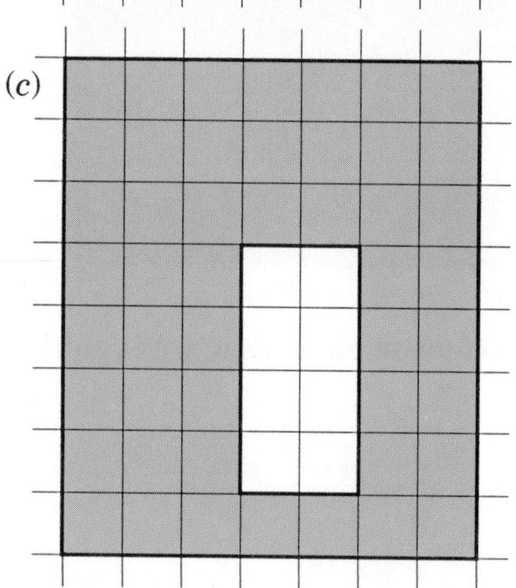

(*d*)

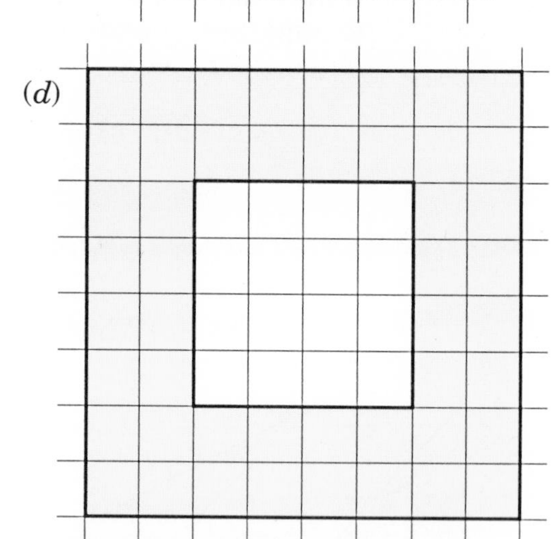

2 Remove a square hole from inside each of the squares shown so that the shape which is left is equable.

(*a*)

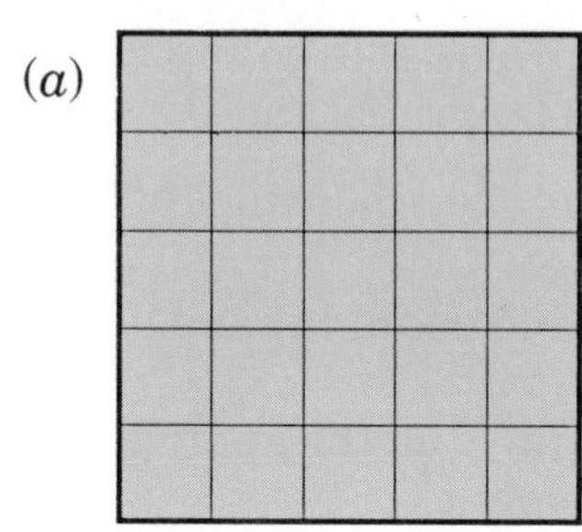

(*b*)

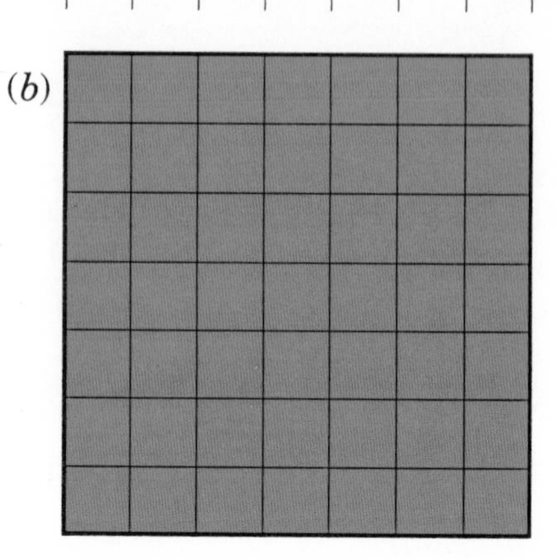

3 Remove a square hole from each of the rectangles shown so that the shape which is left is equable.

(*a*)

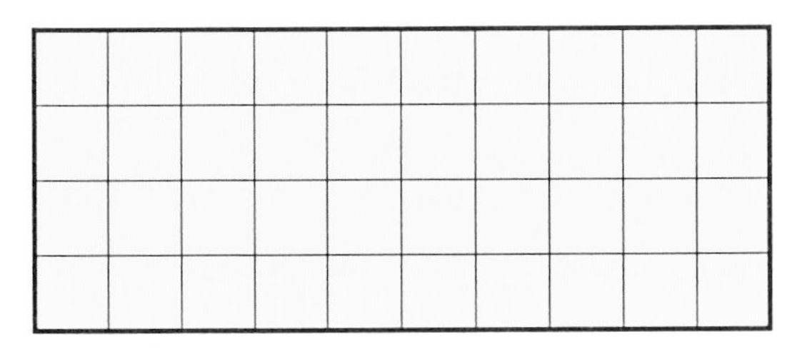

(*b*)

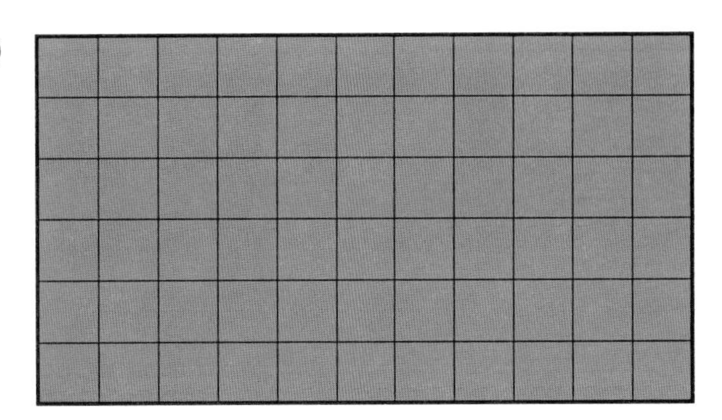

4 (*a*)

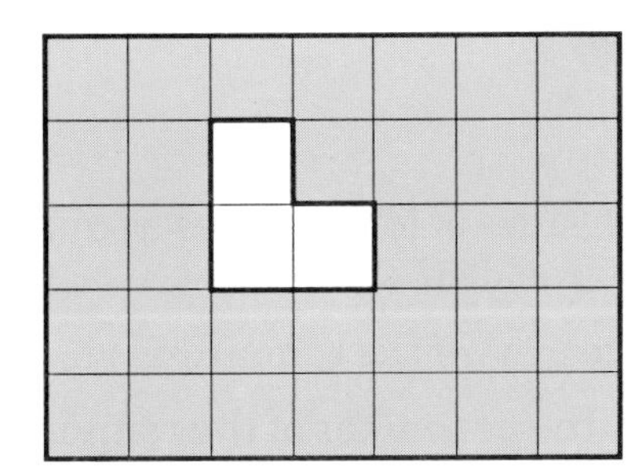

The shape above is equable. Show this by finding its area and perimeter.

(*b*)

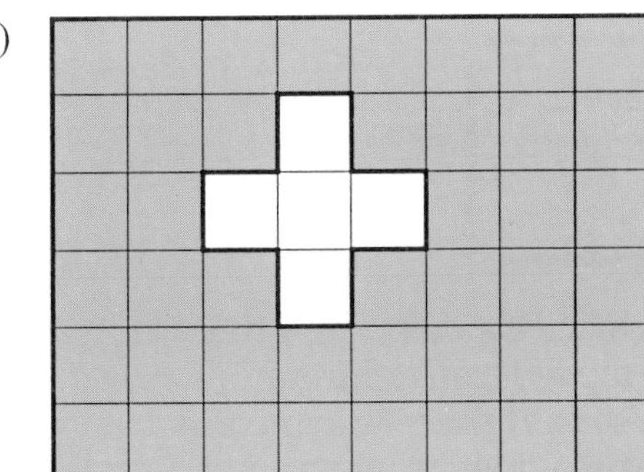

The shape above is not equable. Show this by finding its area and perimeter.

(*c*) Place the hole shown on the left inside a suitable rectangle to produce an equable shape.

5 Which of the following shapes are equable?

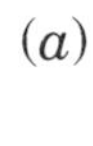

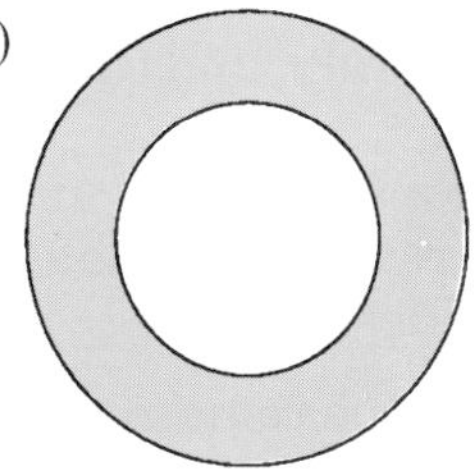

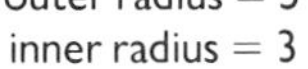

(*b*)

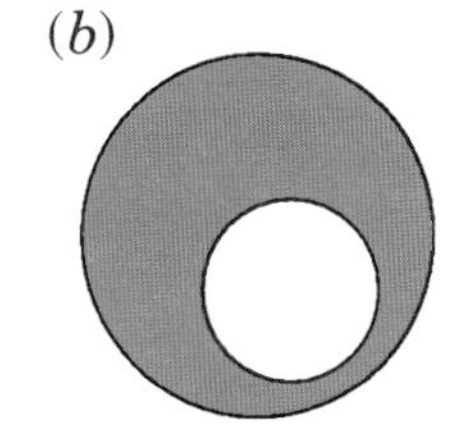

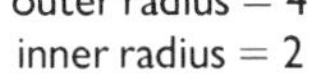

(*c*)

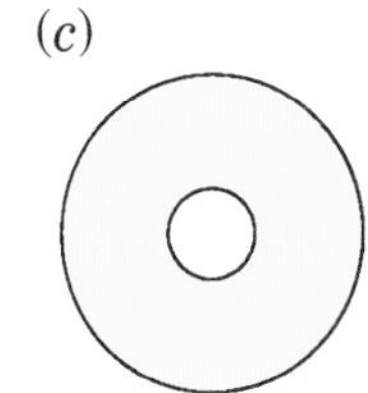

outer radius = 3.5
inner radius = 1

6 Which of the following shapes is equable?

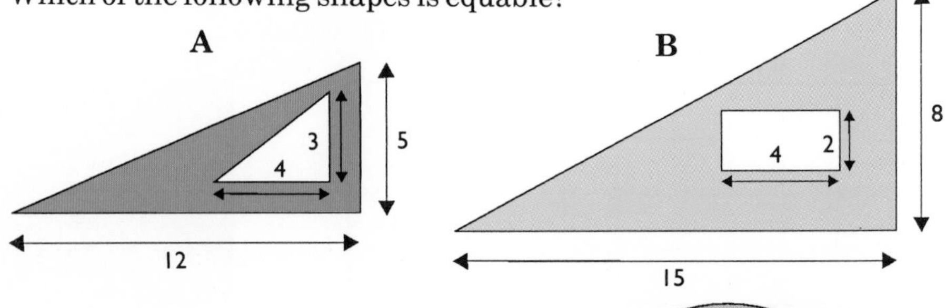

7 (*a*) What is the perimeter of this shape?

(*b*) What is the area of this shape?

(*c*) Is this shape equable?

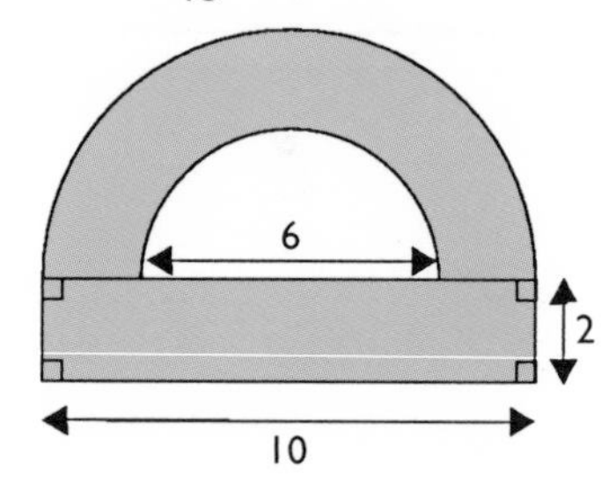

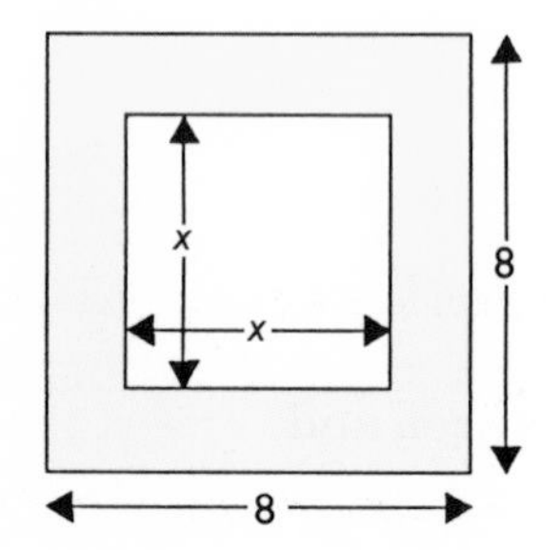

8 A square with sides of length 8 has a square with sides of length x removed from inside it.

(*a*) What is the area of the remaining shape?

(*b*) Show that the perimeter of the remaining shape is $4(8 + x)$.

(*c*) If the remaining shape is equable find the value of x.

> In questions 9 and 10 you will need to be able to multiply out brackets. This was explained in Chapter 16.

9 A rectangle with sides of length x and y is removed from a larger rectangle so that there is a margin of 1 at the top and bottom and 3 at the sides.

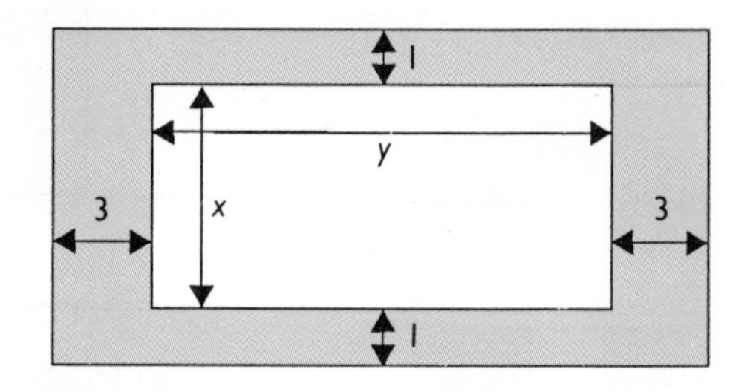

(*a*) Show that the area of the remaining shape is $6x + 2y + 12$.

(*b*) If this shape is equable show that $x - y = 2$.

(*c*) If in addition the perimeter of this shape is 84 write down another equation involving x and y, and find x and y.

10 A rectangle with sides of length $x+3$ and x is removed from a larger rectangle so that there is a margin of 2 on all sides.

(*a*) Show that the area of the remaining shape is $8x + 28$.

(*b*) For what values of x is the remaining shape equable?

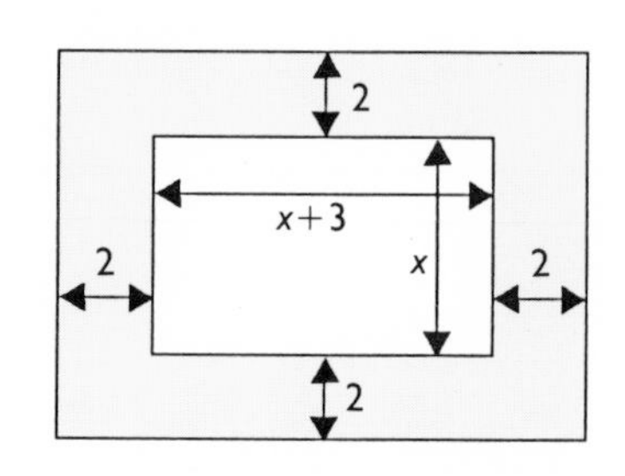

One way of answering questions 11 and 12 is to solve a quadratic equation by factorising. If you want help with this look at the box on page 128.

11 A right-angled triangle whose sides are 8, 15 and 17 has a triangle of the same shape removed from inside it.

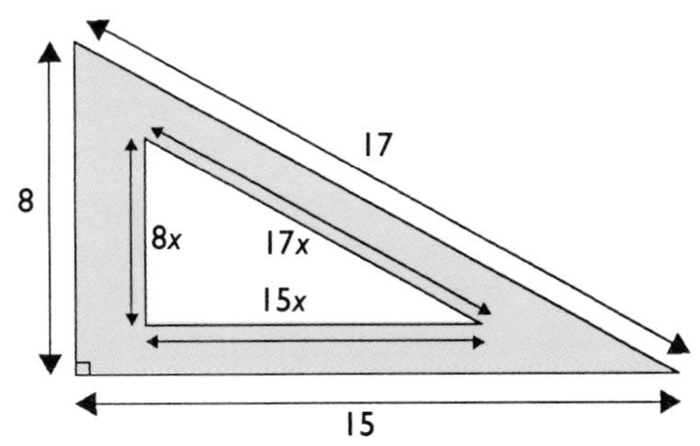

The sides of the inner triangle have lengths $8x$, $15x$ and $17x$.

(*a*) Show that the area of the remaining shape is $60 - 60x^2$.

(*b*) Show that the perimeter of the remaining shape is $40 + 40x$.

(*c*) If the remaining shape is equable find the value of x.

12 (*a*) The diagonals of a rhombus are of lengths 6 and 8. Find the area and perimeter of the rhombus.

(*b*) A rhombus of the same shape is removed from inside this rhombus.

The diagonals of the rhombus which is removed are of lengths $6x$ and $8x$.

Show that the area and perimeter of the remaining shape are $24 - 24x^2$ and $20 + 20x$.

(*c*) If the shape remaining is equable find the value of x.

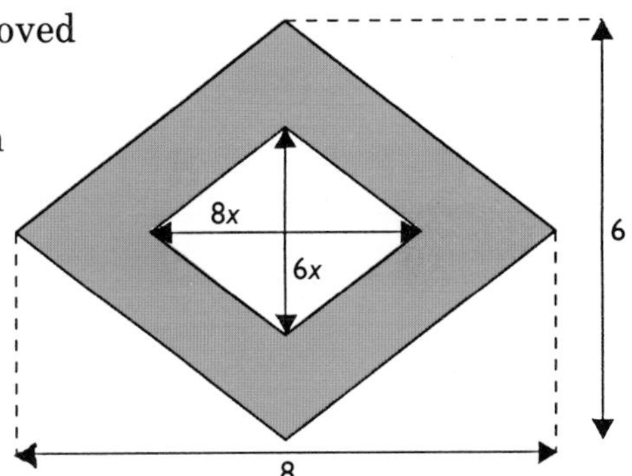

One way of answering questions 13 and 14 is to use the formula for the solutions of a quadratic equation. If you want help with this look at the box on page 128.

13 The rectangle shown below can be made equable by removing a square hole from inside it.

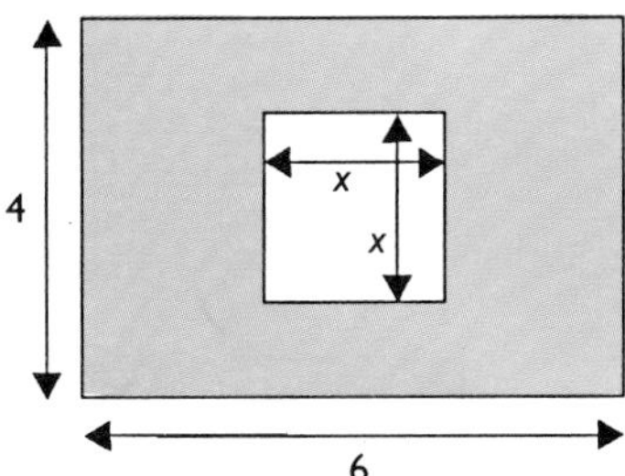

How big should the square hole be?

14 A rectangle whose sides are in the ratio 2:1 has a square of area 9 removed from inside it.

If the remaining shape is equable find the dimensions of the rectangle, correct to one decimal place.

(*Hint:* make the shorter side of the rectangle x).

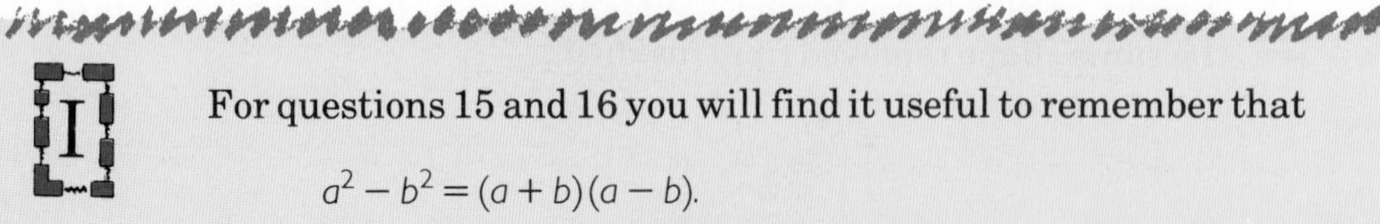

For questions 15 and 16 you will find it useful to remember that

$$a^2 - b^2 = (a + b)(a - b).$$

15 A square with sides of length x has a square with sides of length y removed from inside it.

(*a*) What is the area of the remaining shape?

(*b*) What is the perimeter of the remaining shape?

(*c*) If the remaining shape is equable show that $x - y = 4$.

16 A circle of radius r has a circle radius s cut from inside it.

(*a*) What is the area of the remaining shape?

(*b*) What is the perimeter of the remaining shape?

(*c*) If the remaining shape is equable find the value of $r - s$.

FURTHER COURSEWORK TASKS

1⟩ Design some interesting equable shapes. You might wish to include shapes with one or more holes.

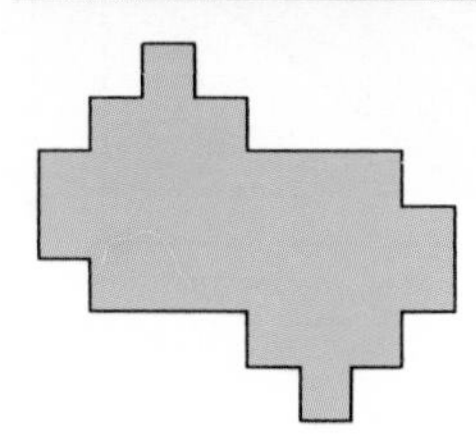

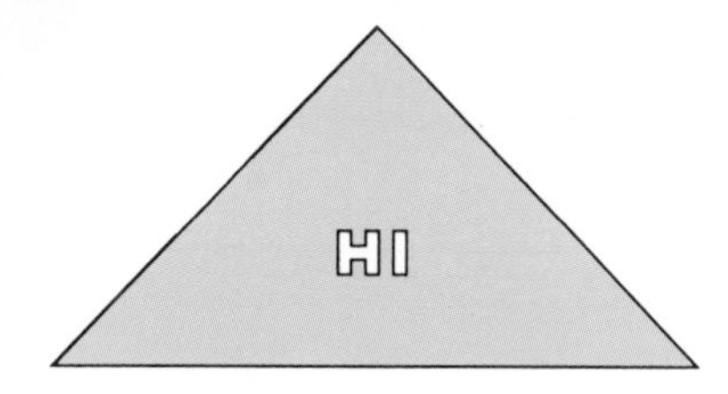

2⟩ Question 3 of Section A was about adding a bump to an equable shape so that the new shape obtained was still equable.

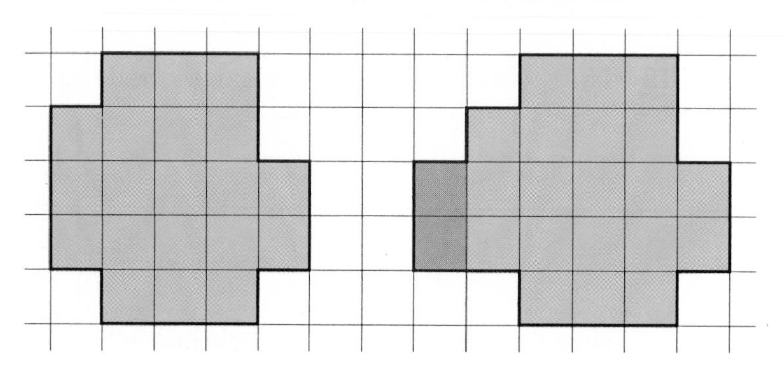

The bump suggested for that question is not the only shape of bump that can be used for this purpose.

Here are some other bumps that could be used, and there are many more.

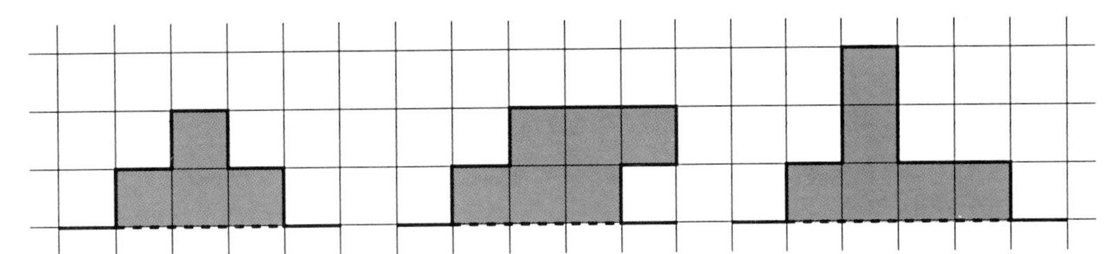

Find other bumps which could be used. Explain how you know that your bumps will work.

Classify your bumps according to the length of the join. You might like to try to find all the possible bumps for a given length of join. How do you know when you have found them all?

3⟩ A solid shape could be called equable if its surface area is numerically equal to its volume.

Find some equable solids.

Explore equable solids of a particular type in more detail. For example, you might want to write a computer program to find equable cuboids with edges which are integers.

4⟩ Explore the relationship between the equable circle and other equable shapes.

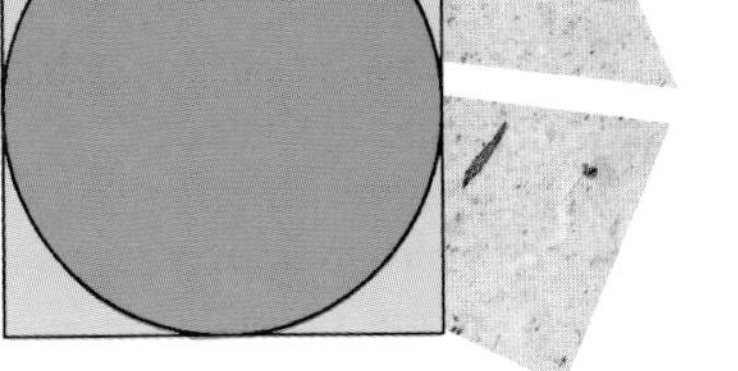

DISSECTING CUBES

There are many different ways of cutting a cube into two pieces.

For example, it can be cut in two to make two cuboids:

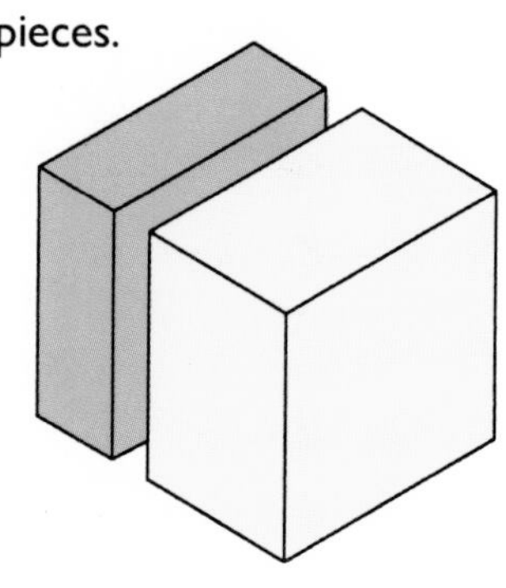

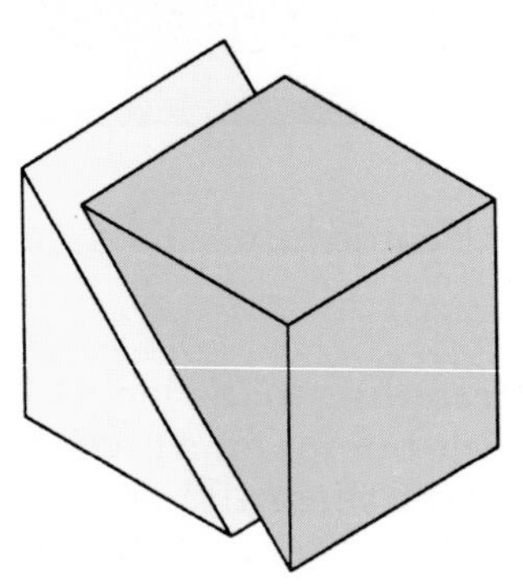

or to make two triangular prisms.

There are also many ways of cutting a cube into more than two pieces.

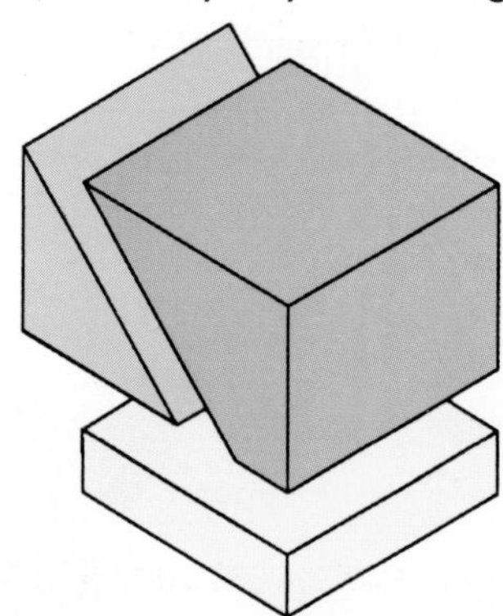

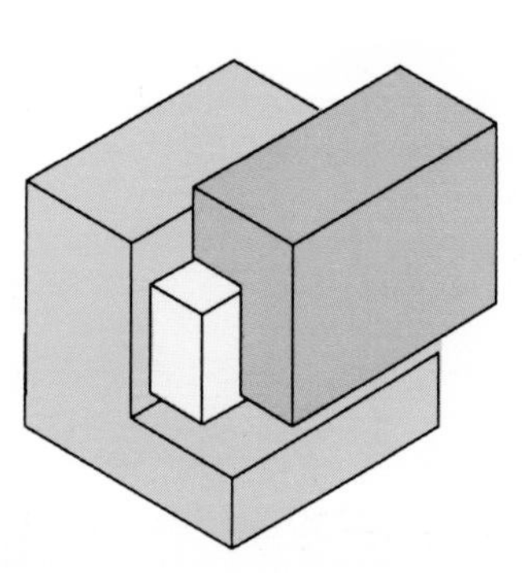

The pieces obtained when you cut a cube up are sometimes called a **dissection** of the cube.

Make your own dissection of a cube. You might want to do this as follows.

1. Cut a net of a cube out of a sheet of paper and fold it up to make a cube. Secure all the edges with flaps or sticky tape.
2. Imagine a way of cutting the cube. Draw lines on your net to show the position of the cut or cuts.
3. Cut your net along the lines you have just drawn.
4. Flatten out each piece. This will give you the net of each piece but the faces which come from making your 'cuts through the cube' will be missing.
5. Draw a net for each of the pieces by adding the faces which come from making the cut.
6. Fold up your nets to obtain the pieces and check that they fit together to make a cube.

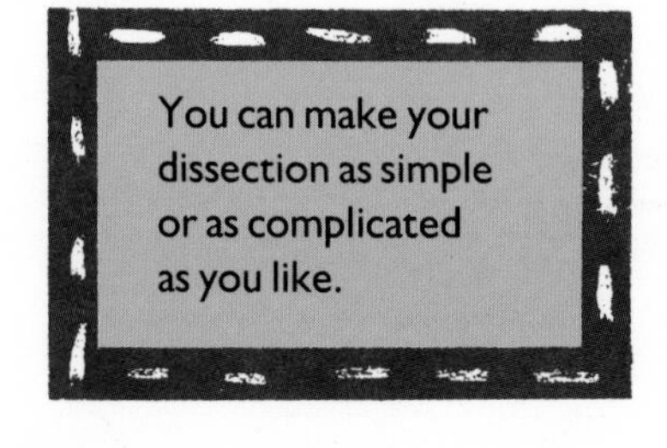

SECTION A

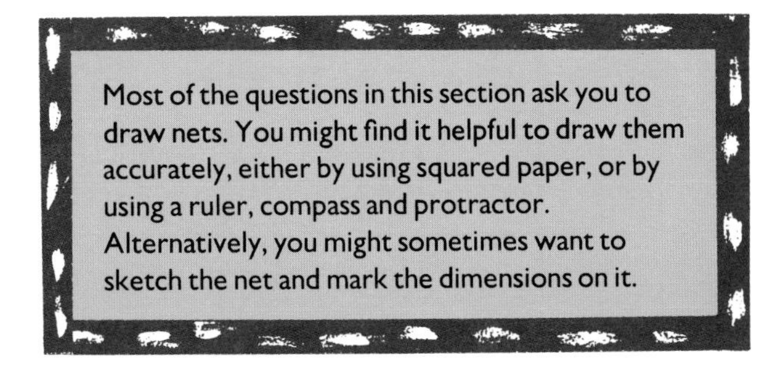

1 Here is a net of a cube.

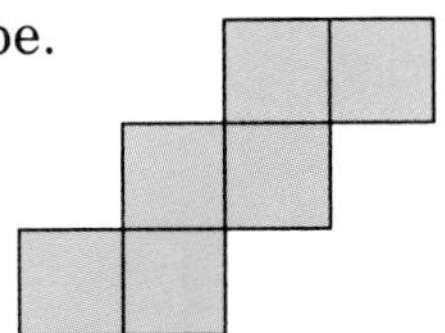

(*a*) There are several other different nets of a cube. Draw them. (You might find it helpful to cut some of them out, to check that they work.)

(*b*) A cube is cut along the line shown to produce two equal cuboids.

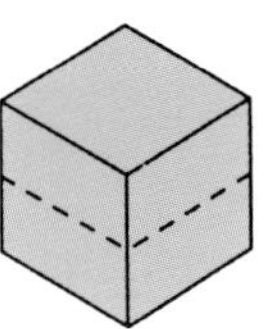

On the net on the right one of the ways in which this cut can be drawn is shown.

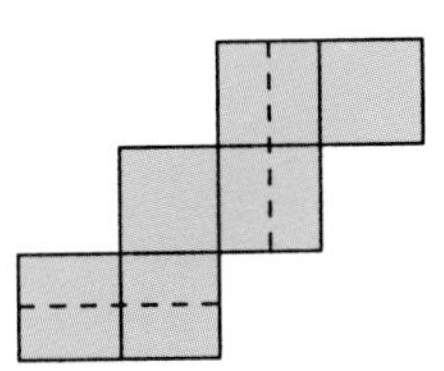

Draw one way of making the cut on some of the nets you drew for part (*a*).

(*c*) None of the arrangements below is the net of a cube. For each one, explain what stops it from being a net.

(i)

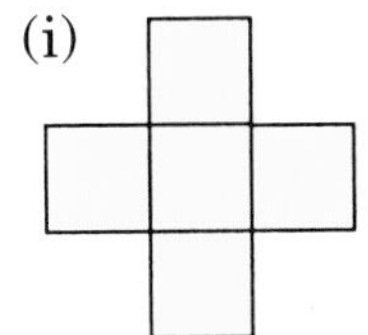

(ii)

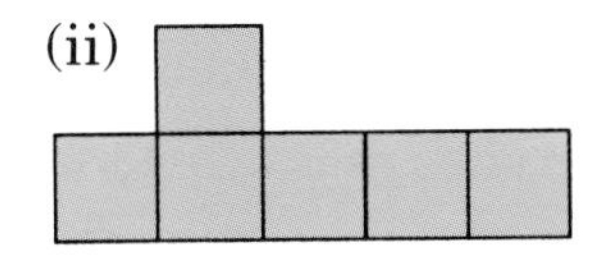

(iii)

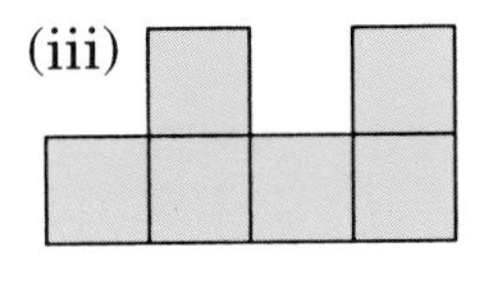

2 The net of a cuboid is rather like the net of a cube. But, for a cuboid, some or all of the six faces are rectangles instead of squares.

(*a*) Some of the pictures below are nets of cuboids and some are not. In each case say whether the picture *is* or *is not* a net of a cuboid.

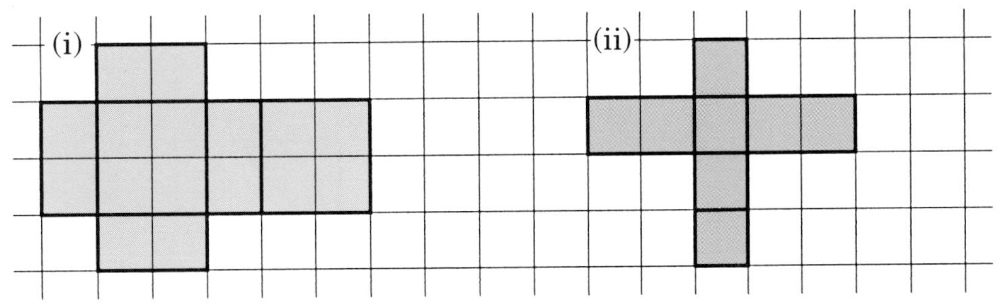

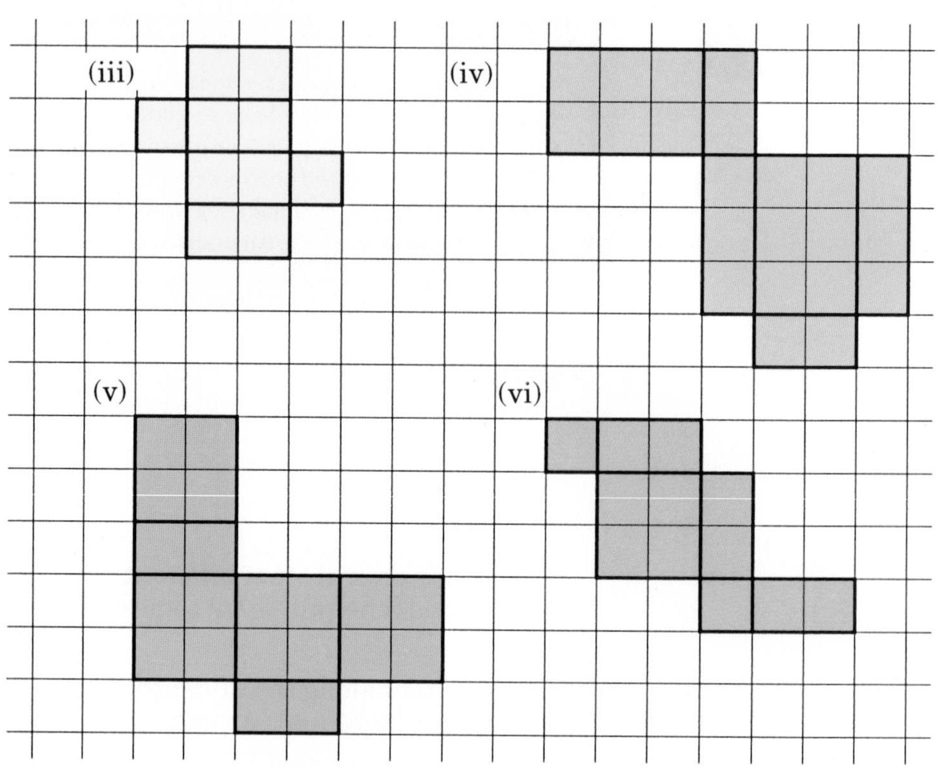

(*b*) For each of the questions below, if your answer is *yes* draw a suitable net. If your answer is *no* explain why it is not possible.

Is it possible to have a cuboid with exactly:

(i) 1 rectangle face and 5 square faces?
(ii) 2 rectangle faces and 4 square faces?
(iii) 3 rectangle faces and 3 square faces?
(iv) 4 rectangle faces and 2 square faces?
(v) 5 rectangle faces and 1 square face?
(vi) 6 rectangle faces and 0 square faces?

3 Every solid shape has several *different* possible nets.

Each of the nets below is of a solid shape which can be obtained by dissecting a cube.

In each case draw a *different* net for the *same* shape.

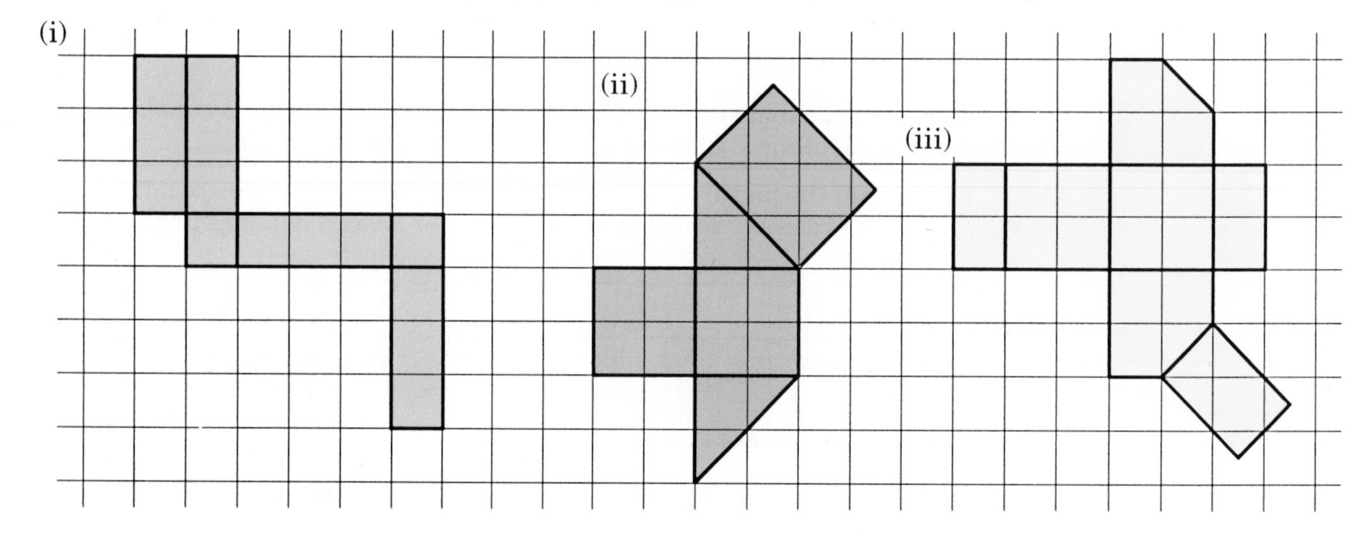

4 The net below is the net for a half of a cube.

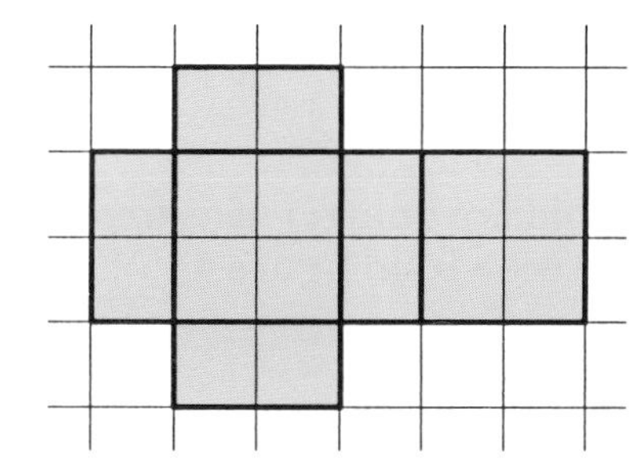

This half-cube is now cut into two *identical* pieces. Here is one way of doing this, together with a net for the pieces.

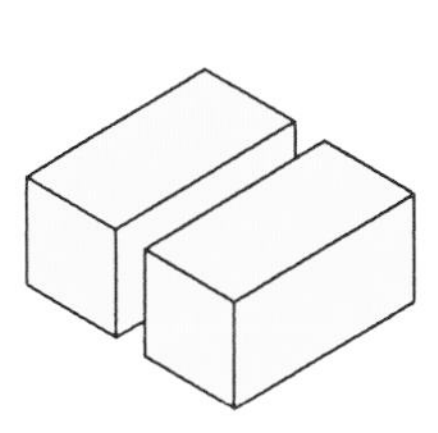

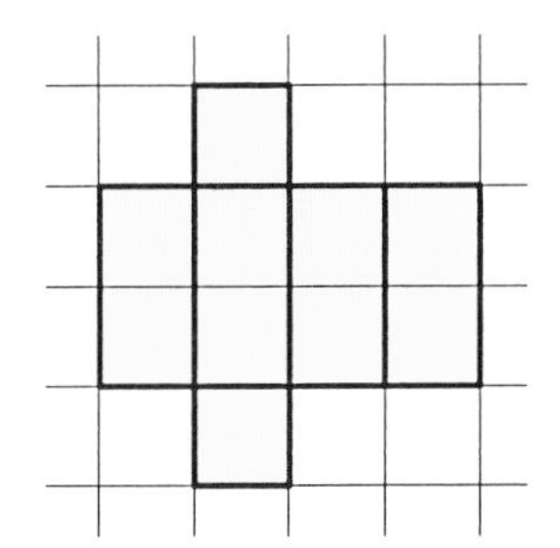

(*a*) Think of *4 more* ways of doing this. Draw a rough sketch to show each of your ways.

(*b*) For 2 of your 4 ways, draw a net for the pieces you get.

5 (*a*) A cube is cut into two pieces, as shown in figure 1.

Figure 1

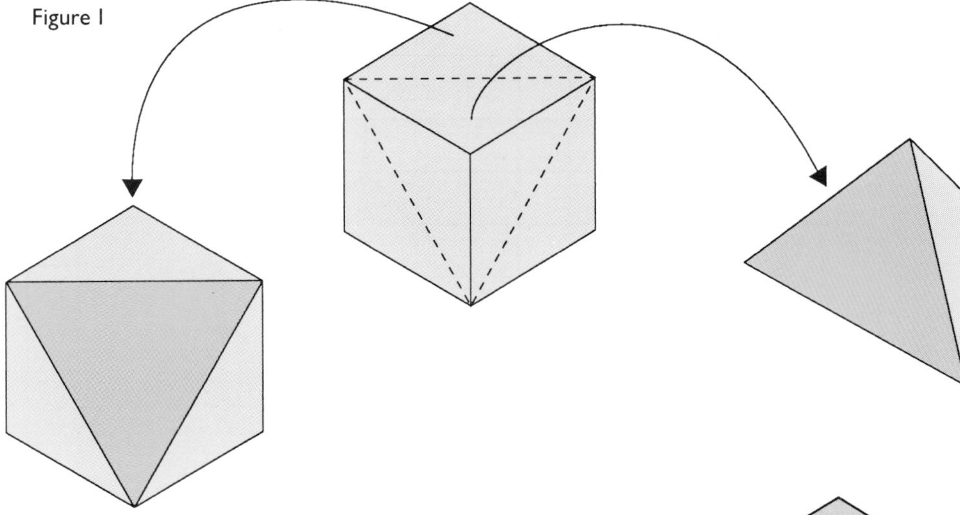

Draw a net for each of the two pieces obtained.

(*b*) A corner is cut off a cube as shown in figure 2. The cut goes through the midpoints of three of the edges.

Draw a net for each of the two pieces obtained.

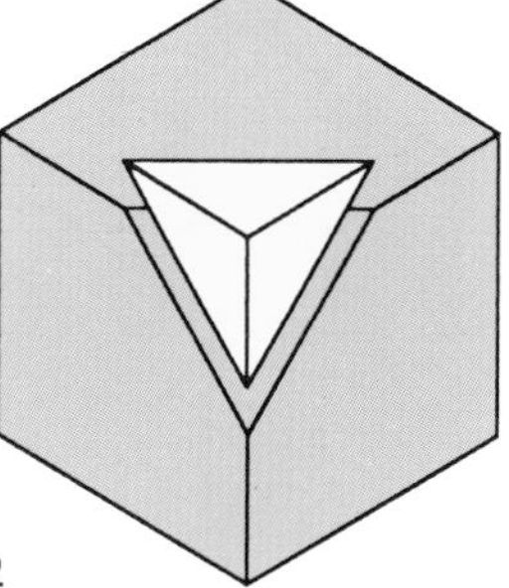

Figure 2

6 Figure 3 shows the net of a cuboid.

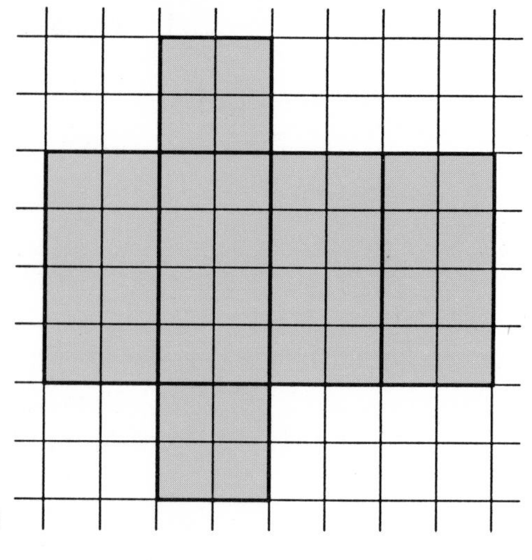
Figure 3

This cuboid is a quarter of a cube, as can be seen from figure 4

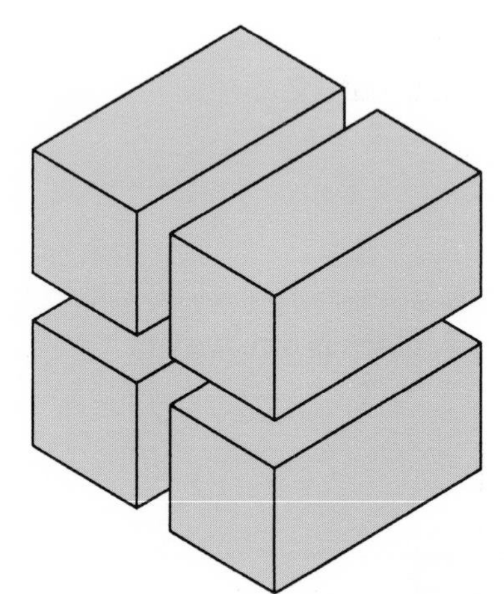
Figure 4

What fraction of a cube is each of the following?

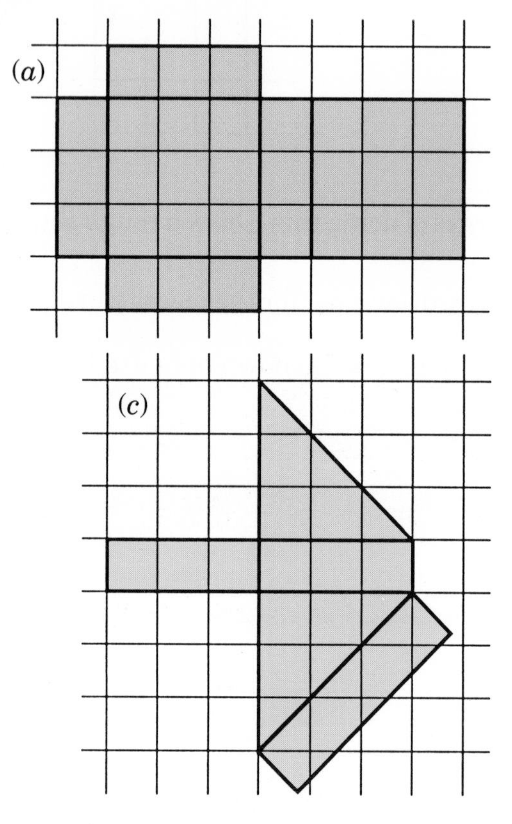

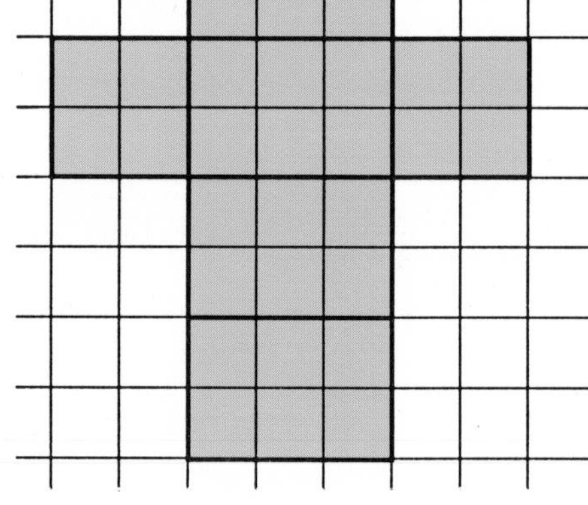

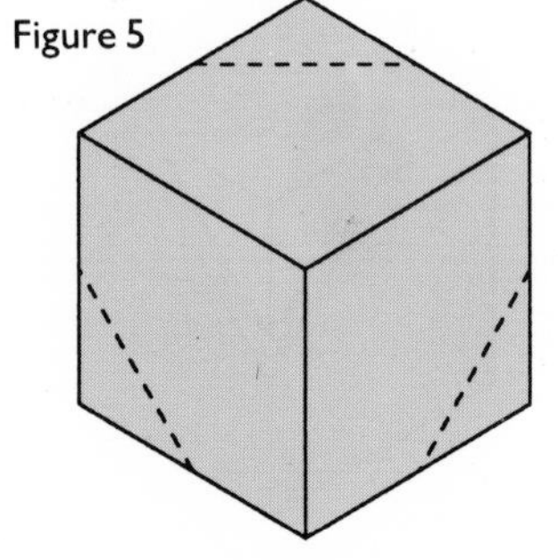
Figure 5

7 Figure 5 shows the position of a cut which dissects the cube into two identical halves.

Draw a net for one of these halves.

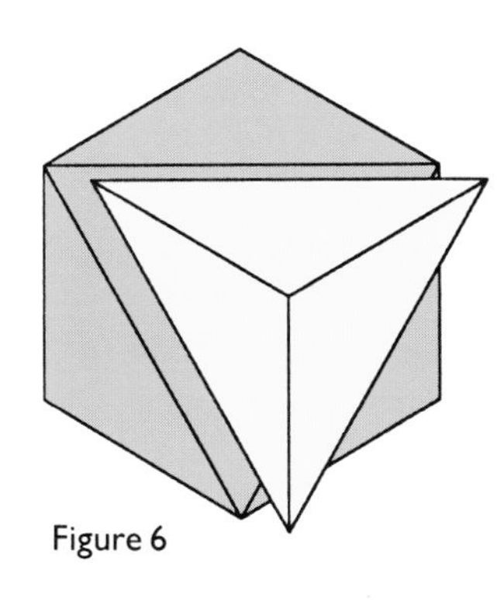
Figure 6

8 Figure 6 shows a cube dissected into two pieces.

This is the same dissection as in question 5(a).

Each piece is now dissected into two *identical* pieces.

(a) Draw a net for one of the pieces the tetrahedron is cut into.

(b) Draw a net for one of the pieces the heptahedron (shape with 7 faces) is cut into.

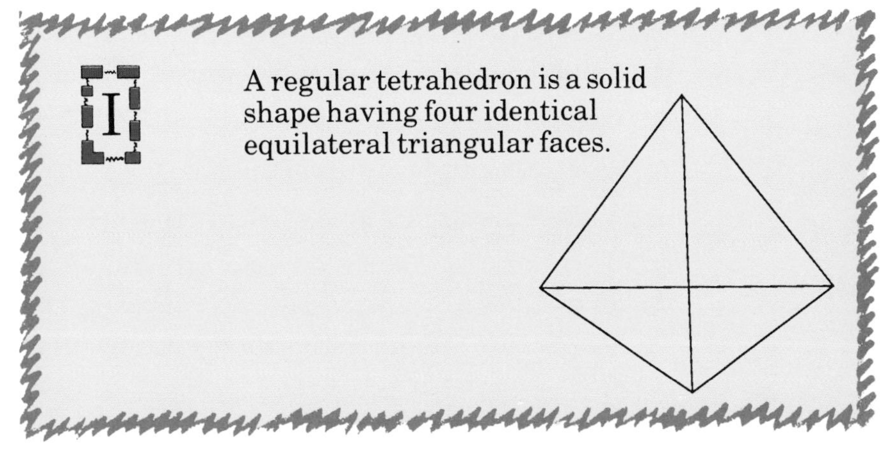

9 Figure 7 shows one way of cutting a regular tetrahedron in half.

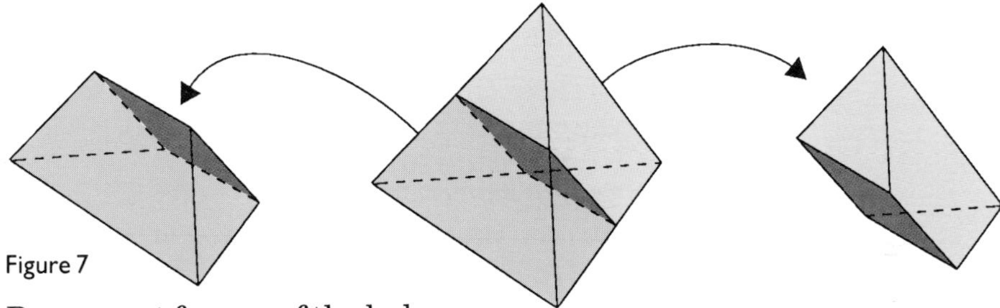
Figure 7

Draw a net for one of the halves.

10 'Any plane cut through the *centre* of a cube cuts the cube into two identical pieces.'

Is this statement true? Justify your answer.

SECTION B

1 Figure 8 shows the net for half of a cube.

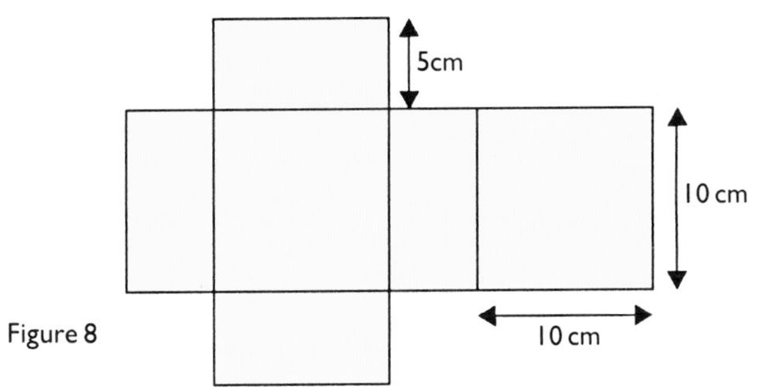

Figure 8

(a) What is the volume of this shape?

(b) What is the surface area of this shape?

2 A cube is dissected into two pieces as shown.

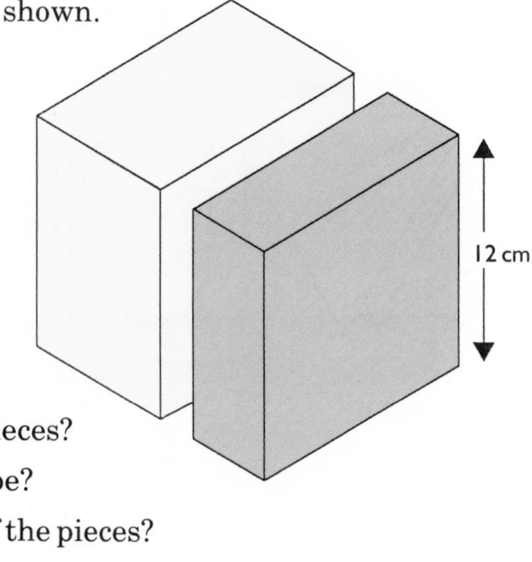

The volume of one of the pieces is twice the volume of the other.

(*a*) What is the volume of each of the pieces?

(*b*) What is the surface area of each of the pieces?

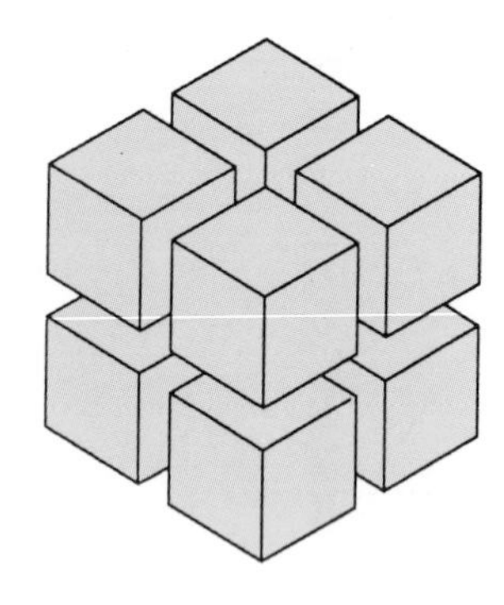

3 A cube of edge 10 cm is dissected into eight identical pieces, as shown.

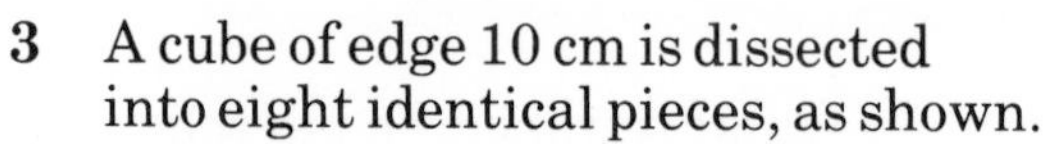

(*a*) What is the volume of one of the pieces?

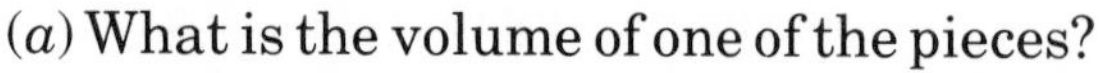

(*b*) What is the surface area of the cube?

(*c*) What is the surface area of each of the pieces?

(*d*) What is the total surface area of all eight pieces?

(*e*) What connection is there between the answer to (*b*) and the answer to (*d*)? Explain this connection by thinking about the cube.

4 A cube is dissected into several pieces by slicing it, like a loaf of bread.

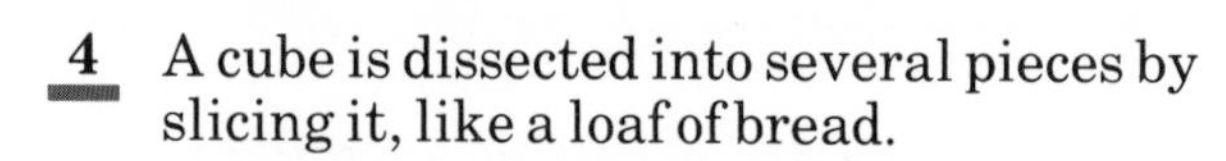

14 cm

(*a*) How many pieces are there if the total surface area of the pieces is exactly

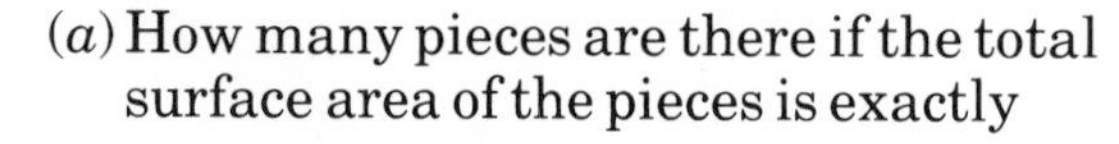

(i) three times the surface area of the cube?
(ii) twice the surface area of the cube?
(iii) ten times the surface area of the cube?

(*b*) For the answers to part (*a*), does it matter whether the slices are all the same thickness or not? Explain your answer.

> You will need to use Pythagoras' theorem to help you answer some of the following questions. If you want to be reminded of Pythagoras' theorem look at page 281.

5 A cube is dissected into two triangular prisms, as shown on the right.

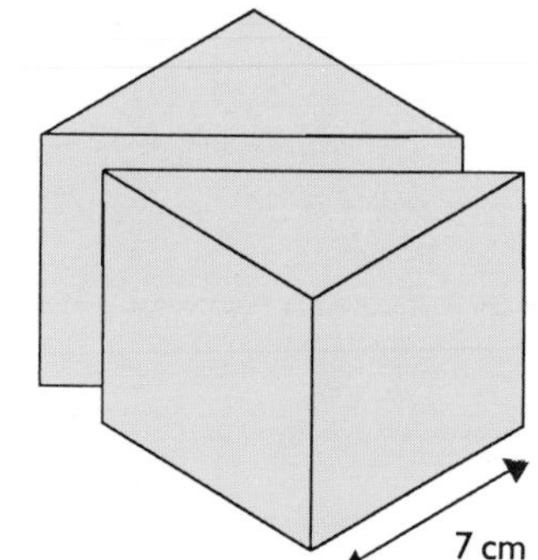

(*a*) What is the volume of each of the pieces?

(*b*) Calculate the surface area of each of the pieces.

6 A cube is dissected into two pieces as shown.

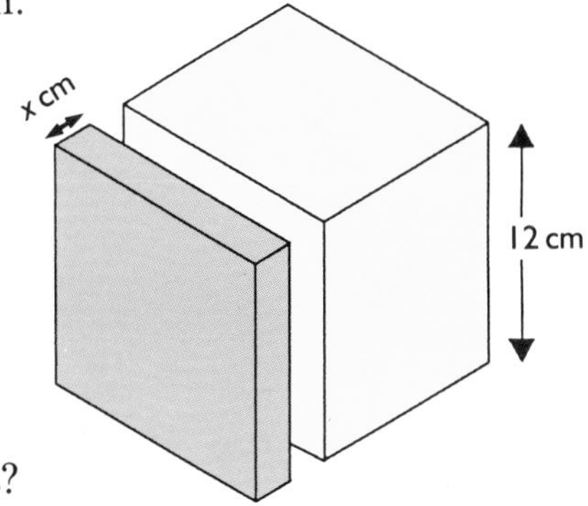

The surface area of one of the pieces is twice the surface area of the other.

(*a*) Find the value of x.

(*b*) What is the surface area of each of the pieces?

(*c*) What is the volume of each of the pieces?

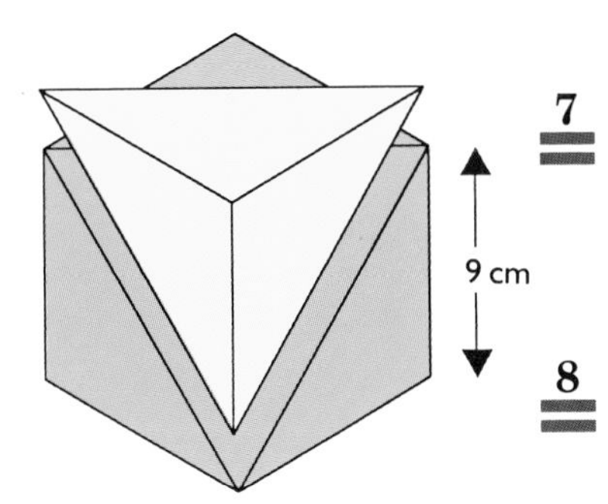

7 A cube is dissected into two pieces, as shown on the left.

(*a*) What is the volume of each of the pieces?

(*b*) What is the surface area of each of the pieces?

8 The eight corners of a cube are cut off. The cuts go through the midpoints of the edges of the cube.

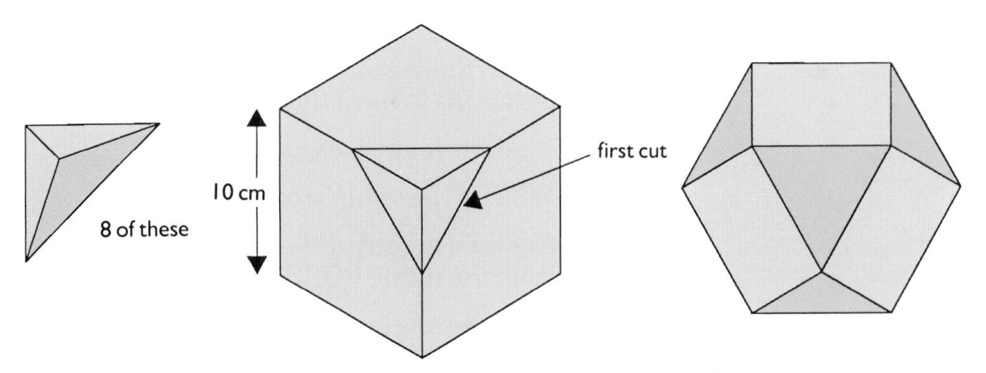

Nine pieces are obtained. Eight of these are tetrahedra. The other one is called a cuboctahedron.

(*a*) How many faces, edges and vertices does the cuboctahedron have?

(*b*) What is the volume of one of the tetrahedra?

(*c*) What is the volume of the cuboctahedron?

(*d*) What is the surface area of the cuboctahedron?

> You will need to use sines, cosines and tangents to help you answer some of the following questions. If you want to be reminded about how these are used, look at page 282.

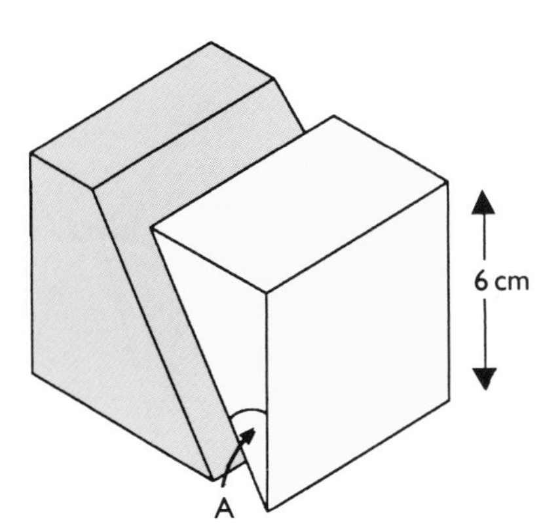

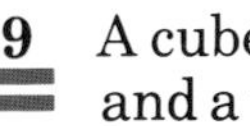

9 A cube is dissected into a triangular prism and a trapezoidal prism, as shown on the right.

(*a*) If the angle marked A is 30°, find the volume of the triangular prism.

(*b*) If the volume of the triangular prism is a quarter of the volume of the cube, find the size of angle A.

(*c*) If the volume of the triangular prism is a third of the volume of the cube, find the size of angle A.

(*d*) What are the largest and smallest sizes for the volume of the triangular prism?

10 A cube is dissected into six identical square-based pyramids.

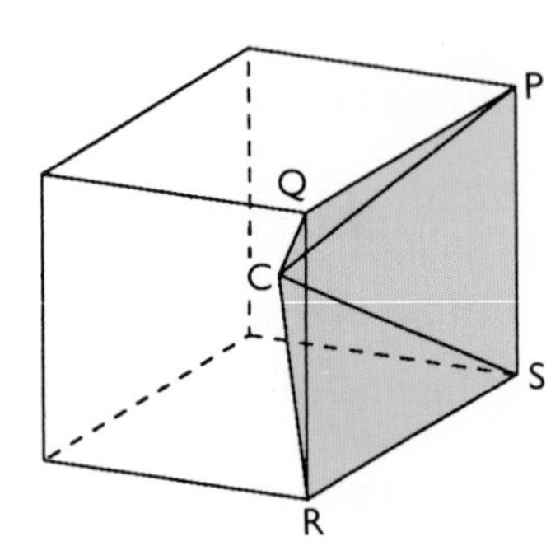

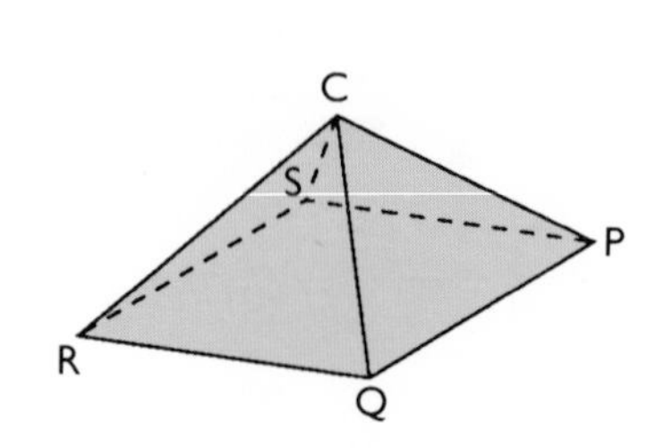

The length of one edge of the cube is 1 unit.

(*a*) When the pyramid shown is put together with the other five pyramids to form the cube, where will the point marked C be?

(*b*) Find the length of the edge CP.

(*c*) What is the volume of the pyramid?

(*d*) Find the height of the pyramid (in other words, the distance of C from the plane PQRS).

(*e*) Find the angle between the edge CP and the face PQRS.

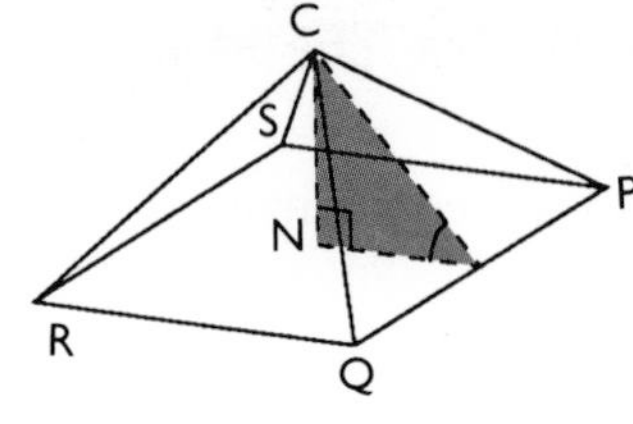

(*f*) Find the angle between the face CPQ and the face PQRS.

11 The edges of a regular tetrahedron are all of length 1 unit.

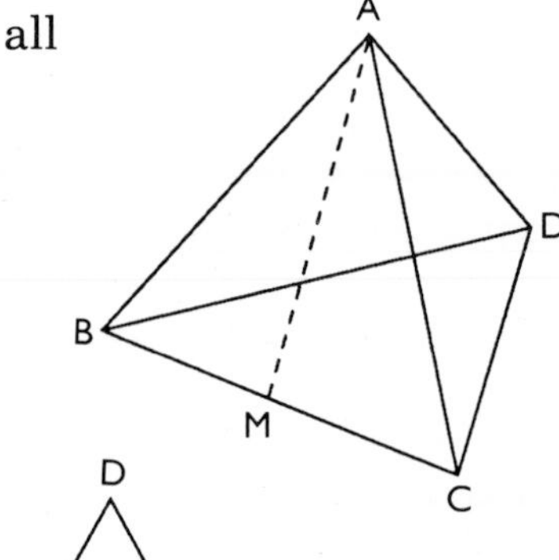

(*a*) The line AM is perpendicular to the line BC. Find the length of AM.

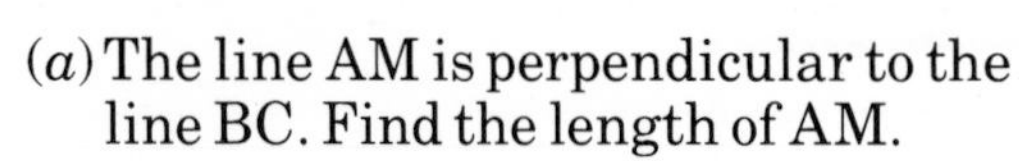

(*b*) Find the surface area of the tetrahedron.

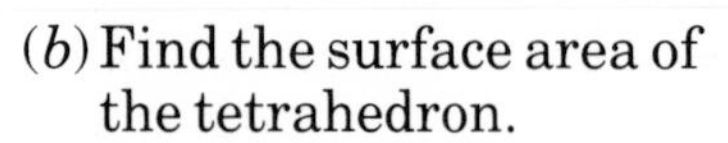

The line AN is perpendicular to the face BCD.

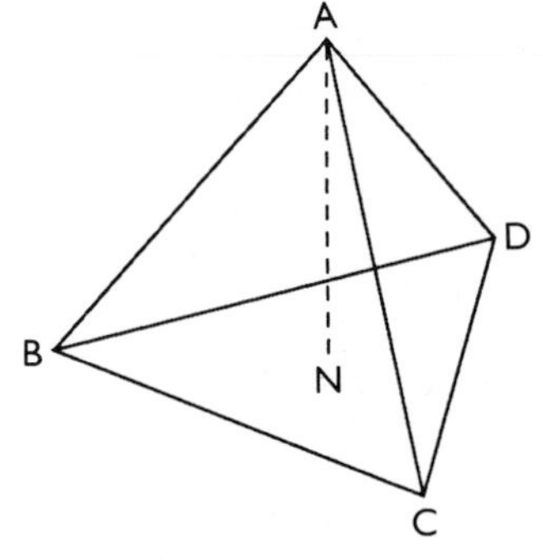

(*c*) By copying the diagram opposite and adding suitable lines, show where N lies.

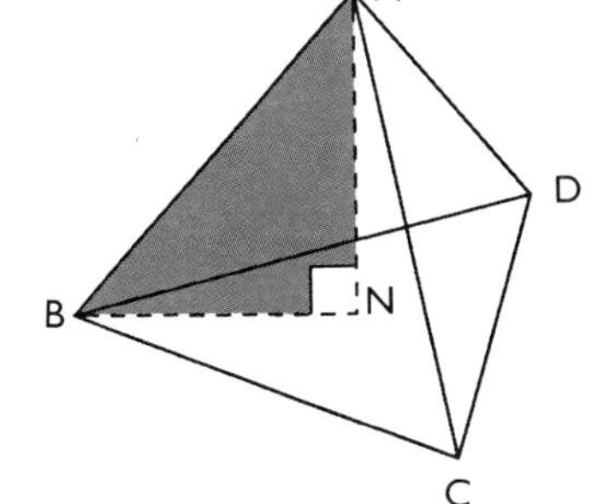

(*d*) Find the length of BN.

(*e*) Find the length of AN.

(*f*) Find the volume of the tetrahedron.

12 A regular tetrahedron is dissected into two identical pieces, as shown in figure 9.

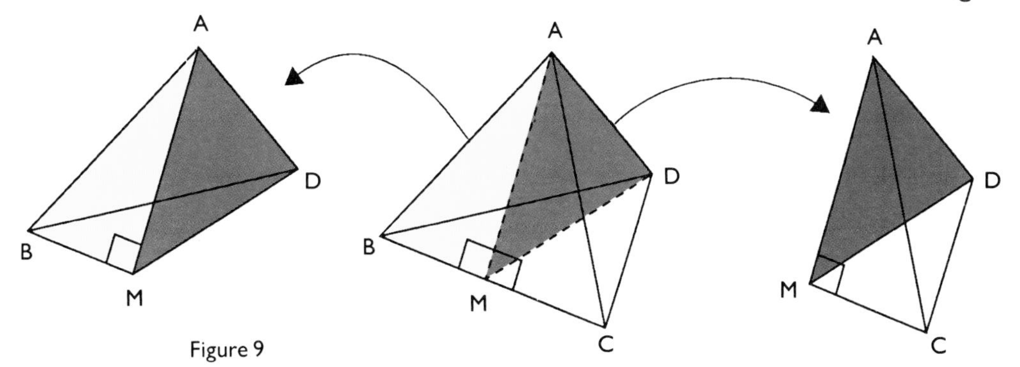

Figure 9

(*a*) Using your answer to question 11, find the volume of each piece.

(*b*) Find the surface area of each piece.

13 Figure 10 shows a regular tetrahedron dissected into two pieces.

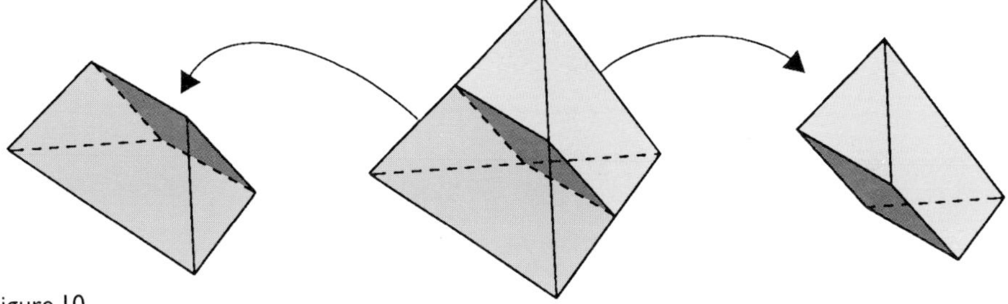

Figure 10

This is the same dissection as in question 9 in Section A.

The length of one edge of the tetrahedron is 1 unit.

(*a*) Find the surface area of each piece of the tetrahedron.

(*b*) Compare your answer to part (*a*) with your answer to question 12(*b*).

Figure 11

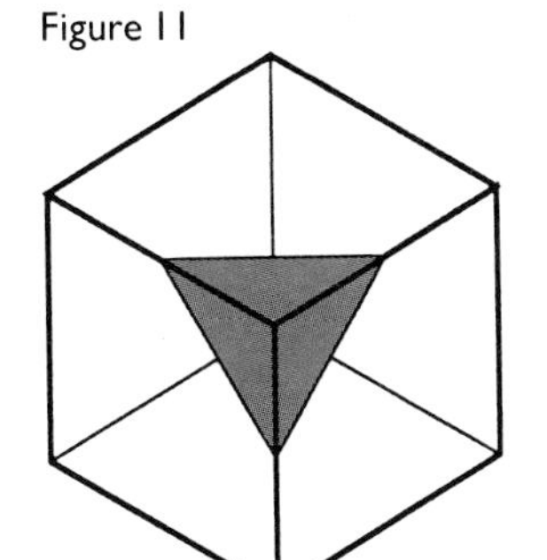

14 If a cube is dissected into two pieces by a plane cut, the new face made on each piece by the cut is called a **section** of the cube. The area of the section means the area of this new face.

Figure 11 shows an equilateral triangular section.

The length of each edge of the cube is 1 unit.

(*a*) What is the area of the largest equilateral triangular section of the cube?

(*b*) What is the area of the smallest equilateral triangular section of the cube?

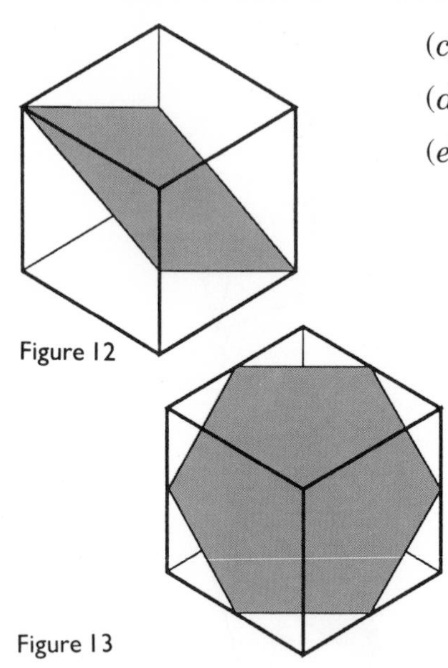

Figure 12

Figure 13

(*c*) What is the area of the largest rectangular section of the cube?

(*d*) What is the area of the smallest rectangular section of the cube?

(*e*) Figure 12 shows the largest rhombic section of the cube.

(i) What is the area of this section? (You might find it helpful to calculate the lengths of the diagonals of the rhombus.)
(ii) What are the angles at the corners of the rhombus?

(*f*) Figure 13 shows a regular hexagonal section of the cube. What is its area?

(*g*) What do you guess is the area of the largest section of the cube?

(*h*) What do you guess is the area of the smallest section of the cube which dissects the cube into two equal pieces?

1⟩ Make a cardboard model of a dissection of a cube. You can dissect the cube into as many pieces as you wish.

Here are some ideas you might want to think about when choosing what dissection to make.

- You might want to dissect the cube into shapes that you think are attractive.
- You might want to dissect the cube into several identical pieces.
- You might want your dissection to be symmetrical in some way, or to produce pieces which are symmetrical.
- You might want the pieces to all have the same volume, but to be different shapes.
- You might want to create a kind of 3-D jigsaw puzzle, in which it is difficult for someone else to know how to fit the pieces together.

Write about how you chose your dissection, and about how you made it. Include nets for the pieces. Also include failures, and try to explain in what ways you went wrong, and what you did to correct your mistakes.

2⟩

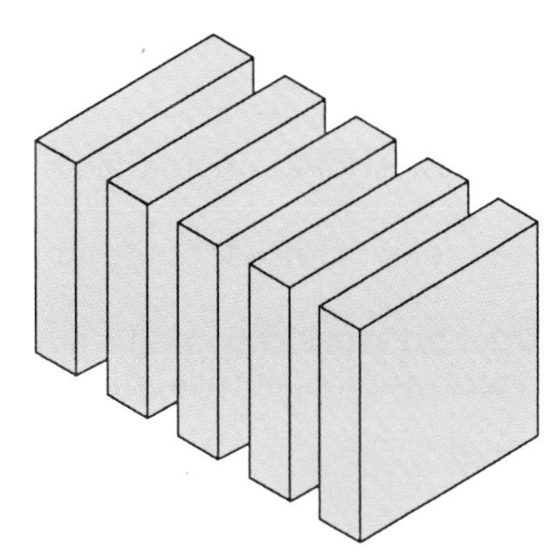

Questions 2, 3, 4 and 6 of Section B are all about slicing a cube into cuboids.

Explore this situation further.

If you cut a cuboid into two cuboids, you might want to consider how to make the surface area of one of the cuboids p times the surface area of the other.

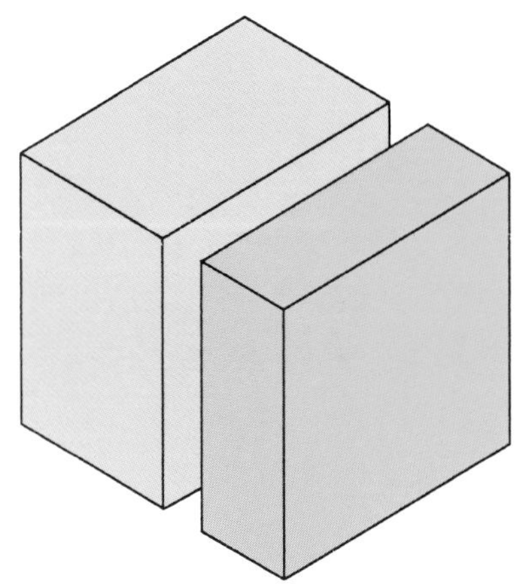

You might want to consider several different ways of cutting a cube into two pieces so that one piece has twice the volume of the other.

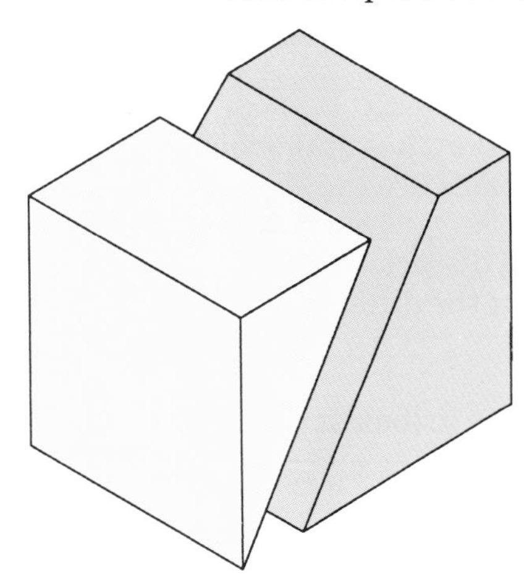

or three times the surface area of the other.

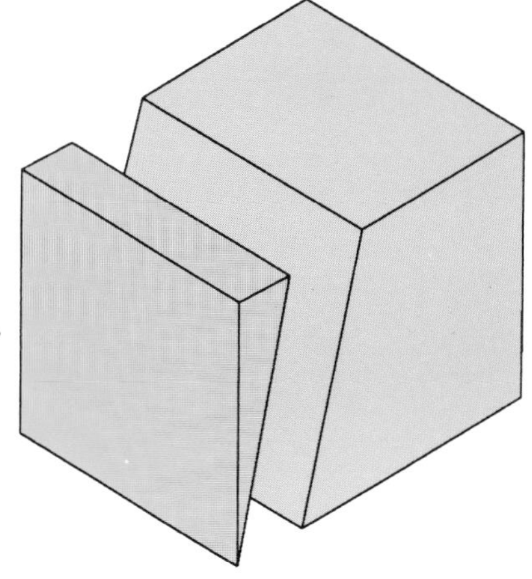

3⟩ Investigate the different sections of a cube (the shapes you create when you cut a cube with a plane cut).

Here are some of the questions you might want to explore.

- What are the ways of getting a triangular section?
- Is it possible to get all types of triangle: equilateral, isosceles, scalene, acute-angled, right-angled, obtuse-angled?

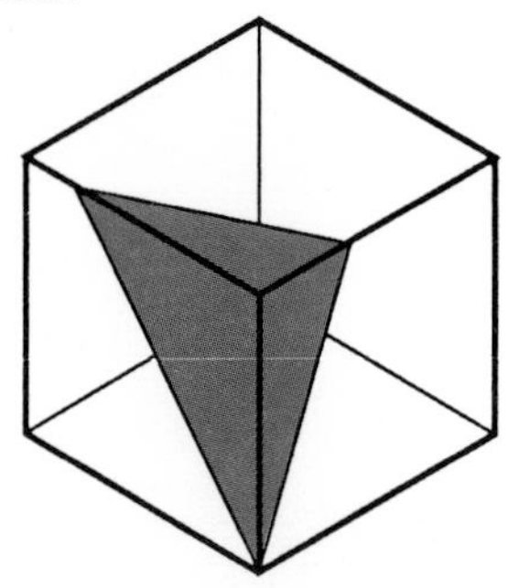

- How do you get a section which is a rectangle? Or a rhombus? Or a parallelogram? Or a trapezium? What types of quadrilateral section are possible?
- What type of pentagonal or hexagonal sections are possible?

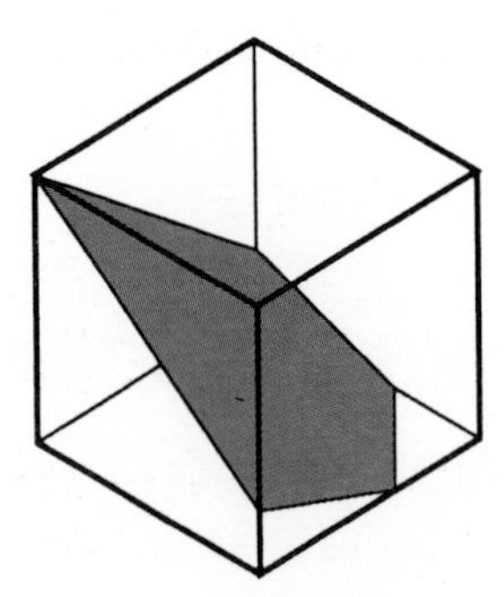

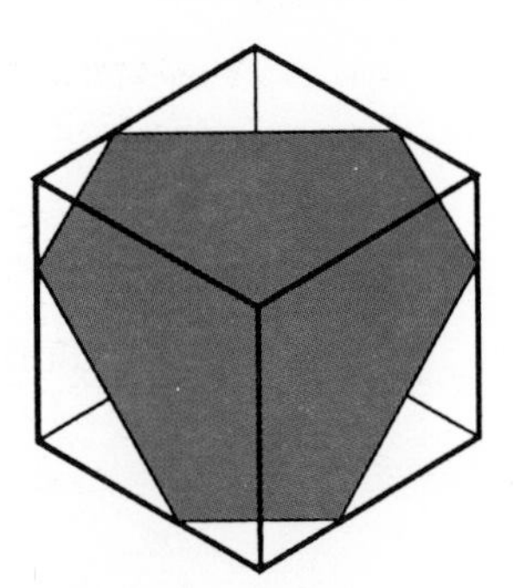

Your write up could contain sketches or models of the sections, and also explanations of why the sections are the shapes they are.

4⟩ Make a cardboard model of a dissection of some shape other than a cube. Or alternatively, write about the different ways of dissecting some other shape.

You could, for example, choose to look at dissections of a tetrahedron, or a cylinder.

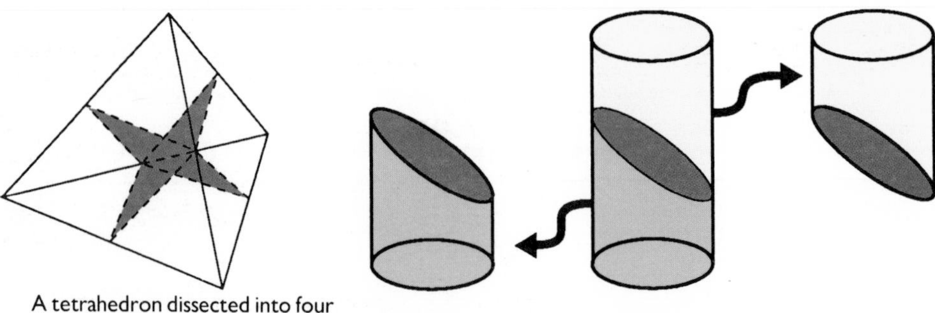

A tetrahedron dissected into four identical pieces.

REVIEW EXERCISES C

EXERCISE 27 Fractions and decimals

1 What fraction of each of the following diagrams is shaded? Give each fraction in its simplest form.

(*a*) 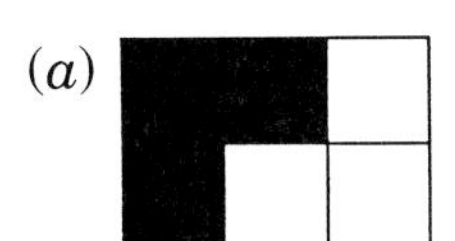 (*b*) 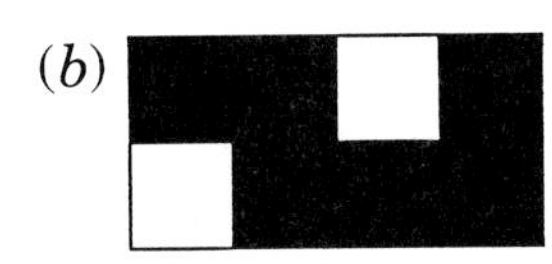

(*c*) 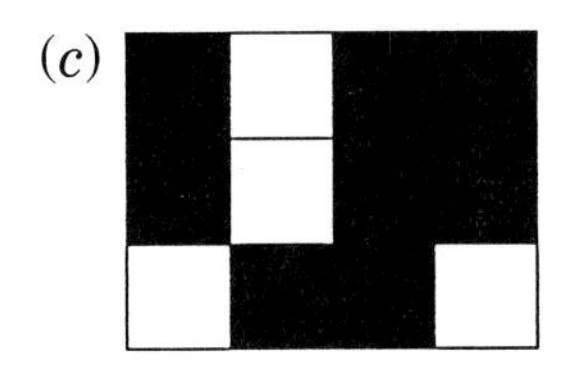 (*d*) 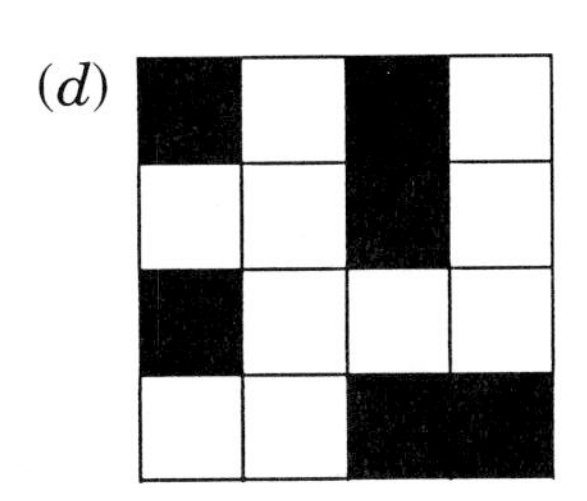

2 Copy each of the following diagrams and shade the fraction stated.

(*a*) (*b*)

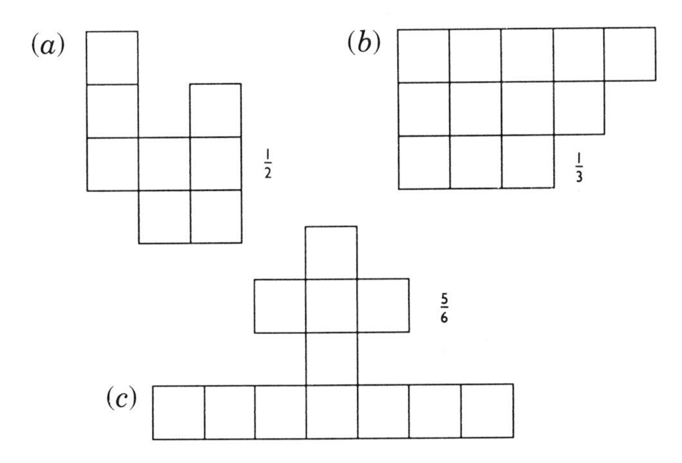

3 State (i) what fraction and (ii) what percentage of each of the following shapes is shaded.

(*a*) (*b*)

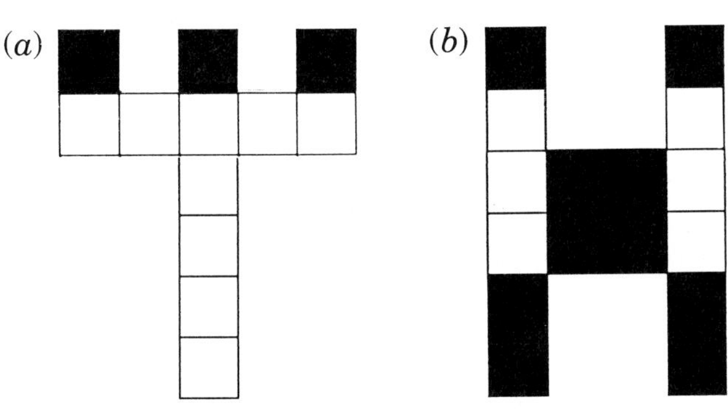

4 60 students applied to go on a rock-climbing course. $\frac{3}{4}$ of them were girls.

(*a*) How many girls applied?

(*b*) What percentage of the students who applied were boys?

5 $\frac{2}{3}$ of the 240 vehicles passing the hospital on a particular morning were cars. How many cars passed the hospital?

6 When Barbara Fox retires next year her pension will be $\frac{3}{5}$ of her present salary. Her present salary is £12 500. What will her pension be?

7 Mrs Brown left £120 000 in her will. She made the following bequests:

One half of her money should go to her daughter, one third to her grandson, one twelfth to the Cancer Research Fund and the remainder to her housekeeper, Miss Grey.

(*a*) How much went to her grandson?

(*b*) How much did Miss Grey receive?

(*SEGB* Summer 1988, Paper 1)

8 Put the following numbers in order, starting with the smallest.

0.36, 0.25, 0.4, 0.6, 0.52

9 5.1, 4.9, 4.11, 4.12, 4.86, 4.75

Some of the numbers above are between 4.8 and 5. Which numbers are they?

10 Put the following numbers in order, starting with the smallest.

$\frac{3}{4}$, 0.7, $\frac{2}{3}$, 1.2, 0.73, 0.4, $\frac{3}{5}$

11 During the first week of a swimming course 24 of the 40 course members were boys.

During the second week of the course 20 of the 36 course members were boys.

(*a*) What fraction of the course members in the first week were boys?

(*b*) During which week was the fraction of boys bigger?

12 The numbers on the right below can all be obtained on a calculator by dividing one whole number by another. The numbers entered into the calculator are all whole numbers less than 50.

For example: 0.6 can be obtained as follows:

$3 \div 5 = 0.6$

Copy the statements below, replacing each question mark with a positive whole number less than 50.

(*a*) $? \div ? = 0.4$ (*b*) $? \div ? = 3.5$

(*c*) $? \div ? = 4.75$ (*d*) $? \div ? = 2.625$

(*e*) $? \div ? = 1.46875$ (*f*) $? \div ? = 1.175$

13

The sweets in a box are classed as creams, caramels or toffees. In a box of Keely's Choice, $\frac{3}{8}$ of the contents are creams, $\frac{1}{4}$ of them are caramels and the remainder are toffees.

(*a*) Work out the fraction of the sweets in the box that are either creams or caramels.

(*b*) What fraction of the sweets in the box are toffees?

(*c*) There are 24 sweets in the box. Work out the number of caramels in the box.

(*LEAG SMP* May 1988, Paper 2)

14 Zenka wants to buy her father a packet of electric drill bits for his birthday.

(*a*) In the first packet that she looks at, there are four different drills and their sizes are marked in inches.

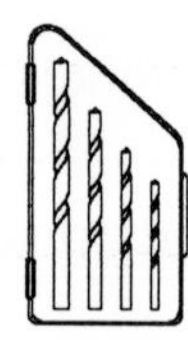

The sizes are $\frac{3}{8}$, $\frac{1}{4}$, $\frac{1}{2}$ and $\frac{1}{8}$.

(i) Which is the larger size drill bit, $\frac{3}{8}$ or $\frac{1}{4}$?
(ii) Write the four sizes in order, starting with the smallest.

(*b*) Zenka looks at a second packet which contains seven drill bits, each increasing in size by $\frac{1}{16}$ of an inch. If the smallest drill bit in the packet is marked $\frac{1}{8}$, write down the sizes of the other six bits.

(You should give the sizes in their simplest form.)

(*NEA* Syllabuses A and B, May 1988, Paper 2)

15 (*a*) Which one of the fractions below is nearest to a half?

$\frac{2}{3}$, $\frac{3}{4}$, $\frac{3}{5}$, $\frac{2}{7}$, $\frac{5}{8}$

(*b*) By how much does it differ from a half?

16 The thickness of two metal sheets are, respectively, $\frac{5}{8}$ of an inch and $\frac{9}{16}$ of an inch.

The sheets are laid one on top of the other. What is their combined thickness?

17 A survey found that the favourite holiday for $\frac{1}{3}$ of people is a seaside holiday abroad, for $\frac{1}{4}$ it was a seaside holiday in Britain and for $\frac{1}{6}$ it was a sports holiday abroad.
For what fraction of people is none of these types of holiday favourite?

18 $\frac{2}{3}$ of a class of children are girls. $\frac{3}{4}$ of the girls play hockey. None of the boys play hockey. What fraction of the class play hockey?

19 When two resistances, R_1 and R_2, are connected in parallel, the formula for the combined resistance is given by the formula

$$\frac{1}{R} = \frac{1}{R_1} + \frac{1}{R_2}$$

(*a*) Find R when $R_1 = 3$ and $R_2 = 6$

(*b*) Find R when $R_1 = 6$ and $R_2 = 4$

(*c*) Find R_2 when $R = 3$ and $R_1 = 12$

(*d*) Find two resistances R_1 and R_2, each whole numbers, whose combined resistance (when connected in parallel) is 8.

20 (*a*) In a sequence of fractions, the next term after $\frac{x}{y}$ is $\frac{y+x}{y+2x}$. For example, the term which follows $\frac{5}{7}$ is $\frac{12}{17}$ $\left(\text{i.e. } \frac{7+5}{7+10}\right)$.

(i) Write down the next three terms in the sequence

$\frac{2}{3}, \frac{5}{7}, \frac{12}{17}, \ldots$

(ii) Copy and complete the following table for the first six terms in the sequence, giving their decimal values to as many decimal places as your calculator will give.

		Decimal value
1st term	$\frac{2}{3}$	
2nd term	$\frac{5}{7}$	
3rd term	$\frac{12}{17}$	
4th term		
5th term		
6th term		

(iii) What do you notice about the decimal values of these terms?

(*b*) In another sequence of fractions, the next term after $\frac{x}{y}$ is $\frac{y-x}{y+x}$.

(i) Write down the first six terms of the sequence which starts with $\frac{2}{3}$.

(ii) What do you notice about the values of these terms?

(*MEG* May 1988, Paper 5)

EXERCISE 28 Probability

1 What is the probability of throwing a tail when an unbiassed coin is tossed?

Give your answer

(*a*) as a fraction, (*b*) as a percentage.

2 Javed and Callum go on a camping weekend together. They take two cans of soup, three cans of beans and two cans of meat. The cans are all exactly the same size and shape.

After they had used one can of soup, it rained heavily and the labels came off all the other cans. When they open the next can, what is the probability that it contains

(*a*) beans? (*b*) soup?

(*MEG*, May 1989, Paper 1)

3 The organisers of a raffle sell 100 tickets. There is one prize. Three friends Ann, Nita and Kathy buy some tickets. Ann and Nita each buy 3 tickets and Kathy buys 5. What is the probability that one of the three friends wins the prize?

4 Each of the positive whole numbers up to 20 is written on a separate piece of paper. The 20 pieces of paper are put into a bag.

A girl picks one of these pieces of paper at random from the bag. What is the probability that she picks

(*a*) a square number?

(*b*) a cube number?

(*c*) a prime number?

5 (*a*) Write down the factors of 24.

(*b*) One of the factors of 24 is chosen at random. What is the probability that it is also a factor of 30?

6 Two bags each contain coloured balls. The first bag contains one black, one red and one green ball. The second bag contains one blue and one green ball. Claire chooses at random one ball from each bag.

(*a*) What is the probability that Claire chooses

(i) a green ball from the first bag?
(ii) a green ball from the second bag?

(*b*) Copy and complete the table to show all possible choices from the two bags.

Ball from 1st bag	Ball from 2nd bag
black	blue
black	green

(*c*) What is the probability that the balls chosen by Claire are both green?

(*NEA* Syllabus C, May 1988, Paper 1)

7 A game uses a special pack of cards. The cards are either red or green, and the picture on each card is either a rabbit or a tulip. The table below shows the number of cards of each type.

	Rabbit	Tulip
Red	6	7
Green	8	9

(*a*) The cards are shuffled well and the first player picks up the top card. What is the probability that:

(i) it is red; (ii) it has a tulip on it?

(*b*) Before players can start they must either pick up a red rabbit or a green tulip. What is the probability that the first player can start with the first card?

8 A bag contains 7 red and 3 yellow sweets. Susan takes a sweet at random and eats it. Jimmy then takes a sweet at random.

Susan's sweet	Jimmy's sweet	Outcome	Probability
red ($\frac{7}{10}$)	red	red, red	–
	yellow	red, yellow	–
yellow ($\frac{3}{10}$)	red	yellow, red	–
	yellow	yellow, yellow	–

(*a*) Complete this tree diagram to find the probabilities of the possible outcomes:

(*b*) What is the probability that both sweets taken are the same colour?

(*NEA* Syllabus B, May 1988, Paper 3)

9 Kirsty and Jan are playing a game. They shuffle five cards, three of which are red and two of which are black.

First Kirsty picks a card at random and keeps it. Then Jan picks a card at random.

The incomplete tree diagram below shows the probabilities and outcomes.

Kirsty's card	Jan's card	Outcome	Probability
red ($\frac{3}{5}$)	red	red, red	–
	black	red, black	–
black ($\frac{2}{5}$)	red	black, red	–
	black	black, black	–

(*a*) Copy and complete the tree diagram.

(*b*) What is the probability that both cards drawn are red?

(*c*) They decide that Jan wins if the two cards drawn are of different colours. What is the probability that Jan wins?

10 Two cards are picked from a normal pack. The first is not replaced before the second is picked.

(*a*) What is the probability that they are both black?

(*b*) What is the probability that they are both aces?

11 The probability that it rains on any particular day in May is $\frac{1}{3}$.

(*a*) Assuming that the weather on any one day is independent of the weather on any other, what is the probability of it raining on two consecutive days in May?

(*b*) Why is the assumption mentioned in part (*a*) not very sensible?

12 The Post Office estimates that 46% of all letters are posted first class and 54% are posted second class. It claims that 88.5% of all first class letters and 94.4% of all second class letters are delivered by the delivery target. The delivery target for first class mail is the next working day after collection, and for second class mail is the third working day after collection.

(*a*) Fill in the missing probabilities on the tree diagram.

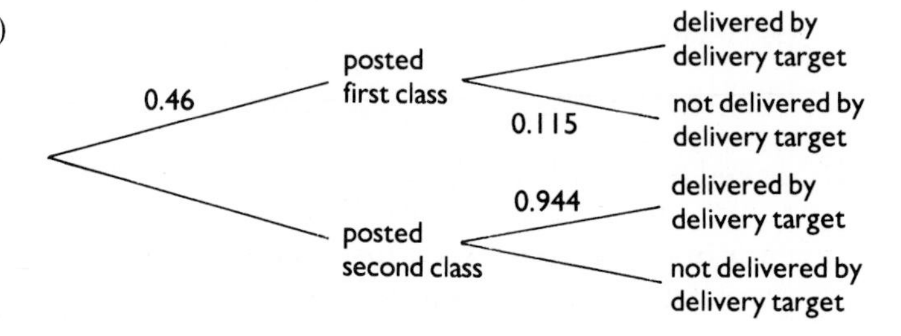

(*b*) What percentage of all letters, whether posted first or second class, are delivered by their delivery target?

(*NEA* May 1989, Syllabus C Paper 3)

You might find it helpful to use Venn diagrams for questions 13 to 16.

13 Nine of the children in a class of thirty have a computer at home and twenty one have a video at home. All the children who have a computer also have video.

What is the probability that a child from the class, chosen at random, has either a computer *and* a video or else *neither* of these?

14 In a set of 28 stamps there are 3 which have no words on and 5 which have no pictures on. 22 of the stamps have both words and a picture.

Find the probability that a stamp, chosen at random, has neither a word nor a picture.

15 A survey on three childhood diseases amongst 200 twelve-year olds produced the following results:

Individual frequencies
30 children have had none of the diseases.
120 children have had measles.
110 children have had German measles.
80 children have had chicken pox.

Joint frequencies
90 children have had exactly two diseases.
25 children have had all three diseases.
All the children who have had chicken pox have also had at least one other disease.
10 of the children have had German measles and chicken pox only.

(*a*) Why is the total of the individual frequencies greater than the number of children in the survey?

The universal set, $\mathscr{E}$ = {all the children in the survey}
M = { children who have had measles}
G = { children who have had German measles}
C = { children who have had chicken pox}

(*b*) Copy the Venn diagram and indicate the number of children in each region.

(*c*) Find the number of children who are in both G and C. Find the number of children who are in C but *not* in G. Interpret your answers.

A nurse claims that a child who has had German measles is more likely to have had chicken pox than a child who has not had German measles.

(*d*) 110 children have had German measles. What proportion of these have also had chicken pox?

(*e*) (i) How many children have not had German measles?
(ii) What proportion of these have had chicken pox?

(*f*) Comment on the nurse's claim.

(*SEG* Summer 1988, Mathematics B Paper 4)

16 There are 28 dominoes in a standard set (see page 4).

(*a*) How many of the dominoes in this set have at least one 5 on them?

(*b*) If a domino is chosen at random from this set, what is the probability that one or both of the numbers on it is a 5 or a 6?

17 Two neighbours Jean and Sheila both go to work on the same bus route. Sometimes they travel on the same bus.

The probability that Jean catches an earlier bus than Sheila is $\frac{3}{10}$. The probability that Sheila catches an earlier bus than Jean is $\frac{2}{5}$.

Assume that Jean's behaviour is independent of Sheila's behaviour.

(*a*) What is the probability that they both catch the same bus?

(*b*) What is the probability that Jean catches an earlier bus than Sheila on two consecutive days?

(*c*) How many times in a month (of 20 working days) would you expect Jean and Sheila to catch the same bus?

18 Two friends Neil and Mark both cycle to school sometimes. When they do not cycle they catch a bus.

On average Neil cycles to school 1 day in every 4 and Mark cycles to school 1 day in every 3.

(*a*) On the assumption that Neil's behaviour is independent of Mark's, find the probability that on a particular day

(i) they both cycle to school,
(ii) neither of them cycles to school.

(*b*) Why is the assumption suggested in part (*a*) an unlikely one?

19 

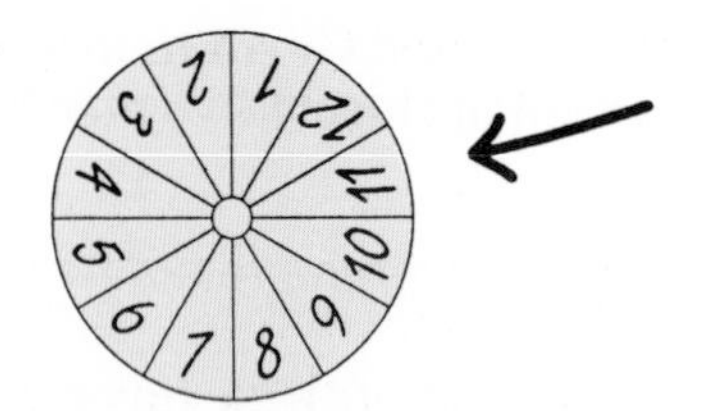

(*a*) What is the probability that the wheel will stop with the pointer opposite a multiple of 5?

(*b*) What is the probability that on the second spin the wheel will stop opposite the same number as in the first spin?

(*c*) What is the probability of getting a multiple of 3 on two consecutive spins?

(*d*) The scores on two consecutive spins are added. What is the probability of getting a multiple of 4?

20 (Give the answers to this question as fractions in their lowest terms.)

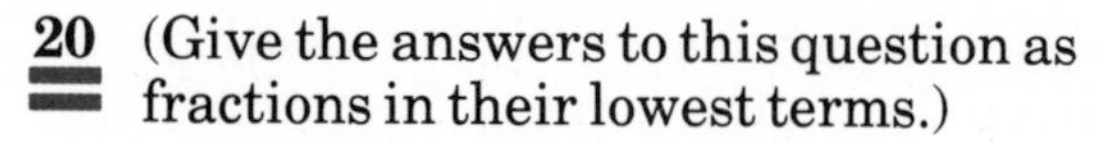

In a game, one red die and one blue die are used. Both dice are unbiased but the faces of the red die are numbered 1, 1, 2, 3, 4, 5 and the faces of the blue die are numbered 1, 1, 2, 2, 4, 4.

(*a*) The two dice are thrown together. Find the probability of each of the following events.

(i) The score on the red die is an odd number.
(ii) The score on the blue die is greater than the score on the red die.
(iii) The scores on the two dice are equal.

(*b*) The two dice are thrown together on two occasions. Find the probability that the score on the blue die is greater than the score on the red die on both occasions.

(*MEG* May 1988, Paper 6)

21 A bag contains 5 red discs, 4 white discs and 1 blue disc.

Two discs are to be chosen at random, without replacement.

(*a*) Copy and complete the probability tree diagram.

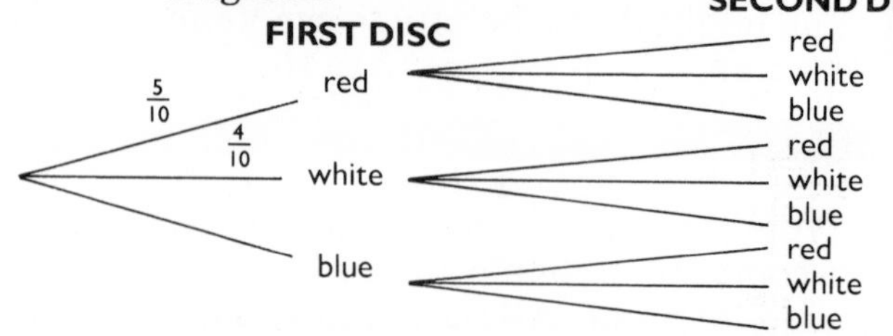

(*b*) Find the probability that

(i) both discs will be red,
(ii) both discs will be blue,
(iii) both discs will be the same colour,
(iv) the two discs will be different colours.

(*LEAG* June 1988, Paper 4)

22 A bag contains five discs, identical in every way except that one is white and the other four are red. Two boys, Alan and Ben, play a game whereby each takes it in turn to draw a disc at random from the bag without replacing it. The first one to draw the white disc is the winner. Given that Alan goes first, find the probability that

(*a*) Alan wins at his first attempt,

(*b*) Ben wins at his first attempt,

(*c*) Ben wins.

(*NEA* November 1988, Syllabus C Paper 4)

23 When a biased 6-sided die is thrown, a score of 6 is twice as likely as a score of 5, a score of 5 is twice as likely as a score of 4 and scores of 1, 2, 3, 4 are equally likely.

(*a*) Calculate the probability of a score of 1.

(*b*) Calculate the probability of a score of 6.

(*c*) Calculate the probability of scoring an even number.

(*NEA* Syllabus B, May 1988, Paper 4)

24 A box of sweets contains 20 chocolates. There are eight orange, six mint and six strawberry flavours. Two sweets are taken at random from the box. Express, as fractions in their lowest terms, the probability that (*a*) both sweets are orange-flavoured,

(*b*) both are the same flavour,

(*c*) they are different flavours. .

(*NEA* May 1989, Syllabus A Paper 4)

25 In a game of darts, the probabilities of three players Ann, Brian and Chetan scoring a double are $\frac{1}{2}$, $\frac{3}{4}$ and $\frac{2}{5}$ respectively.

Each of the players throws one dart.

Calculate the probability that

(*a*) all three players score a double,

(*b*) only Ann will score a double,

(*c*) only one of the three players will score a double.

(*LEAG* June 1989, A Paper 4)

26 A group of 200 thirty-five year old men were asked about their smoking habits: 116 were non-smokers, 53 were moderate smokers (1–24 cigarettes per day) and 31 were heavy smokers (25 or more cigarettes per day).

(*a*) If a man is picked at random from the group, what is the probability that he will be:

(i) a non-smoker, (ii) a smoker.

(*b*) Why is it not possible, using the above information, to calculate a sensible estimate for the mean number of cigarettes smoked each day by the men?

(*c*) The probability that a moderate smoker in the group will die before he is 65 is 0.24. How many of the moderate smokers can be expected to reach this age?

(*d*) The probability, x, that a heavy smoker will die before the age of 65 is twice that for a non-smoker. If 41 of the 200 men die before the age of 65, find a value for x.

(*LEAG SMP* June 1989, Paper 4)

27 Ann and Bill are playing a game in which each player has a die with one face painted red, two faces painted blue and three painted white. The two dice are thrown: if they show the same colour the game is a draw. Otherwise, a player whose die shows red beats one whose die shows blue; similarly, blue beats white and white beats red.

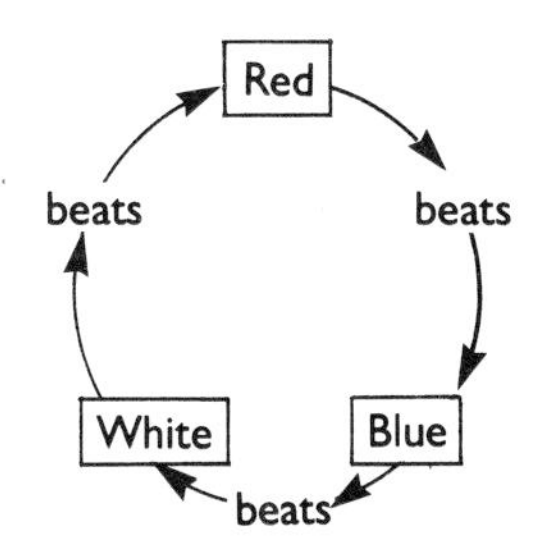

Find the probabilities of Ann winning, Bill winning or a draw.

Bill tries to improve his chance of winning by repainting his die: he paints two of the white faces red. Find how this changes the probabilities of the three possible outcomes.

If you are playing against Ann and she invited you to paint your own die, find out how you should do this to give yourself the best possible chance of winning against her unchanged die.

(*MEG* Specimen 1990 and 1991, Extension paper)

28 Three unbiased dice are thrown.

(*a*) What is the probability that the three numbers obtained are the lengths (in metres) of the sides of a triangle?

(*b*) What is the probability that the three numbers obtained are the lengths (in metres) of the sides of an obtuse-angled triangle?

29 Four women are playing tennis. To decide who will be partners they spin their rackets. The rackets stop either 'rough' or 'smooth'.

If all the rackets are rough or all the rackets are smooth, the players all spin again.

If two of the rackets are rough and two are smooth, this shows who the partners will be.

If one racket is different from the other three, the person with this racket waits while the other three spin again until one racket is different from the other two. The owner of this racket then partners the waiting player.

(*a*) What is the probability that partners will be decided after the first set of spins?

(*b*) What is the probability that partners will be decided after two sets of spins?

(*c*) What is the probability that partners will *not* be decided after three sets of spins?

EXERCISE 29 Networks and flow charts

1 Jan Kirby uses a code to send messages to her friends. Each letter is changed to a pair of numbers using the grid shown below.

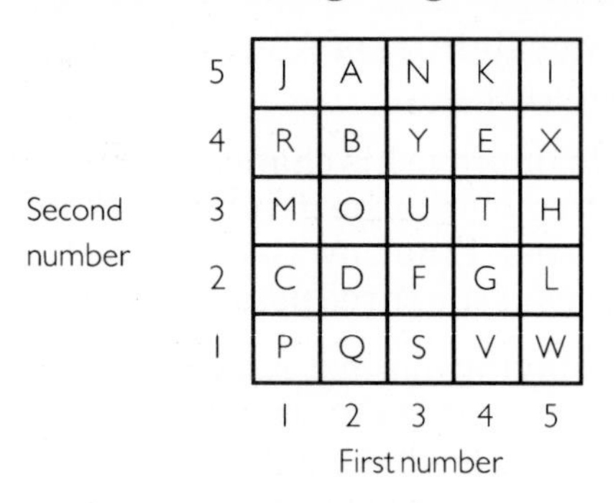

(*a*) Put COSY into code.

(*b*) What word, written in code, is (3,5)(5,5)(4,2)(5,3)(4,3)?

(*c*) Suggest a code for the letter Z.

(*MEG* November 1988, Paper 1)

2 A woman who lives in Manchester orders a dress, which costs £39.99, from a newspaper advertisement. Use the flow chart below to find the cost of the postage and packaging.

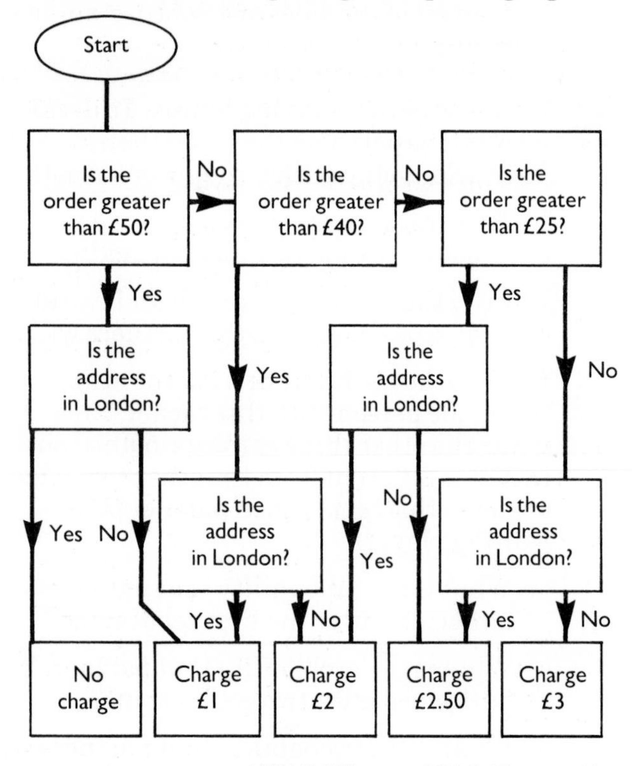

(*SEG* Winter 1988, Paper 1)

3

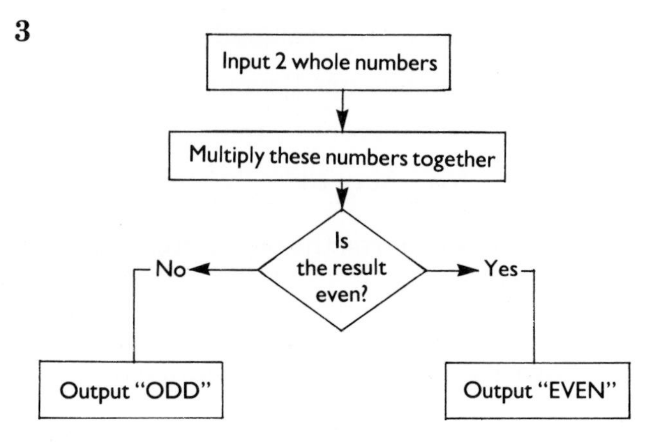

(*a*) State whether the output is 'ODD' or 'EVEN' when the input is

(i) 4 and 3

(ii) 3 and 7.

(*b*) Ann inputs 5 and another number. The output is 'EVEN'. Write down a possible second number for the input.

(*c*) Alfred inputs 2 and another number. He says that the output is 'ODD'. Is he correct? Explain your answer.

(*SEG* Summer 1989, Mathematics A Paper 2)

4

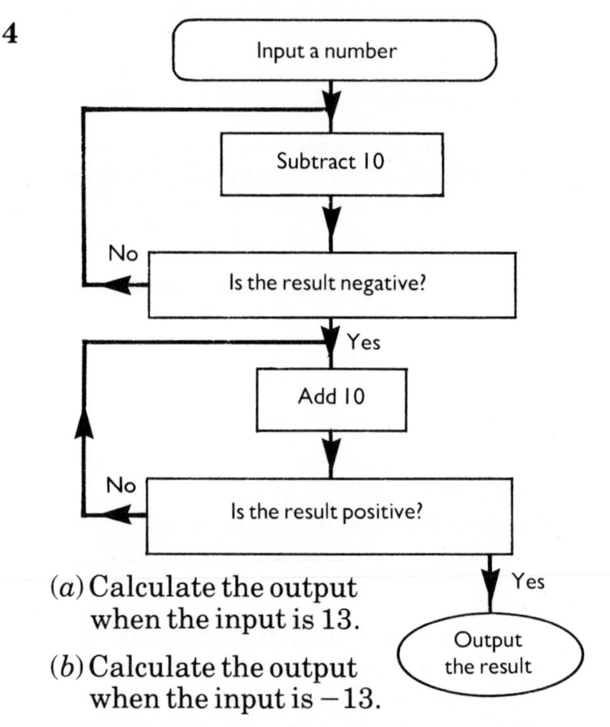

(*a*) Calculate the output when the input is 13.

(*b*) Calculate the output when the input is −13.

(*c*) Find a positive input *and* a negative input, both of which give an output of 6.

(*d*) When a number is input the answer at both decision boxes is *yes* first time. What can you say about the number?

5

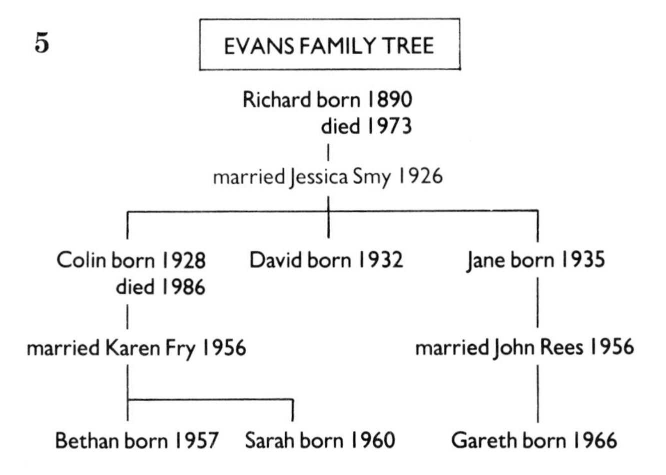

(*a*) How many children did Richard and Jessica have?

Colin dies just after his birthday in 1986.

(*b*) How old was Colin when he died?

Gareth was born on Jane and John's wedding anniversary.

(*c*) For how many years had Jane and John been married when Gareth was born?

The modern Olympic games are held every four years. In 1956 they were held in Melbourne.

(*d*) How many Olympic Games have there been during Bethan's lifetime, up to and including those in 1988?

(*LEAG SMP* January 1989, Paper 2)

6

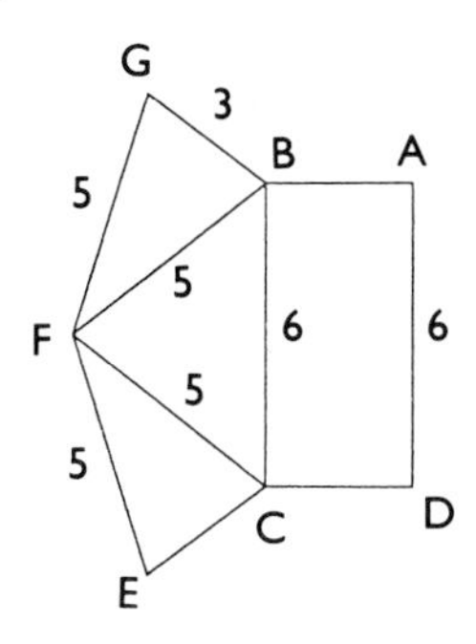

The sketch shows part of the net of a pyramid. All measurements are in cm.

(*a*) Make a full size drawing of the net of the pyramid, adding the missing triangle. (There are several possibilities. Only **one** is required.)

(*b*) How many edges will the pyramid have when it is made?

(*c*) Fred the fly walks from F to A along *edges* of the pyramid. What is the shortest route he can take and how long is it?

(*d*) Freda, his ladyfriend, walks from F to A, but takes the shortest possible route over the outside surface of the pyramid. Draw on your net the route she takes and measure its length.

(*MEG SMP* Mode 2 Specimen)

7 (*a*) (i) A(4,3), B(1,−4), C(−6,−4), D(−3,3). Mark and label these points on a diagram on squared paper.

(ii) Draw the lines AB, BC, CD and DA. Write down the special name given to the quadrilateral ABCD.

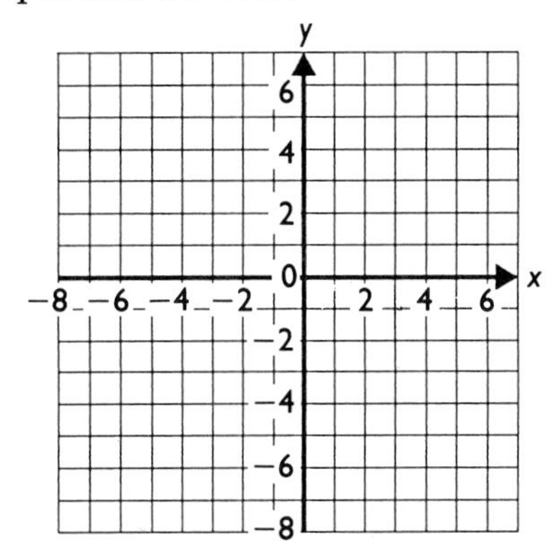

(*b*) Mark and label the point E(6,−8) on the diagram. Draw the lines EA, EB and EC.

(*c*) The points A, B, C, D and E represent five villages. The seven lines you have drawn represent roads. There are six possible routes that could be taken by a car when driving from village D to village E. (The car must not pass through any village more than once.)

One route is D to C to B to E.

Write down five other routes.

(*MEG* November 1988, Paper 4)

8 The diagram shows the distances in miles between towns on major routes.

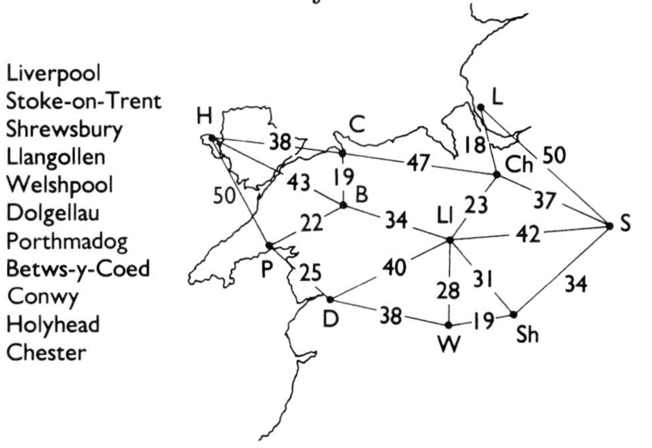

(*a*) A woman who lives at Stoke-on-Trent wants to drive to Holyhead.
(i) If she takes the shortest route, which towns will she pass through?
(ii) On the way home she agrees to drop a friend off at Welshpool. She again wants to drive as few miles as possible. How much longer is her return journey?

(*b*) A commercial traveller, whose home is in Dolgellau, has to visit all the towns shown on the diagram and then return to Dolgellau.

In which order should she visit the towns to make her route as short as possible?

9 Here is a list of things to be done when making a cup of tea.

get cup out
pour milk in cup
pour tea in cup
put boiling water in pot
put tea in pot
put water on to boil

This list of things to do is in alphabetical order, not in a sensible order. One way of explaining a sensible order is to draw a diagram.

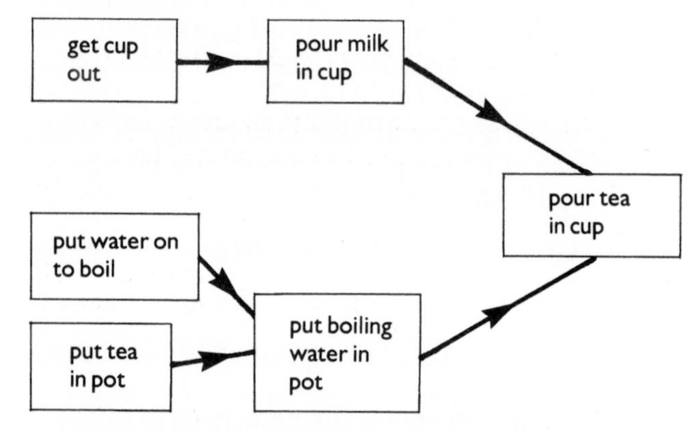

The diagram shows, for example, that you must get a cup out before you can pour milk in it. It shows this by the arrow connecting the 'get cup out' box to the 'pour milk in cup' box. The diagram also shows that you can get the cup out before or after you boil the water or make the tea. This is because there are no arrows connecting these boxes.

(*a*) Some people think you should warm the pot before adding the tea.

Copy the diagram and add a box with an arrow to it to show this extra thing to be done.

(*b*) Some people do not mind whether the milk is put in before or after the tea. Change your diagram to show what they think.

10 Here is a list of what some people do when making poached eggs on toast.

add salt to water
add vinegar to water
break egg
butter toast
cook toast
cut bread for toast
put egg in boiling water
put water on to boil
take egg from water and put on toast

Draw a diagram, similar to that in question 9, to show the order in which these things must be done.

11 Peter is preparing a meal and the following jobs need to be done.

Job	Time needed in minutes
prepare potatoes	5
prepare meat	5
cook potatoes	20
cook meat	15
prepare salad	10

The potatoes and meat can cook at the same time, and while they are cooking the other preparation can be done. Only one preparation job can be done at a time.

(*a*) To have the meal ready for 6.30 p.m., what is the latest time Peter must start to prepare it?

(*b*) Write a possible timetable for him, starting at the time you gave in your answer to part (*a*).

(*MEG SMP* 11–16 November 1988, Paper 3)

12

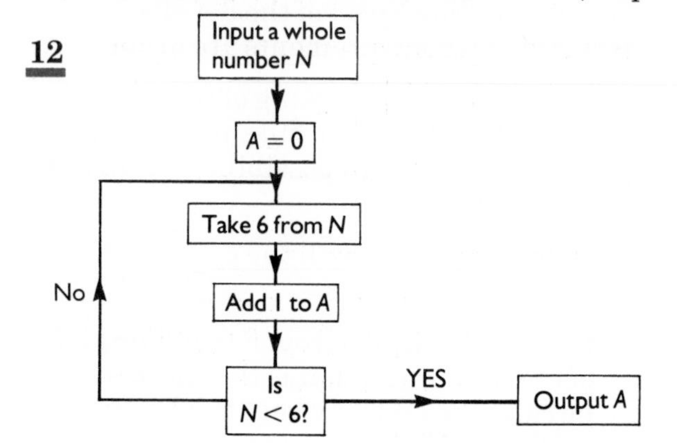

(*a*) What is the output when the input is

(i) 18?
(ii) 24?
(iii) 26?

(*b*) There are six different inputs which produce an output of 5. What are they?

(*c*) What is the output if the input is

(i) 300?
(ii) 400?

13 

A $y = -\frac{1}{4}x + 2$
B $x = 2y - 2$

A method of solving these simultaneous equations uses the following iteration.

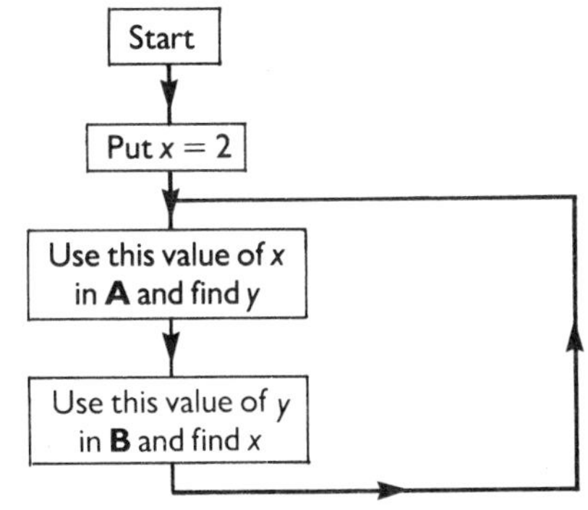

(*a*) Use this loop three times and list the values of x and y you obtain at each stage.

(*b*) (i) By substituting $-\frac{1}{4}x + 2$ for y in **B** solve the equation for x.
(ii) Use your value of x from part (*b*)(i) in **A** to solve the equation for y.

(*c*) Comment on the apparent inconsistency between the results obtained in parts (*a*) and (*b*).

(*LEAG SMP* January 1989, Paper 4)

14  (*a*) Calculate the height of an equilateral triangle of side 1 unit in the form $p\sqrt{3}$, where p is a fraction in its lowest terms.

(*b*) A computer program, when run, moves a cursor on a screen according to the following instructions.

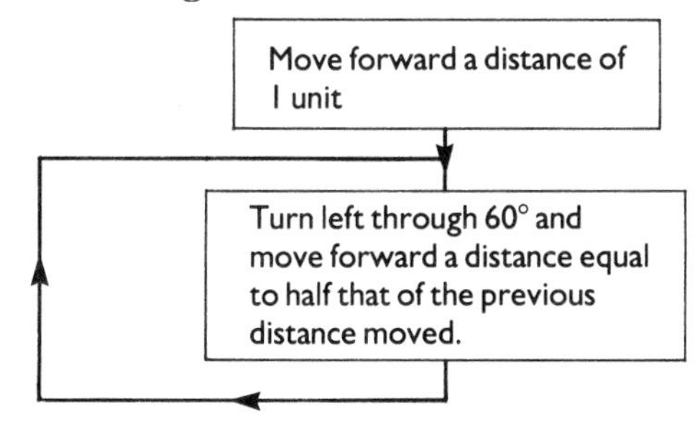

Part of the path traced out is shown below.

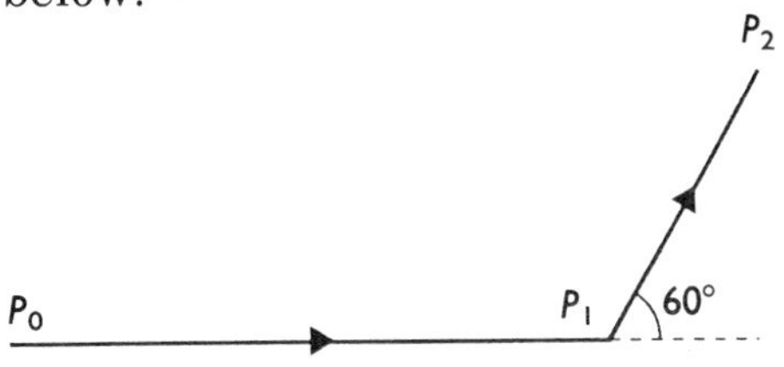

Continue the diagram to show the positions of P_3 and P_4.

(*c*) Given that P_0 is (0,0) and P_1 is (1,0), calculate the coordinates of P_2 in the form $(a, b\sqrt{3})$, where a and b are rational numbers.

(*NEA* May 1989, Syllabus B Paper 4)

EXERCISE 30 Combinatorics

1

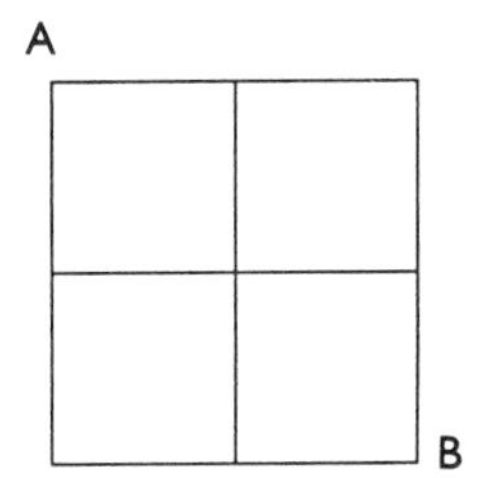

Following the lines of the grid, find how many *different* routes there are to travel from A to B. Do not follow any line in the grid more than once in each route. Do not cross any point in the grid more than once in each route.

(*NEA* November 1988, Syllabuses A and B Paper 1)

2

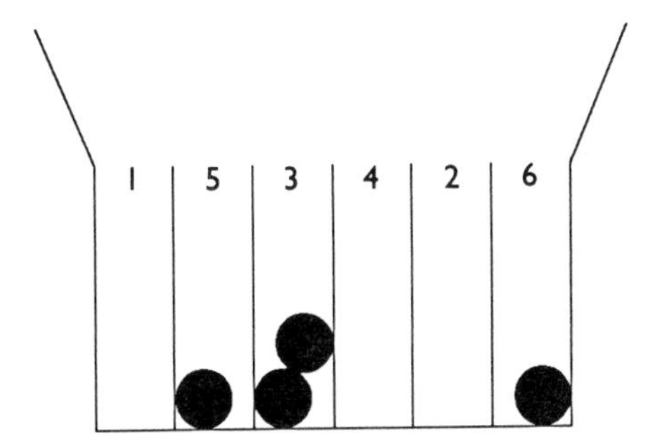

John plays Roll-a-Ball at the fairground. He has to roll six balls, all of which must score. When he has rolled four balls, the position is as shown. So far he has scored

$5 + 3 + 3 + 6 = 17.$

Winning totals are

6, 10, 18, 20, 25, 29, 32, 36

(*a*) Which of these winning totals can John still achieve?

(*b*) List all the possible ways in which he can score 8 with the last two balls.

(*MEG* May 1988, Paper 4)

3 The diagram shows a dartboard.

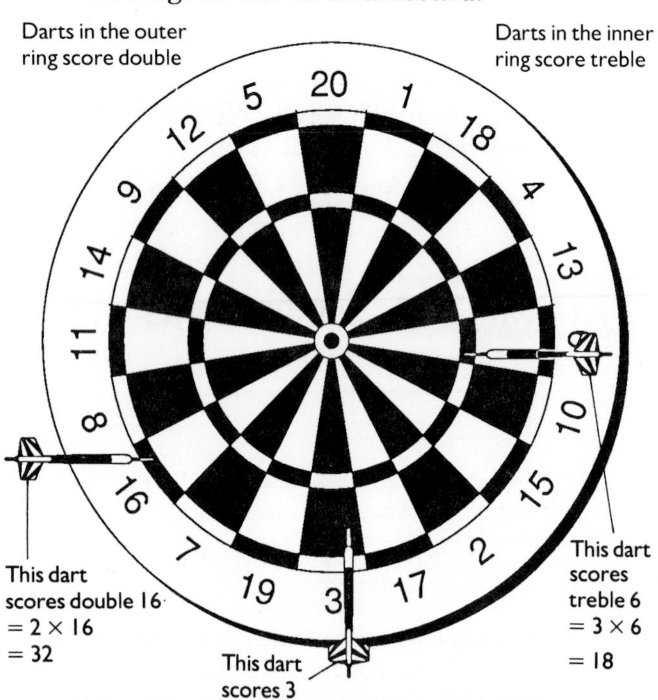

To win a competition, the *last* dart must go into the outer ring, to score a double. Jane has 3 darts to score a total of 29 to win. She scores 20 with her first dart.
To win, she can throw her remaining two darts in five different ways. Two different ways are

1, double 4;
7, double 1.

Find the three other ways.

(*MEG* November 1987, Paper 4)

4 Here is the menu for a restaurant.

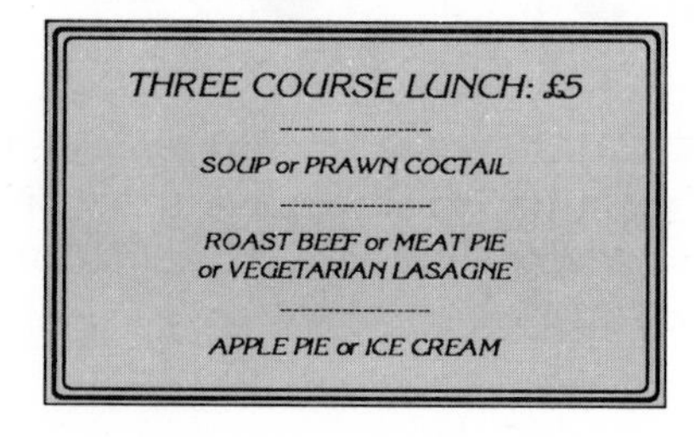

THREE COURSE LUNCH: £5

SOUP or PRAWN COCTAIL

ROAST BEEF or MEAT PIE or VEGETARIAN LASAGNE

APPLE PIE or ICE CREAM

(*a*) How many different three course meals could be chosen from this menu?

(*b*) How many different three course meals could you choose if you did not want to have pie twice?

5 Car parking costs 60p. You get a ticket from a machine and no change is given. You can use coins of any value.

I have five coins in my pocket which will exactly pay the 60p. What might these coins be? Give all the possibilities.

6 A milkman receives milk from the dairy in three different sized packs.

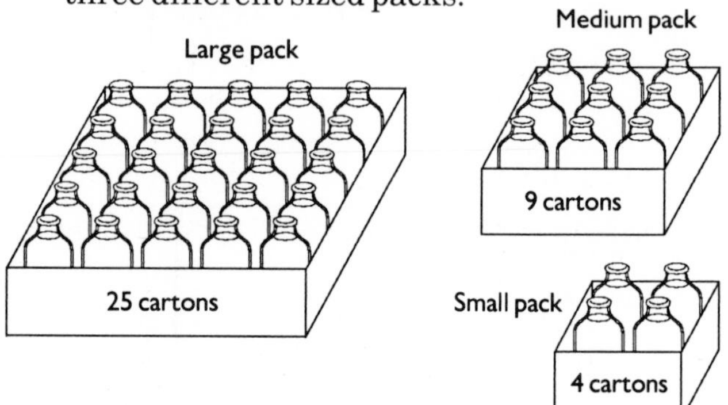

(*a*) Using the *least* number of complete packs, how would the milkman deliver

(i) 29 cartons,
(ii) 47 cartons?

(*b*) One morning the milkman receives four packs of milk. He did not record the number of cartons he received. However, he knew that when he had delivered all the cartons, the number of cartons was between 80 and 90.

How many cartons exactly did he deliver?

(*Welsh* May 1988, Paper 1)

7 In a hockey league each team plays each other team twice. There are 3 points for a win, 1 point for a draw and no points for losing. Complete the table below:

Team	Played	Won	Drawn	Lost	Points
Oak Rangers	8				21
Birchfield United	8	4		2	
Ashtree Rovers	8	3	1		
Willow Sports	8		1		7
Chestnut Athletic	8		2		5

(*SEG* Summer 1989, Mathematics C Paper 2)

8 Rectangles with dimensions 4 cm by 3 cm are needed to make tickets.

What is the largest number of these rectangles which can be cut from a square sheet of card measuring 16 cm by 16 cm? Draw a diagram to show how these tickets should be cut from the sheet.

9 A hockey team has played eight games this season. They have won only one game and lost the other seven. They have scored 3 goals and have had 8 goals scored against them.

List all the possible scores of the game they won.

10 Gwyn and Andrea sell Coke to their friends at breaktime. They charge 10p for a small cup and 20p for a large cup. A small cup holds 150 ml. A large cup holds 400 ml.

(*a*) One breaktime they sell 6 small cups and 3 large cups.

(i) How much money do they take?
(ii) What volume of Coke do they sell?

(*b*) At the end of one breaktime they have taken £1.20.

(i) List all the ways they could have taken £1.20.
(ii) For their £1.20 they find they have sold 2 litres of Coke. How many small cups and how many large cups did they sell?

(*Welsh* May 1989, Paper 2)

11 The following table shows the positions of the top six teams in Division One of the Football League at the end of one week in the season.

1 Liverpool
2 Arsenal
3 Manchester United
4 Nottingham Forest
5 Tottenham Hotspur
6 West Ham

After the following week's games, these changes occurred:

Nottingham Forest went down two places;
Luton Town entered the top six but in the lower half;
Liverpool were still ahead of Arsenal and both teams remained in the top six;
Manchester United became the new leaders;
Tottenham Hotspur remained in the same position.

Show the new order at the top of Division One.

(*NEA* May 1989, Syllabuses A and B Paper 2)

12 At a meeting four men discovered that they each had three children and that each child had two pets.

(*a*) How many pets were there altogether?

(*b*) Some of the pets were mammals, some were birds and some were insects. (Each insect had 6 legs and 2 wings.)

Altogether the pets had 88 legs and 20 wings. How many mammals, how many birds and how many insects were there?

13 Garages are allocated number plates which fit the following pattern.

F * * * SJT

The three stars (* * *) are replaced by different numbers.

Each garage is given a different set of numbers to use.

(*a*) One garage is given the numbers 1, 2 and 3. Each number plate must use all three numbers.

(i) List all the possible number plates.
(ii) Mr Smith buys a car from this garage. He asks for a number plate which is a multiple of 4. What number plate should he be given?

(*b*) Another garage is given the numbers 4, 5, 6 and 7. Each number plate must use three of the numbers. The garage usually sells 15 to 20 cars each year. Will they be able to allocate a different number plate to all the new cars they usually sell? Explain how you reached your answer.

(*SEG* 1991 Specimen, Mathematics B Paper 1)

14 Six players take part in a table-tennis competition.

Each player plays one game against each of the other players.

(*a*) How many games are played by one of the players?

(*b*) How many games are played altogether?

The outright winner is the player who wins more games than any of the other players.

(*c*) What is the *smallest* number of games which the outright winner could win?

There might not be an outright winner. There are joint winners if more than one player wins the largest number of games.

(*d*) What is the *biggest* number of joint winners there can be?

15

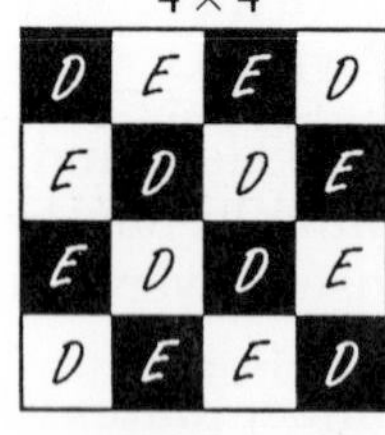

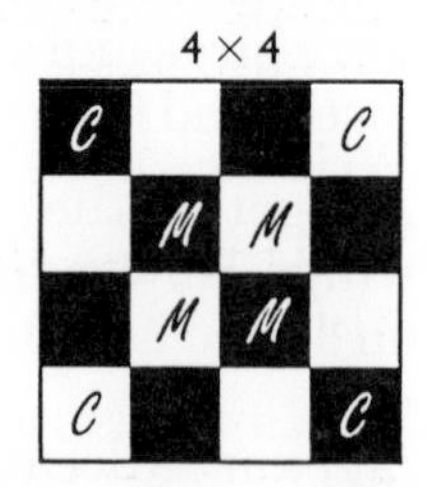

A 'chessboard' consists of four different types of square. They are denoted by

C, corner squares, of which there are four,
E, edge squares, which lie along the edge of the board, but are not corner squares,
M, middle squares, which are neither edge nor corner squares,
D, diagonal squares, which lie along both diagonals of the square.

(Some squares may be more than one type of square simultanteously.)

The diagrams above show the same 4×4 chessboard labelled in two different ways.

The table below shows the number of each type of square for various size boards.

Size of board	Type of square			
	C	E	M	D
3 × 3	4	4	1	5
4 × 4	4	8	4	8
5 × 5	4	12	9	9
6 × 6				

(*a*) Find the number of each type of square for a 6×6 board.

(*b*) How many middle squares will an 8×8 board have?

(*c*) A board has 48 edge squares. How many diagonal squares does it have?

(*d*) A board has 225 middle squares. How many edge squares does it have?

(*e*) Find the number of each type of square for a 100×100 board.

(*NEA* May 1989, Syllabus C Paper 3)

One method of tackling questions 16 and 17 is to use Venn diagrams.

16 For WJEC Mathematics, GCSE candidates are entered for *either* papers 1 and 2, *or* papers 2 and 3, *or* papers 3 and 4.

In one school in 1989, 51 candidates were entered for paper 1, 114 candidates were entered for paper 2 and 112 candidates were entered for paper 3.

How many candidates were entered for paper 4?

(*Welsh* May 1989, Paper 4)

17 A palindromic number is a number which stays the same if the digits are reversed. For example, 484 is a palindromic number.

Among three-digit numbers there are 143 prime numbers, 22 square numbers and 90 palindromic numbers.
3 of the numbers are both square *and* palindromic.
15 of the numbers are both prime *and* palindromic.

(*a*) How many of the numbers are both square *and* prime?

(*b*) If all the prime, square and palindromic three-digit numbers are listed, how many *different* numbers will be listed?

18 The Bargain Bus Company has buses and coaches for hire. A bus can carry 70 passengers and costs £87 a day.
A coach can carry 42 passengers and costs £65 a day.
A sponsored walk raised £400. This is to be used on transport for an old people's outing.

Find the largest number of people that can be taken.

Show all your trials.

Show clearly how many buses and how many coaches are needed.

(*LEAG SMP* 11–16 June 1987, Paper 4)

19 A security code consists of three digits. Each digit is one of the numbers 1 to 6. How many different security codes are possible?

20 In a tiddlywinks tournament, each match involves three players. The first player to get all his counters into the pot is the winner. You are arranging a tournament so that every player competes against every other player exactly once.

(*a*) How many matches would be needed if seven players were involved?

(*b*) Could you arrange a tournament like this for eight players? Give a reason for your answer.

(*SEG* 1990 Specimen, Extension Paper)

EXERCISE 31 Properties of shapes

1

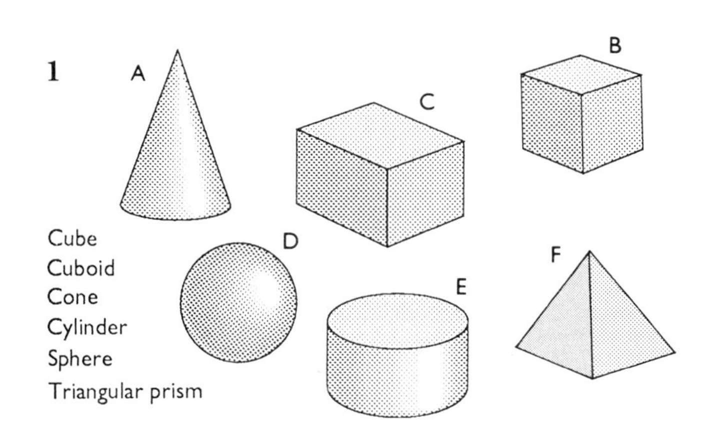

(*a*) Which of the objects in the picture is a cylinder?

(*b*) Which of the shapes on the list is not shown in the picture?

(*c*) Which object in the picture has a shape which is not on the list?

2 (*a*) Plot the points A(2,0), B(−3,3) and C(−1,−5) and join them up.

(*b*) Select one name from column 1 and one from column 2 to describe triangle ABC.

Column 1	Column 2
Equilateral Isosceles Scalene	Acute-angled Obtuse-angled Right-angled

(*MEG* June 1988, Paper 4)

3

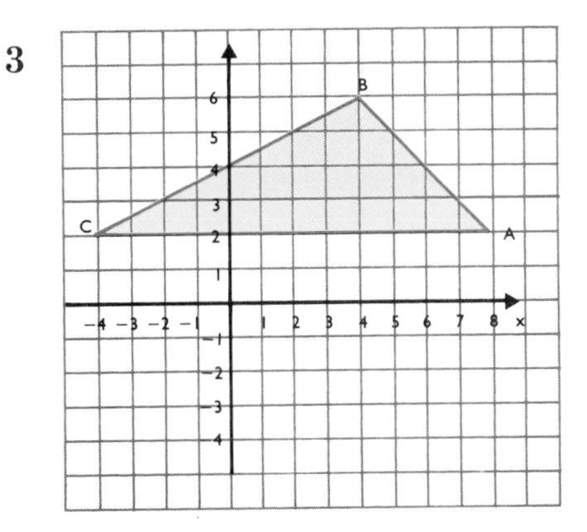

In the diagram A is the point with coordinates (8,2) and B is the point with coordinates (4,6).

(*a*) Write down the coordinates of C.

(*b*) Find the area, in square units, of triangle ABC.

(*c*) The line AC is a line of symmetry of quadrilateral ABCD.

(i) Write down the coordinates of point D.
(ii) What special type of quadrilateral is ABCD?

(*MEG* May 1989, Paper 4)

4

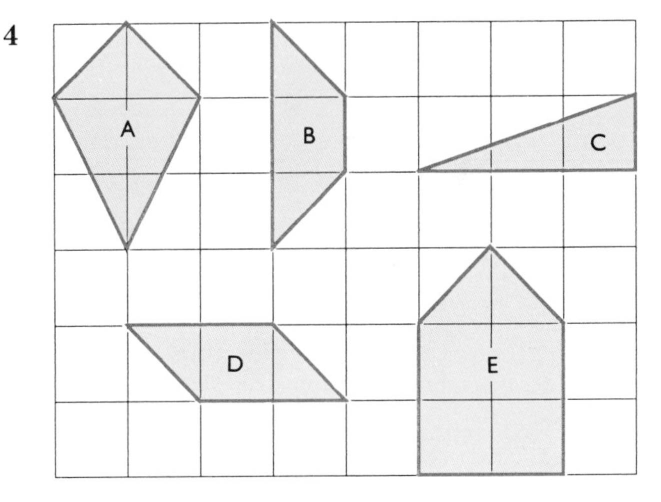

On the grid of 1 cm squares above, five shapes are drawn.

(*a*) Which of these shapes is a trapezium?

(*b*) Which of these shapes have a line of symmetry?

(*c*) What is the sum of the five angles of shape E?

(*d*) Find the area of shape C.

(*MEG* November 1988, Paper 1)

5 Triangle ABC is an equilateral triangle.

Triangle DEF has an angle D = 90°.

Triangle HGK has the length of HG equal to the length of HK.

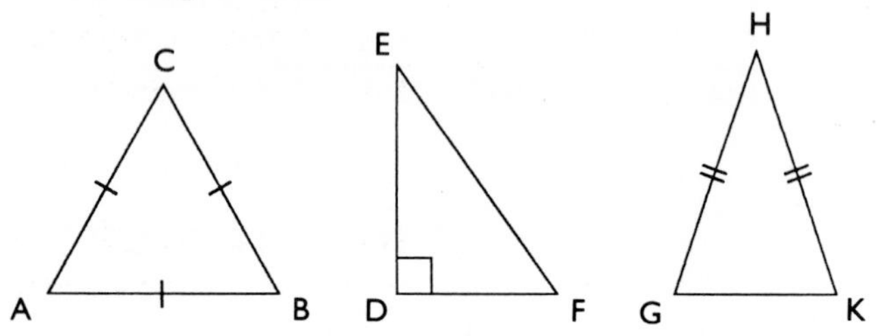

(*a*) Given that angle A = angle F, write down the number of degrees in

(i) angle F, (ii) angle E.

(*b*) Given that angle E = angle H, write down the size of angle G.

(*SEG* Summer 1989, Paper B1)

6 These shapes are displayed on a mathematics classroom wall.

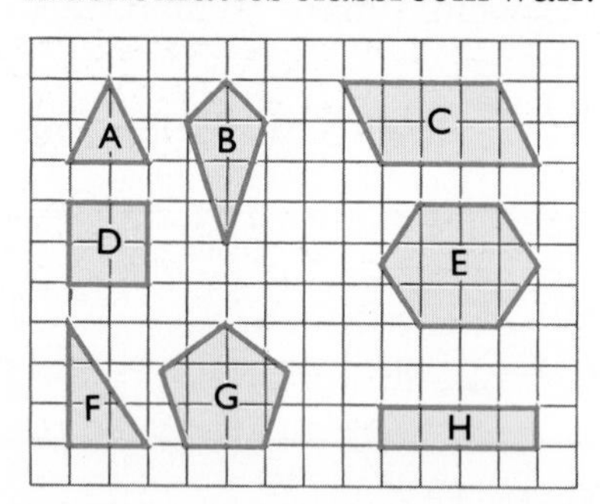

Someone removes one of the shapes from the display. It has less than five sides and does not have any right angles.

(*a*) Give the letters of the shapes which could have been removed.

Here is some more information about the missing shape. It has two obtuse angles and its opposite sides are parallel.

(*b*) Give the letter of the shape which has been removed.

(*c*) What is the name of this shape?

(*NEA* May 1988, Paper 2)

7 Sian makes a square out of geo-strips as shown in the diagram.

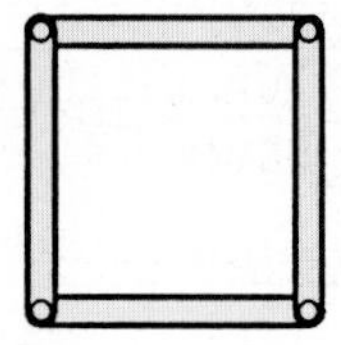

(*a*) How many lines of symmetry does the square have?

Sian pushes her square over to give the following shape.

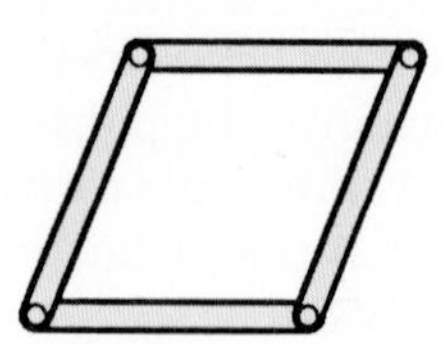

(*b*) What is the name of this shape?

(*c*) Describe *one* difference between a square and the shape above.

Sian next makes a rectangle out of geo-strips.

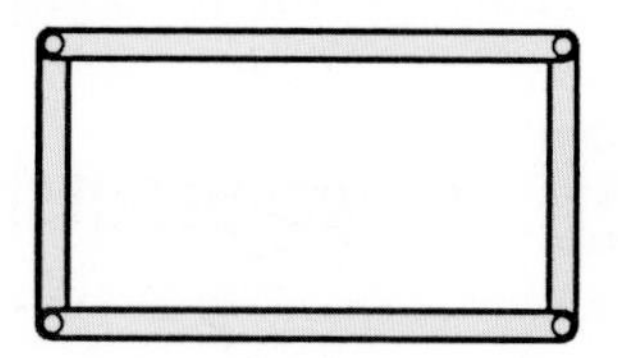

(*d*) Draw the shape that Sian will obtain when she pushes the rectangle over.

(*e*) How many lines of symmetry does the new shape have?

(*NEA* November 1988, A and B, Paper 2)

8

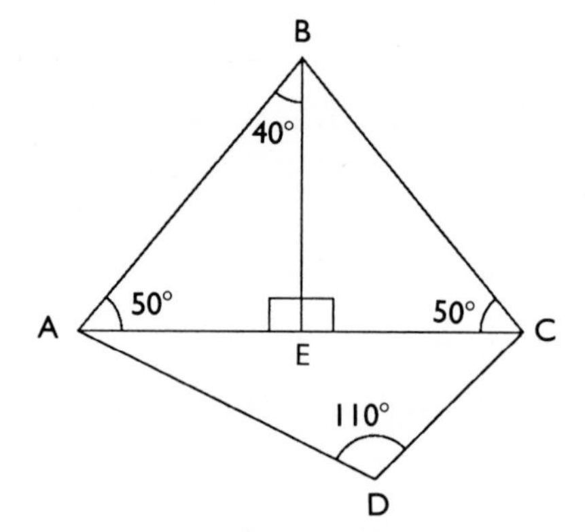

Name any triangle in the above diagram which is

(*a*) a right-angled triangle,
(*b*) an isosceles triangle.

(*SEG* Summer 1989, B Paper 2)

9 In an isosceles triangle one angle is 40 degrees. What are the other two angles?

There are two possible answers. Give both of them.

10

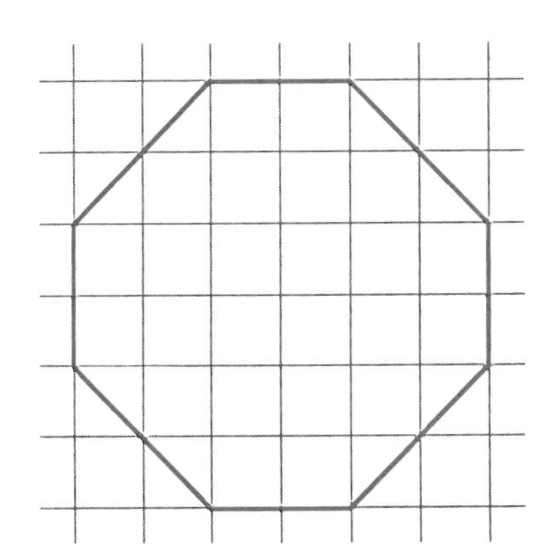

(*a*) Make a copy of the octagon shown above. Draw a line which divides it into two pentagons.

(*b*) Make a copy of the octagon shown above. Draw a line which divides it into a septagon and a triangle.

(*c*) Make a copy of the octagon shown above. Draw a line which divides it into an octagon and a quadrilateral.

11 A piece of wire is 60 cm long. It can be made into any one of the following shapes.

No wire is wasted.

(*a*) Equilateral triangle.
What is the length of each side?

(*b*) Square.
What is the length of each side?

(*c*) Rectangle.
The rectangle is 10 cm wide. What is its length?

(*d*) Cuboid.

The skeleton framework is shown in the diagram.

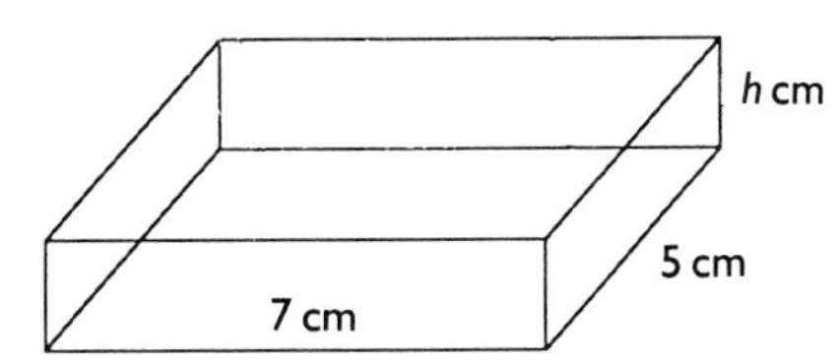

What is the height, h cm, of this cuboid?

(*MEG SMP* November 1988, Paper 2)

12 (*a*) Draw a regular hexagon. Divide it into one rectangle and two triangles. What type of triangles are they?

(*b*) Draw a regular hexagon. Divide it into an equilateral triangle and three isosceles triangles.

(*c*) Draw a regular hexagon. Divide it into two quadrilaterals. What type of quadrilaterals are they?

(*d*) Draw an irregular hexagon which can be divided into a square and two equilateral triangles. What are the sizes of the six angles at the corners of this hexagon?

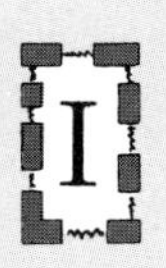

Two shapes are **congruent** if they are the same shape *and* the same size.

For example, the two triangles shown below are congruent.

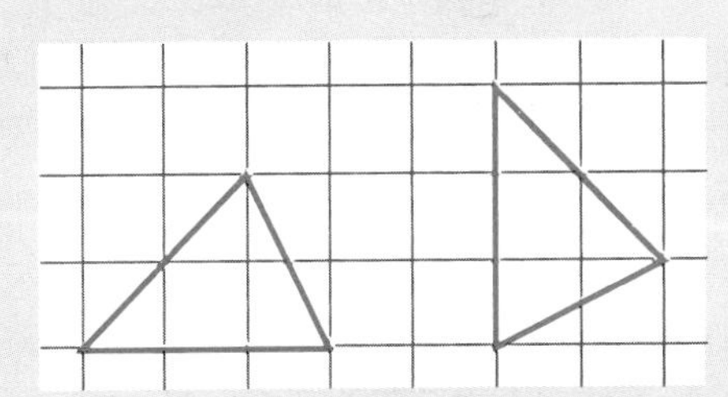

Two shapes are **similar** if they are the same shape. They do not have to be the same size.

For example, the two triangles shown below are similar.

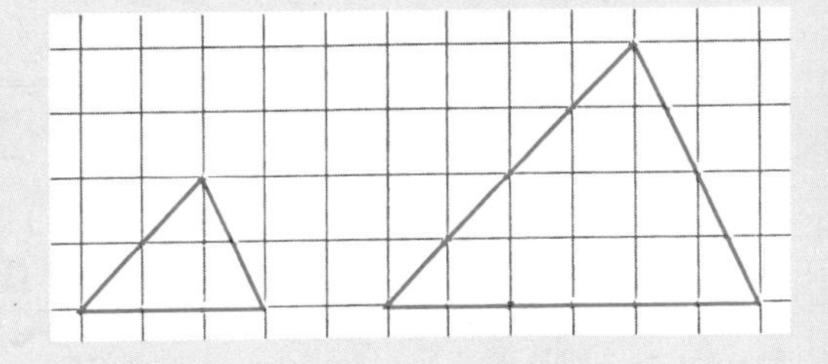

13

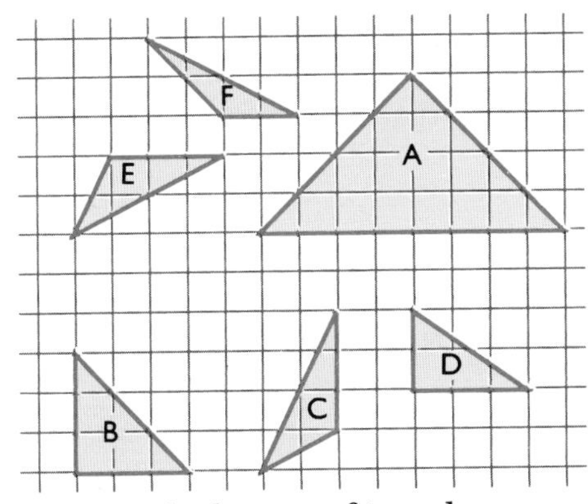

(*a*) Write down the letters of two shapes which are congruent.

(*b*) Write down the letters of two shapes which are similar but not congruent.

14

(*a*) Write down the letters of two shapes which are congruent.

(*b*) Write down the letters of two shapes which are similar but not congruent.

15

In the triangle ABC, D is the midpoint of AB and E is the midpoint of CD. BE = BD and angle BDE $= x°$.

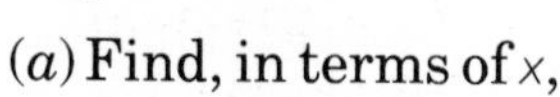

(*a*) Find, in terms of x,

(i) angle ADE,
(ii) angle BEC.

(*b*) Name a triangle which is congruent to triangle BEC.

(*MEG* November 1986, Paper 1A/B)

16 Draw on squared paper

(*a*) a triangle with one line of symmetry,

(*b*) a quadrilateral with rotational symmetry, but no line of symmetry,

(*c*) a hexagon with rotational symmetry and two lines of symmetry.

17 Quadrilaterals A, B, C and D are to be formed according to the rules below.

In each of A, B, C and D one diagonal is to be drawn to divide the quadrilateral into two pieces.

(*a*) Draw quadrilateral A so that the diagonal divides it into two congruent right-angled isosceles triangles. What type of quadrilateral is A?

(*b*) Draw quadrilateral B so that the diagonal divides it into two congruent obtuse-angled isosceles triangles. What type of quadrilateral is B?

(*c*) Draw quadrilateral C so that the diagonal divides it into two congruent right-angled scalene triangles. What type of quadrilateral is C?

(*d*) Draw quadrilateral D so that the pieces are two right-angled isosceles triangles which are similar but *not* congruent. What type of quadrilateral is D?

18

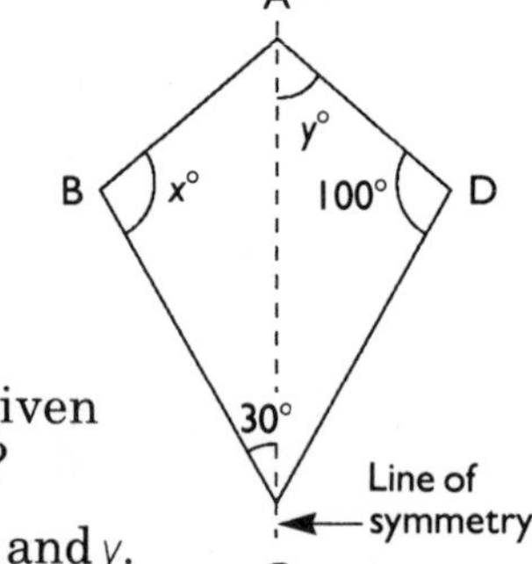

(*a*) What is the name given to the shape of ABCD?

(*b*) Find the values of x and y.

19 Here is a list of statements which are true for a square.

A Its sides are all the same length.
B Its diagonals are the same length.
C Its opposite sides are parallel.
D Its angles are all 90 degrees.
E Its diagonals bisect each other.
F Its diagonals meet at right angles.
G It has mirror symmetry.
H It has rotational symmetry.

(*a*) Two of the statements above are *not* true for all rectangles. Which are they?

(*b*) Two of the statements above are *not* true for all rhombuses. Which are they?

(*c*) How many of the statements above are not true for all kites? Which are they?

(*d*) How many of the statements above are not true for all isosceles trapezia? Which are they?

(*e*) Draw a quadrilateral for which B, F and G are true, but all the other statements are not true.

20

A regular hexagon ABCDEF is divided into four triangles as shown in the diagram.

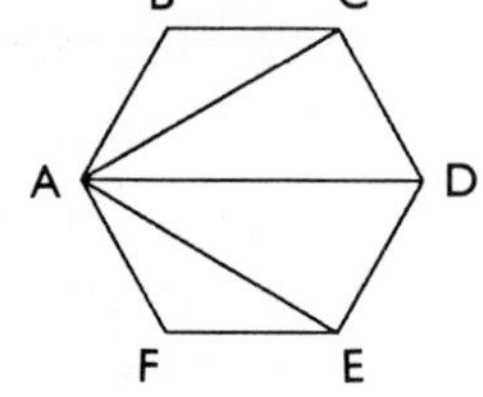

(*a*) Find the sizes of the three angles of triangle ABC.

(*b*) Describe fully the single transformation which will map triangle ABC onto triangle AFE.

(*c*) Show how a regular hexagon can be divided into four triangles, three of which are congruent.

(*MEG* November 1988, Paper 2)

21

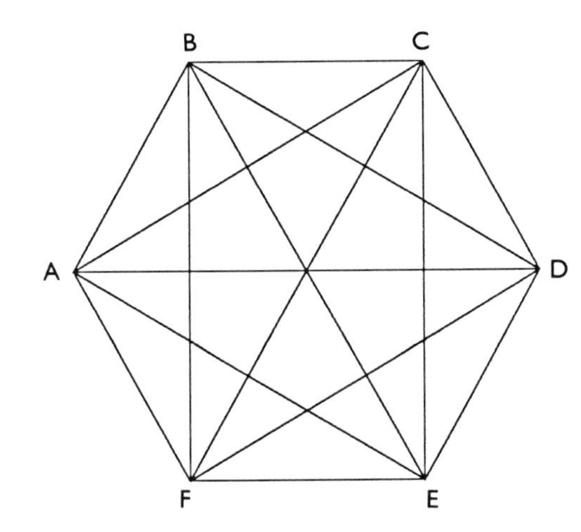

ABCDEF is a regular hexagon.

(*a*) Using only the letters given in the diagram,

(i) name two congruent equilateral triangles,
(ii) name two congruent right-angled triangles.

(*b*) Find the values of (i) $F\hat{A}B$, (ii) $F\hat{B}A$ (iii) $A\hat{C}E$.

(*Welsh* May 1989, Paper 3)

22

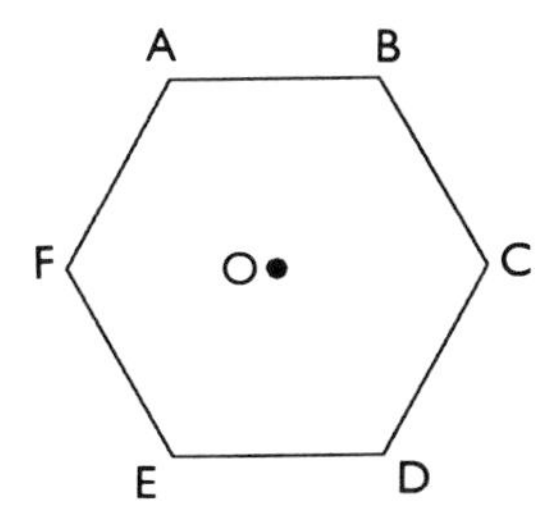

ABCDEF is a regular hexagon. Point O is the centre of the hexagon.

(*a*) What is the order of rotational symmetry of this hexagon?

(*b*) What type of triangle is triangle AOB?

(*c*) If the area of triangle AOB is 2 cm^2, what is the area of the hexagon?

(*d*) What type of quadrilateral is

(i) AEDB?
(ii) BODC?

(*e*) Use *three* of the letters A, B, C, D, E and F in each case to name

(i) an equilateral triangle,
(ii) a right-angled triangle.

(*NEA* May 1989, Syllabus B Paper 3)

23 Draw four separate circles each with radius 3 cm.

(*a*) (i) On the first circle draw a triangle ABC with A, B and C on the circumference of the circle and angle B = 90°.
(ii) Describe briefly how you decided where to place A, B and C.

(*b*) On the second circle draw an equilateral triangle DEF with D, E and F on the circumference of the circle.

(*c*) (i) On the third circle draw two diameters GH and KL which do not intersect at 90°.
(ii) State the precise mathematical name for quadrilateral GKHL.

(*d*) On the fourth circle draw a regular hexagon MNPQRS with all the points M, N, P, Q, R and S on the circumference of the circle.

(*SEG* Summer 1989, B Paper 3)

24 Here are some facts about four triangles ABC, DEF, GHI and JKL.

AB = DE = GH = JK = 5 cm.

BC = EF = HI = KL = 4.5 cm

$\hat{A} = \hat{E} = \hat{H} = \hat{J} = 60°$

(*a*) Which two triangles described above *must* be congruent?

(*b*) Explain with the aid of a diagram why the other pair of triangles need not be congruent.

25 (*a*) Draw and name a quadrilateral which has rotational symmetry of order 2 but no lines of symmetry.

(*b*) A quadrilateral has *m* lines of symmetry.

Write down all possible values of *m*.

(*c*) A quadrilateral has rotational symmetry or order *n*.

Write down all the possible values of n.

(*d*) There are some quadrilaterals for which $m = n$.

For each of these values draw or name an example.

(*LEAG* June 1989, Paper 4)

26 (*a*) The triangle ABC is equilateral. Points D, E, F, G, H and I are a third or two thirds of the way along the sides.

Is the hexagon DEFGHI equilateral? Give a reason for your answer.

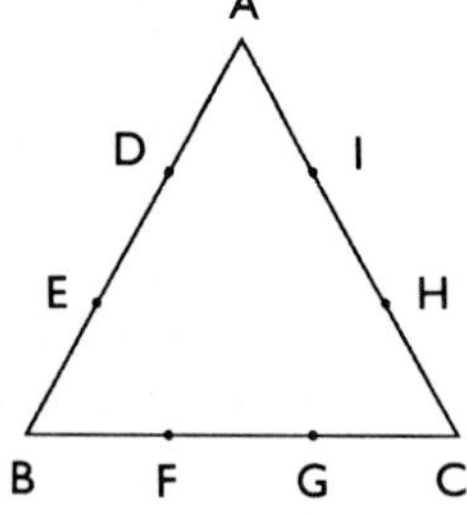

(*b*)

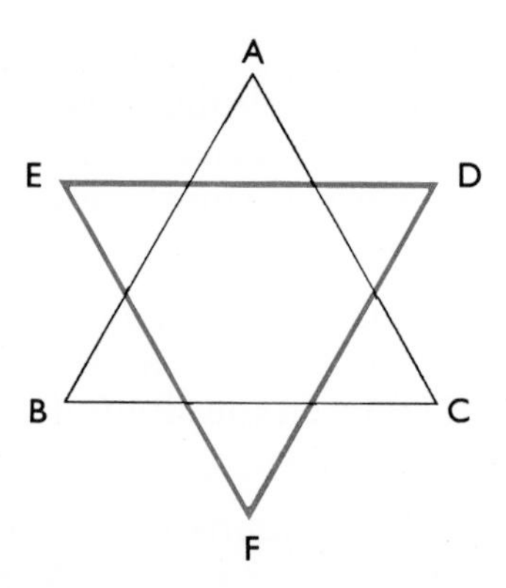

The triangle DEF is obtained by rotating the equilateral triangle ABC through 60° about its centre.

Is the overlap of the two triangles a regular hexagon? Give a reason for your answer.

(*c*) ABCD is a square. The points E, F, G, H, I, J, K and L are a third or two thirds of the way along the sides of the square.

Is EFGHIJKL a regular octagon? Give a reason for your answer.

(*d*) A regular polygon with N sides is rotated about its centre to give a second regular polygon, just as the triangle was rotated in part (*b*).

Is it always possible, for any value of N, to rotate it so that the overlap of the two polygons is a regular polygon with $2N$ sides? Give a reason for your answer.

EXERCISE 32 Algebraic manipulation

1 (*a*) Calculate the value of each of the following

(i) $(1 + 2) \div 3$
(ii) $(3 + 4 + 5) \div 4$
(iii) $(6 + 7 + 8 + 9) \div 5$
(iv) $(10 + 11 + 12 + 13 + 14) \div 6$

(*b*) What special name is given to the numbers you obtained as answers to part (*a*)?

(*c*) Write down the next expression in this pattern and calculate its value.

(*d*) Write down the values of the next two expressions without calculating them.

2 (*a*) Work out the following

(i) $(53 \times 76) + (47 \times 76)$
(ii) $(68 \times 49) + (32 \times 49)$
(iii) $(70 \times 36) + (30 \times 36)$

(*b*) What pattern is followed by your answers to part (*a*)?

(*c*) Write down two expressions of the same type as those in part (*a*).

3 Insert brackets into the following statements to make them correct.

(*a*) $6 \times 7 + 3 = 60$

(*b*) $4 \times 3 + 6 \times 3 = 30$

(*c*) $12 - 7 - 5 = 10$

(*d*) $12 + 8 \times 12 - 8 = 80$

4 Write the following without brackets, and simplify your answers.

(*a*) $3(a + b) + 2(a - b)$

(*b*) $4(p + q) - 3(p - 2q)$

(*c*) $5(r + s + t) + 4(r - s + t) - 6(r + s - t)$

(*d*) $3(2a - b) - 2(a - 3b)$

5 Factorise the following

(*a*) $3x - 6y$

(*b*) $4a^2 - 6ab$

(*c*) $6p^2q - 9pq$

6 If $p = 5$ and $q = -4$ evaluate

(*a*) $p + 2q$

(*b*) $(p + 2q)(p - q)$

(*c*) $p^2 - q$

(*d*) $2p^3 - q$

7 The two-digit number x has tens digit p and units digit q. The relationship between x, p and q is $x = 10p + q$.

The two-digit number y has tens digit q and units digit p.

(*a*) Express y in terms of p and q.

(*b*) Write down an expression for $x + y$ in terms of p and q, and show that $x + y$ is divisible by 11.

(*c*) Find a number greater than 1 which is a factor of $x - y$.

(*MEG* November 1988, Paper 2)

8

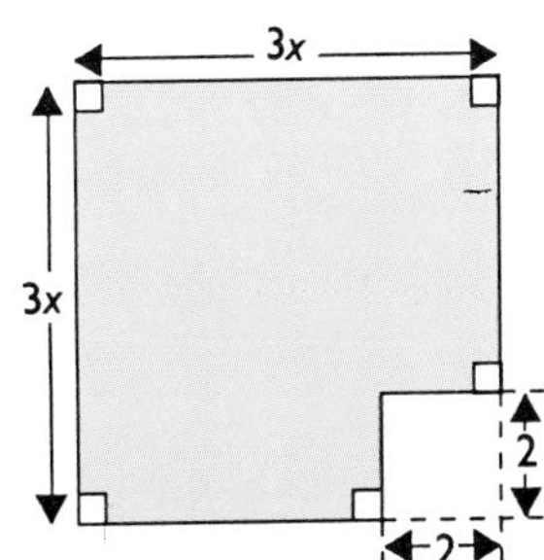

(*a*) Write down, in terms of x, an expression for the area of this shape.

(*b*) Multiply out $(3x + 2)(3x - 2)$, giving your answer in its simplest form.

(*c*) By making one cut and reassembling, the above shape can be made into a rectangle. Using your answers to (*a*) and (*b*), draw a diagram to show how this can be done. Mark the dimensions of the rectangle on your diagram.

(*NEA* May 1988, Syllabus C Paper 3)

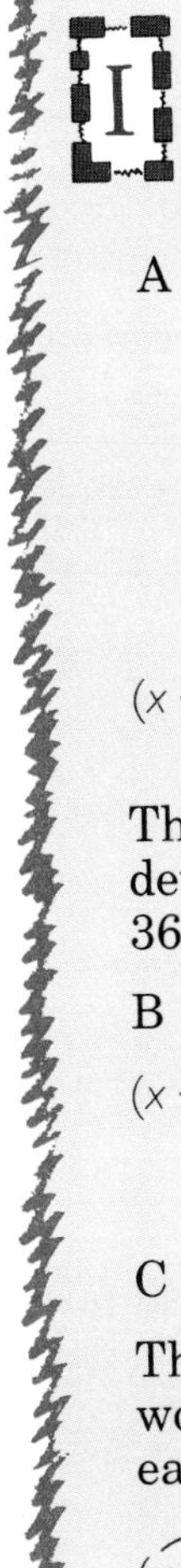

When you multiply out $(x + 3)(x - 4)$ there is only one correct answer, but there are several ways of getting it. Here are three of them.

A Geometrical method

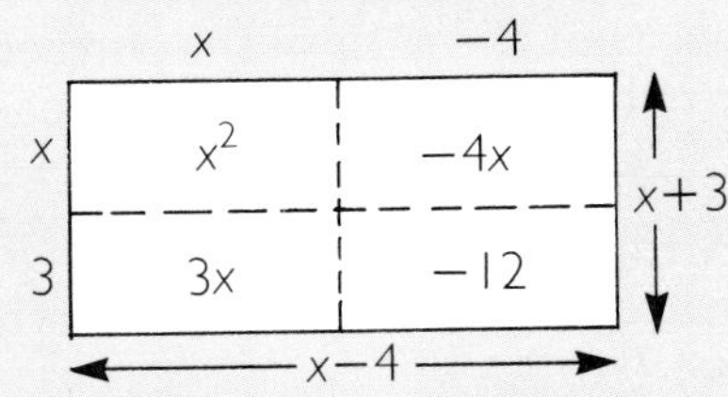

$$(x + 3)(x - 4) = x^2 + 3x - 4x - 12$$
$$= x^2 - x - 12$$

This method was explained in more detail in Section B of Chapter 16 on pages 36 to 39.

B Distributive law

$$(x + 3)(x - 4) = x(x - 4) + 3(x - 4)$$
$$= x^2 - 4x + 3x - 12$$
$$= x^2 - x - 12$$

C Eyebrows, nose and mouth

This is a 'rule for remembering' which works when there are just two terms in each bracket.

$$(x + 3)(x - 4) = x^2 + 3x - 4x - 12$$
$$= x^2 - x - 12$$

9 Write the following without brackets, as simply as possible.

(*a*) $(a + 3)(a - 3)$

(*b*) $(p + 2)(p + 4)$

(*c*) $(c + 3d)(c + 2d)$

(*d*) $(x - y)(x + 2y)$

(*e*) $(3a + 2b)(4a - 6b)$

(*f*) $x(2x + 3y)(2x - 3y)$

10 Factorise

(*a*) $x^2 + 4x + 3$

(*b*) $x^2 - 5x + 4$

(*c*) $2x^2 + 5x + 2$

11 (*a*) Factorise the following

(i) $x^2 + 7x + 10$
(ii) $x^2 - 11x + 10$

(*b*) Both of the expressions in part (*a*) are of the form

$$x^2 + kx + 10$$

where k is an integer.

Find all the other integer values of k for which $x^2 + kx + 10$ factorises.

12 Factorise the following

(*a*) $x^2 - 25$

(*b*) $4x^2 - 49y^2$

(*c*) $12a^2 - 75b^2$

(*d*) $3pq^3 - 12p^3q$

13 (*a*) Calculate $501^2 - 399^2$.

(*b*) By factorising the expression given in part (*a*), explain why your answer to part (*a*) ends with two zeros.

(*c*) How many zeros are there at the end of the answer to the following

$$3000000002^2 - 1999999998^2$$

Explain your answer.

14 (*a*) Factorise $x^3 - x$.

(*b*) Use your answer to part (*a*) to explain that, if x is a positive integer, $x^3 - x$ is a multiple of 6.

15 (*a*) Factorise $n^2 - 1$.

(*b*) 3 is a prime number and is followed by 4, which is a square number.

Use your answer to part (*a*) to explain why there is no other prime number which is immediately followed by a square number.

16

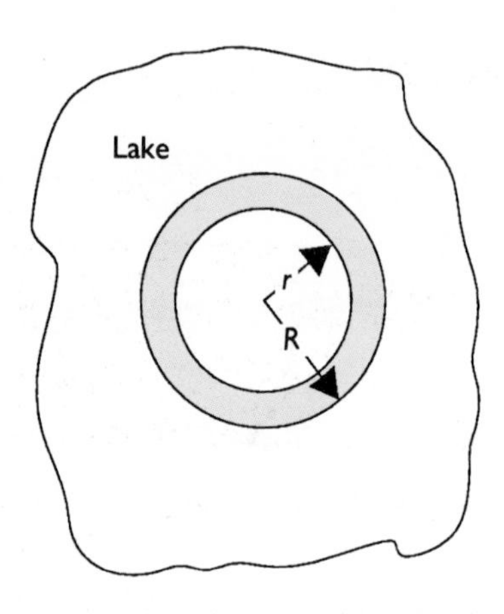

For breeding purposes, fish are kept in an area of a lake enclosed by two concentric circles as shown by the shaded area in the diagram.

(*a*) Write down an expression for the shaded area in terms of R and r, the radii of the circles, and π.

(*b*) If the shaded area is 1180 m^2, and $(R + r)$ is 25 metres, calculate the value of $(R - r)$ to the nearest whole number.

(*c*) Using the rounded value of $(R - r)$ found in part (*b*), calculate the values of R and r.

(*NEA* May 1988, Syllabus B Paper 4)

17

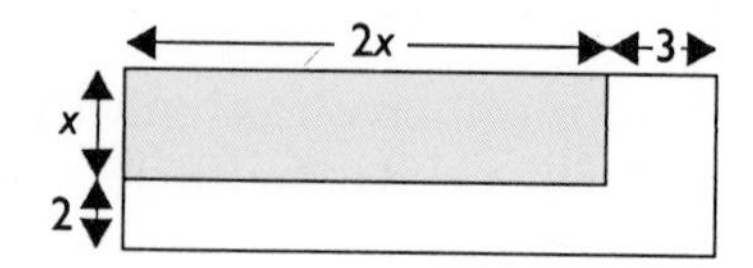

The outer rectangle in the above figure measures $(2x + 3)$ by $(x + 2)$.

(*a*) Express the area of the shaded rectangle in terms of x.

(*b*) Express the area of the unshaded region in terms of x, in as simplified a form as possible.

(*c*) Calculate the value of x when the area of the shaded region is 2 square units less than the area of the unshaded region.

(*NEA* May 1988, Syllabus A Paper 4)

18 The surface area of a cylinder which is closed at one end is $2\pi rh + \pi r^2$.

(*a*) Factorise this expression for the surface area.

(*b*) Deduce that the ratio of the surface area of the cylinder to the area of the base is $(2h + r):r$.

(*c*) The ratio of the surface area of a cylinder to the area of its base is 4:1. Find the ratio of h to r.

19

0	3	6	9	12	....
4	7	10	13	16	....
8	11	14	17	20	....
12	15	18	21	24	....
16	19	22	25	28	....
.	.	.	.	.	
.	.	.	.	.	

The questions below refer to the numbers on the grid above.

The diagonal difference for any 2 × 2 square on the grid is defined as $qs - pr$, where p, q, r and s are numbers in the square shown below.

p	q
s	r

Squares are identified by the number in the top left-hand corner. This square is called a 'p' square.

(*a*) Find the diagonal difference for the '14' square.

(*b*) Investigate diagonal differences for *two* other squares on the grid. Write down your results and any observations that you can make.

(*c*) Complete the 'n' square below.

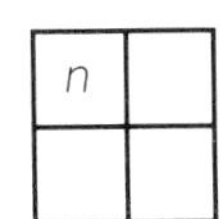

(*d*) Using your 'n' square from part (*c*), work out and simplify the diagonal difference for the square. Show all your working clearly.

(*NEA* November 1988, Syllabus A Paper 4)

20 (*a*) Given that $u_1 = 1$ and $u_{n+1} = u_n + (n+1)^2$, show that

(i) u_2 can be written as the sum of two squares,
(ii) u_3 can be written as the sum of three squares.

(*b*) Calculate the values of u_2, u_3 and u_4.

(c) Given that $S_n = n(n+1)(2n+1)$, calculate the values of S_1, S_2, S_3 and S_4.

(*d*) Hence suggest a formula to find the value of $1^2 + 2^2 + 3^2 + ... + n^2$.

(*NEA* May 1989, Syllabus B Paper 4)

21  Here are four consecutive numbers: 13, 14, 15, 16.

If you multiply the middle pair, you get $14 \times 15 = 210$.

If you multiply the outer pair, you get $13 \times 16 = 208$.

(i) Do a calculation like this for a different set of four consecutive numbers of your own.
(ii) Repeat (i) twice more. You should notice a general rule. State this clearly in words.
(iii) Use algebra to prove that your rule always works with any four consecutive numbers.
(iv) Find a similar rule which works if you start with four consecutive *odd* numbers (such as 17, 19, 21, 23). Use algebra to prove this rule.

(*LEAG SMP* 11–16, June 1987 Extension Paper)

EXERCISE 33 Money 2

1

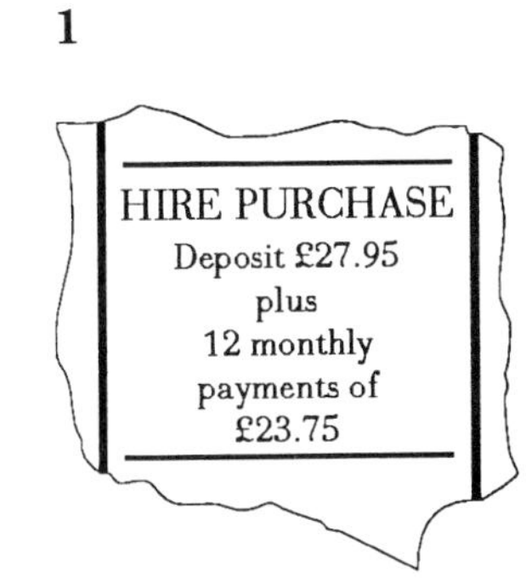

(*a*) Robin buys this television on hire purchase. Calculate

(i) the total cost of the monthly payments,
(ii) the total hire purchase price.

(*b*) Susan pays the cash price of £279.95 for a similar television.
How much more than Susan did Robin pay for his television?

(*Welsh* May 1989, Paper 1)

2

Derek buys the washer/dryer shown in the above advertisement for £429.90.

He pays a deposit of £69.90 and then has to make nine equal monthly payments to pay the balance.

How much will Derek pay each month?

(*Welsh* May 1988, Paper 2)

3 A garden centre buys a tray of 24 plants for £15 and sells each plant for 90p.
Calculate the profit made on the sale of a tray of plants.

(*LEAG* January 1989, Paper 2)

4 A dress shop allows a discount of 12p in the pound off all its marked prices.

How much has to be paid for a dress marked at £42?

(*LEAG* May 1989, Paper 2)

5

(*a*) Mary and Derek were organising a Valentine disco.

(i) Mary wanted to use 'HAM DISCO' and finish at 3.00 a.m. How much would it cost?
(ii) Derek wanted to use 'Andy's Disco', but was only prepared to pay £70. At what time would the disco have to finish?

(*b*) 'Banex Disco', who also had a fixed charge with a $\frac{1}{2}$ hour rate after midnight, said that, if their disco was used, they would charge

£47 to finish at 2.00 a.m.
or £63 to finish at 3.00 a.m.

Calculate

(i) the $\frac{1}{2}$ hour rate after midnight,
(ii) the fixed charge.

(*NEA* May 1989, Syllabus A Paper 3)

6

The members of a Youth Club have decided to hold a Grand Draw in aid of a local charity.
The draw prizes and their values are given in the table.

Prizes	Value
1 Black and white portable TV	£70
1 Personal stereo	£25
2 Food hampers	£15 each
5 Turkeys	£7.50 each
5 Bottles of wine	£2.50 each

The tickets cost 20p each.

After paying for the prizes, all other money received from the ticket sales will be given to the charity.

(*a*) Calculate the total value of the prizes.

(*b*) Calculate the value of the TV as a percentage of the total value of the prizes.

(*c*) Calculate the least number of tickets that must be sold to cover the cost of the prizes.

(*d*) If 2365 tickets are sold, how much money would be given to the charity?

(*e*) How many tickets would have to be sold to raise £500 for the charity?

(*LEAG* June 1989, Paper 3)

EXERCISE 34 Ratio

1 Kirandeep and Ann are paid £45 for some painting work. They decided that Kirandeep did much more work than Ann and that they would share the money in the ratio 4 to 1.

How much was Kirandeep's share?

2 A garage agreed to pay John and Dipaak a total of £125 for cleaning all the cars in its forecourt. John spent 30 hours cleaning cars and Dipaak spent 20 hours.

They decided to split the money fairly between them. How much was John's share?

3 In a tennis club the ratio of women members to men members is 2:1. There are 40 women members. How many members does the tennis club have altogether?

4 A newsagent delivers 800 papers each day and finds that, on average, this is six times as many as he sells across the counter. How many papers does he expect to sell each day across the counter?

(*NEA* November 1988, Syllabus C Paper 1)

5

Colour	Ratio of blue paint to yellow paint
Dark green	3 to 1
Mid-green	1 to 1
Light green	1 to 3

When yellow paint and blue paint are mixed together a green paint is formed. The table shows the ratios of blue and yellow paint required to make three shades of green. Write down the shade of green you get when you mix together

(*a*) 9 parts of blue paint and 3 parts of yellow paint,

(*b*) 4 parts of yellow paint and 4 parts of blue paint.

(*LEAG* January 1989, Paper 1)

6 In a certain recipe sugar and flour are mixed in the ratio of 1 to 3.

What weight of sugar should be used with 600 g of flour?

7 The total area of a garden is 360 m^2. Donna-Marie decides that some of the garden area is to be lawn and some is to be for flowers. The ratio of lawn area to flowers area is to be 2 to 1.

What will be the area of the lawn?

8 The label of a squash bottle says, 'Mix one part squash to four parts water.'

Darren wants to make 1 litre of drink. How much squash does he need to use? (1 litre = 1000 ml)

9 A primary school has two classes in its first year, 1W and 1C.
In class 1W there are 16 boys and 10 girls.
In class 1C there are 10 boys and 15 girls.

(*a*) (i) What is the total number of children in 1W and 1C?
(ii) How many more boys are there than girls in the first year?

(*b*) For the class 1W, write the number of girls to the number of boys as a ratio in its simplest form.

(*SEG* Winter 1988, Mathematics A Paper 1)

10 To make concrete, a builder mixes 240 kg of sand with 60 kg of cement.

Give the ratio of sand to cement in its simplest terms.

11 There are 180 pupils in the first year of Bronglais Comprehensive School.
The ratio of the number of boys to the number of girls in the first year is 5:4.
How many girls are in the first year?

(*Welsh* May 1988, Paper 2)

12 Some pupils decided to have a sponsored tiddlywink game to raise money for charity. They could not agree whether to collect money for Oxfam or for NSPCC.

In the end they decided that they would split the money between Oxfam and NSPCC in the ratio 5:3.

The event raised £200. How much was sent to Oxfam?

13 A discount store is offering a box containing 64 tins of baked beans for £8. Frank and Sharon decide to buy the box between them. Sharon pays £5 and Frank pays £3.

The beans are shared in the same ratio as the money they paid. How many tins of beans does Sharon get?

14 The Fibonacci sequence begins as follows:

1, 1, 2, 3, 5, 8, 13, 21, 34, 55, ...

Pick a *pair* of numbers from this sequence to satisfy each of the following conditions.

(*a*) One number is four times the other.

(*b*) One number is sixteen more than the other.

(*c*) The ratio of the numbers is 4:1.

(*d*) The ratio of the numbers is 17:4.

15 The money left in Mrs Patel's will was to be divided between three people in the ratios 3:5:7.

Mrs Patel left £18 000. How much did each person receive?

16 In the 1983 General Election, 650 Members of Parliament were elected. Shortly before the election, an opinion poll indicated these voting intensions:

Conservative 38%,
Labour 32%.

If Members of Parliament had been elected in the same proportions as the poll results, find how many MP's of parties other than Conservatives or Labour would have been elected.

(*MEG* June 1987, Paper 3)

EXERCISE 35 Rate and proportion

1

The bottle shown contains 400 ml of medicine.
How long will the medicine last if it is taken as shown on the label?

2

Zulfika hired a car from Speedy Car Hire early on Monday to go to see her mother who lived about 300 miles away. She took the car back late on the Tuesday.

Roughly how much did she have to pay Speedy Car Hire?

3 Brenda works a basic 40-hour week. She is paid at the rate of £5.40 per hour.

(*a*) How much does Brenda earn for a basic 40-hour week?

(*b*) The following table shows the number of hours Brenda worked each day during a particular week.

Day	Monday	Tuesday	Wednesday	Thursday	Friday
Hours worked	9	9	10	8	8

For any hours over 40 hours worked, Brenda is paid overtime.

(i) How many hours of overtime does she work?
(ii) The overtime rate is £8.40 per hour. How much does Brenda earn for overtime?
(iii) Find the total amount earned by Brenda for this particular week.

(*Welsh* May 1989, Paper 2)

4 Abdul Hassan's standard working week is 40 hours from Monday to Friday. Overtime worked in the evenings is paid for at time and a quarter and all work on Saturdays is paid at double time.
His normal rate is £3.60 per hour. Last week he worked 56 hours, 12 of which were in the evening and 4 on Saturday morning.

(*a*) (i) How much is Abdul paid for a standard working week?
(ii) What is the evening overtime rate?
(iii) What is the Saturday overtime rate?
(iv) How much did Abdul earn last week?

(*b*) Abdul pays $7\frac{1}{2}$ % of his wages into the firm's pension fund. How much did he pay into the pension fund last week?

(*NEA* November 1988, Syllabus C Paper 1)

5

Services 33

Jo is driving her car on the motorway.

She passes a road sign which shows that a service area is 33 miles away.

The time is 12.20 p.m.

Jo is to meet a friend at this service area at 12.50 p.m.

At what speed, in miles per hour, must she travel to meet her friend on time?

(*NEA* May 1989, Syllabuses A and B Paper 1)

6 Mrs McDonald lives 8 miles from the nearest railway station and it takes her 20 minutes to drive there in her car.

(*a*) What is her average speed, in miles per hour, for this journey?

(*b*) Mrs McDonald's son is due to arrive at the station at 1815 hours. She wants to be there when he arrives. She will allow herself 10 minutes to park the car and walk to the station.

What is the latest time she could set off from home?

(*MEG* November 1988, Paper 1)

7

The Morley Bus Service						
Hansom	06.50	07.50	09.50	13.50	17.50	20.50
Toft	07.10	08.10	10.10	14.10	18.10	21.10
Neston	07.40	08.40	10.40	14.40	18.40	21.40

(*a*) At what time does the first afternoon bus leave Hasom?

(*b*) How many minutes does the bus take to travel from Hasom to Toft?

(*c*) Brian lives in Neston. He finishes work at Hasom at 7.30 p.m. At what time does the next bus leave Hasom?

(*d*) Hasom to Toft is 10 miles. How far is it from Toft to Neston, assuming that the bus travels at the same average speed for both parts of the journey?

(*MEG* November 1988, Paper 4)

8

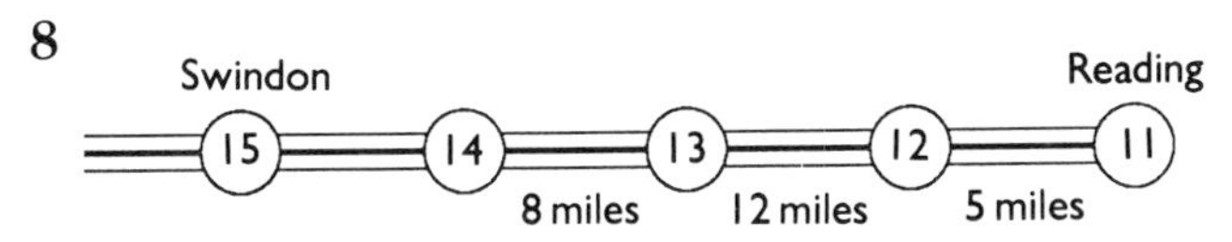

The diagram shows a simplified map of part of the M4 motorway.
The motorway passes near to Reading and Swindon.
The numbers in circles are the exit numbers for the roads leaving the motorway.
The distances between some of the exits are also given.

(*a*) Work out the distance from exit 12 to exit 14.

Whilst the road is being repaired, it takes a car 10 minutes to travel from exit 11 to exit 12.

(*b*) Work out, for this part of the journey, the average speed of the car in,

(i) miles per minute,
(ii) miles per hour.

A car travels at 60 miles per hour from exit 14 to exit 15. The journey takes 12 minutes.

(*c*) Work out the distance between exit 14 and exit 15.

(*LEAG SMP* January 1989, Paper 1)

9 In a journey of 356 miles a car uses about 8 gallons of petrol. What is the average fuel consumption in miles per gallon? Give your answer to the nearest whole number.

10 (*a*) Gary buys a second hand moped for £200. The road tax is £10 a year. The insurance is £85 a year. A crash helmet costs him £28. Find the total of these four costs.

(*b*) The moped uses 1 litre of petrol every 24 miles. The petrol tank holds 9 litres. How many miles can he drive on a tankful of petrol?

(*c*) Petrol costs 38.4 pence for a litre. How much will 9 litres cost? Give your answer to the nearest penny.

(*d*) Gary wants to go to Skegness for the day, a distance of 72 miles each way.

(i) How much petrol will he use?
(ii) How much will this petrol cost? Give your answer correct to the nearest penny.

(*MEG* May 1988, Paper 4)

11

MACARONI CHEESE	MACARONI CHEESE
100g macaroni	g macaroni
60g cheese	g cheese
25g cornflower	g cornflower
700ml milk	ml milk
SERVES FOUR	SERVES TWELVE

(*a*) Copy the second box of the list of ingredients for macaroni cheese for 12 people and fill in the gaps.

(*b*) How much cheese would you need to serve 10 people?

(*Welsh* May 1989, Paper 2)

12

Kamal is filling the tank from a pipe which supplies water at the rate of 1.25 litres per second.

How long will it take him to fill the tank? Give your answer to the nearest minute.

(*NEA* November 1988, Syllabus C Paper 2)

13 A book of 200 pages is 3 cm thick.

(*a*) What would be the thickness of a book of 300 pages, made from the same paper?

(*b*) What is the thickness, in mm, of one of the pages?

14 A librarian wants the books on a set of shelves to be reorganised. She estimates that two library assistants will take 10 hours to do the job.

Just as they are about to start a third library assistant becomes available. If she puts him onto the job as well, and if he works at the same rate as the other librarians, how long will her estimate now be? Give your answer correct to the nearest hour.

15

NESWELL CO 300g £4.38 | NESWELL CO 200g £2.98 | NESWELL CO 100g £1.53 | NESWELL CO 50g 79p

(i) (ii) (iii) (iv)

Neswell coffee is sold in four different sized jars, as shown above.

(*a*) Work out the cost of 100 g of coffee for each of the jars (i), (ii) and (iv).

(*b*) Neswell are to introduce a new size of jar which will contain 400 g of coffee. Estimate how much this new jar will cost.

(*MEG SMP* November 1988, Paper 2)

16 A supermarket sells its own brand of ginger ale in bottles of 3 sizes. One week a 500 ml bottle costs 33p, a litre bottle costs 63p and a 2 litre bottle costs £1.23.

(*a*) Which of the sizes offers ginger ale at the cheapest price per litre?

(*b*) Give one reason why someone might choose to buy ginger ale in a bottle of a different size from your answer to part (*a*).

17 The following advertisement for a breakfast cereal was displayed in the window of a supermarket.

Which is the most economical way of buying the breakfast cereal at this supermarket? Explain your answer.

18 Karen and Sam are on a touring holiday. They fill their car with petrol when the reading on the mileometer is

034569

Next time they fill the car, the mileometer reading is

034905

On this second occasion the petrol costs £1.93 per gallon and they have to pay £15.36.

How many miles per gallon has the car done on average between the first and second fillings? Give your answer to the nearest whole number.

19 Titan Tools hire out concrete mixers. The charges are shown on the graph.

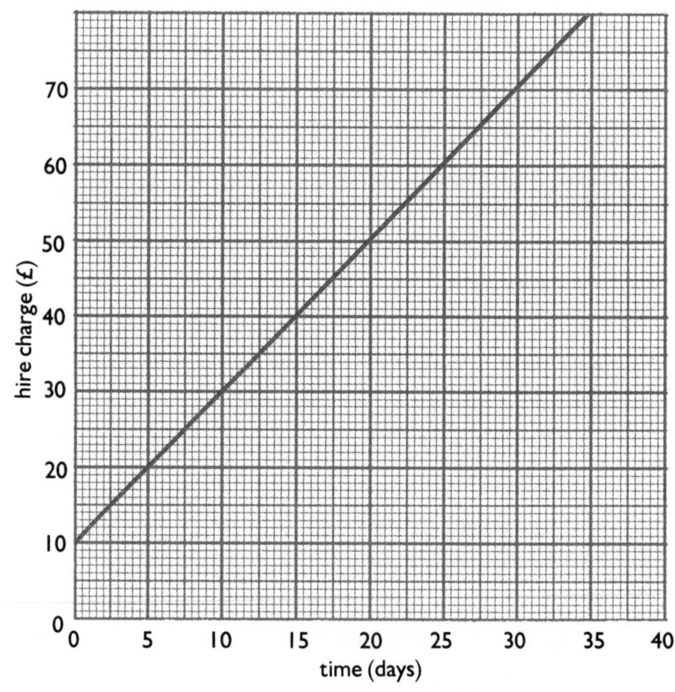

(*a*) (i) What is the charge for 30 days?
(ii) For how many days is the charge £40?
(iii) For how many days is the charge £62?

(*b*) The charge is made up of £10 plus a fixed amount per day. What is the fixed amount per day?

Heavy Hire charge £30 plus £1 per day.

(*c*) Copy and complete the table below.

Number of days	10	20	30
Heavy Hire charge			

(*d*) Copy the graph shown on page 120. On your graph show the Heavy Hire charges.

(*e*) (i) Which firm is cheaper for 25 days?
(ii) Explain your answer to (i).

(*SEG* Winter 1988, Mathematics B Paper 2)

20 In a cookery book it says that the time needed to roast meat is '20 minutes per pound plus an extra 20 minutes'.

(*a*) How long will it take to roast a piece of meat weighing 5 pounds?

It is given that 1 kilogram is equivalent to 2.2 pounds.

(*b*) How long will it take to roast a piece of meat weighing 1 kilogram?

(*c*) Write down a rule for the time needed to roast meat when the weight is known in kilograms.

(*LEAG* January 1989, Paper 3)

21 The radius of a car's wheel is 26 cm.

(*a*) Calculate the circumference of the car's wheel.

(*b*) Calculate, to the nearest whole number, the number of times the wheel rotates every second when the car is travelling at 80 km per hour.

(*c*) The radius of a lorry's wheel is 52 cm. How many times does the lorry's wheel rotate every second when the lorry is travelling at

(i) 80 km per hour?
(ii) 60 km per hour?

22 (*a*) A rectangular lawn is 60 m long and 40 m wide. What is its area?

Two brothers, David and Alan, take it in turns to cut the grass.

David cuts the grass in one hour using his father's old lawn-mower, which he prefers.

(*b*) How many square metres does David cut in one minute?

Alan only takes 40 minutes, using his father's new lawn-mower.

(*c*) How many square metres does Alan cut in one minute?

(*d*) One day they both go out to cut the lawn together. How long do they take?

(*MEG SMP* 11–16, November 1988, Paper 3)

23 (*a*) p is directly proportional to q. Copy and complete the table below.

p	3	4	5	6	7	8
q					84	

(*b*) p is inversely proportional to q. Copy and complete the table below.

p	3	4	5	6	7	8
q					84	

24

x	2	4	6	8
y	576	144	64	36

Which of the following could represent the relationship between x and y?

A y is directly proportional to x.
B y is inversely proportional to x.
C y is directly proportional to x^2.
D y is inversely proportional to x^2.

25 The area of a rectangle is 120 m^2. The two unequal sides of the rectangle are of length x cm and y cm.

If x is changed, y changes.

Which of the following statements is true?

A y is directly proportional to x.
B y is inversely proportional to x.
C y is neither directly nor inversely proportional to x.

Draw a sketch graph to show the relationship between x and y.

26

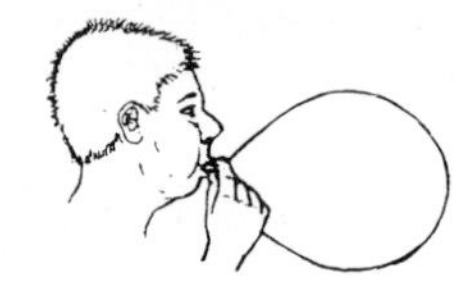

The pressure needed to blow up a balloon varies as the cube of its radius.

When the radius is 5 cm, the pressure needed is 80 g/cm^2.

(*a*) What pressure is required when the radius is 15 cm?

(*b*) What is the radius of the balloon when the pressure needed is 640 g/cm^2?

(*Welsh* May 1988, Paper 4)

27 (*a*) Which of the following is directly proportional to the area of the flat face of a hemisphere:

A the radius of the hemisphere?

B the total surface area of the hemisphere?

C the volume of the hemisphere?

(*b*)

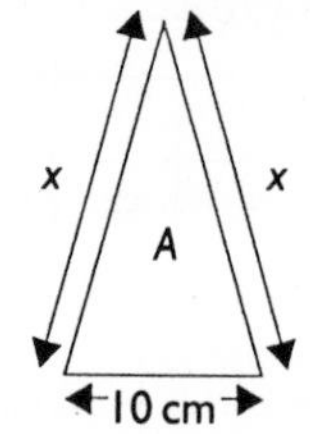

The length of one side of an isosceles triangle is 10 cm. The length of the other two sides is x cm. The area of the isosceles triangle is A cm^2.

Which of the following statements is true.

A A is directly proportional to x.

B A is inversely proportional to x.

C A is directly proportional to the square of x.

D None of **A**, **B** and **C** is true.

Give a reason for your answer.

28

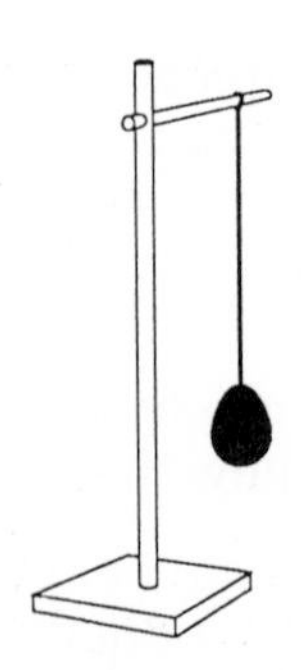

In a Science class a pupil is attempting to find how the length of a pendulum (l) affects the time of the swing (t). The following results are obtained.

Length l (cm)	0	20	40	60	80
Time t (s)	0	0.89	1.27	1.55	1.80

(*a*) Explain how you can tell, from the table, that t is not directly proportional to l.

(*b*) It is suspected that t is directly proportional to $\sqrt{l}$. Complete the table of values for t and $\sqrt{l}$.

$\sqrt{l}$	0	4.47		7.75		10
t	0	0.89	1.27	1.55	1.80	2.00

(*c*) On graph paper draw the graph of t against $\sqrt{l}$.

(*d*) Explain why the graph suggests that t is directly proportional to $\sqrt{l}$.

(*NEA* May 1989, Syllabus A Paper 4)

29 (*a*) The ratio of the frequencies of note C to note F above it is 3:4 and the ratio of the frequencies of note F to note G above it is 8:9. What is the ratio of the frequency of note C to that of note G above?

(*b*) The frequency of a string is inversely proportional to its length.
A particular string, 36 cm long, produces a note C.
By how much should it be shortened to produce note G above?

(*Welsh* May 1989, Paper 4)

30 A firm has research chemists working on a new washing powder, which is to be made by mixing two ingredients, X and Y. In this question x and y denote the number of grams of X and Y respectively in 100 g of the powder, and E is a quantity giving the effectiveness of the powder.

(*a*) One of the chemists, Arthur, thinks that E varies jointly as y and the square of x. Write down an equation (involving an unknown constant) which expresses Arthur's law.

(*b*) Another chemist, Bert, thinks that the law is $E=ax^2 - bx^3$, where a and b are constants. Use the fact that $y = 100 - x$ to show that Arthur's and Bert's laws may both be correct, and find the relation between a and b if both are in fact correct.

(*c*) Experiments are carried out, using various values of x and y, with results as follows:

x	0	25	50	75	100
y	100	75	50	25	0
E	0	30	40	30	0

Show that these results prove that Arthur's and Bert's laws are wrong.

(*d*) Suggest a simple law that *is* supported by the results of the experiments and show that it is supported by them.

(*MEG* Specimen Extension Paper 1990 & 1991)

4 The area of England is 1.304×10^5 km^2 and the area of Wales is 2.1077×10^4 km^2.

(*a*) Find the total area of England and Wales, giving your answer in standard form.

(*b*) Find the ratio of the area of England to the area of Wales, giving your answer in the form $n:1$, with n correct to two significant figures.

(*MEG* November 1988, Paper 2 and 3)

5 (*a*) What is the reciprocal of

(i) 0.4?
(ii) 2.5?

(*b*) The formula $\frac{1}{f} = \frac{1}{u} + \frac{1}{v}$ is used to find the focal lenth (f) of a lens.

Find f when $u = 2.50$ and $v = 0.4$.

Give your answer to 2 decimal places.

(*SEG* Winter 1988, Mathematics A paper 4)

EXERCISE 36 Indices and exponential growth

1 Calculate the following, giving all your answers correct to two decimal places.

(*a*) $\frac{1}{5.5}$ (*b*) $(3.2)^3$ (*c*) $(3.5)^2 + \frac{1}{(3.5)^2}$

2 A telephone directory is 3.2 cm thick. The number of the highest page in the directory is 1010.

Find, in centimetres, the thickness of one page of the directory. Give your answer in standard form.

3 On the Forth Bridge, an area of 586 000 m^2 of metal has to be painted.

(*a*) Write this number in standard form.

(*b*) 32 000 litres of paint are used. Find the thickness of the coat of paint in metres, giving your answer in standard form correct to 2 significant figures. [1 m^3 = 1000 litres]

(*LEAG* June 1989, Paper 3)

When two powers of the same number are multiplied, the indices are added.

Example: $n^2 \times n^3 = n^5$

When two powers of the same number are divided, the indices are subtracted.

Example: $n^7 \div n^4 = n^3$

To work out the power of a power the indices are multiplied.

Example: $(n^3)^4 = n^{12}$

Negative indices

Example: n^{-2} means $\frac{1}{n^2}$

Fractional indices

$n^{\frac{1}{m}}$ means the mth root of n.

Examples:

$125^{\frac{1}{3}} = 5$

$64^{\frac{2}{3}} = (64^{\frac{1}{3}})^2 = 4^2 = 16$

6 Calculate the value of x^{-2}

(a) when $x = 3$ (b) when $x = -\frac{1}{2}$

7 Simplify the following

(a) $x^3 \times x^5$ (b) $N^3 \div N^5$

(c) $P^{\frac{2}{3}} \div P^{\frac{1}{6}}$ (d) $(h^6)^{\frac{1}{2}} \div (h^2)^{\frac{1}{6}}$

8 (a) Calculate

(i) 2^5 (ii) 2^9

(b) Using your answers to part (a), or otherwise, solve the equation

$32^x = 512$

9 Solve the following equations.

(a) $3^x = 9$

(b) $9^n = 3$

(c) $25^p = 125$

(d) $(0.16)^y = 2.5$

(e) $(0.37)^u = 1$

10 (a) Which is greater 3^{-4} or 4^{-3}?

(b) Find two solutions to the equation

$2^x = x^2$

11 If $A = x^{\frac{1}{3}}$, $B = x^{\frac{1}{12}}$ and $A = 3B$, find the value of x.

12 Mark used his credit card to pay for a hi-fi system costing £300.

At the end of the month Mark pays back £30 to the credit card company.

The credit card company then charge 2% interest on what remains and add it to his account.

Each calculation is rounded to the nearest penny.

Write down the calculations for Mark's account with the credit card company as far as calculating the third interest charge of 2%.

How much does he still owe the credit card company?

(*Welsh* May 1989, Paper 3)

13 During the first few weeks of its life, an octopus increases its body weight by 5% each day. An octopus was born with a body weight of 150 grams.

How much will it weigh after

(a) 1 day?

(b) 3 days?

(*NEA* November 1988, Syllabus A Paper 3)

14 A motorist has just purchased a car for £4000. She wants to estimate what its value will be in the future. She is told that prices for this make of car are depreciating at about 30% per year.

Estimate the value of the car

(a) after one year,

(b) after two years,

(c) after four years,

(d) after six months.

15 An infectious disease is being successfully reduced using antibiotics.

In 1990, 4000 people suffered from the disease. It appears the number of people catching the disease each year is 12% fewer than the previous year.

Assume that this reduction happens in the years following 1990.

(a) Complete the following table

Year	1990	1991	1992	1993	1994
Number of people catching disease	4000				

(b) Find the year in which the number of people catching the disease falls below 1000.

16 A flower is placed in a vase. During the course of each day, it loses 5% of its water content. It will begin to droop after losing 25% of its original water content.

(a) What percentage of its original water content will it lose after two days?

(b) If the flower had drooped after x days, what is the minimum possible value of x?

(*NEA* 1988, Syllabus B Paper 4)

17 A man invests £200 in a savings account at an annual rate of interest of 7%. He makes no further deposits or withdrawals. Interest is added each year and then itself earns extra interest (i.e. compound interest).

(*a*) How much will he have in his account at the end of the second year?

(*b*) After how many complete years will he first have more than £300 in his account?

(*MEG SMP* June 1988, Paper 4)

18 A biologist measures the number of cells in a culture at the end of each day. Her results, expressed to the nearest thousand, are as follows.

Day	1	2	3	4	5	6	7
Number of cells	10 000	15 000	23 000	34 000	51 000	76 000	114 000

Estimate the number of cells there will be at the end of the next day.

(*SEG* 1991 Specimen, Mathematics B Paper 4)

19

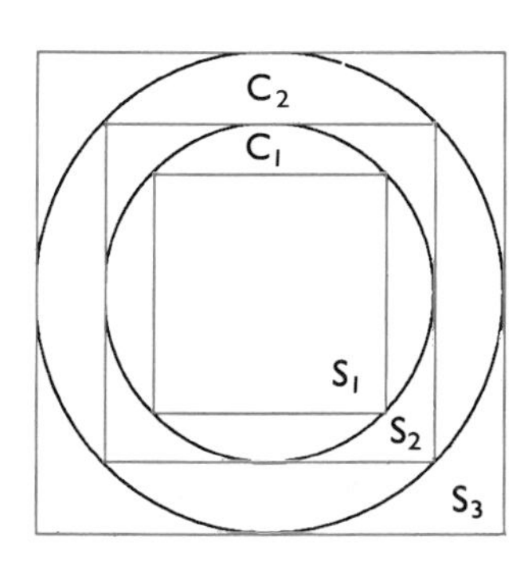

The design shown in the figure above is formed by repeatedly circumscribing a square with a circle and then circumscribing the circle with a square.

The squares and circles are lettered S_1, S_2, S_3 . . . and C_1, C_2 . . . respectively from the inside as shown.

The inner square S_1 has an area of 4 square units.

(*a*) What is the radius of circle C_1?

(*b*) What is the area of square S_2?

(*c*) What is the area of square S_3?

(*d*) What is the area of square S_{10}?

(*e*) What is the area of square S_n?

(*NEA* May 1989, Syllabus B Paper 4)

EXERCISE 37 Equations 2

1 In 1978 it cost x pence to send a letter by first class post and 2 pence less to send the same letter by second class post.

(*a*) Write down, in terms of x, the cost of sending a letter by second class post.

(*b*) I posted 19 similar letters, 12 by first class post, the rest by second class post, and I spent £1.57.

Express this statement as an equation in x and solve it.

(*c*) Joanne posted 23 similar letters, 8 by first class post and 15 by second class post.

How much change did she get from £2?

(*NEA* November 1988, Syllabus C Paper 3)

2 Solve the equations:

(*a*) $18 + 3x = 30$

(*b*) $12 + 6y = 21$

(*c*) $30 + 4z = 10$

(*d*) $12 - 10t = 40$

(*e*) $3u + 4 = -17$

(*f*) $6(3 - 2w) = 36$

3 A field 100 metres square is divided into two trapeziums and a triangle, as shown in the diagram. BD is x metres long.

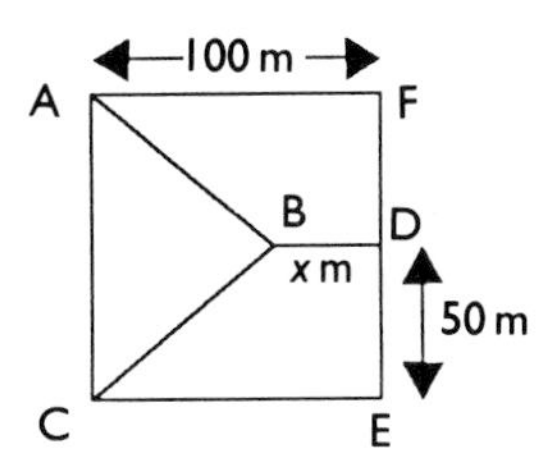

(*a*) What is the perpendicular distance from B to AC in terms of x?

(*b*) What is the area of trapezium CBDE in terms of x?

(*c*) Each of the three parts of the field has the same area. What is the length of BD?

(*Welsh* May 1988, Paper 4)

There are several different ways of solving simultaneous equations.

One way is to use trial and improvement.

Another way is to draw a graph of each equation and find the point where the graphs meet.

Algebraic methods can also be used.

The first algebraic method is the **substitution method**.

Example: To solve the simultaneous equations

$$x + 2y = 7$$
$$2x + 3y = 12$$

rearrange one of the equations so that it is in the form $x = \ldots$ or $y = \ldots$

In this case

$x = 7 - 2y$

Now substitute for x in the other equation.

$2(7 - 2y) + 3y = 12$

This equation in y can now be solved in the usual way to give $y = 2$.

This value of y can now be substituted into an equation to find that $x = 3$.

The second algebraic method is the **elimination method**.

Example: To solve the simultaneous equations

$$2x + 3y = 17$$
$$3x - 2y = 6$$

First multiply one or both equations by a number, so that you make either the x term or the y term the same in both equations.

In this case multiply the first equation by 2 and the second by 3.

$$4x + 6y = 34$$
$$9x - 6y = 18$$

Now either add or subtract the equations (add in this case) so that either x or y is eliminated.

$13x = 52$

Thus $x = 4$.

This value of x can now be substituted into an equation to find that $y = 3$.

Use whatever method you think is suitable when answering the following questions.

4 (*a*) On the same axes draw the graphs of the lines

(i) $y = 2x - 4$,
(ii) $x + y + 7 = 0$.

(*b*) From the graphs find the values of x and y which satisfy both equations simultaneously.

5 (*a*) Draw the graphs of the lines

(i) $2x + 3y = 9$,
(ii) $4x - 3y = 0$.

(*b*) From the graphs find the values of x and y which satisfy both equations simultaneously.

(*NEA* May 1989, Syllabus B Paper 3)

6 The cost of printing a leaflet is a fixed charge of £F and an additional charge of r pence per copy.

(*a*) Write down a formula for the cost, in pounds, of printing 1000 copies.

(*b*) Two different printing processes are available. In the first process $F = 5, r = 3$; in the second process $F = 20, r = 1.2$.

Complete this table to show the cost, in pounds, of printing different quantities using each process.

Number of copies	200	400	600	800	1000
Cost by first process					
Cost by second process					

(*c*) Draw graphs to show the cost of printing different quantities by each process.

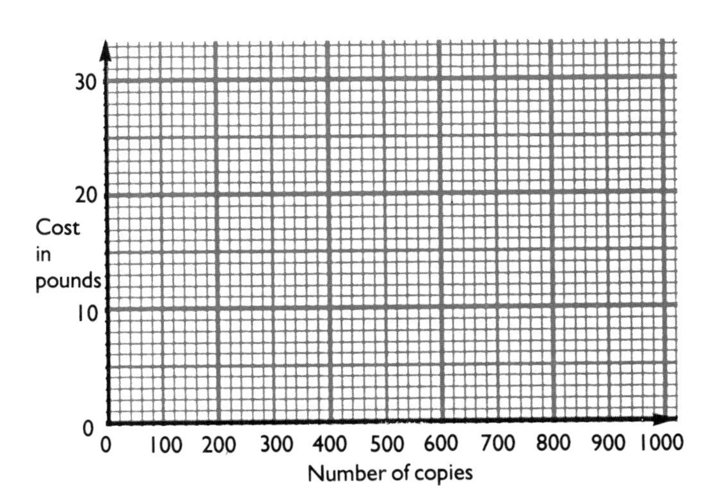

(*d*) Use your graph to answer the following questions.

(i) For what number of copies is the cost the same by both processes?
(ii) When is the cost by the second process cheaper than by the first process?

(*NEA* May 1988, Syllabus B Paper 3)

7 Joseph decides to treat himself to some sweets. Twirls cost 15p each. Twizzles cost 20p each. Joseph buys x Twirls and y Twizzles.

(*a*) Altogether he buys 12 sweets. Write down an equation connecting x and y.

(*b*) He spends a total of £2.05 on the sweets. Write down another equation connecting x and y.

(*c*) By solving your equations, or by another method, calculate how many of each type of sweet he buys.

(*SEG* 1991 Specimen, Paper 4)

8 Some students went on a trip using cars and minibuses. Let x be the number of cars and y the number of minibuses used.

(*a*) 5 students travelled in each car and 14 in each minibus.

(i) Write down an expression, in terms of x and y, for the total number of students on the trip.
(ii) The total number of students was 53. Write down an equation in x and y.

(*b*) Petrol costs were £4 for each car and £6 for each minibus. The total petrol cost was £32. Write down an equation in x and y.

(*c*) Use both your equations to find the number of cars and minibuses used.

(*SEG* Summer 1989, Mathematics A Paper 4)

9 Solve the simultaneous equations

$$4x - 3y = 16$$
$$5x - 6y = 2$$

10 (*a*) Expand and simplify $(x - a)(x + a)$.

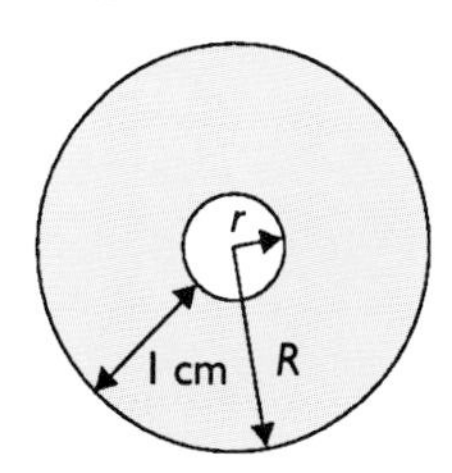

The sketch shows a washer. The area of the washer (shaded) is 20 cm^2. The inner and outer radii are r and R cm respectively.

(*b*) Show that $\pi(R + r) = 20$.

(*c*) Calculate the values of R and r, correct to 3 significant figures.

(*NEA* May 1988, Syllabus A Paper 4)

11 The first three hexagonal numbers 1, 7 and 19 are shown in the following dot patterns.

(*a*) Find the fourth hexagonal number.

(*b*) The nth hexagonal number is given by an expression of the form $an^2 + bn + 1$, where a and b are numerical constants. Using the information above, write down two simultaneous equations in a and b, and solve them to find a and b.

(*c*) Verify that the 7th, 9th, 10th and 16th hexagonal numbers all contain the same three digits.

(*NEA* November 1988, Syllabus C Paper 4)

12

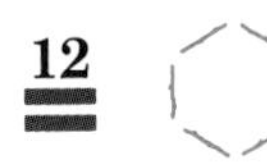

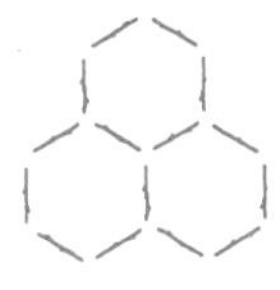

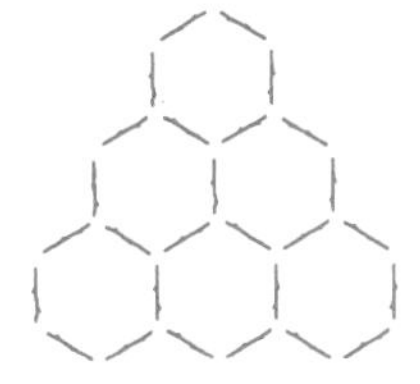

Bridget is doing an investigation which involves making patterns with hexagons with sticks. The first three of these patterns are shown below.

(a) Copy and complete this table.

Number of rows, n	1	2	3	4	5
Number of hexagons, h	1	3			
Number of sticks, s	6				

(b) Write down a formula for h in terms of n.

(c) The formula for s in terms of n is of the form

$$s = an^2 + bn,$$

where a and b are constants.

Find the value of a and the value of b.

(*MEG* November 1988, Paper 6)

EXERCISE 38 Polynomial equations

Some of the ways of solving polynomial equations were explained in Chapters 13 and 16.

A quadratic equation is a special type of polynomial equation. There are several methods of solving **quadratic equations**.

(a) **Trial and improvement**
This method can be used to solve any equation, not just quadratic equations. You continue the process of trial and improvement until the desired degree of accuracy is reached.

Advantages of this method. It is easy to apply and works with all quadratic equations, whether they factorise or not. It also works with equations of other types. It is quick to use with a calculator and even quicker with a programmable or graphical calculator, or a spreadsheet. *This method is strongly recommended now that calculators are universally available.*

Disadvantages of this method. It might be slower than other methods in some cases. Careful thought is needed to decide which number to try next. If you do not know how many solutions an equation has this method will not help you to decide.

(b) **Iteration**
This method (explained in Chapter 16 on page 25) can be used in such a way that you can be sure to find both solutions of a quadratic equation.

Suppose, for example, you want to solve the equation

$$x^2 - 8x - 5 = 0$$

This can be rearranged to give

$$x(x - 8) = 5$$

The equation can now be rearranged in two different ways to get an x on its own.

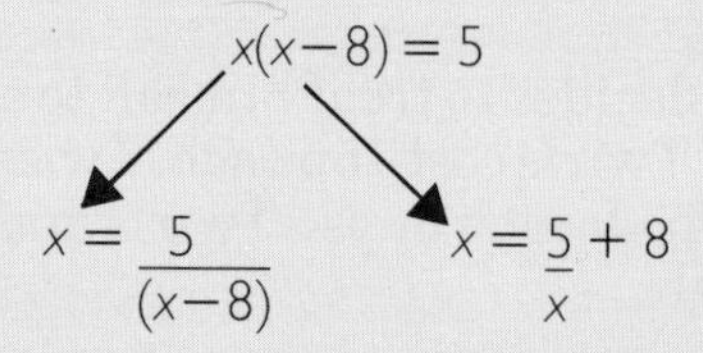

Each of these rearrangements can now be used to solve the equation iteratively.

$$x_{NEW} = \frac{5}{(x-8)} \quad\quad x_{NEW} = \frac{5}{x} + 8$$

$$\downarrow \quad\quad\quad\quad \downarrow$$

$$-0.5826 \quad\quad\quad\quad 8.5826$$

Using this method of producing two different arrangements you *always* get both solutions.

Advantages of using this method. It is straightforward, provided that you have a suitable calculator, and always gives both solutions.

Disadvantages of using this method. It assumes that you can rearrange equations. (But once you have practised on two or three equations you should know how to deal with all other equations). It is a bit clumsier if you do not have a calculator with an ANS button.

(*c*) **Factorising**
First example: to solve
$x^2 + 5x + 4 = 0$

First factorise the left-hand side of the equation.

$$(x + 4)(x + 1) = 0$$

This gives two numbers whose product is zero. One of these numbers must be zero.

$x + 4 = 0$ or $x + 1 = 0$

Thus $x = -4$ or $x = -1$

Second example: to solve
$4z^2 - 5z = 6$

First take all terms to one side of the equation.

$$4z^2 - 5z - 6 = 0$$

Then factorise

$(4z + 3)(z - 2) = 0$

So $4z + 3 = 0$ or $z - 2 = 0$

$z = -\frac{3}{4}$ or $z = 2$

Advantages of using this method. It is a quick method if you are able to factorise quickly. It gives both solutions.

Disadvantages of using this method. It will not work if there are no factors. It can be time-consuming to find factors.

(*d*) **Formula**
There is a formula for solving a quadratic equation.

If a, b and c stand for numbers, the equation

$$ax^2 + bx + c = 0$$

has solutions

$$x = \frac{-b \pm \sqrt{b^2 - 4ac}}{2a}$$

First example: $3z^2 + 6z + 2 = 0$

In this case $a = 3$, $b = 6$ and $c = 2$.

So $z = \frac{-6 \pm \sqrt{36 - 24}}{6}$
$= \frac{-6 \pm \sqrt{12}}{6} = \frac{-6 \pm 3.464}{6}$

So $z = \frac{-9.464}{6} = -1.57$ to 2 decimal places

or $z = \frac{-6 + 3.464}{6} = \frac{-2.536}{6}$
$= -0.42$ to 2 decimal places

Second example: $3x^2 + 4x + 5 = 0$
In this case $a = 3$, $b = 4$ and $c = 5$.

So $x = \frac{-4 \pm \sqrt{16 - 60}}{6}$
$= \frac{-4 \pm \sqrt{-44}}{6}$

Since it is not possible to have a square root of a negative number this equation does not have any solutions.

Advantages of this method. The formula can be applied to any quadratic equation. It tells you whether or not the equation has any solutions.

Disadvantages of this method. You have to look up the formula. It is easy to make mistakes when substituting a, b and c into the formula. A different method might be quicker for some equations.

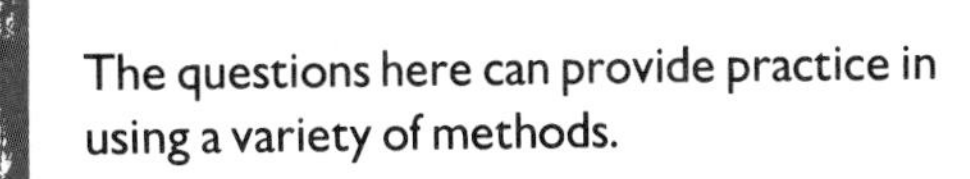
The questions here can provide practice in using a variety of methods.

1 Solve the following equations

(*a*) $3x^2 + 15x = 0$

(*b*) $12p^3 - 3p^2 = 0$

(*c*) $12n^3 = 3n$

2 Solve the following equations

(*a*) $x^2 + x - 12 = 0$

(*b*) $y^2 - 3y - 28 = 0$

(*c*) $x^2 - 9x - 22 = 0$

(*d*) $3x^2 - 10x + 3 = 0$

3 Find the value of $3x^2 + 4x$, when $x = 5$. Find the other value of x, which gives the same value of $3x^2 + 4x$.

4 The quadratic equation $x^2 + bx + c = 0$ has solutions $x = 3$ and $x = 5$.

Find b.

5 (*a*) Solve $x^2 - 4x = 5$

(*b*) Sketch $y = x^2 - 4x - 5$.

(*c*) Draw the line of symmetry on your sketch.

(*d*) What is the equation of the line of symmetry?

6 Solve

(*a*) $(x - 1)^2 = 3$

(*b*) $(5 - x)^2 = 2$

(*c*) $(x + 2)(x - 3) = 6$

7 'Think of a number. Square it. Add twice the number you first thought of. What is your answer?'

'15'

(*a*) Form an equation to describe the situation above.

(*b*) There are two possible numbers that could have been thought of. What are they?

8

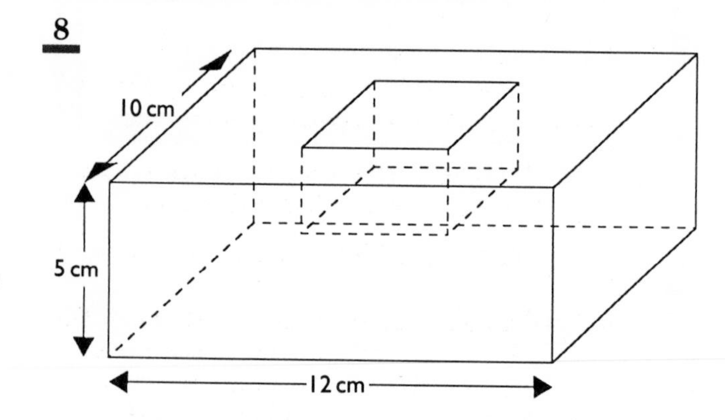

The inner cavity of the rectangular box shown in the diagram is to have a volume of 300 cm^3. The thickness of the container walls and of the base is x cm.

(*a*) The box is 5 cm deep. Write down, in terms of x, an expression for the depth of the inner cavity.

(*b*) Obtain, in terms of x, an expression for the volume of the inner cavity.

(*c*) Form an equation in x, and show that it simplifies to $(6 - x)(5 - x)^2 = 75$.

(*d*) Find, and write down, two consecutive positive whole numbers between which the solution to the equation lies.

(*NEA* May 1989, Syllabus A Paper 4)

9

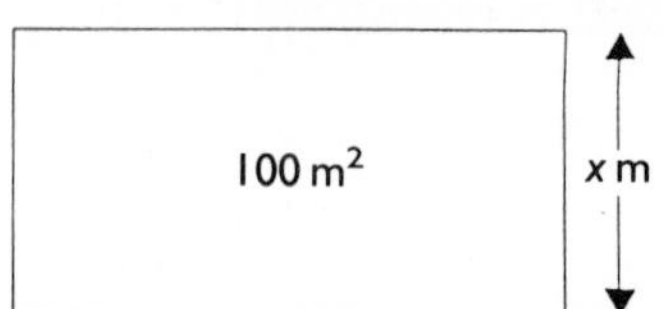

The length of a rectangle is 10 m longer than its breadth and its area is 100 m^2.

(*a*) If the breadth of the rectangle is x m, show that x satisfies the equation

$$x(x + 10) = 100$$

(*b*) Solve the equation to find x.

(*c*) What is the perimeter of the rectangle?

10

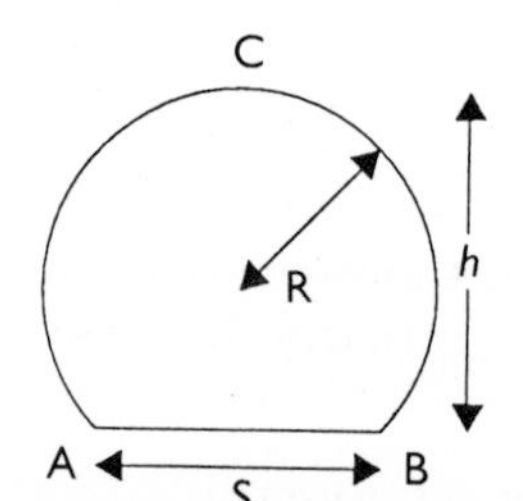

The diagram represents the cross-section of a tunnel. The points A and B are at the same horizontal level and AB = s metres. ACB is a major arc of a circle with radius R metres. C is the highest point of the arc and the height of C above AB is h metres.

The relation between R, s and h is

$$s^2 = 8Rh - 4h^2$$

For a particular tunnel, $s = 8$ and $R = 5$.

(*a*) Show that, for this tunnel, $h^2 - 10h + 16 = 0$.

(*b*) Factorise $h^2 - 10h + 16$.

(*c*) Find the value of h for this tunnel.

(*MEG* November 1987, Paper 2)

11 Solve the following equations

(*a*) $x^3 + 5x^2 + 6x = 0$

(*b*) $2x^3 - 5x^2 = 3x$

12 The stopping distance, d metres, of a car travelling at a speed of v km/h is given by

$$d = \frac{1}{5}\left(v + \frac{v^2}{30}\right)$$

(*a*) Find the stopping distance for a car travelling at 60 km/h.

(*b*) (i) Given that $d = 12$, form an equation in v and show that it simplifies to $v^2 + 30v - 1800 = 0$.
(ii) Solve the equation $v^2 + 30v - 1800 = 0$ and, hence, find the speed at which a car is travelling when its stopping distance is 12 m.

(*MEG* June 1986, Paper 3)

13

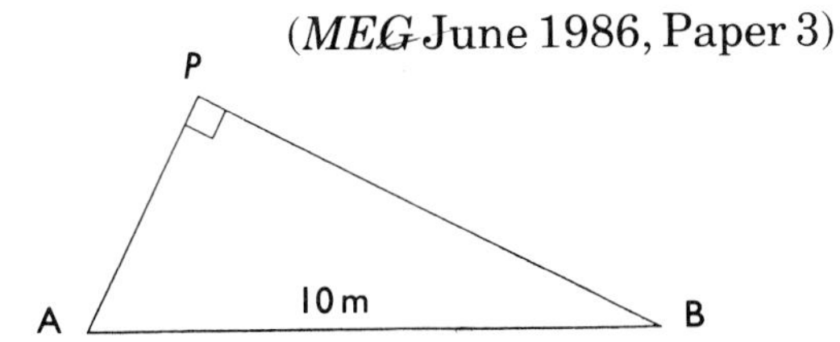

Derrick has to plant out a triangular flower bed ABC, as shown in the diagram above. The distance AB must be 10 m and the angle APB must be 90°. The lengths of the other two sides, AP and BP, must total 13 m.

(*a*) Taking the length of AP as x metres, form an equation in x, and show that it simplifies to $2x^2 - 26x + 69 = 0$.

(*b*) Solve this equation to find the two possible values of x, correct to 2 decimal places.

(*MEG* May 1988, Paper 3)

14 The nth term, a_n, of a sequence is $\frac{n(n+1)}{2}$.

(*a*) Find a_1, a_2, a_3 and a_{20}.

(*b*) Find $a_n - a_{n-1}$.

(*c*) Explain why a_n is the sum of the first n positive whole numbers.

(*d*) If the sum of the first x positive whole numbers is 378, show that x satisfies the equation

$$x^2 + x = 756$$

Solve the equation to find x.

15 (*a*) Show that the equation $2x^3 - 18x^2 - 108x + 120 = 0$ has a solution between -5 and -4.

(*b*) Use trial and improvement to find this solution correct to 2 decimal places.

(*c*) Between which two consecutive whole numbers is the largest solution of $2x^3 - 18x^2 - 108x + 120 = 0$?

16 If x is an approximation to the cube root of a number N (that is $x \simeq N^{\frac{1}{3}}$), then a better approximation y can be obtained by using the formula

$$y = \frac{1}{3}\left(2x + \frac{N}{x^2}\right)$$

(*a*) Explain briefly why 2 would be a sensible first approximation to the cube root of 7.

(*b*) Use the formula to obtain a second approximation.

(*Welsh* May 1989, Paper 4)

17

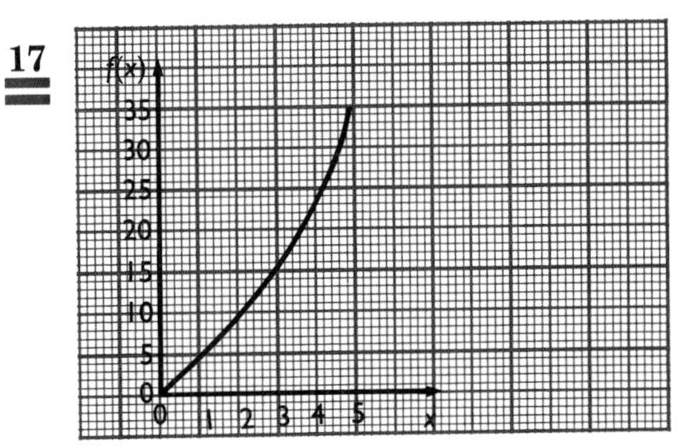

The graph of the function f, where

$$f(x) = x(x+2)$$

is drawn for $0 \leqslant x \leqslant 5$.

(*a*) From the graph, obtain an approximate solution to the equation $x(x+2) = 10$.

(*b*) By a trial and error method, obtain this solution correct to 2 decimal places.

(*NEA* November 1988, Syllabus A Paper 4)

18 (*a*) P is the point (12,0) relative to horizontal and vertical axes 0x, 0y respectively. A line drawn through P is at an angle of 45° to the positive horizontal axis. Find the equation of the line.

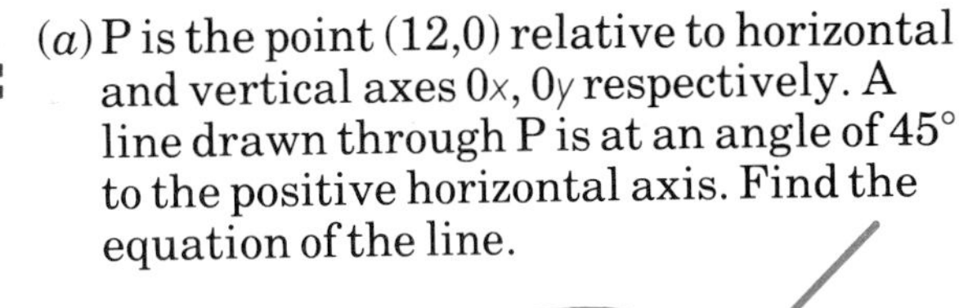

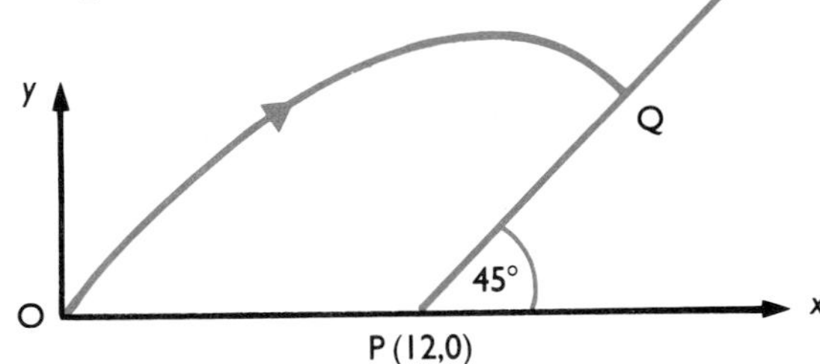

(*b*) A ball is thrown from 0 such that its path relative to $0x$ and $0y$ is given by

$$y = 2x - \frac{1}{16}x^2$$

The ball strikes the plane which rises at an angle of 45° to the horizontal from P. Find the coordinates of Q, the point of impact of the ball and the plane.

(*Welsh* May 1989, Paper 4)

19 The diagram shows part of the graph $y = x^2 - 6x + 3$.

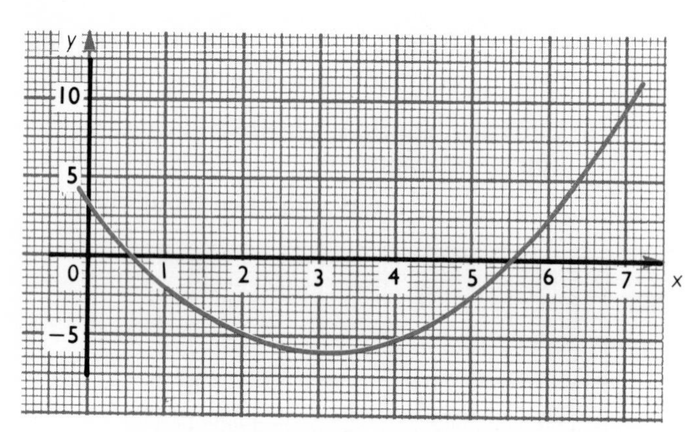

(*a*) Use the graph to give the smaller of the two solutions of the equation $x^2 - 6x + 3 = 0$, correct to one decimal place.

(*b*) Show that $x^2 - 6x + 3 = 0$ can be rearranged to give $x = \frac{x^2 + 3}{6}$

(*c*) Use the iteration $x_{n+1} = \frac{x_n^2 + 3}{6}$, starting with $x_1 = 0$, to solve the equation $x^2 - 6x + 3 = 0$, correct to two decimal places. Give all figures on your calculator until you state your answer.

(*d*) The equation can also be rearranged to give $x = \sqrt{6x - 3}$ and solved by the iteration $x_{n+1} = \sqrt{6x_n - 3}$.
(You are **not** asked to prove this.)

(i) Starting with $x_1 = 1$ find the values of x_2, x_3, x_4 and x_5.
(ii) Comment on your results in (i).

(*MEG SMP* November 1988, Paper 4)

20 If p and q are numbers and you are told that $p \times q = 0$, then you can deduce one of the following statements.

(*a*) Both p and q are zero.

(*b*) Either p is zero or q is zero (or possibly both).

(*c*) Either p is zero or q is zero (but not both).

Which of these is the correct deduction?

Find as many different pairs of numbers x and y as you can such that

$(x + y - 1)(x - y) = 0$
and $x(x + y - 2) = 0$

(You will only get good marks if you show a method which makes sure that you have found all the answers.)

(*LEAG SMP* 11–16 June 1987, Extension Paper)

EXERCISE 39 Rearranging formulae

The following examples explain the methods involved.

1 Rewrite $v = u + at$ in the form $t =$

Rearrange terms so that term in t is on its own.

$v - u = at$
or $at = v - u$

Divide by the letter in front of t.

$t = \frac{v - u}{a}$

2 Rewrite $F = \frac{9}{5}C + 32$ in the form $C =$

Multiply by 5 to remove fraction.

$5F = 9C + 160$

Rearrange terms so that term in C is on its own.

$5F - 160 = 9C$
or $9C = 5F - 160$

Divide by the number in front of C.

$C = \frac{5F - 160}{9}$ or $\frac{1}{9}(5F - 160)$

3 Rewrite $A = P + \frac{PRT}{100}$ in the form $T =$

Multiply by 100 to remove fraction.

$100A = 100P + PRT$

Rearrange terms so that term in T is on its own.

$100A - 100P = PRT$
or $PRT = 100A - 100P$

Divide by the quantity in front of T.

$T = \frac{100A - 100P}{PR}$

4 Rewrite $L = W - I^2 R$ in the form $I =$

Rearrange terms so that term in I^2 is on its own.

$I^2R = W - L$

Divide by the letter in front of I^2

$I^2 = \frac{W - L}{R}$

Lastly, take the square root of both sides to get I.

$I = \sqrt{\frac{W - L}{R}}$

5 Rewrite $T = 2\pi\sqrt{\frac{l}{g}}$ in the form $l =$

Rearrange terms so that the square root is on its own.

$\frac{T}{2\pi} = \sqrt{\frac{l}{g}}$

Square both sides to remove square root.

$\frac{T^2}{4\pi^2} = \frac{l}{g}$

Multiply by $4\pi^2 g$ to remove fractions.

$T^2g = 4\pi^2 l$
or $4\pi^2 l = T^2 g$

Divide by the quantity in front of l.

$l = \frac{T^2 g}{4\pi^2}$

6 Rewrite $S = 180 - \frac{360}{n}$ in the form $n =$

Multiply by n to remove fraction.

$Sn = 180n - 360$

Rearrange terms so that terms in n are on *one* side.

$360 = 180n - Sn$
or $180n - Sn = 360$

Factorise to isolate n.

$n(180 - S) = 360$

Divide by the bracket.

$n = \frac{360}{180 - S}$

7 Rewrite $V = \frac{12R}{r + R}$ in the form $R =$

Multiply by $(r + R)$ to remove fraction.

$V(r + R) = 12R$

Multiply out bracket.

$Vr + VR = 12R$

Rearrange terms so that terms in R are on one side.

$Vr = 12R - VR$
or $12R - VR = Vr$

Factorise to isolate R.

$R(12 - V) = Vr$

Divide by the bracket.

$R = \frac{Vr}{12 - V}$

8 Rewrite $\frac{1}{f} = \frac{1}{u} + \frac{1}{v}$ in the form $v =$

Rearrange terms so that term in v is on its own.

$\frac{1}{v} = \frac{1}{f} - \frac{1}{u}$

Express fractions as a single fraction.

$\frac{1}{v} = \frac{u - f}{uf}$

Invert both sides (note that you can *only* do this when you have a *single* fraction on each side).

$v = \frac{uf}{u - f}$

1 The relationship between A and P is given by

$$P = 3(A + 20)$$

(*a*) Find P when $A = 15$.

(*b*) Find A when $P = 15$.

(*c*) Find P when $A = P$.

(*d*) Express A in terms of P.

2 To join a film club you pay £10 a year and then £2 for each film you see.

A member goes to see N films in a year. The total amount he pays is £A.

(*a*) Write down an expression for A in terms of N.

(*b*) Rewrite it to express N in terms of A.

3 Make t the subject of

(*a*) $v = u + at$,

and

(*b*) $s = \frac{1}{2}at^2$.

4 The relationship between power (P), voltage (V) and resistance (R) is given by the equation:

$$P = \frac{V^2}{R}$$

(*a*) Rearrange this equation to make R the subject.

(*b*) Rearrange this equation to make V the subject.

5 W Morgan's 'East Africa' gives the formula

$$T = 24.5 - 0.69H$$

for the mean minimum temperature T°C at a height H measured in hundreds of metres above sea level in Uganda.

(*a*) The maximum recommended height for growing coffee is 1800 m. What is the mean minimum temperature given by the formula for this height?

(*b*) Above what height could you expect a mean minimum temperature of less than 0°C?

(*c*) Give a formula for H in terms of T.

(*MEG SMP* June 1988, Paper 3)

6 At a particular disaster relief depot, the daily weight of grain supplied can be estimated during the first month by using the following formula:

$$s = 13n + nt$$

where s = number of tonnes of grain supplied,
n = number of days since the disaster,
t = number of times TV coverage has been made.

(*a*) Factorise the right-hand side of the formula.

(*b*) Transform the formula to make n the subject.

(*c*) What was the date of the disaster if on 28th May, after 5 TV coverages, the depot was supplied with 198 tonnes of grain?

(*NEA* May 1989, Syllabus A Paper 3)

7

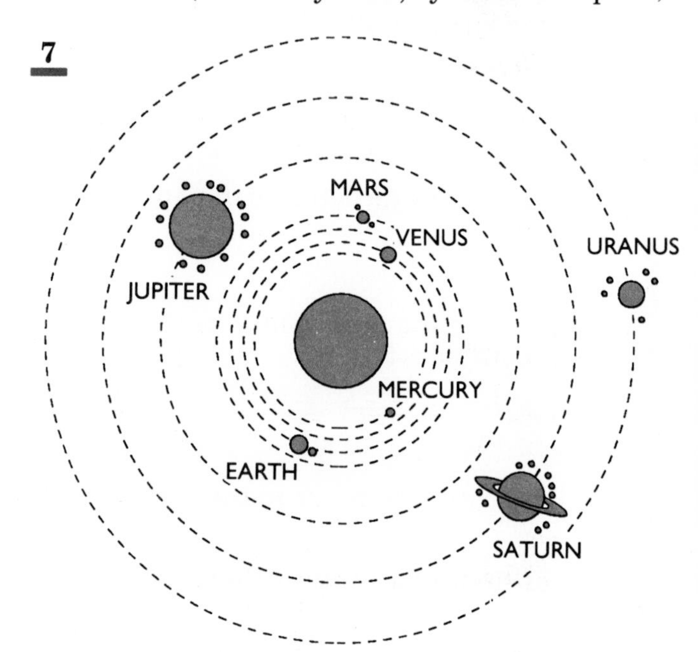

Kepler's third law says that

$$T = \frac{\sqrt{R^3}}{5}.$$

Here R is the distance of a planet from the Sun in millions of kilometres, and T is the time in days it takes to go round the Sun.

(*a*) For Mars $R = 228$. Calculate the number of days Mars takes to go round the Sun.

(*b*) For the Earth, taking $T = 365$,

(i) calculate R^3,
(ii) show that R is approximately 150.

(*c*) Give a formula for R^3 in terms of T.

(*MEG SMP* November 1988, Paper 3)

8 Four rods are used to make a square.

Rods are then added to make a row of 2 squares, then 3 squares and so on.

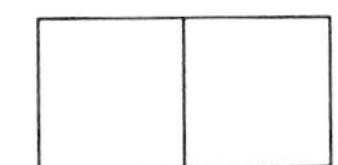

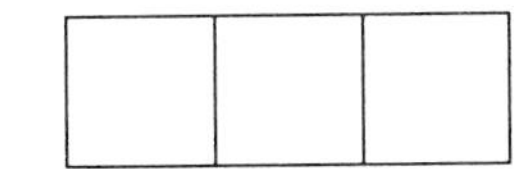

(*a*) How many rods are needed to make a row of

(i) 5 squares,
(ii) 6 squares,
(iii) 15 squares?

(*b*) Find a formula which gives the number of rods, r, needed to make a row of s squares in the form:

$$r =$$

(*c*) Use your formula to find how many squares could be made using 70 rods.

(*d*) Rearrange your formula in (*b*) in the form:

$$s =$$

(*e*) What is the greatest number of squares you can make in a row with 120 rods? How many rods will you have left over?

(*Welsh* May 1988, Paper 3)

9

1	2	3	4	5	36	37	38	39	40	71	72	73	74	75
6	7	8	9	10	41	42	43	44	45	76	77	78	79	80
11	12	13	14	15	46	47	48	49	50	81	82	83	84	85
16	17	18	19	20	51	52	53	54	55	86	87	88	89	90
21	22	23	24	25	56	57	58	59	60	91	92	93	94	95
26	27	28	29	30	61	62	63	64	65	96	97	98	99	100
31	32	33	34	35	66	67	68	69	70					

The numbers from 1 to 100 are arranged in rows of 5 as indicated above. From the array we may choose a 'box' of 4 numbers in a square.

Two of these are shown:

the '8 box' which has a total of 44,
the '49 box' which has a total of 208.

(*a*) What is the total of the '72 box'?

(*b*) Which box has the largest total, and what is its total?

(*c*) (i) Write down, in terms of n, the four numbers in the 'n box',
(ii) What is the total, t, of the 'n box'? Write your answer in the form $t = \ldots$

(*d*) Rearrange your formula in (*c*) in the form $n = \ldots$

(*e*) Which box has a total of 156?

(*SEG* Summer 1988, Mathematics A Paper 3)

10 The formula for the surface area, A, of a closed circular cylinder of radius r and height h is

$$A = 2\pi r(r + h)$$

(*a*) Make h the subject of the formula.

(*b*) Find the radius, in cm to one decimal place, of a cylinder whose surface area is 120π cm^2 and whose height is 12 cm.

(*LEAG* Specimen 1991, Paper 4)

11 (*a*) l and b are the length and breadth of an equable rectangle. The relationship between l and b is given by the equation

$$l = \frac{2b}{b - 2}$$

Rearrange this equation to express b in terms of l.

(*b*) r is the radius of the base and h is the height of an equable cone.

The relationship between h and r is given by the equation

$$h = \frac{6r^2}{r^2 - 9}$$

Rearrange this equation to express r in terms of h.

12 (*a*) (i) The focal length (f) of a lens is connected to the distance (u) of an object from the lens and the distance (v) of its image by the following formula

$$f = \frac{uv}{u + v}$$

Rearrange this equation to express v in terms of u and f.
(ii) An object is 40 cm from a lens of focal length 30 cm. Find the distance of the image from the lens.

(*b*) (i) The combined resistance (R) of two resistances R_1 and R_2 in parallel is given by the formula

$$R = \frac{R_1 R_2}{R_1 + R_2}$$

Rearrange this equation to express R_2 in terms of R_1 and R.
(ii) What resistance should be used in parallel with a resistance of 40 ohms to produce a combined resistance of 30 ohms?

13 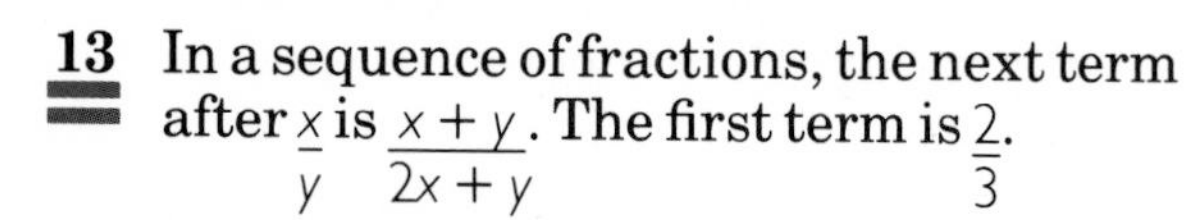
In a sequence of fractions, the next term after $\frac{x}{y}$ is $\frac{x+y}{2x+y}$. The first term is $\frac{2}{3}$.

(*a*) Write down the first six terms of the sequence

$$\frac{2}{3}, \frac{5}{7}, \ldots$$

(*b*) Find the squares of the values of these six terms to as many decimal places as your calculator will give. What do you notice about these squares of values?

(*c*) Find the term in the sequence which comes immediately before $\frac{2378}{3363}$.

(*d*) One term in the sequence is $\frac{p}{q}$. Find, in terms of p and q, the term which comes immediately before $\frac{p}{q}$.

(*MEG* May 1988, Paper 6)

14 

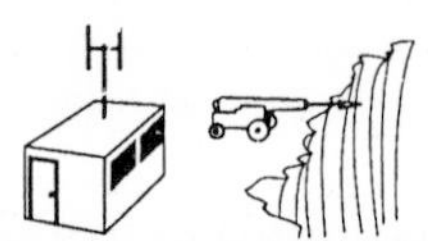

A rescue harpoon is fired horizontally from a cliff-top. The horizontal distance, x metres, it has travelled after t seconds is given by

$$x = 250t$$

The distance of the harpoon below the cliff-top, y metres, is given by $y = 5t^2$

(*a*) (i) Write t in terms of x.
(ii) Write an equation which connects y and x, but does not include t, in the form $y = \ldots$

(*b*) How many centimetres below the cliff-top will the harpoon be when it is 50 metres horizontally from the firing gun?

(*Welsh* May 1988, Paper 4)

15 $y = \frac{1}{2}\left(\frac{A}{x} + x\right)$

(*a*) (i) Use your calculator to find, from the above formula, the value of y when $A = 55$ and $x = 7$. Write down all the figures that your calculator displays for the answer.
(ii) Write your value of y correct to 6 significant figures.
(iii) Taking $A = 55$ again, but x as your answer to (*a*) (ii) instead of 7, use the formula again to find a new value of y. Write down the full answer display from your calculator and then correct it to 6 significant figures.
(iv) Repeat this process with the same formula, each time taking $A = 55$ and the value of x as the previous 6 figure value of y, until the newly calculated value of y is the same as the previous value of y, correct to 6 significant figures.

(*b*) Given that $x = \frac{1}{2}\left(\frac{A}{x} + x\right)$, express x in terms of A.

(*c*) Explain what has been calculated in part (*a*).

(*MEG* November 1987, Paper 6)

16 

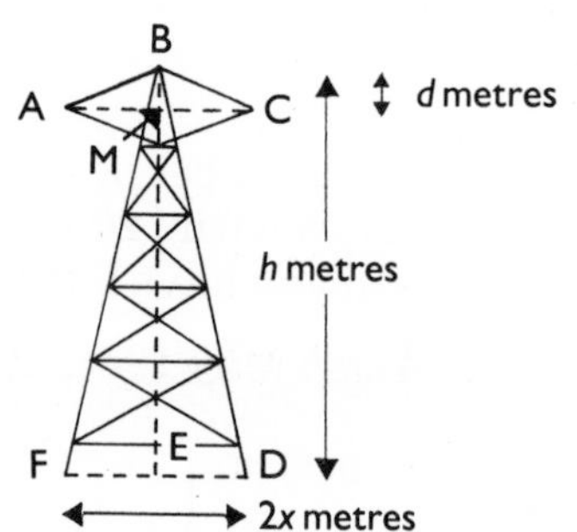

The diagram represents the side view of a symmetrical electricity pylon standing on horizontal ground. The line AC is horizontal with the points A and C vertically above the points F and D respectively. The vertical height BE is h metres, the distance BM is d metres and the distance FD is $2x$ metres.

The triangles BMC and FEB are similar.

(*a*) Copy and complete the following equation

$$\frac{\text{BM}}{\text{FE}} = \frac{\text{MC}}{}$$

(*b*) Rewrite this equation

(i) using the letters d, h and x,
(ii) with d as the subject.

(*c*) Calculate the height of A above F, given that $h = 12$ and $x = 3$.

(*LEAG* June 1989, Paper 4)

EXERCISE 40 Nets and polyhedra

1 Here is the net of a solid.

(*a*) What is the name of the solid?

(*b*) How many faces does the solid have?

(*c*) How many vertices does the solid have?

2

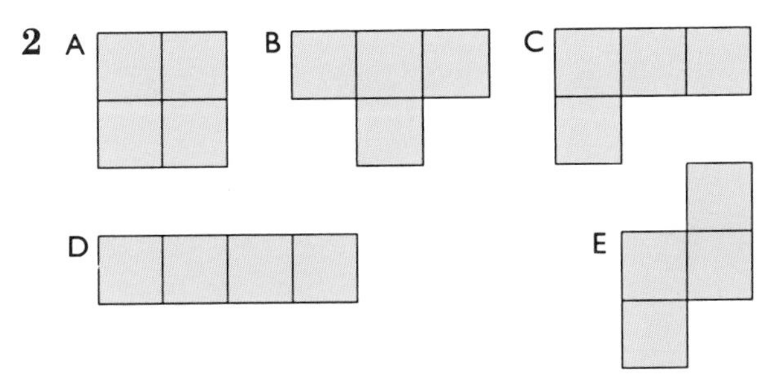

(*a*) Four of the drawings above are *part* of the net of a cube. Which drawing is *not*?

(*b*) Copy the four drawings which are part of the net of a cube onto squared paper.

Add two squares to each drawing to turn it into the net of a cube. Shade the two squares you add.

3

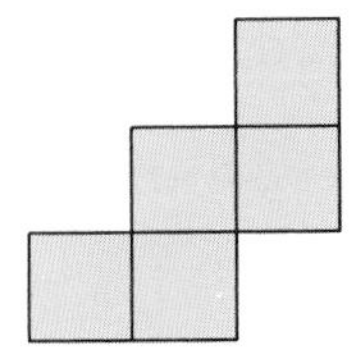

The diagram above shows part of the net of a cube. Another square needs to be added to complete the net.

Make several copies of the diagram and complete the net in as many different ways as possible.

4 A cuboid has dimensions 4 cm by 2.5 cm by 1 cm.

(*a*) Calculate the volume of the cuboid.

(*b*) Draw accurately, on centimetre squared paper, a net for the cuboid.

(*c*) Calculate the surface area of the cuboid.

5

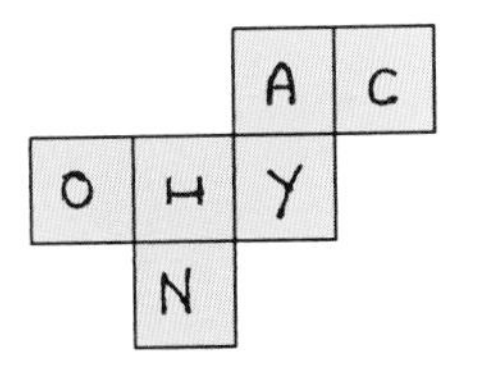

A cube is folded from the net shown above. Figure 1 shows the cube but the letters on two of the faces are missing.

Figure 1

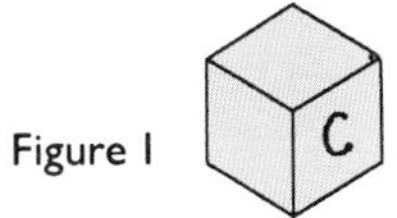

Copy the picture of the cube and put in the missing letters.

6

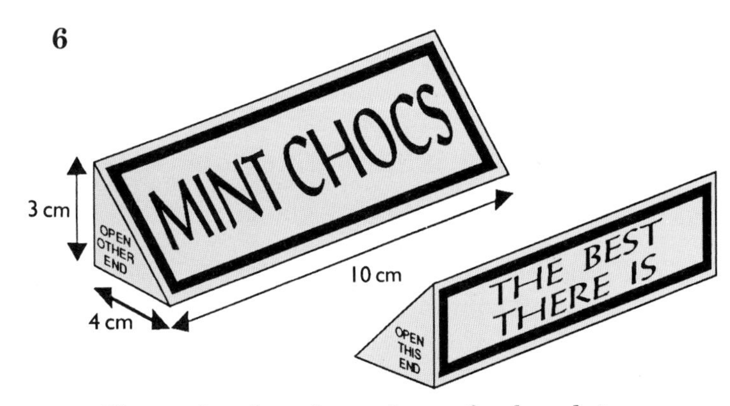

These sketches show views of a chocolate box.

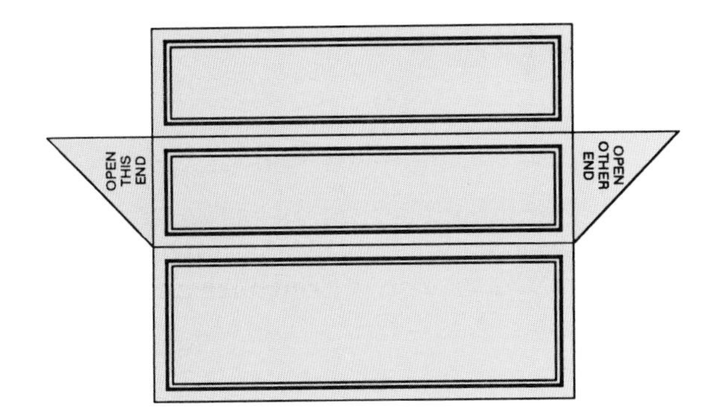

When it is opened out with the outside showing, it looks like this.

This is called the *net* of the box.

(*a*) Put the words MINT CHOCS and THE BEST THERE IS in the correct places on your sketch of the net.

(*b*) Draw the net of the box, full size, with the outside showing.

(*Welsh* May 1989, Paper 2)

7

The diagram above represents a winner's stand used at athletics championships. The stand consists of six boxes glued together. Each box is a cuboid with base 50 cm by 50 cm and height 20 cm.

(*a*) Calculate the volume of one box.

(*b*) The outside of the stand (but not the part on the ground) is to be painted.

(i) How many squares 50 cm by 50 cm are to be painted?
(ii) How many rectangles 50 cm by 20 cm are to be painted?
(iii) What is the total area to be painted?

(*MEG* November 1988, Paper 1)

8 This diagram shows a cuboid made out of centimetre cubes. The measurements of the cuboid are 8 cm by 4 cm by 2 cm.

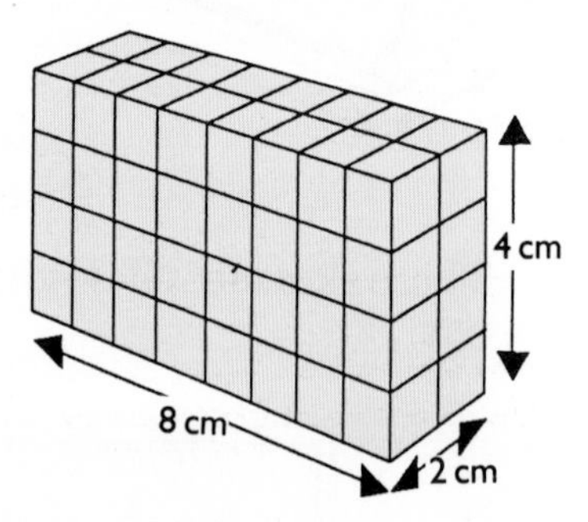

(*a*) How many centimetre cubes have been used to make the cuboid?

(*b*) The cuboid is painted red on all its six faces. How many of the centimetre cubes will have paint on one face only?

(*NEA* November 1988, Syllabuses A and B Paper 2)

9

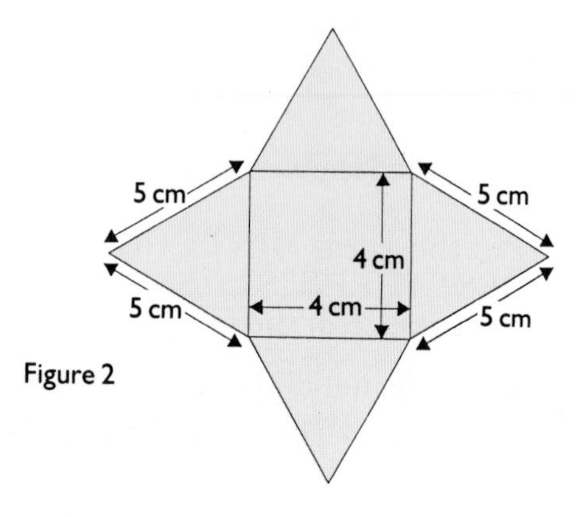

Figure 2

Figure 2 shows the net of a solid. It is not drawn accurately.

(*a*) Name the solid which can be made from this net.

(*b*) Draw an accurate net for this solid, using the lengths shown.

(*c*) Measure any lengths you need from your drawing and find the area of the net.

(*d*) The net is to be made from the smallest possible square piece of card.

(i) What size is the card?
(ii) What area of card is wasted?

10 (*a*) How many edges does a cube have?

(*b*) How many edges does a square-based pyramid have?

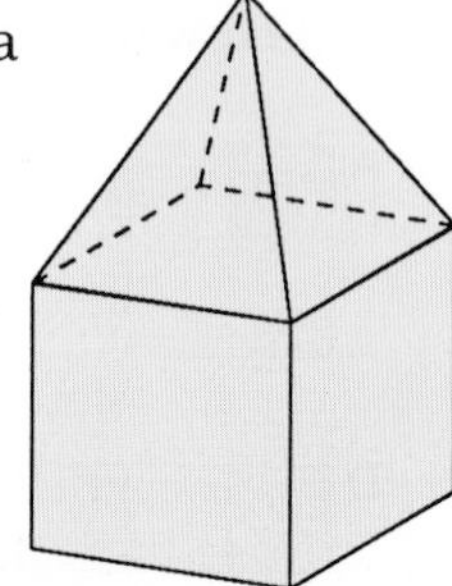

Figure 3

(*c*) The shape shown in figure 3 is formed by sticking together one face of a cube with the square face of the square-based pyramid. How many edges does this shape have?

(*d*) Another shape is formed by sticking together a cube and six square-based pyramids. The square face of a pyramid is stuck onto each face of the cube.

How many edges does this shape have?

11 Figure 4 shows pyramids with bases of different shapes.

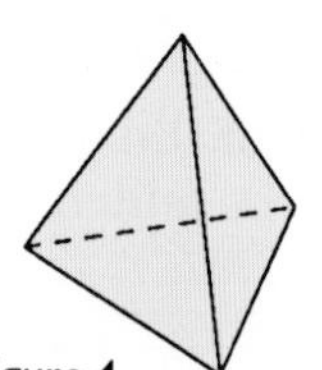

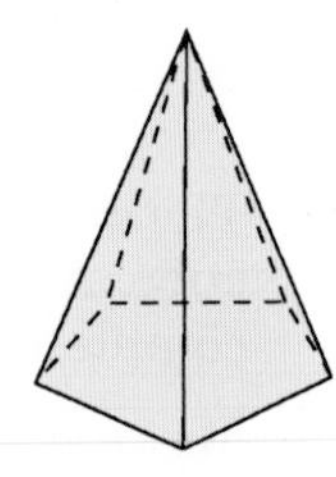

Figure 4

(*a*) How many edges does a triangular-based pyramid have?

(*b*) How many edges does a square-based pyramid have?

(*c*) How many edges does a pentagonal-based pyramid have?

(*d*) How many edges does a pyramid have if its base is a polygon with 20 sides?

12 (*a*) How many faces, edges and vertices does a pentagonal prism have?

(*b*) How many faces, edges and vertices does a hexagonal prism have?

(*c*) How many faces, edges and vertices does a prism have if its cross-section is a polygon with N sides?

13 Here is the net for a prism.

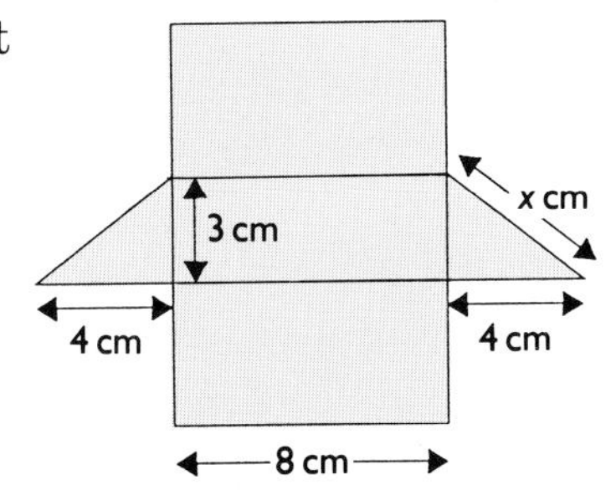

(*a*) Calculate the length of the side marked x.

(*b*) Calculate the surface area of the prism.

(*c*) Calculate the volume of the prism.

14 The figure ABCDE represents a square-based pyramid. The base ABCD is horizontal and the vertex E is vertically above C.

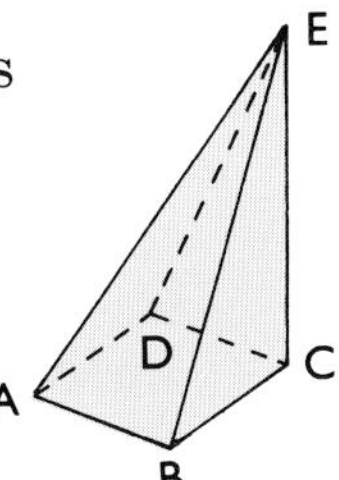

(*a*) Draw a sketch of a net of this pyramid.

(*b*) Name two congruent faces of the pyramid.

(*NEA* May 1989, Syllabus A Paper 3)

15 Draw a net of a square-based pyramid in such a way that each face on the net touches not more than two other faces.

16

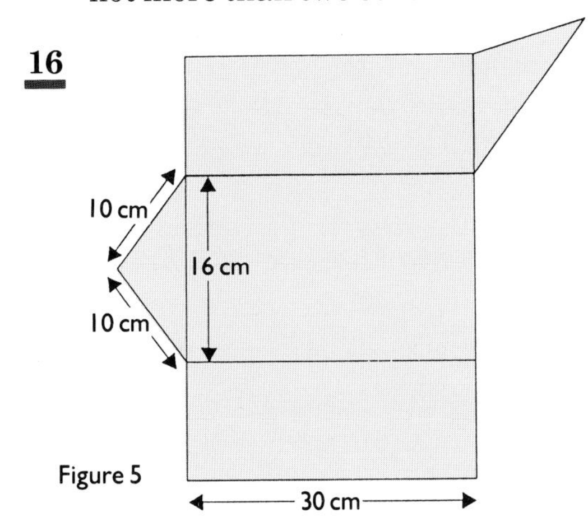

Figure 5

Figure 5 is a sketch of the net of a solid.

(*a*) Explain why the two triangular faces must be congruent.

(*b*) Calculate the area of one triangular face.

(*c*) Calculate the volume of the solid.

17

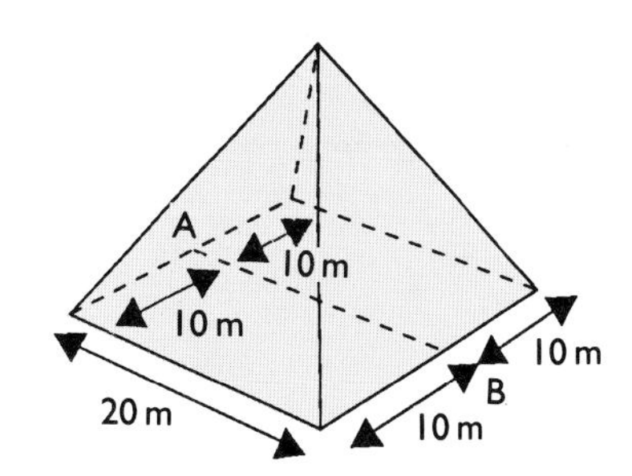

At an exhibition, one of the buildings is in the shape of a pyramid with a square base.

The height is 8 m.

A vertical wall 3 m high is to be built up from AB. It touches the sloping sides.

Make an accurate drawing of this wall. Use a scale of 1 cm to 2 m.

(*LEAG SMP* 11–16 June 1988, Paper 3)

18

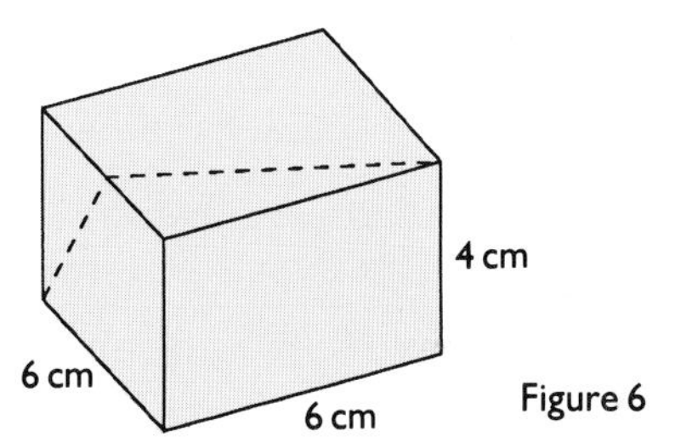

Figure 6

Figure 6 shows a path drawn on the surface of the cuboid, which joins opposite corners of the cuboid.

Find the length of the shortest path on the surface of the cuboid which joins opposite corners.

Hint: You might find it helpful to draw different nets of the cuboid.

19

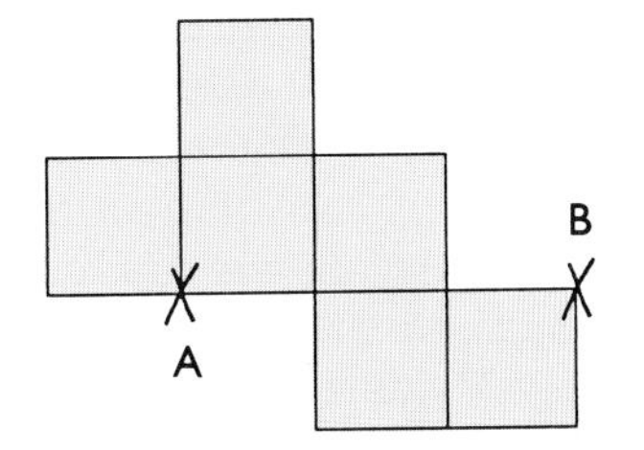

Figure 7 shows the net of a cube. The picture is not the correct size. Each edge of the cube is 5 cm long.

(*a*) When the cube is folded up, what will be the shortest distance between A and B?

(*b*) When the cube is folded up, a path is drawn betwen A and B on the surface of the cube. This path is made as short as possible. What is its length?

20 The drawing shows the net of an open box with points A and B marked on it. It is not drawn to scale.

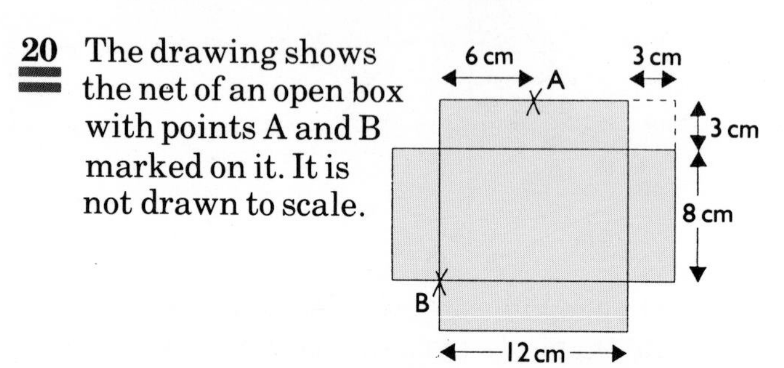

(*a*) Calculate the shortest distance on the net from A to B.

(*b*) The net is folded to form an open box as shown. Copy the drawing and mark the points A and B.

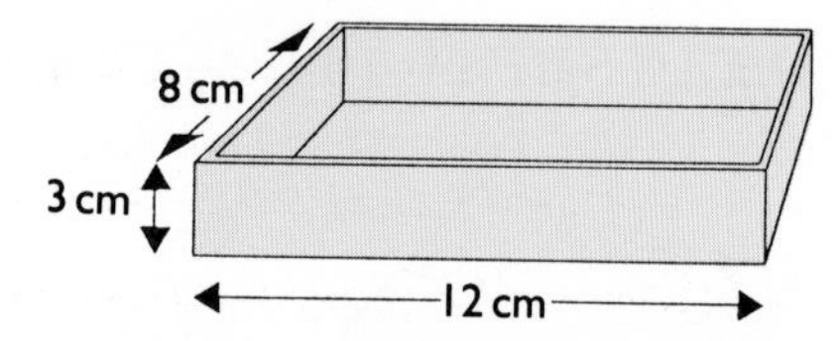

(*c*) Calculate the distance from A to B on a straight line passing through the box.

(*NEA* May 1988, Syllabus A Paper 4)

21

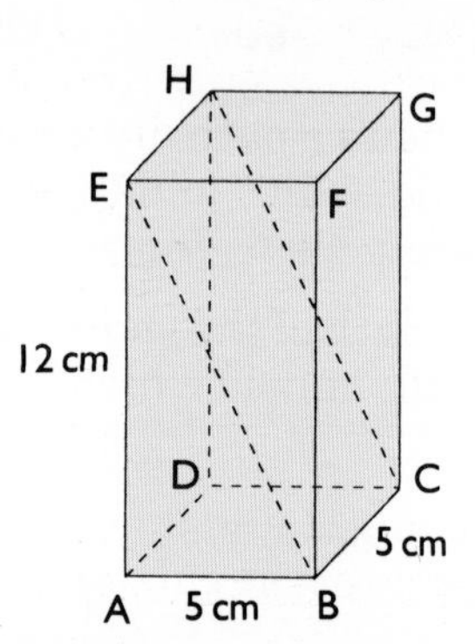

ABCDEFGH is a cuboid. The faces ABCD and EFGH are squares of side 5 cm. AE = BF = CG = DH = 12 cm. The cuboid is divided into two parts by a cut made along the plane EBCH, as shown in the diagram. The upper part is discarded. The remaining part is then cut into two parts along the plane EDC, leaving a pyramid on a square base ABCD, with its vertex at E, after the other part has also been discarded.

(*a*) Calculate the length of BE.

(*b*) Using a scale of 1 cm to represent 2 cm, draw accurately the net of the pyramid EABCD.

(*MEG* June 1987, Paper 3)

22

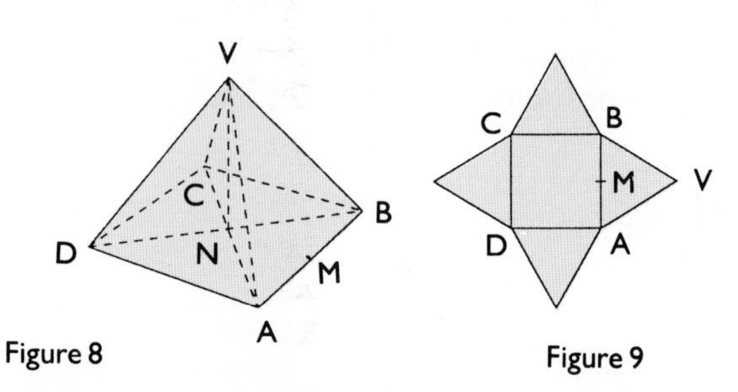

Figure 8 Figure 9

Figure 8 represents a pyramid VABCD on a square base ABCD. The length of each side of the square is 4 cm. The vertex V is 5 cm vertically above N. The midpoint of AB is M.

(*a*) Calculate the length of VM. Give your answer in cm, correct to two decimal places.

The pyramid was constructed from the net shown in figure 9. The net was drawn on a square piece of card.

(*b*) Calculate the length of the side of the smallest square of card that could have been used. Give your answer in cm, correct to two decimal places.

(*LEAG* June 1989, Paper 4)

23

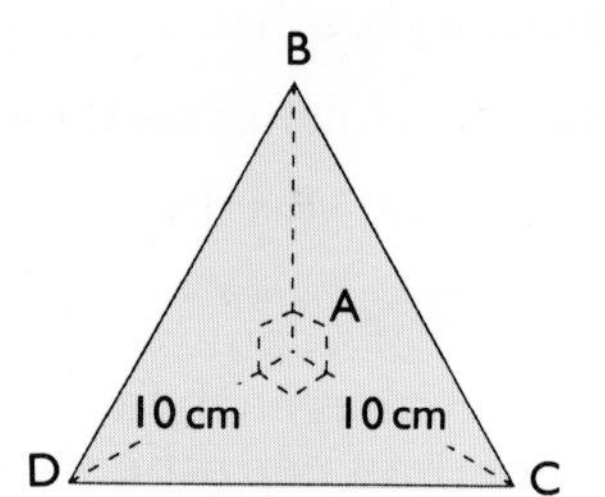

Figure 10

Figure 10 shows a tetrahedron in which angles DAC, DAB and CAB are all right angles. The lengths of AD and AC are both 10 cm.

(*a*) Calculate the length of DC, correct to three significant figures.

(*b*) Angle DBC is 72°. Calculate the length of BD, correct to three significant figures.

(*c*) Calculate the length of AB, correct to three significant figures.

(*d*) Calculate the surface area of the tetrahedron, correct to two significant figures.

24

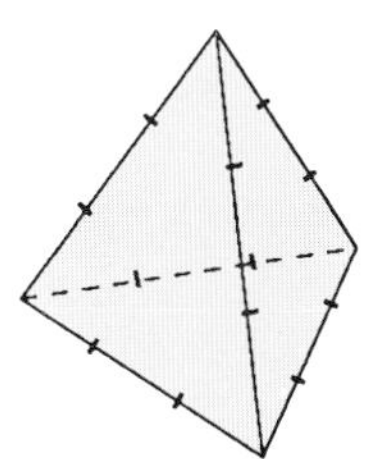

The diagram shows a solid tetrahedron. (The dotted line indicates an edge which you cannot see from the front.) Small marks are made one-third and two-thirds of the way along each edge. At each of the four vertices, a pyramid is then cut off the tetrahedron by slicing along the plane through the three marks closest to that vertex. Make a copy of the diagram in pencil (it need not be drawn accurately) and then on your copy ink over the edges of the solid that is left after the pyramids are cut off. Draw in as solid lines those edges which you can see from the front, and dotted lines those edges which you cannot see.

For the solid that is left, write down

(i) what kinds of faces it has, and how many of each kind;
(ii) how many vertices it has;
(iii) how many edges it has.

Find also the ratio of the volume of the new solid to the volume of the original tetrahedron.

Each edge of the new solid now has marks placed one-third and two-thirds of the way along it. At each of its vertices, a pyramid is again cut off by slicing along the plane through the three marks closest to that vertex. For the solid that is now left, write down

(iv) what kinds of faces it has and how many of each kind;
(v) how many vertices it has;
(vi) how many edges it has.

(*LEAG SMP* 11–16 June 1987, Extension Paper)

EXERCISE 41 Pythagoras' theorem and trigonometry in three dimensions

1 The diagram shows the internal dimensions of a pencil box with a rectangular base and vertical sides. EH = AD = 4 cm, FG = BC = 6 cm, AB = 5 cm, AE = 20 cm.

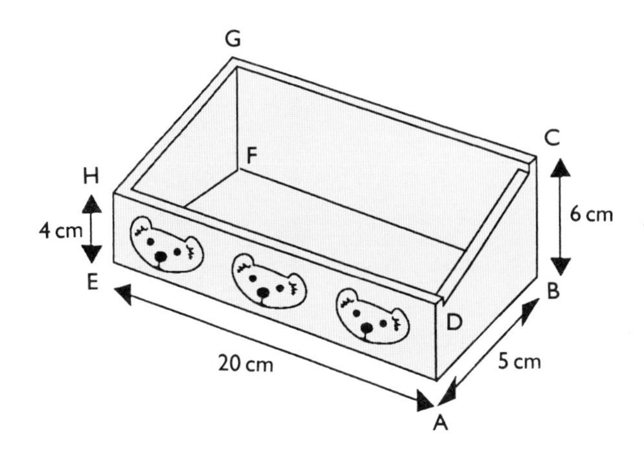

(*a*) How many planes of symmetry has the box?

(*b*) Calculate

(i) the area of the end ABCD,
(ii) the volume of the box.

(*c*) Calculate the length of the longest pencil which will fit into the box. You should ignore the thickness of the pencil.

(*SEG* Winter 1988, Mathematics A Paper 4)

2

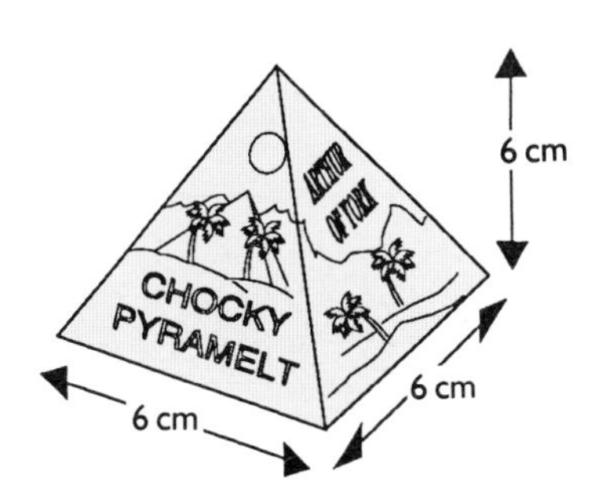

The box for a chocolate mint is a square-based pyramid with its point vertically above the middle of the base. The sides of the base of the box are 6 cm long and the box is 6 cm tall.

(*a*) (i) Calculate the diagonal distances across the base.
(ii) Calculate the length of the sloping edge.

(*b*) Sketch a net for the box, indicating the lengths of the sides.

(*Welsh* May 1988, Paper 4)

3

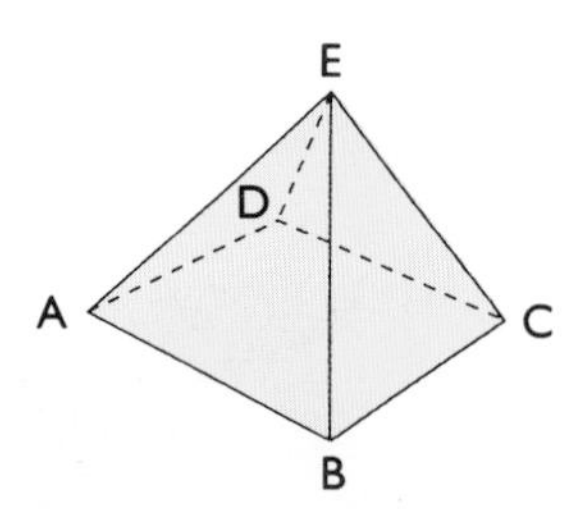

A model of a square-based pyramid is to be made with each edge 2 cm long.

(*a*) Calculate the height of E above the plane ABCD.

(*b*) Calculate the angle between the face ABE and the plane ABCD.

(*NEA* November 1988, Syllabus A Paper 4)

4

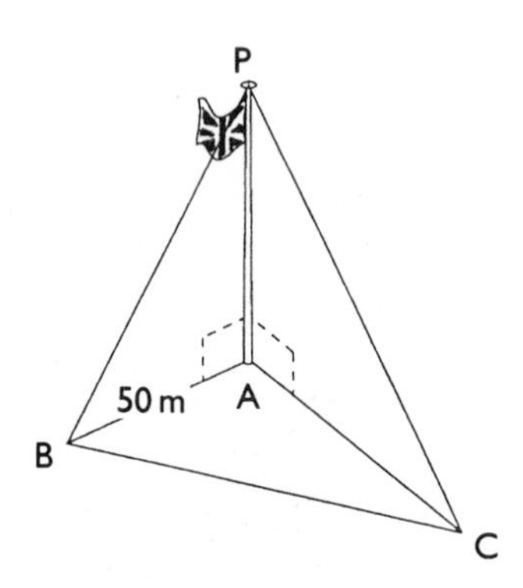

The line AP represents a vertical mast. The point B is 50 m due South of A, the foot of the mast. The angle of elevation of P from B is 20°.

(*a*) Find the height of the mast.

(*b*) A woman walks due East from B until she reaches a point C from which the angle of elevation of P is 10°. How far is C from B?

5

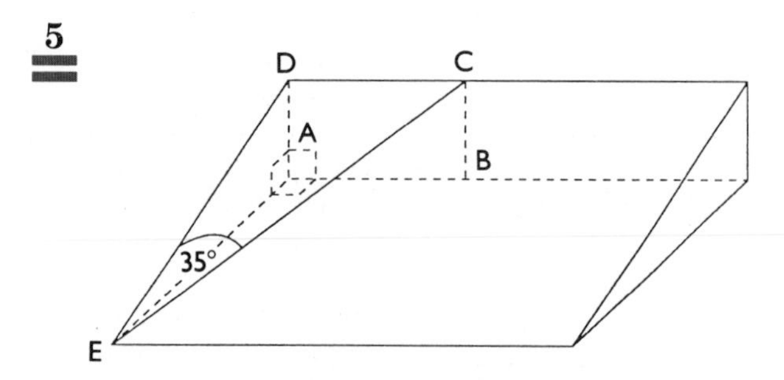

The diagram shows that part of a hillside whose gradient is 1 in 5, that is, for every 1 m rise in the direction AD, the increase in the direction ED is 5 m. A straight path, EC, is inclined at 35° to a line of greatest slope, ED. Find the gradient of the path in the form 1 in *n*, where *n* is given correct to two significant figures.

(*NEA* May 1988, Syllabus C Paper 4)

6

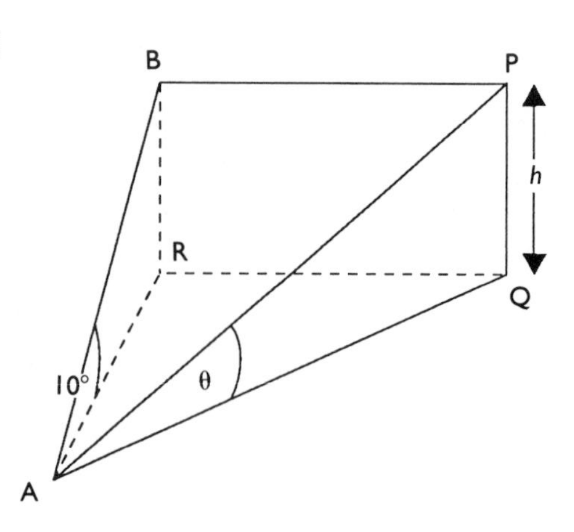

A line of greatest slope, AB, of a hill makes an angle of 10° with the horizontal AR, as shown in the digram. The bearing of R from A is N25°E.

An engineer decides to build a straight road, AP, on the hill, bearing N67°E.

In the diagram, h is the height of the hill above the horizontal plane, ARQ, and BP is parallel to RQ.

The line RQ is on a bearing of 115°.

(*a*) (i) Explain why the angle ARQ is 90°.
(ii) Express AR in terms of h.
(iii) From the triangle ARQ, find AQ in terms of h.

(*b*) If the gradient of the road is given by tan θ, calculate the value of the gradient of the road.

(*NEA* November 1988, Syllabus B Paper 4)

7

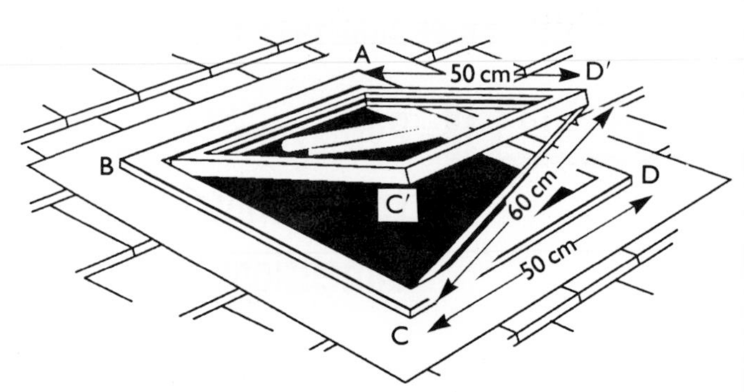

A square rooflight is hinged along one edge and its closed position, ABCD, is horizontal. Its open position is ABC′D′ and it is maintained in this position by a stay CD′, as shown in the diagram. The length of each side of the rooflight is 50 cm and the length of the stay is 60 cm.

(*a*) Explain why angle CDD′ is a right angle.

(*b*) Calculate the angle of inclination to the horizontal of the rooflight in the open position.

(*NEA*, November 1988, Syllabus C Paper 4)

8 (In this question *all* answers should be given to three significant figures.)

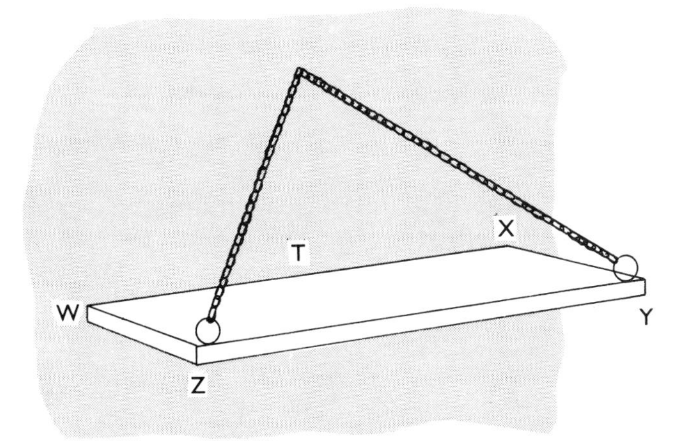

The drawing above shows a rectangular shelf WXYZ which is hinged to a vertical wall along the line WX. The midpoint of WX is T and WX = 2.4 m, XY = 0.5 m. The shelf is held in a horizontal position by two straight chains joining Y and Z to a point U on the wall and vertically above T. Each chain is of length 1.7 m.

(*a*) Calculate
(i) the length of UT,
(ii) the size of angle UYT.

The chains are now rehung so that they are directly above the edges XY and WZ, the chain from Z being fixed to the wall at the point P, vertically above W. The shelf remains horizontal.

(*b*) Calculate
(i) the size of the angle WPZ,
(ii) the length of PW.

(*LEAG* June 1986, Paper 4)

9 ABCDE is a square-based pyramid. The length of one side of the base is 60 m.

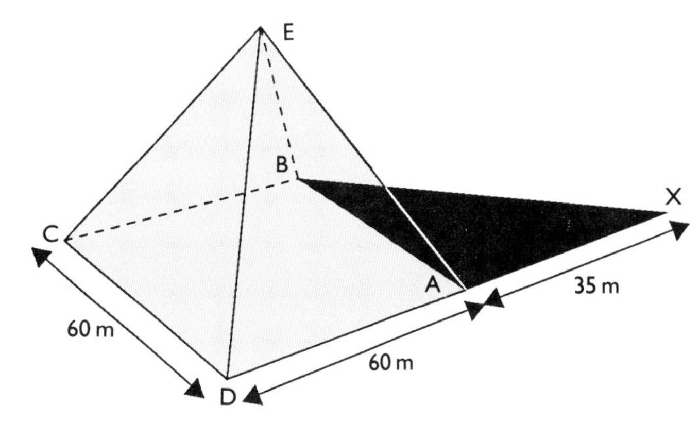

At one time the shadow of the pyramid cast on the ground is the triangle ABX, XAD is a straight line and the length of XA is 35 m.

At the same time a vertical post of height 3 m, casts a shadow on the ground of length 5 m.

(*a*) Calculate the angle of elevation of the sun at this time.

(*b*) Calculate the height of the pyramid.

10

A vertical, rectangular advertisement hoarding faces due North. It is 4 m high and 10 m long. Sketch two plans showing the shapes of the shadows of the hoarding on the level ground

(i) at mid-day, when the sun is due South at an angle of 60° above the horizon,
(ii) at a time in the afternoon when the sun is in a South-West direction at an angle of 45° above the horizon. Mark the direction of north on your plans.

In each case calculate the lengths of the sides of the shadow and mark the angles on your sketches. (You may give your answers either using whole numbers and square roots, or in decimal form using a calculator where necessary.)

(*MEG LEAG SMP* 11–16 June 1987 Extension Paper)

11 An aeroplane is flying in a horizontal circle of radius r, at a height h above level ground: it is observed from a point O on the ground. When the aeroplane is due North of O, its angle of elevation from O takes its largest value, which is 45°; when the aeroplane is due South of O, its angle of elevation from O takes its smallest value which is the angle whose tangent is $\frac{1}{2}$.

(*a*) Show that $h = \frac{2}{3}r$

(*b*) Find, in terms of r, the distance in a straight line from O to the centre of the circle in which the aeroplane is flying.

(*c*) Calculate the angle of elevation of the aeroplane from O when it is due West of O.

(*MEG* Specimen 1990 and 1991, Extension Paper)

12 Do not use a calculator in this question.

AD, BD and CD are the three legs of a surveyor's tripod, which stands on level ground. Each leg is 60 inches long when fully extended.

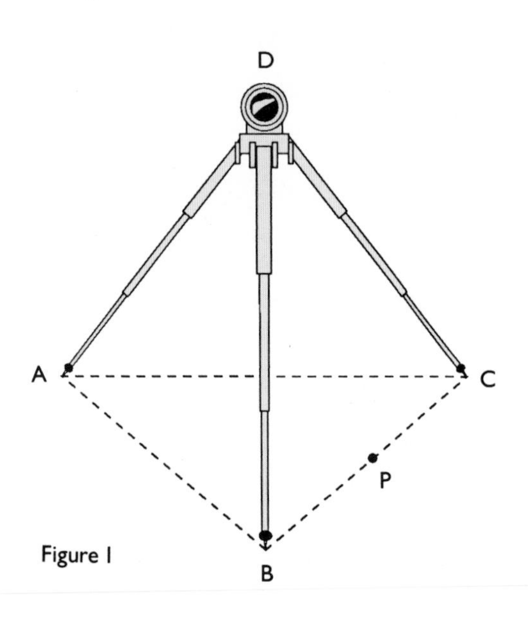

Figure 1

The tripod is first set up with all its legs fully extended and stands so that ABCD forms a regular tetrahedron, as in figure 1. The ground plan is shown in figure 2. The midpoint of BC is denoted by P.

(i) Use letters in figure 1 to label the angle which the leg AD makes with the ground,

(ii) Without doing any calculation, state whether this angle is less than, equal to, or greater than 60°. Give a reason for your answer.

(iii) Find the length AP. Give your answer in inches in the form $p\sqrt{q}$, where p and q are whole numbers and q is as small as possible.

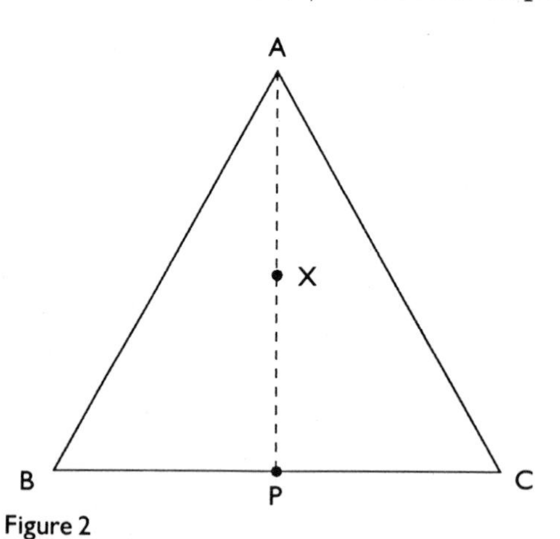

Figure 2

The surveyor now adjusts the tripod by shortening the leg AD, so that D comes directly above X, the midpoint of AP. This is shown in figure 3.

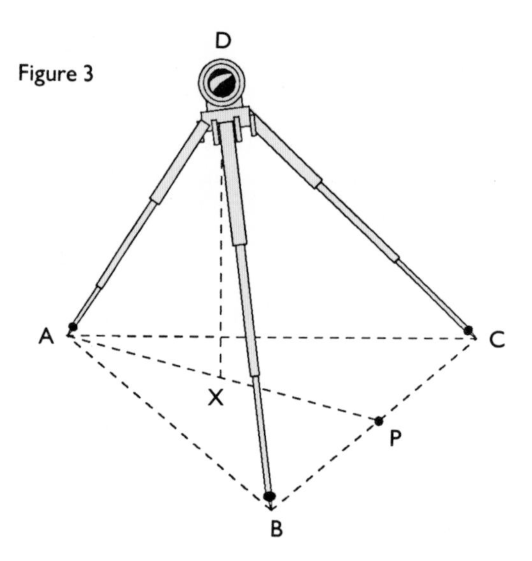

Figure 3

(iv) Which of the four triangles making the tetrahedron are still equilateral?

(v) Draw out the triangle ADP, and mark on it all the lengths you know.

(vi) Find the angle which the leg AD now makes with the ground.

(vii) Find the height of the point D above the ground.

(*MEG* and *LEAG SMP* 11–16 Specimen 1990 and 1991 Extension Paper)

20 REPEATING PATTERNS

The line below shows a week. The marked portions are the times during which someone was asleep during that week.

The pattern of sleep is a repeating pattern, but not as exact repeating pattern.

Each of the lines below represents a week.

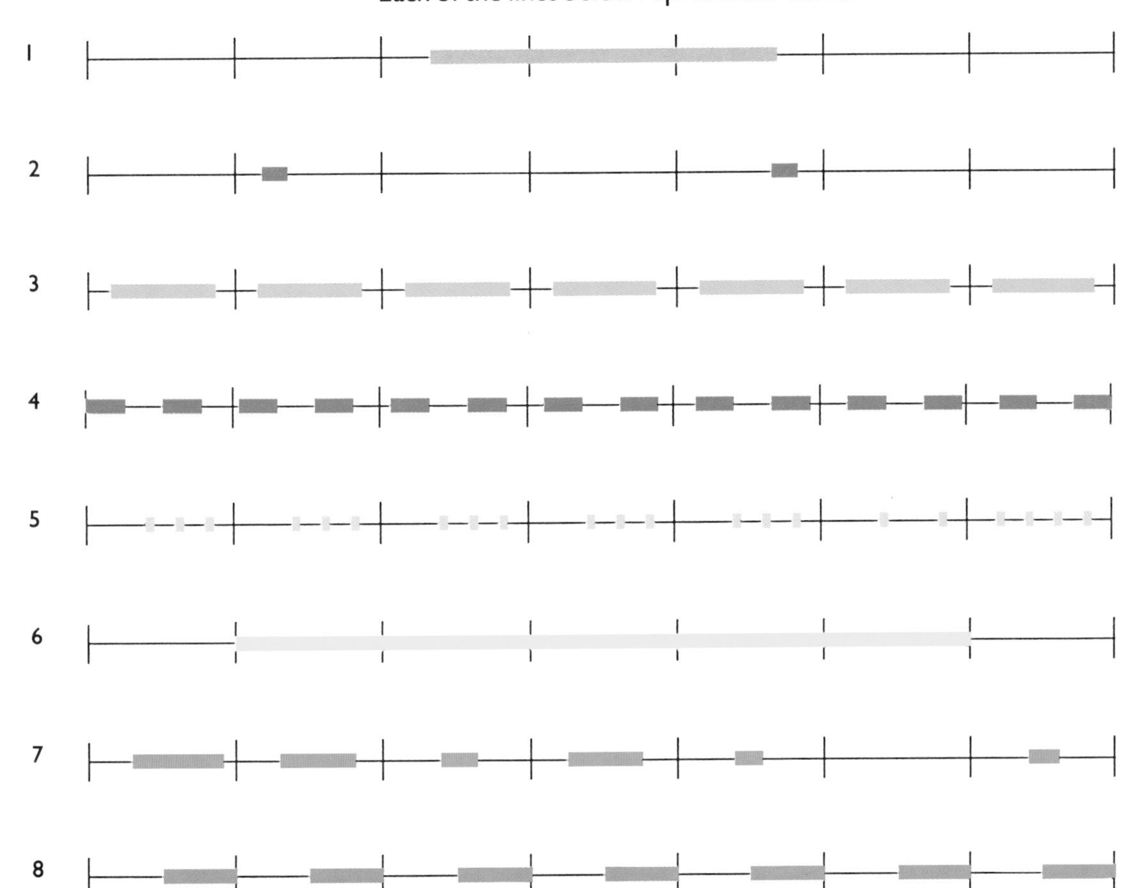

The marked portion of each line represents *one* of the following happenings.

A the times during which someone is eating;

B daylight in September;

C the time when someone has flu;

D days containing the letter '*t*';

E daylight in July;

F the times during which someone is watching television;

G the time someone is at the cinema;

H a.m. times;

I weekdays;

J the times someone is at school;

K the times when the temperature is above 10 °C;

L the times someone is on an aeroplane during a trip to Paris;

M the times when the tide is going out on Cromer beach;

N p.m. times;

O the times when it is raining.

- Decide what you think each of the lines might describe. Draw lines to describe the other happenings.
- Think of different happenings and draw lines to describe them.
- Which of the happenings are *regularly repeating* patterns? Which are *nearly regularly repeating* patterns? Which are *irregularly repeating* patterns? Which are *not* repeating patterns at all?

SECTION A

1 (*a*) How many hours during a week is it p.m.?

(*b*) The line below shows the p.m. times during a five-day period.

How many hours is it between A and B?

2 Each of the graphs below shows one of the following situations:

A the amount of money someone has in the bank throughout a year;

B the length of a day somewhere in Britain during a period of several years;

C the temperature during a period of several days;

D the position of someone walking at a steady speed up and down the street near a bus stop, while waiting for a bus;

E the angle the string makes to the vertical when a pendulum swings.

Match the graphs with the situations.

Give reasons for your answers.

1

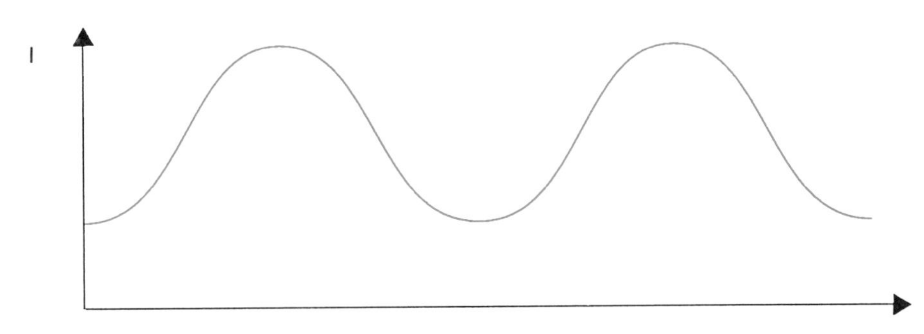

2

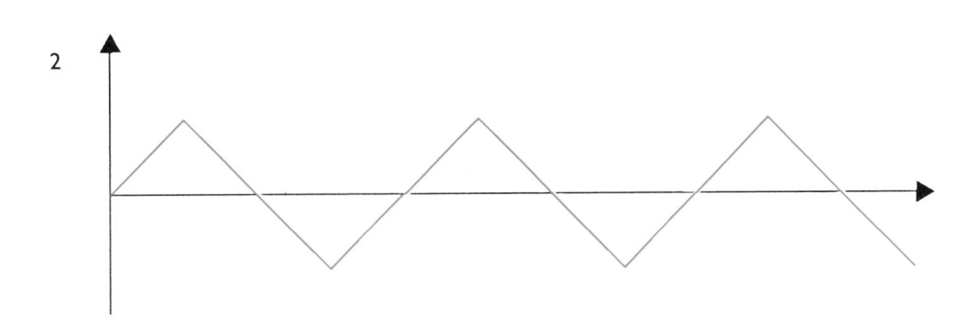

3

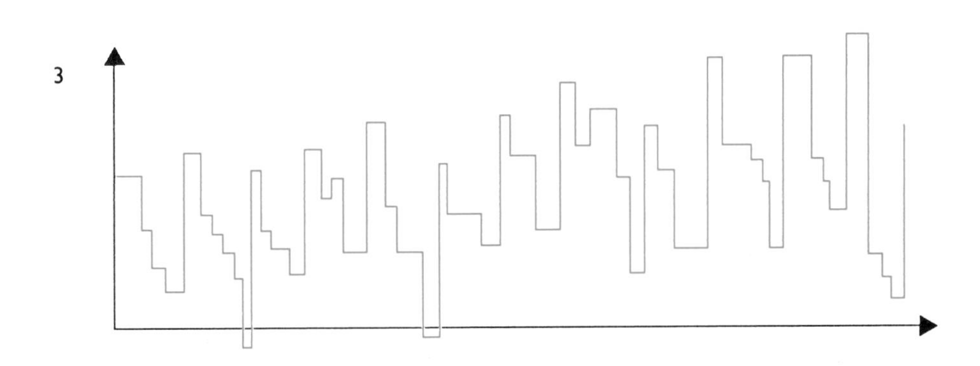

4

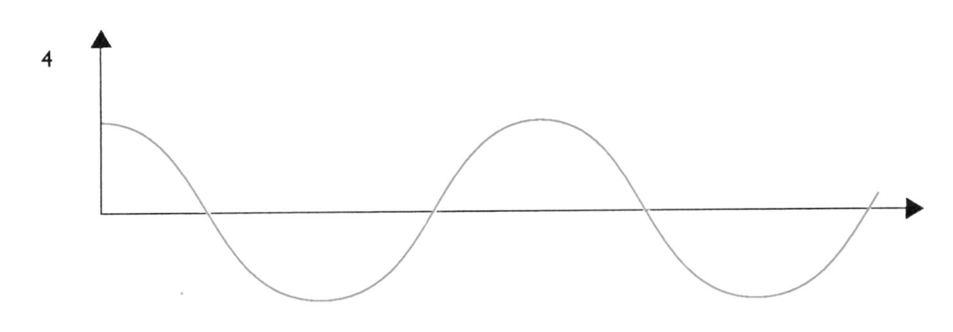

5

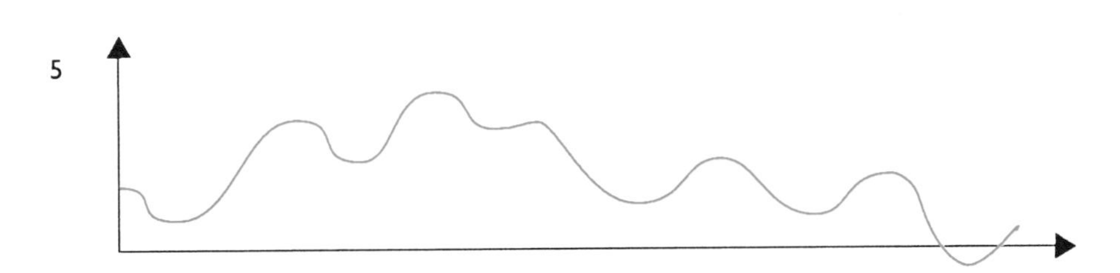

3 Draw a sketch graph for each of the following situations:

(*a*) the speed during a journey on a public bus service;

(*b*) the distance from the nearest SOS phone for a car travelling at constant speed along a motorway, if the SOS phones are at equal intervals along the motorway;

(*c*) the height of a tennis ball after it is dropped onto a horizontal concrete surface.

(*d*) the time of sunrise over a four-year period (where you live).

(*e*) the time of sunset over a four-year period (where you live).

4 Three people were asked to describe the pattern of daylight in Birmingham and to say how often the pattern repeated.

The first answer was 'every day'.

The second answer was 'every week'.

The third answer was 'every year'.

(*a*) Two of these answers are correct in a way. Which two?

(*b*) Explain your answer to part (*a*).

5 (*a*) How many hours during a year is it daylight?

(*b*) What assumption did you make?

(*c*) Is your assumption reasonable?

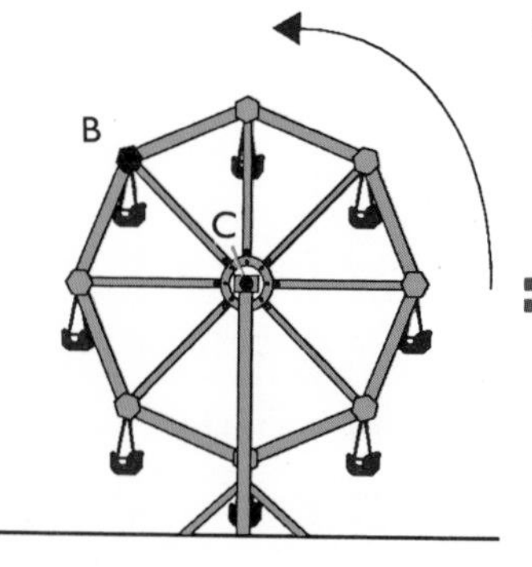

6 A big wheel is travelling at constant speed.

One of the graphs below shows the angle the spoke, CB, makes with the vertical during three complete turns of the wheel.

The other graph shows the height of basket B above the ground during three complete turns of the wheel.

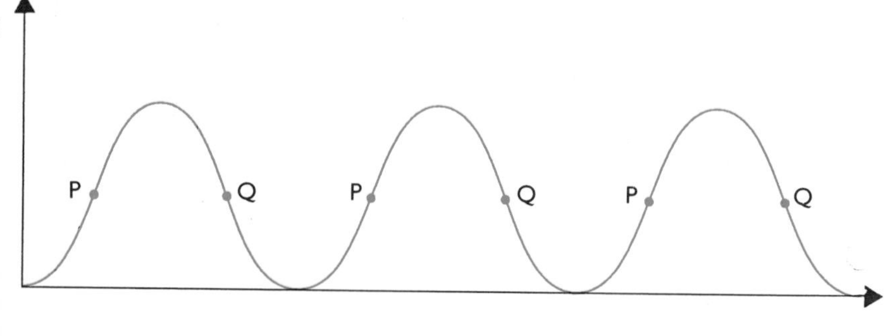

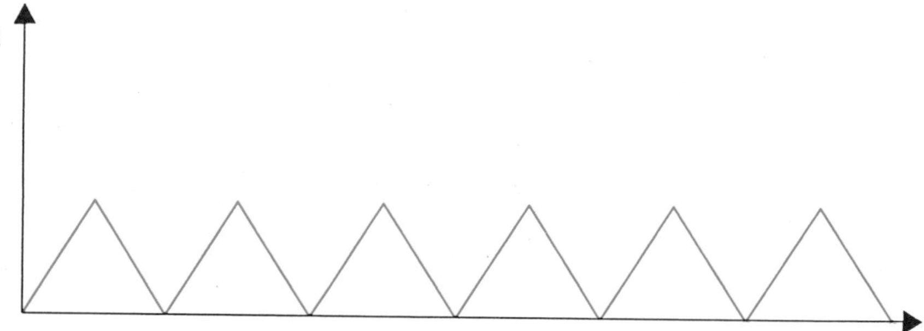

(*a*) Which of the graphs is which? Give a reason for your answer.

(*b*) Where was the basket at the time when the graph starts?

(*c*) Where is the basket B at the points labelled P? Where is it at the points labelled Q? Explain why the graph is steepest at these points?

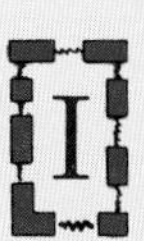

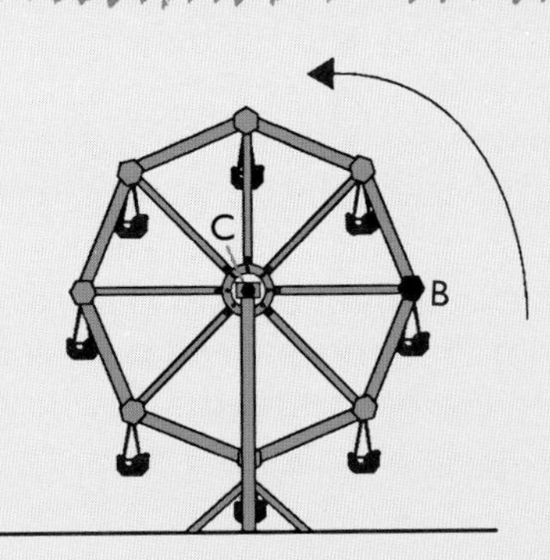

The radius of the wheel is 10 m. This time basket B starts in the position shown above.

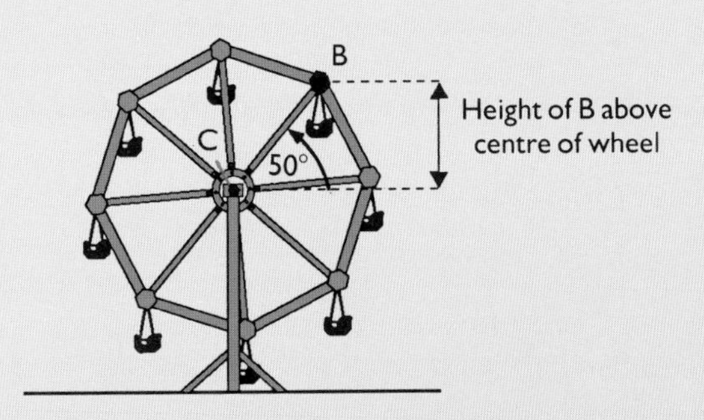

After the wheel has turned through 50° the height of B above the **centre** of the wheel can be found using the sin button on your calculator.

Make sure that your calculator is in 'degrees' mode.

Enter 50 into the calculator. Press the sin button. Then multiply the answer by 10, the radius of the wheel. This should give you an answer of approximately 7.7. So the height of B above the centre of the wheel is 7.7 m.

The number you get when you enter 50 into a calculator and press the sin button is called the sine of 50° and is written as sin 50°.

So the height of B above the centre is $10 \times \sin 50°\ m = 7.7$ m approximately.

This method was first introduced in Chapter 2 (on page 18 of Book 4).

7 (*a*) Find the height of the basket above the centre after the wheel has turned through

(i) 30°, (ii) 120°, (iii) 300°, (iv) 500°.

(*b*) What angle does the wheel turn through before basket B is again level with the centre of the wheel? Check that your calculator agrees with your answer.

(*c*) (i) What is the greatest height for B above the centre of the wheel?
(ii) When does this occur? Check that your calculator agrees.
(iii) What does this tell you about the greatest value you can get from using sin ?

(*d*) Draw a graph of the height of basket B above the centre, using a graphical calculator or a graph-drawing program on a computer. (Use the formula in the box immediately before this question.)

The graph should look rather like one of the graphs in question 6.

SECTION B

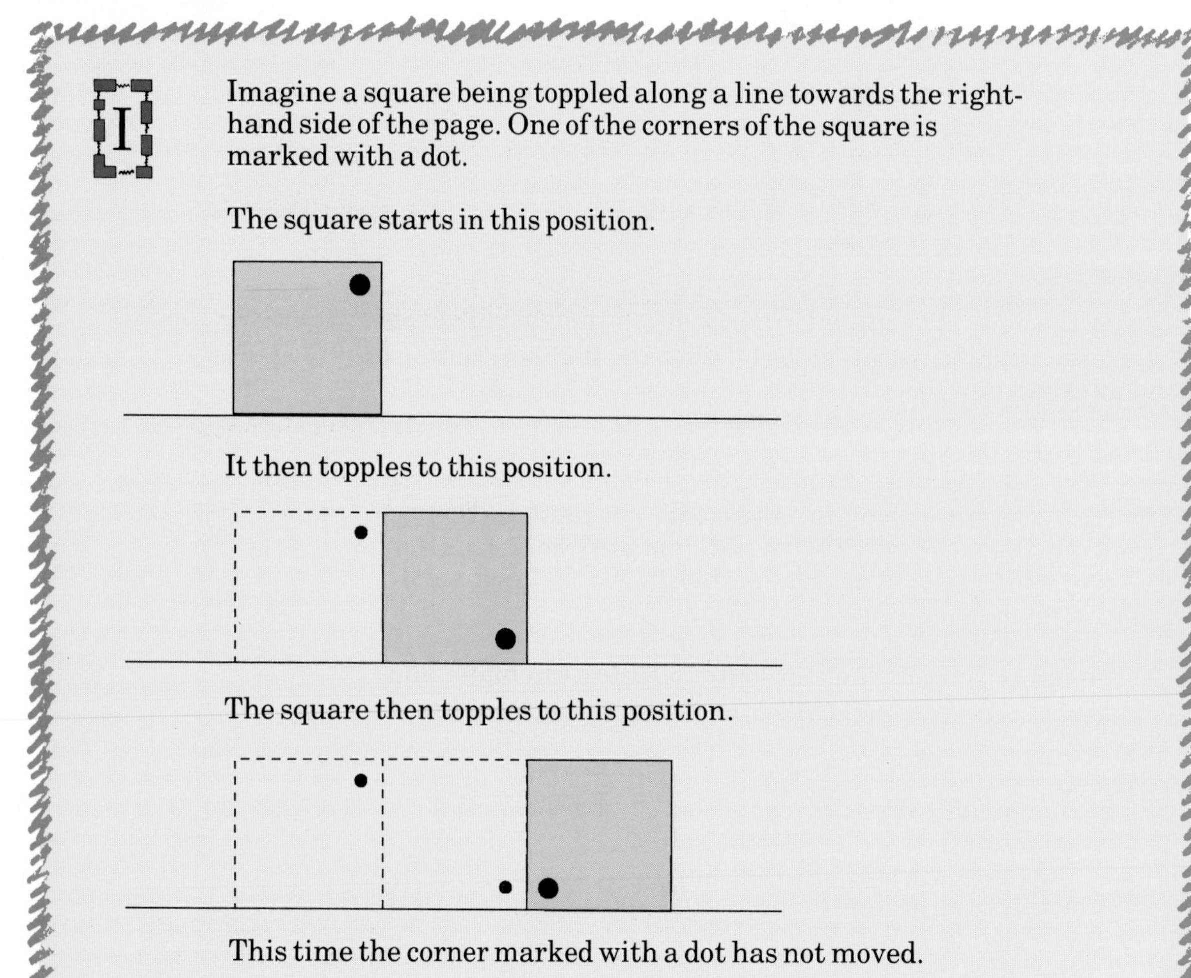

Imagine a square being toppled along a line towards the right-hand side of the page. One of the corners of the square is marked with a dot.

The square starts in this position.

It then topples to this position.

The square then topples to this position.

This time the corner marked with a dot has not moved.

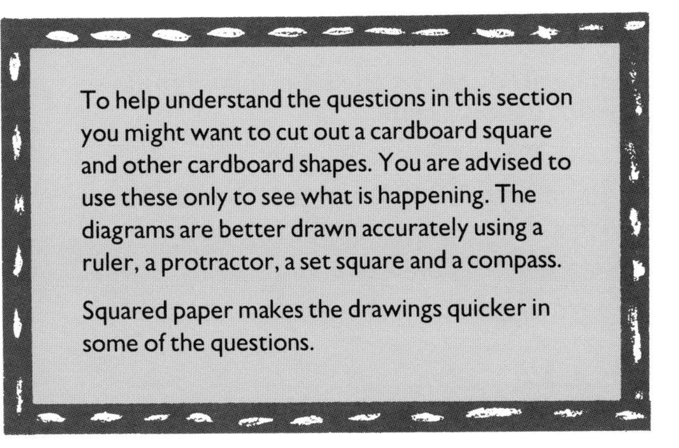

To help understand the questions in this section you might want to cut out a cardboard square and other cardboard shapes. You are advised to use these only to see what is happening. The diagrams are better drawn accurately using a ruler, a protractor, a set square and a compass.

Squared paper makes the drawings quicker in some of the questions.

1 A square with sides of length 2 cm, and with one corner marked with a dot, is toppled as described in the box above.

(*a*) Copy the diagram on page 150, and complete it to show the position of the square after the first four topples. At each stage show the position of the corner marked with a dot.

(*b*) What angle does the square turn through at each topple?

(*c*) Two people are asked how often the pattern produced by the toppling square repeats.

The first person says it repeats after every topple.

The second person says it repeats after every four topples.

Explain why both of these answers are correct in different ways.

2 Figure 1 shows a rectangle 4 cm by 2 cm. One of the corners is marked with a dot.

Figure 1

(*a*) The rectangle is toppled towards the right-hand side of the page. Draw accurately a diagram showing its starting position, and its positions after the first four topples. At each stage show the position of the corner marked with the dot.

(*b*) What angle does the rectangle turn through at each topple?

(*c*) How often does the sequence produced by the toppling rectangle repeat? Give two answers to this question and explain how they are both correct in different ways.

3

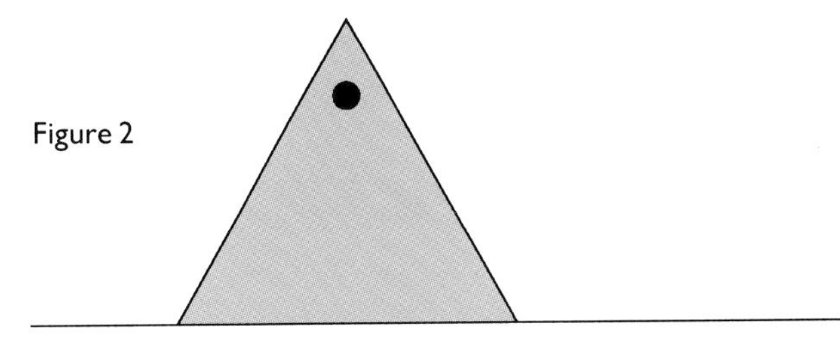

Figure 2

Figure 2 shows an equilateral triangle.

(*a*) The triangle is toppled towards the right-hand side of the page. Draw accurately a diagram showing its starting position and its positions after the first four topples. Show the position of the marked corner at each stage.

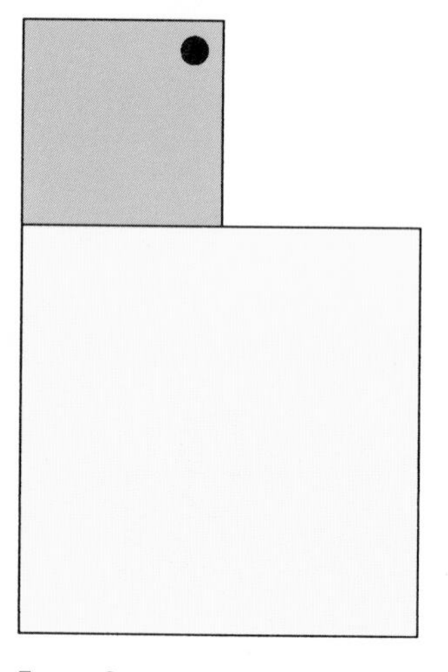
Figure 3

(*b*) What angle does the triangle turn through at each topple?

(*c*) How often does the sequence produced by the toppling triangle repeat? Give two answers to this question.

4 The smaller square (with sides of length 2 cm) in figure 3 is toppled around the larger square (with sides of length 4 cm). Again one corner of the smaller square is marked with a dot.

Figure 4 shows the small square toppling all the way round the big square.

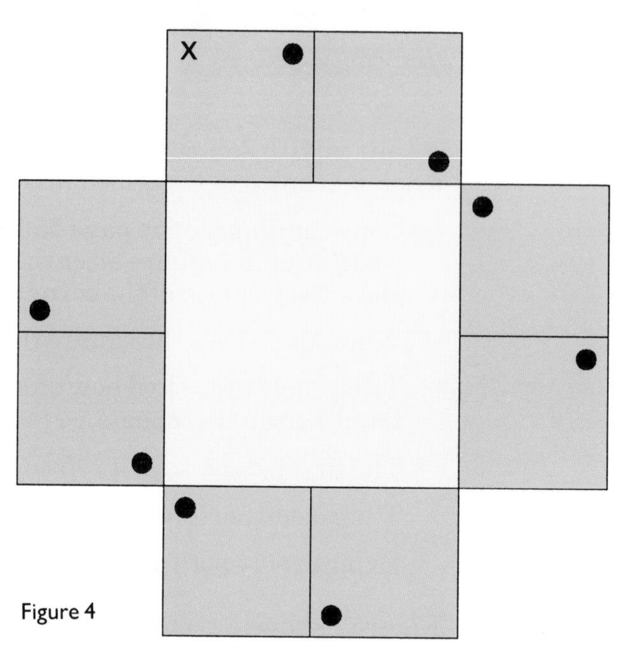

Figure 4

(*a*) Copy figure 4 onto squared paper.

Add crosses to the picture to show the position of the corner marked with the cross at each stage.

(*b*) What angle does the square turn through at each topple? (It is not always the same angle.)

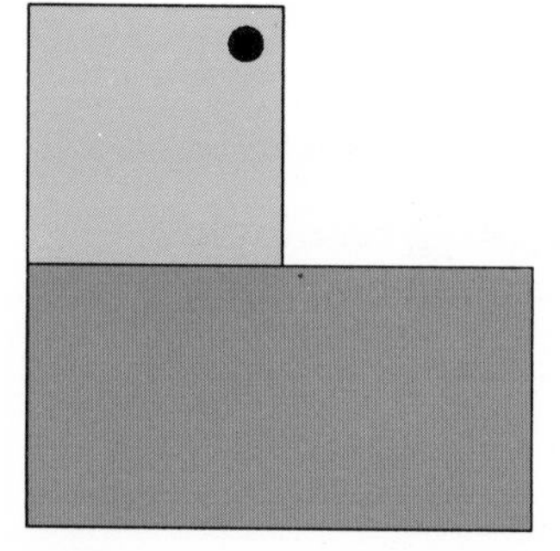
Figure 5

5 The square (with sides of length 2 cm) in figure 5 is toppled around the rectangle (which is 4 cm by 2 cm). One corner of the square is marked.

Figure 6 shows the position of the square after the first two topples.

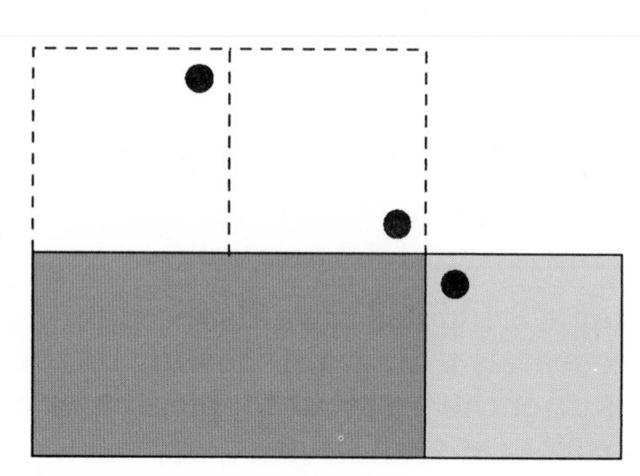
Figure 6

(*a*) Draw accurately a diagram showing the position of the square as it topples all the way round the rectangle.

(*b*) What is the *total* angle the square turns through as it topples all the way round the rectangle?

(*c*) After how many topples does the pattern repeat?

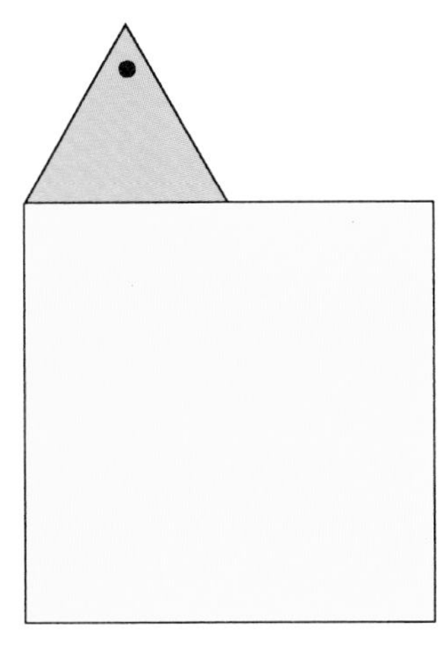

Figure 7

6 The triangle in figure 7 is toppled around the square. One corner of the triangle is marked.

Figure 8 shows the position of the triangle after the first two topples.

(*a*) Draw accurately a diagram showing the position of the triangle as it topples all the way round the square.

(*b*) What is the *total* angle the triangle turns through as it topples all the way round the square?

(*c*) After how many topples does the pattern repeat?

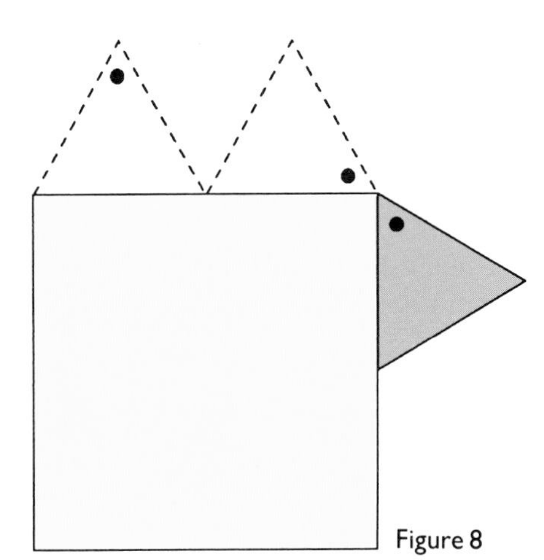

Figure 8

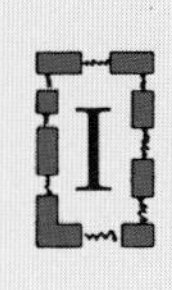

Figure 9 shows the first three stages of a square being toppled along a line.

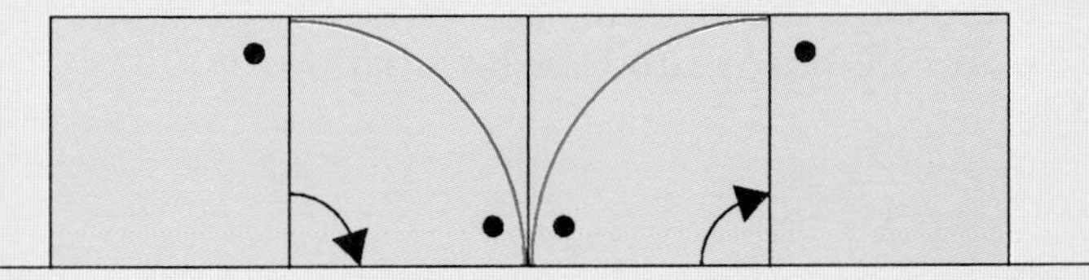

Figure 9

The path (often called the **locus**) of one of the corners is shown. This path is made up of the arcs of circles.

The centres of these arcs are the corners about which the square is turning when it topples.

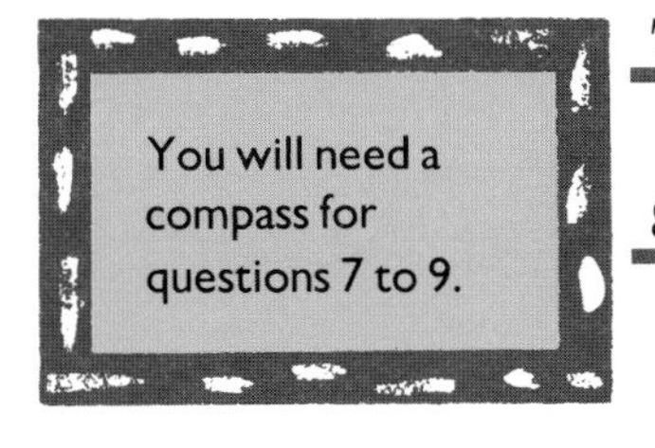

7 Draw accurately the diagram shown in the box above, and add the fourth stage of the toppling.

8 (*a*) Add to the drawing you did for question 2 the locus of the corner marked with a dot.

(*b*) Add to the drawing you did for question 3 the locus of the corner marked with a dot.

(*c*) Add to the drawings you did for questions 4, 5 and 6 the locus of the corner marked with a dot.

9 (*a*) Add to the drawing you did for question 7 the locus of the centre of the square.

(*b*) Add to the drawing you did for question 2 the locus of the centre of the rectangle.

You will need to use Pythagoras' theorem to calculate some lengths in questions 10 to 12. You can find this on page 281. You will also need the formula for the circumference of a circle.

10 A square of side 2 cm is toppled along a straight line. After four topples it has turned completely round once.

(*a*) How far is the square from its starting position after four topples?

(*b*) What is the total length of the locus of the centre of the square during the four topples?

(*c*) What is the total length of the locus of one of the corners of the square during the four topples?

(*d*) Does each of the corners move the same distance during the four topples? Give a reason for your answer.

11 The 4 cm by 2 cm rectangle of question 2 has turned completely round once after four topples.

(*a*) How far is the rectangle from its starting position after four topples?

(*b*) What is the total length of the locus of the centre of the rectangle during the four topples?

(*c*) What is the total length of the locus of one of the corners of the rectangle during the four topples?

(*d*) Does each of the corners move the same distance during the four topples? Give a reason for your answer.

12 What is the length of the locus of each corner of the small square of question 4 as it rolls once round the large square?

13

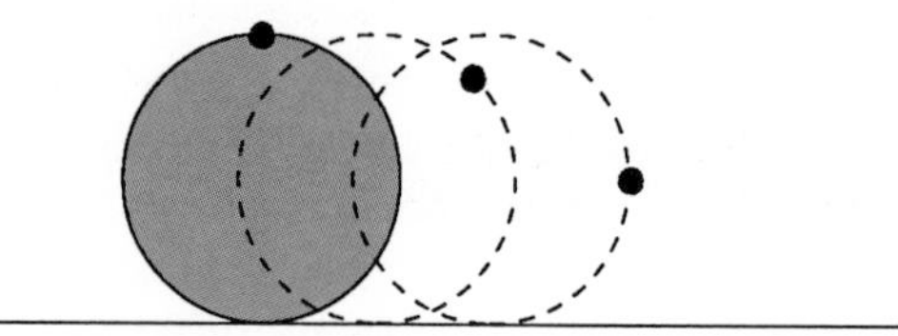

Figure 10

A circle of radius 2 cm, shown in figure 10, is rolling along a straight line. One of the points of the circle's circumference is marked with a dot.

Figure 10 shows three positions of the circle.

(*a*) Draw several positions to show a complete turn of this circle as it rolls along the line.

(*b*) Draw the locus of the centre of the rolling circle.

(*c*) Draw the locus of the marked point on the circumference of the rolling circle. This locus is *not* the arc of a circle.

(*d*) Calculate the distance through which the centre of the rolling circle moves as the circle turns round once.

(*e*) Estimate the distance through which a point on the circumference of the rolling circle moves as the circle turns round once.

Suppose a circle of radius 1 starts rolling towards the left-hand side of the page.

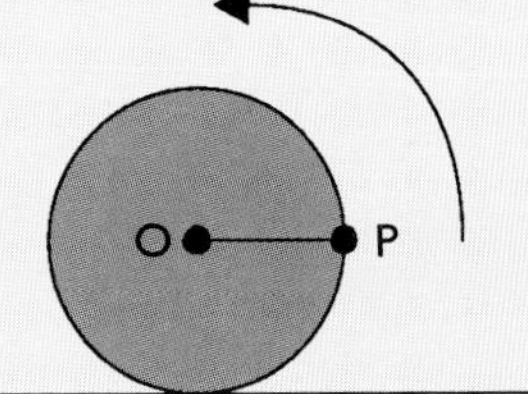

One of the points of the circumference is marked. At the start the radius to this point is horizontal. After the circle has turned through $x°$ the point will be a certain distance *above* the centre O and a certain distance to the *right* of the centre O.

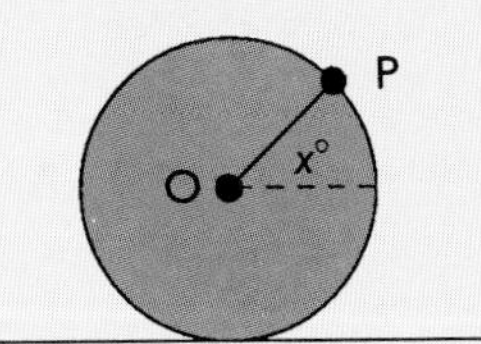

The distance *above* the centre can be found as in question 7 of Section A. It is $\sin x$.

The distance *to the right* of the centre can also be found by using a calculator, but the cos button needs to be used instead of the sin button. The distance is called the cosine of x and is usually written $\cos x$.

The graph below labelled **A** shows the point's distance *above* the centre, plotted against the angle. The equation of this graph is $y = \sin x$. The graph below labelled **B** shows the point's distance to the *right* of the centre, plotted against the angle. The equation of this graph is $y = \cos x$.

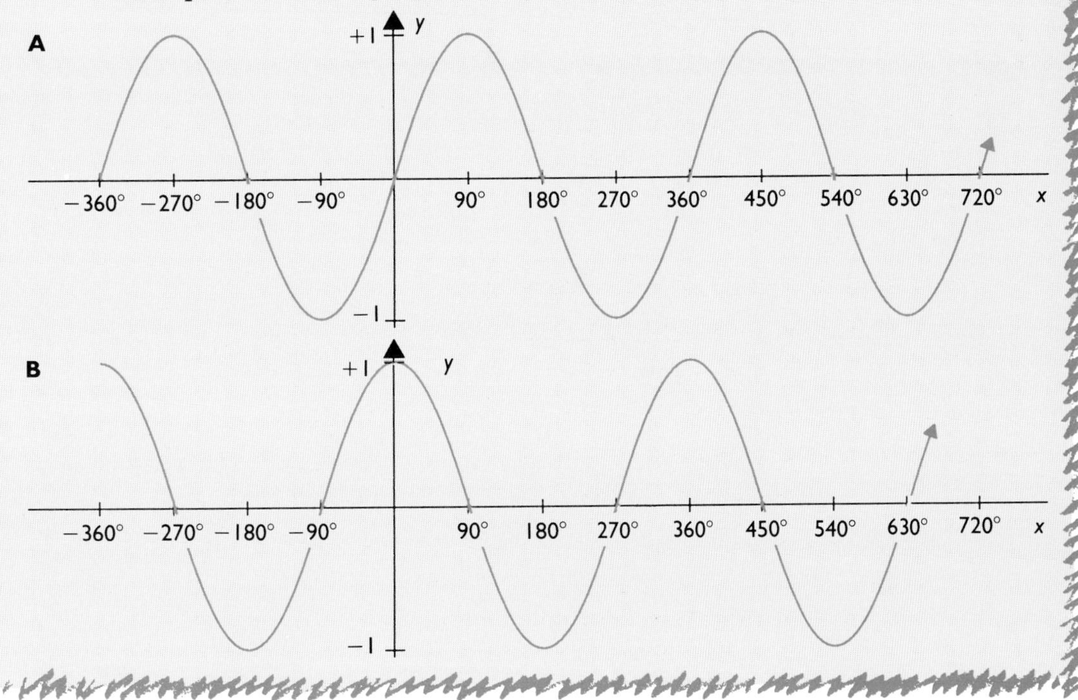

14 (*a*) Both graphs appear to repeat themselves every 360°. Explain this in terms of the rolling circle.

(*b*) (i) Rolling through an angle of 50° has been used to mean rolling to the *left* through an angle of 50°. What meaning might be given to rolling through an angle of −50°.
(ii) Look at the graph of $y = \cos x$. The y-axis is a line of symmetry of this graph.
Use your answer to part (i) to help you explain this symmetry.
(iii) The graph of $y = \sin x$ has rotational symmetry about the origin.
Use your answer to part (i) to help you explain this symmetry.

(*c*) What connection does there appear to be between the graph of $y = \cos x$ and the graph of $y = \sin x$?

15

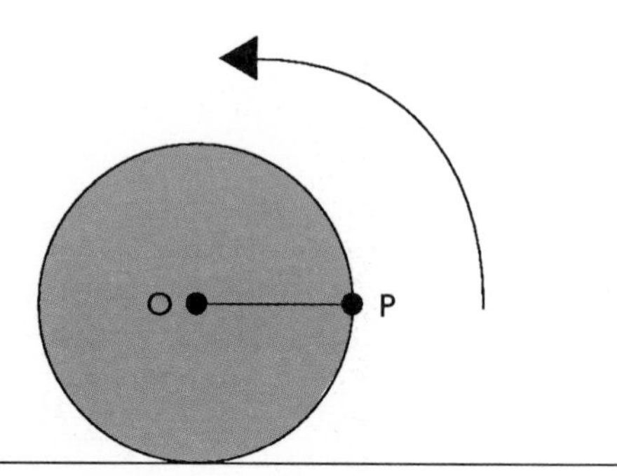

Figure 11

Figure 11 shows the starting position of a circle of radius 1.

The circle rotates anticlockwise about its centre O.

(*a*) When the circle has rotated through 70°, how far to the *right* of the centre will the point P be?

(*b*) When the circle has rotated through 135°, how far *above* the centre will the point P be?

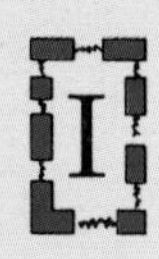

Figure 12 shows the circle of question 15 after it has rotated through 50°. The point Q is the position on the tangent which is on the same straight line as O and P.

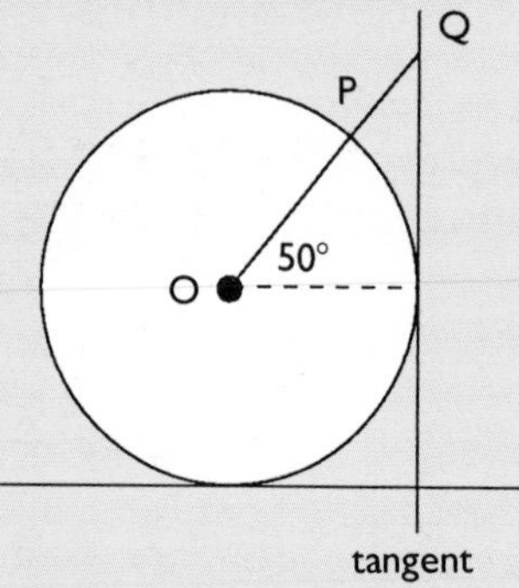

Figure 12

As the circle rotates Q moves along the tangent so that O, P and Q are always in a straight line.

16 

(*a*) Where is Q when the circle is in the starting position?

(*b*) What happens to Q when the circle has nearly turned through 90°?

(*c*) Where is Q when the circle has turned through a little more than 90°?

(*d*) Where is Q when the circle has turned through 180°?

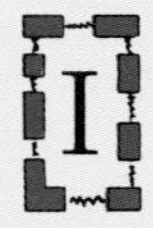

The distance of Q from its starting point can be found using the [tan] button on your calculator.

When the circle has turned through 50° the distance of Q from its starting point is found by putting 50 into the calculator and pressing [tan].

This number is called the tangent of 50° and is written tan 50°. So the distance of Q from its starting point is tan 50° = 1.2 approximately.

(*e*) Find the distance of Q from its starting point when the circle has turned through 70°.

(*f*) Find the distance of Q from its starting point when the circle has turned through 135°.

(*g*) Give an explanation of the negative answer the calculator gives for part (*f*)

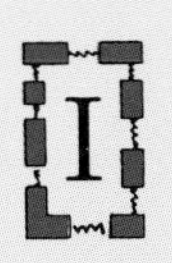

In Chapter 10 (on page 155 of Book 4 of this series) the [tan] button was used to find the ratio of two sides of a right-angled triangle.

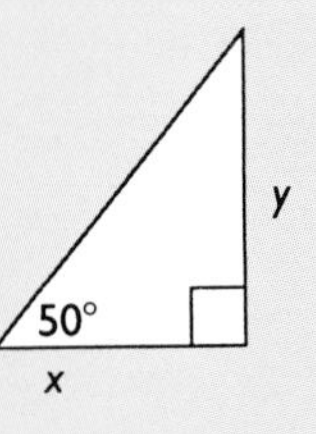

In the triangle above the fraction $\frac{y}{x}$ is tan 50° = 1.2 approximately. This means that, if x is 1, y is 1.2.

The drawing below shows the connection between this use of tangent and the use in question 16.

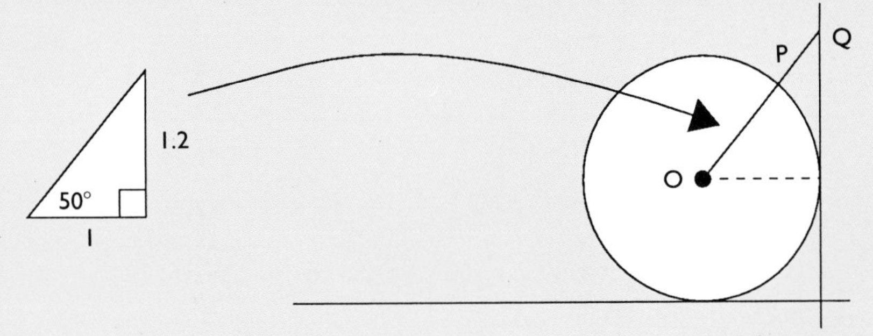

17 Use a graphical calculator, or a graph-drawing program on a computer, to draw a graph of $y = \tan x$. Make sure that the calculator or the program is in 'degrees mode'.

Explain what happens to the graph when x is 90°, 270°, and so on, by referring to point Q in question 16.

1⟩ Investigate what happens when polygons are rolled round other polygons.

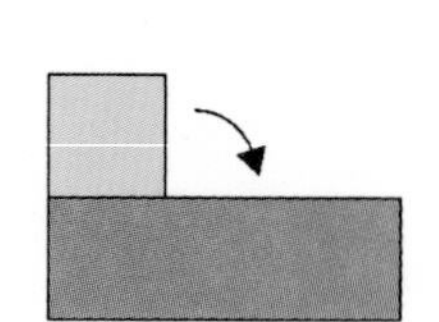
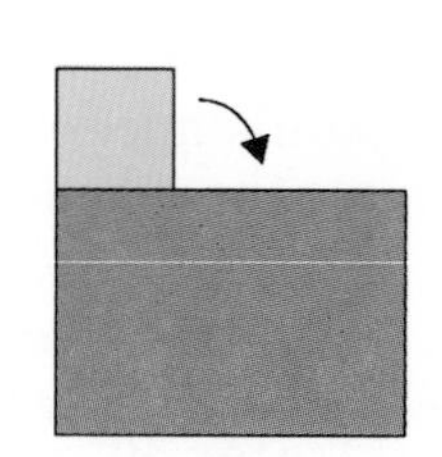
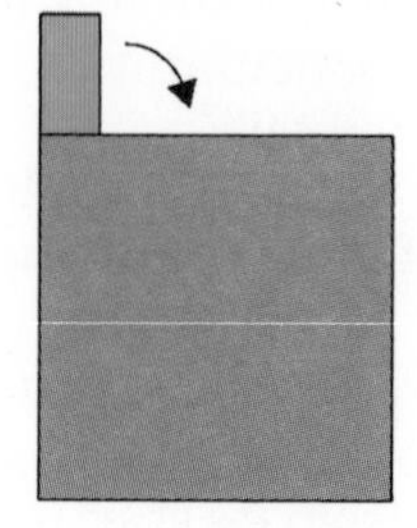
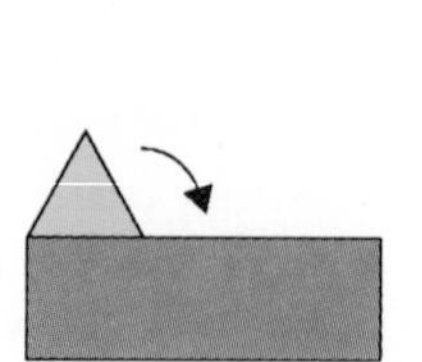
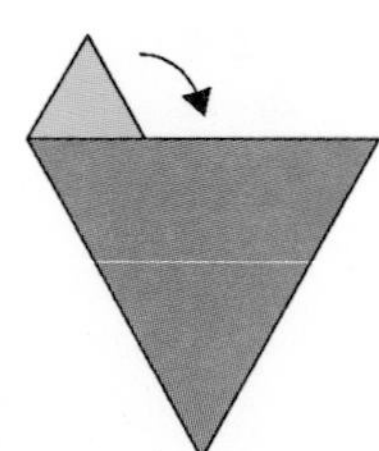

There are many questions to explore. How many times does the toppling polygon need to go round the fixed polygon before the pattern repeats? How far does each vertex of the toppling polygon move? How far does the centre of the toppling polygon move?

If you explore systematically you might discover some rules about the answers to these questions. For example, you could look at squares toppling round rectangles; or triangles toppling round squares; or triangles toppling round triangles; or regular polygons toppling round identical regular polygons.

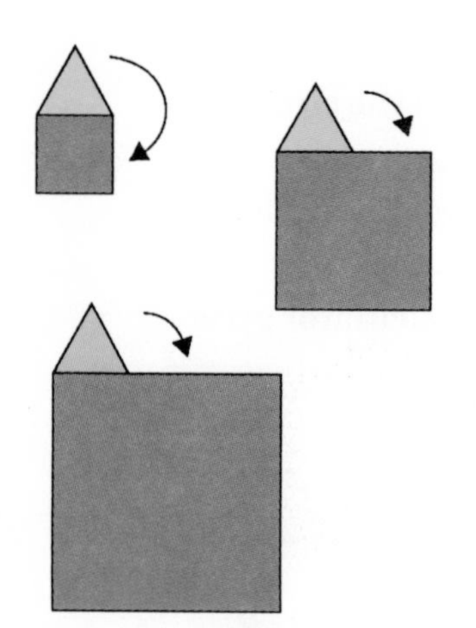

Triangles toppling round squares

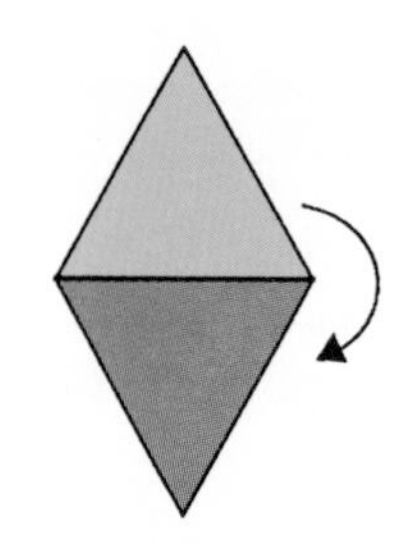
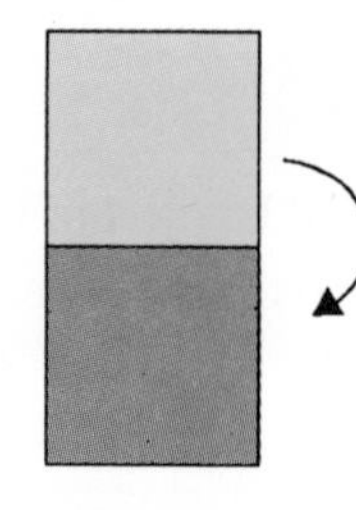
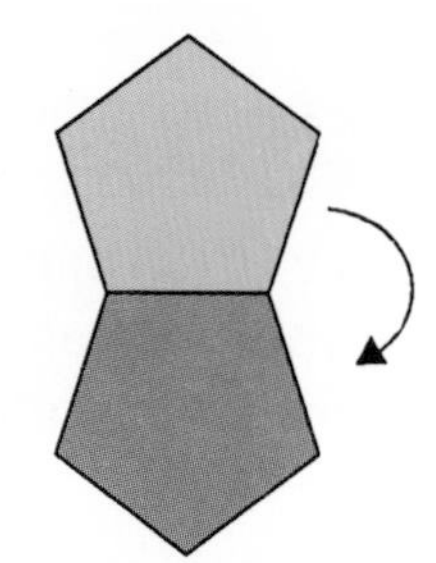
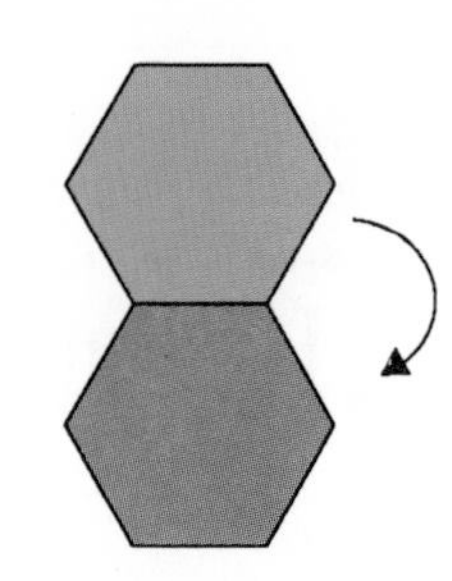

Regular polygons toppling round identical regular polygons.

2⟩ Explore what happens when different shapes are toppled along a line.

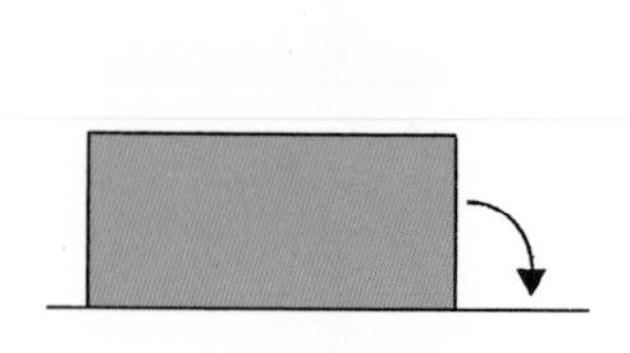
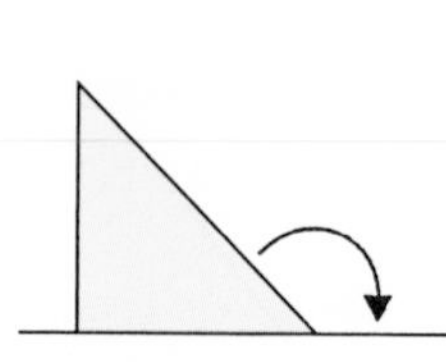
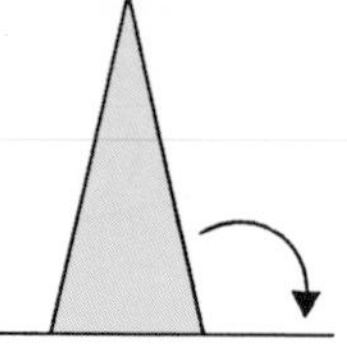
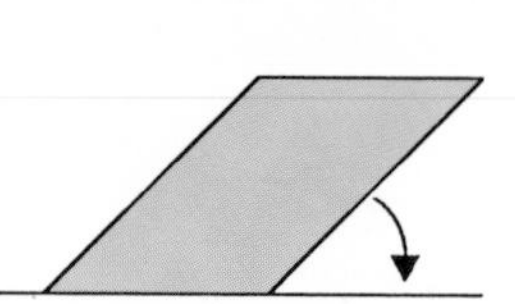
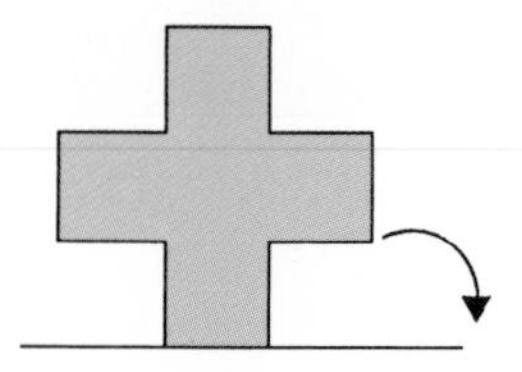

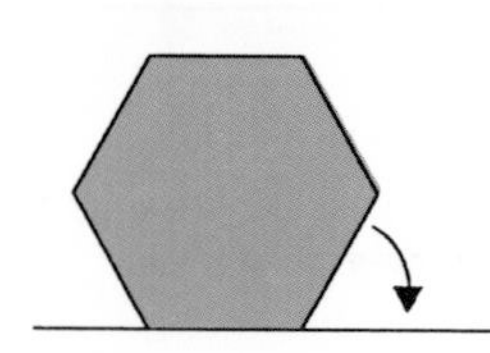

How many topples are needed before the pattern repeats? What is the locus of the different corners of the shape? What is the locus of other points of the shape?

Which point of the shape has the longest locus? Which has the shortest?

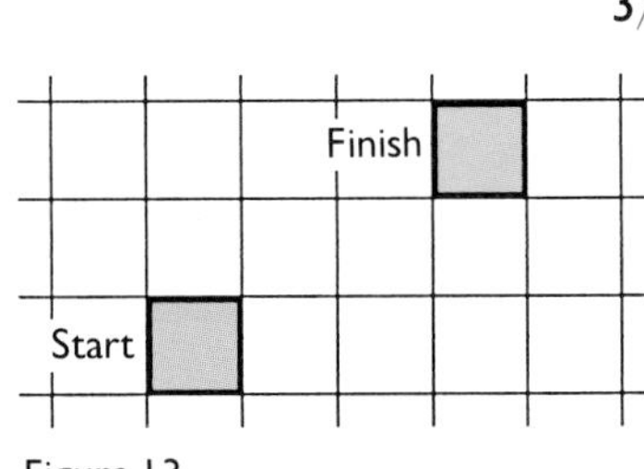

Figure 13

3) Imagine a tea chest in the shape of a cube repeatedly being toppled about one of its edges in a large room.

Suppose it moves from the position labelled *Start* to the position labelled *Finish* in figure 13.

Which way up will the cube be when it arrives at *Finish*? Will it depend on the 'route' it took?

You will need to invent a notation to describe this.

Are there repeating patterns involved in the movement of the cube?

You can, of course, look at different starting and finishing points to see what happens.

You might want to consider the locus of a corner of the cube as it topples from *Start* to *Finish*.

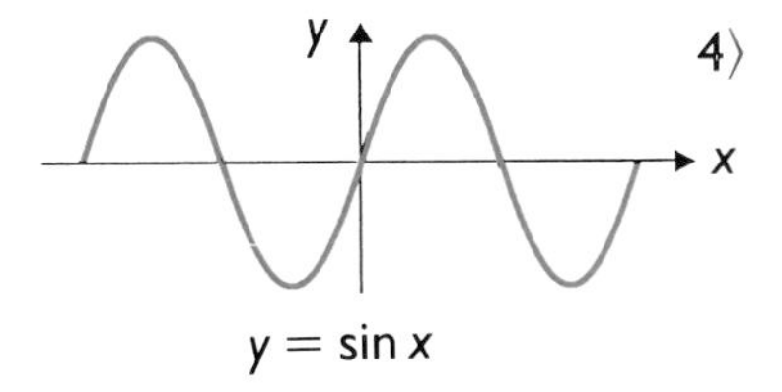

$y = \sin x$

4) Sounds are produced by sound waves. The shapes of waves for musical notes are simpler than shapes of waves for noises. The shape of the wave of a very 'pure' note is a sine graph.

Notes of different pitches have waves of different lengths.

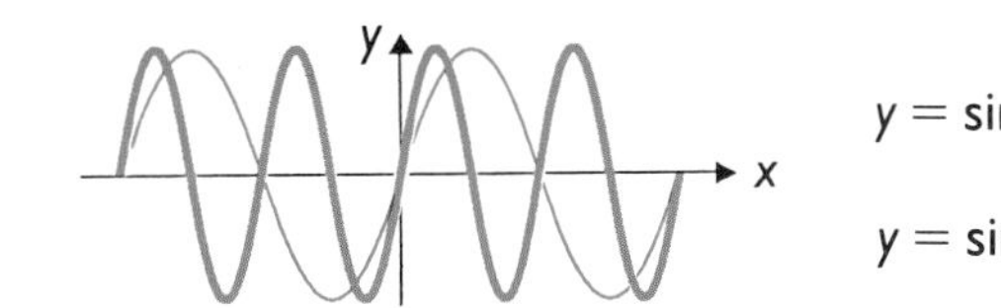

$y = \sin x$

$y = \sin 2x$

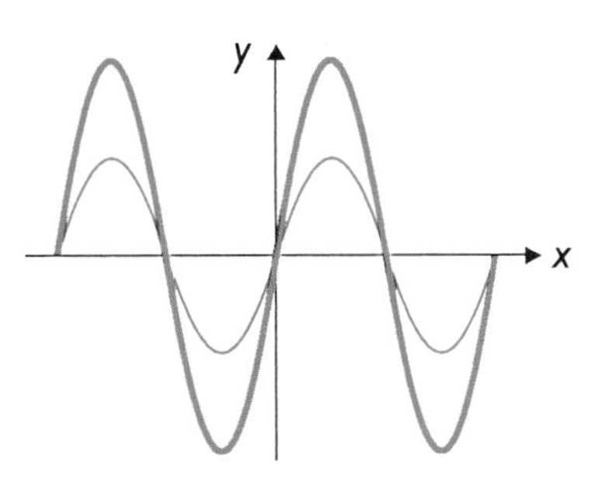

Notes of different loudness have waves of different height.

$y = \sin x$ ——

$y = 2 \sin x$ ——

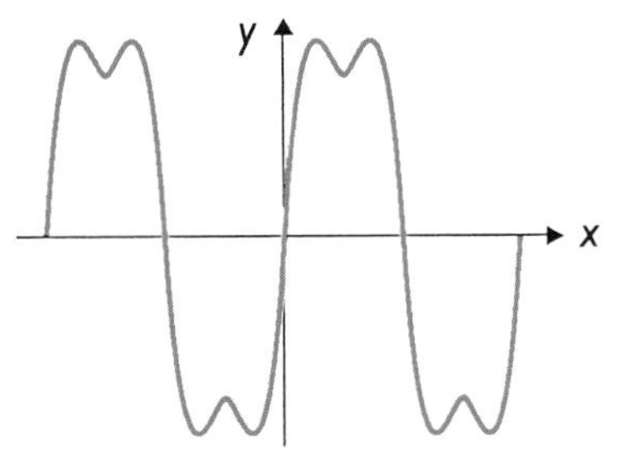

Graphs of interesting shapes can be made by combining sine graphs,

$y = 3 \sin x + \sin 3x$

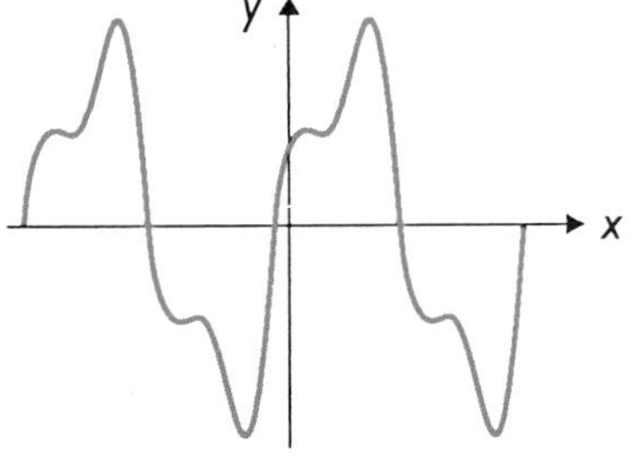

or by combining sine graph with cosine graphs.

$y = 3 \sin x + \cos 3x$

Investigate graphs of this kind. You will probably want to use either a graphical calculator or a graph-drawing program on a computer.

HOW DO YOU DECIDE?

Are the same number of babies born in the Winter as in the Summer?

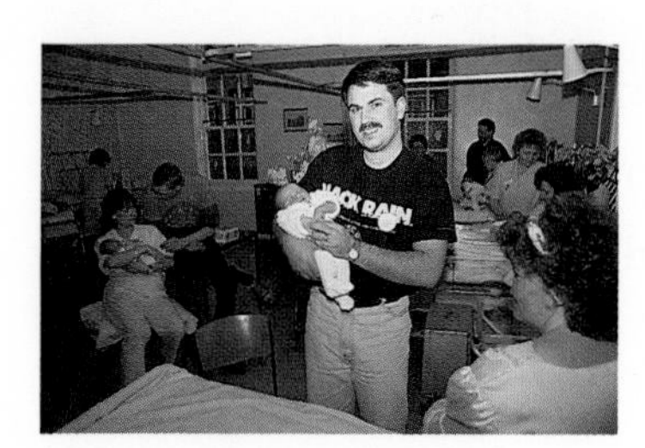

One way of answering this question is to survey a group of people and find out when their birthdays are.

- Collect this information from all members of your class.

Presenting this information as a list of dates is not very interesting, and you will probably not be able to see at a glance how the birthdays are distributed.

One way of making the data easier to read is to put the birthdays into groups.

- Decide whether you want to put people into groups according to the month they were born or according to their birth sign.
- Arrange people in groups according to your decision. Display your results visually; in a barchart, for example.
- What conclusions can you draw from your display? Try answering the following questions.

  Are the same number of people born in the Winter as in the Summer?

  How reliable are your results? What could make them more reliable?

SECTION A

In a statistical survey, information is collected. There are many different ways of displaying that information.

1 40 people were asked which of the following leisure activities they had engaged in during the previous four weeks. The pictogram below shows their replies.

Cinema

Go out for a meal

Go out for a drink

Dancing

Listen to records

Gardening

Reading

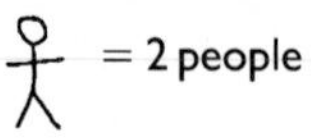

(stick figure) = 2 people

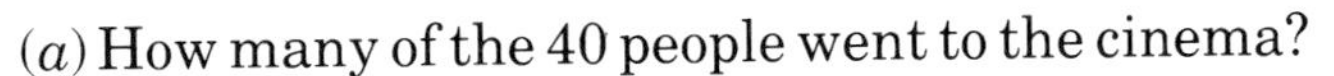

(*a*) How many of the 40 people went to the cinema?

(*b*) What was the most popular leisure activity? How many people engaged in it?

(*c*) Which was more popular: gardening or dancing?

(*d*) If you asked 100 people the same questions how many might you expect to say *yes* to reading? Would you be surprised if exactly that number said *yes* to reading?

2 50 students were asked how they normally travelled to school. Here are their replies.

Cycle	12
Bus	22
Walk	13
Car	3

(*a*) If you show this information on a pictogram, using different symbols for the different ways of travelling, why should all the symbols be the same length?

(*b*) Draw a pictogram to show this information.

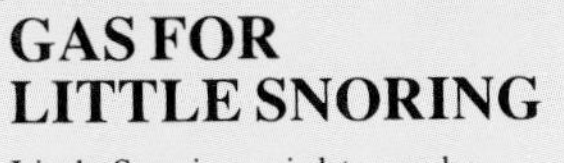
GAS FOR LITTLE SNORING

Little Snoring might soon be getting its own gas supply! Mrs Pamela Smith, who was interviewed by our correspondent, said that there were already provisional plans

3 The pictogram below shows the number of people in two villages who use gas and electricity for cooking.

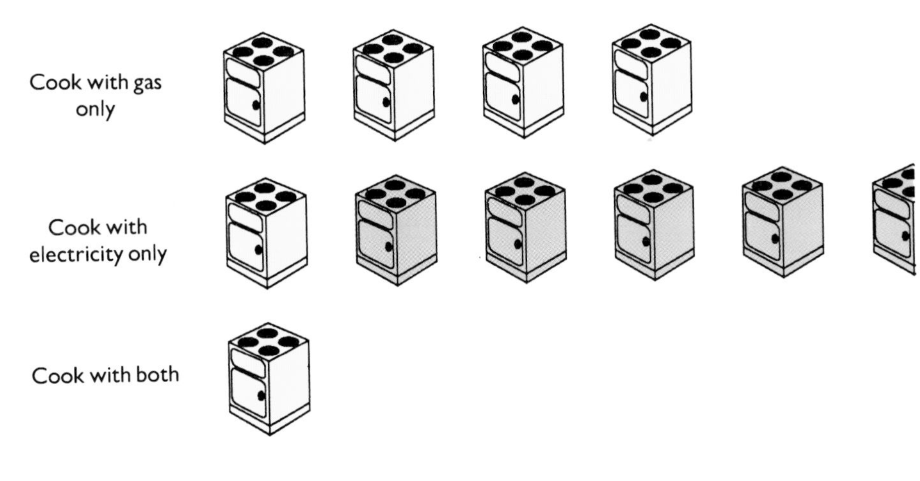

(*a*) How many people in the two villages cook with electricity only?

(*b*) What explanation could you give for the fact that nobody from Little Snoring cooks with gas?

(*c*) Estimate the number of people from Little Snoring who would cook only with gas if they had the choice.

4 25 people were questioned about what they usually had for breakfast. Here are their replies.

Drink only	6
Toast only	5
Cereal only	6
Toast and cereal	2
Cooked breakfast	3

The remainder had no breakfast at all.

Show this information on a barchart. Include on the barchart the people who had no breakfast.

5 40 people were asked to estimate the number of hours they watch television each week. These are their replies.

12, 18, 19, 8, 16, 26, 28, 24, 27, 32, 17, 6, 5, 14, 12, 23, 28, 26, 19, 21, 23, 35, 21, 26, 32, 18, 28, 40, 43, 16, 16, 18, 0, 43, 28, 16, 32, 14, 23, 21.

(*a*) Copy and complete the table below to show the replies of the 40 people.

Number of hours TV viewing	Tally	Frequency
0–4	I	
5–9	III	
10–14		
15–19		
20–24		
25–29		
30–34		
35–39		
40–44	III	3

(*b*) According to *Social Trends 19*, 'in 1987 the average weekly time spent watching the television was 25 hours and 25 minutes per head.' Can you judge from your table whether the 40 people questioned were above or below the national 'average' in the amount of television they watched?

(*c*) How many hours do you watch TV in a typical week?

(*d*) How accurate do you think your answer is to part (*c*)?

6 (*a*) The chart below shows the number of people using a branch library at different hours on a typical *Wednesday*.

Time	Number of people
9 a.m. – 11 a.m.	21
11 a.m. – 1 p.m.	37
1 p.m. – 3 p.m.	53
3 p.m. – 5 p.m.	19

(i) During which time period do most people use the library on a Wednesday?
(ii) How many people use this branch library on a typical Wednesday?

(*b*) The charts below show the use of this library on other days of the week.

Monday	
Time	**Number of people**
9 a.m. – 11 a.m.	7
11 a.m. – 1 p.m.	34
1 p.m. – 3 p.m.	20
3 p.m. – 5 p.m.	5
Tuesday	
Time	**Number of people**
9 a.m. – 11 a.m.	19
11 a.m. – 1 p.m.	28
1 p.m. – 3 p.m.	38
3 p.m. – 5 p.m.	21
Thursday	
Time	**Number of people**
9 a.m. – 11 a.m.	18
11 a.m. – 1 p.m.	30
1 p.m. – 3 p.m.	43
3 p.m. – 5 p.m.	6
Friday	
Time	**Number of people**
9 a.m. – 11 a.m.	12
11 a.m. – 1 p.m.	18
1 p.m. – 3 p.m.	55
3 p.m. – 5 p.m.	39
Saturday	
Time	**Number of people**
9 a.m. – 11 a.m.	48
11 a.m. – 1 p.m.	88

(i) On which day do fewest people use the library?
(ii) On which day do most people use the library?
(iii) On which afternoon (after 1 p.m.) do most people use the library?
(iv) Do more people use the library during the morning (before 1 p.m.) or during the afternoon (after 1 p.m.)?

(c) The library wishes to save some money by reducing the opening hours.

A number of different suggestions for saving money have been made. These are listed below. Place these suggestions in order, starting with the one you think is best.

A Close the library every day at 3 p.m. instead of 5 p.m.
B Close the library all day Monday.
C Close the library all day Friday.
D Close the library on Tuesday and Thursday afternoons.
E Open the library every day at 11 a.m. instead of 9 a.m.
F Close the library on Saturday.

(*d*) There has been another suggestion to close the library all day Monday and Friday morning and open it on Saturday afternoons instead.

(i) Why do you think this suggestion was made?
(ii) Who might not be in favour of this suggestion?

Question 2 was about the way in which 50 students normally travel to school.

Cycle	12
Bus	22
Walk	13
Car	3

This information can be shown on a pie chart.

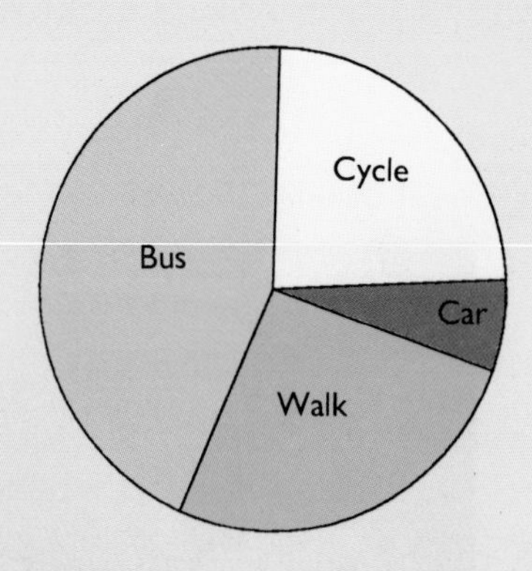

The area of each section of the pie is proportional to the number of students it represents. For example, $\frac{12}{50}$ of the pie represents students who cycle.

To draw a pie like this you need to calculate the angles at its centre. Because there are 360° round the centre and 50 students, you first calculate $360 \div 50$. This gives the angle for one student. To find the angle for the 12 students who cycle you multiply this by 12. This gives 86°, correct to the nearest degree.

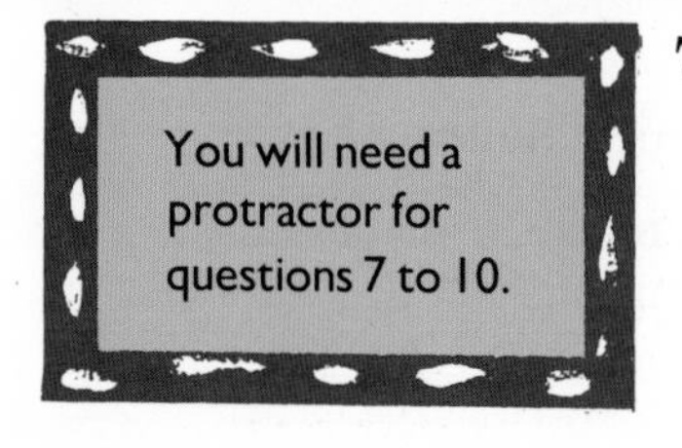

7 The pie chart below shows how a different group of 40 students travel to school.

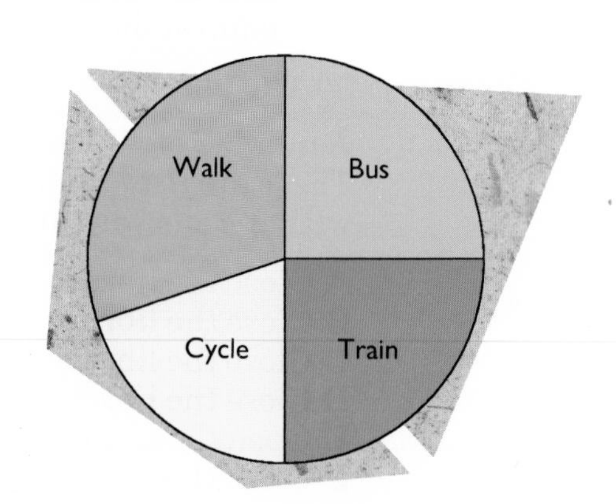

(*a*) Which of the four ways of travelling to school is the most common?

(*b*) What fraction of students travel by bus?

(*c*) How many students cycle?

8 30 people were asked their favourite sport. The table below gives their replies.

Tennis	6
Football	8
Snooker	10
Badminton	3
Basketball	3

Draw a pie chart to display this information.

9 In Britain 57% of the people who smoke are men and 43% are women.

Draw a pie chart to show this information.

10 The pie chart shown below shows the percentage of books of different types available in public libraries.

(*a*) What percentage of the books available are for reference?

(*b*) What percentage of the books available are for adult borrowing?

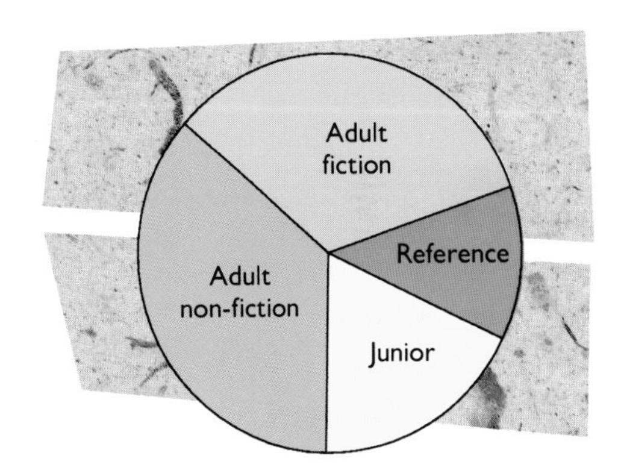

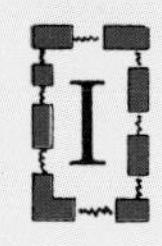

The graph on the right is a bar graph and frequency polygon showing the Wednesday use of the library in question 6.

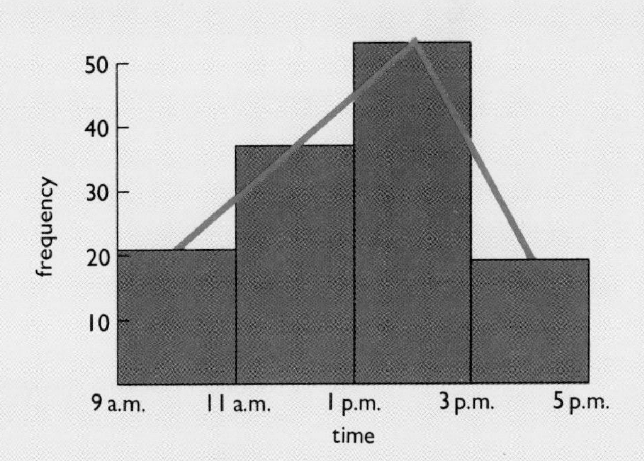

The graph on the left is a frequency polygon showing the Monday use of the library.

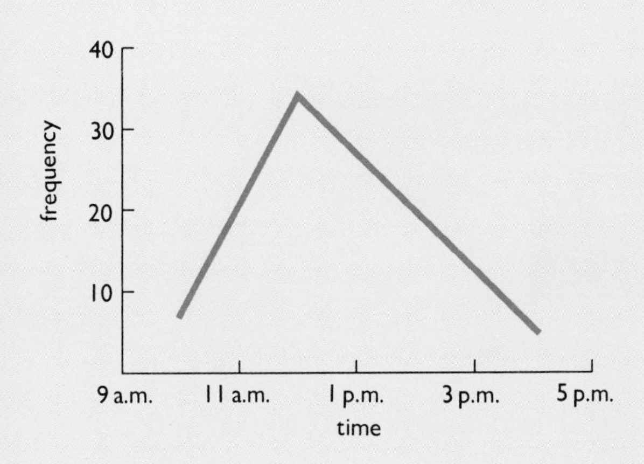

11 (*a*) Draw a frequency polygon showing the Tuesday use of the library of question 6.

(*b*) Draw a frequency polygon showing the Thursday use of the library.

(*c*) On the same graph as for Thursday show the Friday use of the library.

12 The frequency polygon below shows the rise in the number of people from the United Kingdom taking holidays abroad between 1976 and 1987.

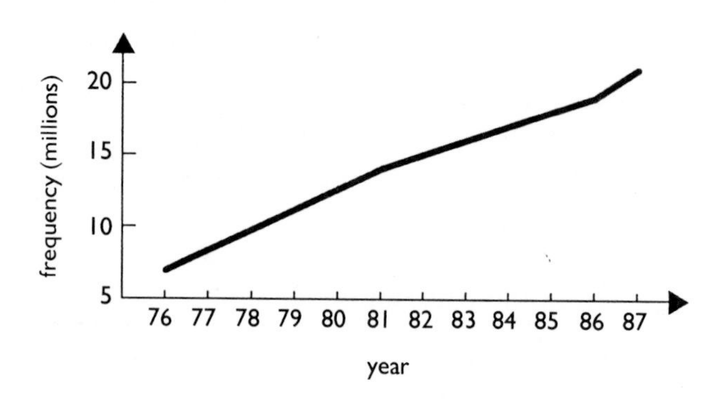

(*a*) How many people took a holiday abroad in 1986?

(*b*) What was the percentage rise between 1986 and 1987?

(*c*) How does the frequency polygon exaggerate the rise between 1976 and 1987?

(*d*) The total population of the United Kingdom in 1987 was 57 million. What percentage of the population took a holiday abroad in that year?

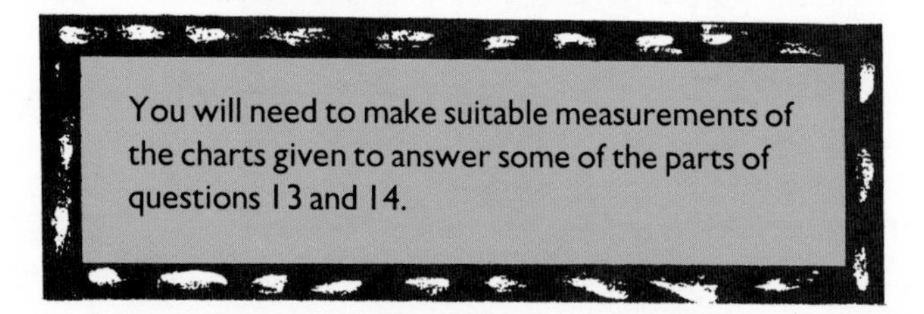

13 The chart below shows how the land area of Britain is divided between England, Wales and Scotland.

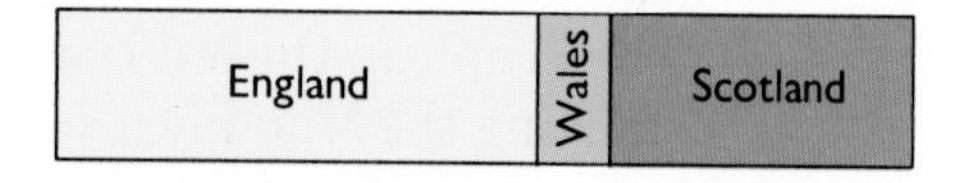

(*a*) Which of the three countries in Britain has the largest land area?

(*b*) What percentage of the total land area of Britain is in Scotland?

(*c*) The total land area of Britain is 230 000 km^2. What is the approximate land area of Wales?

14 The diagrams below show the proportions of the male and female populations of different ages in the United Kingdom in mid-1987.

Male	0–14 yrs	15–29 yrs	30–44 yrs	45–64 yrs	65+ yrs
Female	0–14 yrs	15–29 yrs	30–44 yrs	45–64 yrs	65+ yrs

(a) Why do you think the charts are of different lengths?

(*b*) What percentage of the male population was over 15?

(*c*) What percentage of the total population was over 65?

(*d*) If the total population in mid-1987 was 57 million, what was the approximate male population at that time?

(*e*) Why are the figures described as referring to 'mid-1987' and not simply to '1987'?

15 One way of measuring the influence of a newspaper is to find out how many people read it. The barchart below shows how many men and women regularly read the Sun, the Mail, the Telegraph or the Guardian in 1987.

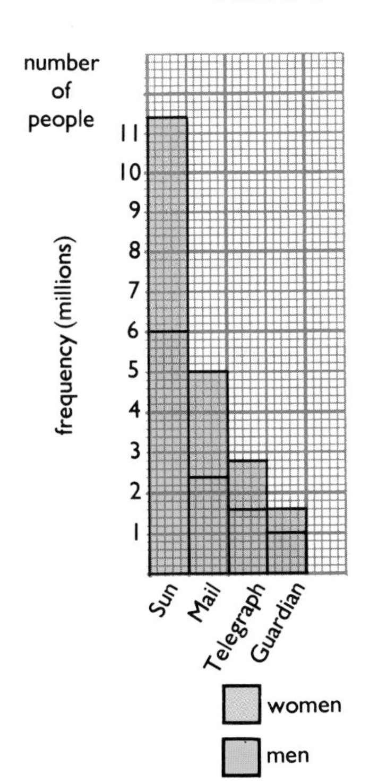

(*a*) How many women read the Daily Mail?

(*b*) How many more people read the Sun than read the other three papers put together?

(*c*) What percentage of the Sun's readers were women?

(*d*) Which of these four papers had the highest percentage of women readers?

(*e*) Does this barchart suggest that more women or more men read daily newspapers?

Why is it not possible to be certain about this from only looking at this barchart?

20 women and 20 men who used a tennis court were asked how many hours of tennis they had played during the previous two months, to the nearest hour. Here are their replies.

Women: 5, 1, 2, 7, 23, 5, 8, 9, 28, 5, 4, 7, 6, 9, 10, 5, 11, 24, 10, 9.

Men: 5, 3, 4, 7, 9, 4, 14, 5, 7, 10, 9, 7, 5, 7, 6, 9, 11, 7, 12, 9.

The replies from the women could be displayed on a histogram as follows:

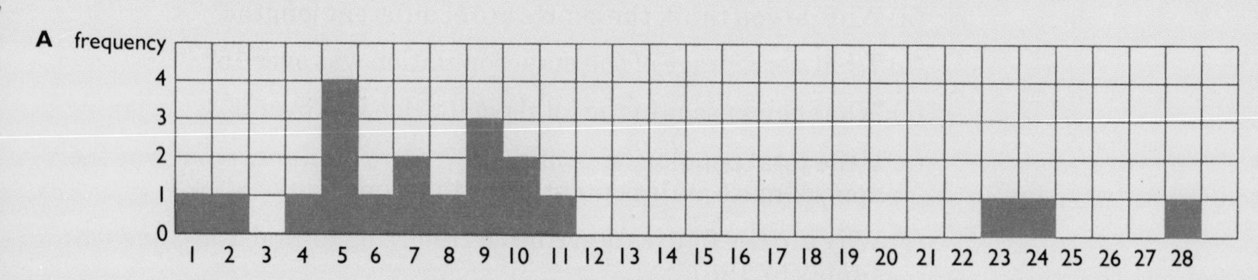

Suppose someone was interested in the ways in which this tennis court was likely to be used over a longer period. The information on the histogram above is too detailed for this purpose. From the information collected you might feel moderately confident in predicting that very roughly 3 in 20, or 15%, of women using the tennis court might use it more than 15 times in a month. But you would probably think it silly to forecast that someone is likely to use it 28 times rather than 27 times in a month. So it might be more meaningful for the histogram to give a rough idea, rather than a precise picture. One way of achieving this is to group the data into intervals of 3 hours, as shown in the table below.

No. of hours tennis played	Frequency
1 – 3	2
4 – 6	6
7 – 9	6
10 – 12	3
13 – 15	0
16 – 18	0
19 – 21	0
22 – 24	2
25 – 27	0
28 – 30	1

This grouped information is represented by the histogram below:

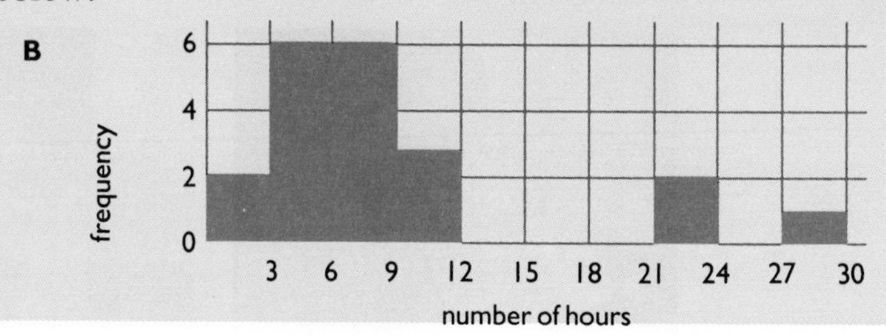

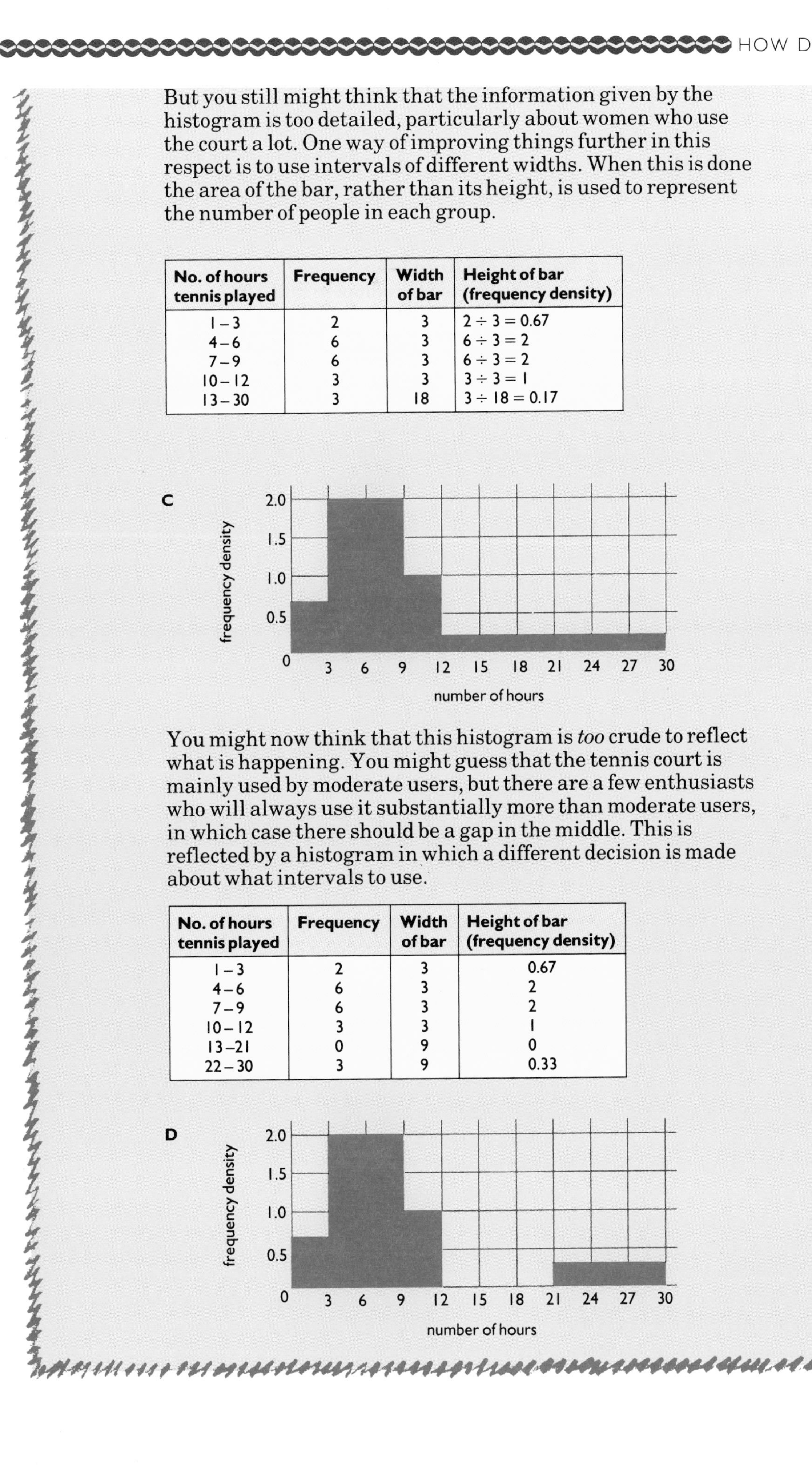

But you still might think that the information given by the histogram is too detailed, particularly about women who use the court a lot. One way of improving things further in this respect is to use intervals of different widths. When this is done the area of the bar, rather than its height, is used to represent the number of people in each group.

No. of hours tennis played	Frequency	Width of bar	Height of bar (frequency density)
1–3	2	3	2 ÷ 3 = 0.67
4–6	6	3	6 ÷ 3 = 2
7–9	6	3	6 ÷ 3 = 2
10–12	3	3	3 ÷ 3 = 1
13–30	3	18	3 ÷ 18 = 0.17

C

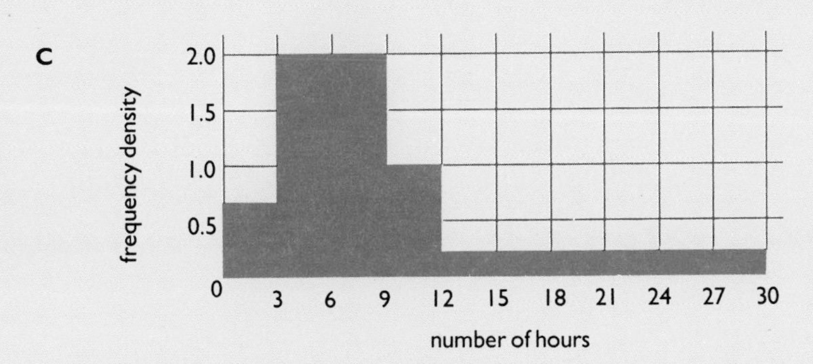

You might now think that this histogram is *too* crude to reflect what is happening. You might guess that the tennis court is mainly used by moderate users, but there are a few enthusiasts who will always use it substantially more than moderate users, in which case there should be a gap in the middle. This is reflected by a histogram in which a different decision is made about what intervals to use.

No. of hours tennis played	Frequency	Width of bar	Height of bar (frequency density)
1–3	2	3	0.67
4–6	6	3	2
7–9	6	3	2
10–12	3	3	1
13–21	0	9	0
22–30	3	9	0.33

D

frequency density
2.0
1.5
1.0
0.5
0
3 6 9 12 15 18 21 24 27 30
number of hours

16 (*a*) Draw a histogram showing the replies of all the 40 tennis players, given on page 168. Use the same intervals as for the histogram marked **B**.

(*b*) Now draw a histogram showing the replies of all 40 tennis players, using the same unequal intervals as for the histogram marked **D**.

17 The following data was obtained from *Social Trends 19*. It describes the age structure of the United Kingdom in mid-1987.

Age	Population (millions)
0–4	3.7
5–14	7.1
15–29	13.5
30–44	11.6
45–59	9.2
60–64	3.0
65–74	5.0
75–84	3.0
85+	0.8

Draw a histogram to display this data. You will obviously need to use the unequal intervals for which the results are given.

Questions 16 and 17 are about how much a tennis court is used by different people. If information about how much *any* sports facility is used by different members of a sports club was collected, you might expect the result to be distributed more or less in the way shown on this graph.

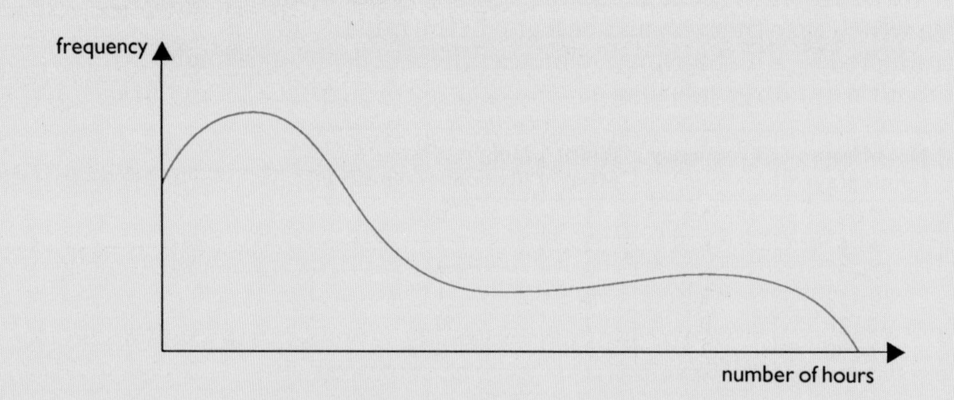

Most people will make a small or average use of the facility. Just a few will use it a great deal.

How information is distributed depends on the nature of that information. One common type of information distribution is called the **'normal distribution'**.

The normal distribution looks like this.

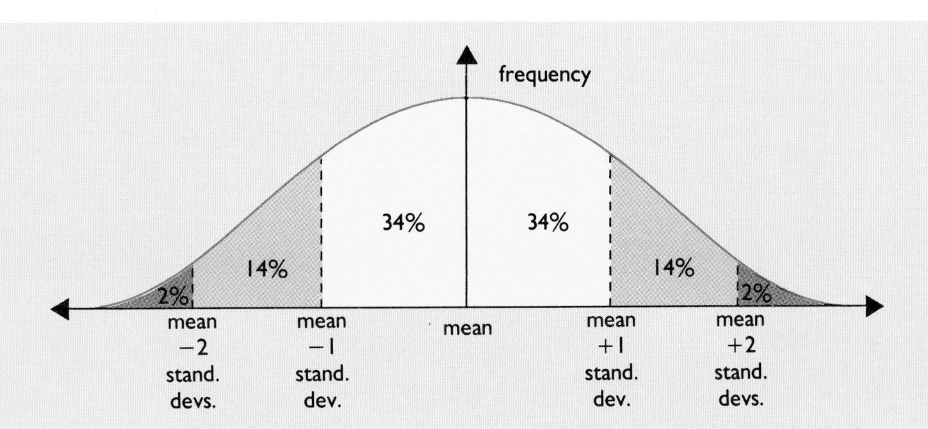

All normal distributions are this shape. You know everything about a normal distribution once you know its **mean** and **standard deviation**. For example, the percentage of the population within one standard deviation of the mean is always 68%.

A normal distribution is symmetrical. This means, for example, that, because 32% of the population is outside one standard deviation from the mean, half of this, 16%, is more than one standard deviation *above* the mean.

People's physical characteristics, such as height, weight, handspan, head circumference, are usually more or less *normally distributed*.

18 The mean weight of adult females in Britain is 60 kg and the standard deviation of weights is 6 kg.

The adult female population of a particular city in the Midlands is approximately 50 000.

Assuming that the distribution of the population is a normal distribution,

(*a*) what percentage of the adult female population weigh less than 54 kg?

(*b*) how many adult females in the city weigh more than 72 kg?

19 The mean height of adult males in Britain is 176 cm and the standard deviation is 7 cm.

The adult male population of a city in Wales is 30 000.

(*a*) Assuming that the distribution of the population is a normal distribution, how many of the adult males in this city are less than 162 cm tall?

(*b*) Someone is designing a door, for which there is not much room. She wants the height of the door to be sufficient so that at least 80% of adult males will be able to use the door without stooping. What is the minimum height she can choose for the door?

SECTION B

When you are finding out about something by collecting results there are a number of stages that you are likely to go through. The first is to choose an appropriate question to investigate.

Suppose you are interested in finding out about traffic which passes the school gate. Your starting question should help you to become clear what you want to do.

Some starting questions are better than others. Here are some examples.

Find out how many cars pass the school gate.

This is vague. Why do you want to find this out? How are you going to use what you find?

Find out if more British or foreign cars pass the school gate.

This does provide a question to answer, but the answer does not tell you very much.

Find out the percentage of British cars passing the gate. Use a book or magazine in the school library or local library to find out if this is above or below the national average.

This provides a more specific focus for the work.

Find out whether the percentages of different types of car used in this area are typical of the country as a whole.

This starting point provides plenty of opportunities to develop a piece of work on statistics. If you used such a starting point you would then need to ask further questions, such as the following.

- Is the school gate the right place to do the survey?
- Does the time of day at which the survey is done make a difference? Does the day of the week make a difference?
- How does the information collected compare with the national average? Does a local library have information about different makes of car in your region?

What are you going to mean by types of car? Does this mean British or foreign? Does it mean small or large? Does it mean saloon or estate? Does it mean cars which use leaded petrol or lead-free petrol? And can you find out what you want to know simply by counting cars as they pass?

Are there special reasons you can think of why a particular type of car is more likely to be used in your area?

1 Someone decides to do a survey about bringing sandwiches to school for lunch.

(*a*) Which of the following do you think would make the best starting question for her work?

A Do more boys or girls bring sandwiches?

B What factors help people decide whether to bring sandwiches?
C How many people bring sandwiches to school?
D Is the number of people who bring sandwiches increasing or decreasing?

(*b*) What facts would you try to find out if you were doing a piece of work to answer the starting question you chose for (*a*)?

2 Someone decides to do a survey about the school library.

(*a*) Which of the following questions do you think would make the best starting question for his work?

A What makes people decide to use the library?
B How many people use the school library?
C How could the school library be improved?
D Which subjects do people use the library for most?

(*b*) What facts would you try to find out if you were doing a piece of work to answer the starting question you chose for (*a*)?

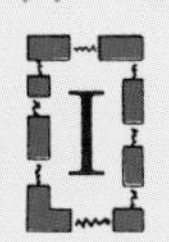

When you try to find something out by making observations and asking questions, the events you observe or the people you ask are called a **sample**.

If you want your results to be reliable you have to think carefully about what sample to use. You should try to ensure that the events you observe or the people you ask are typical representatives.

For example, suppose you were finding out about the people who bring sandwiches for lunch.

The sample of people you asked could be the friends you spend lunch time with.

This would be a very bad sample. Why?

A better sample might be all the people in your maths class or tutor group.

An even better sample might be people chosen **at random** from several classes or tutor groups. If your survey is supposed to be about the whole school you would need to survey people of different ages.

3 Suppose you were interested in finding out whether traditionally popular sports are still as popular as they used to be, and you decided to collect some information.

Your sample could be all the people who play football at the same club as you.

(*a*) Why is this sample *not* a good one?

(*b*) Suggest a better sample.

4 Suppose you were interested in finding out whether more of the food shopping nowadays was being done by men, and you decided to collect some information about it.

Your sample could be all the people in the local supermarket between 10 a.m. and 10.30 a.m. on one particular Thursday.

(*a*) Why is this sample *not* a good one?

(*b*) Suggest a better sample.

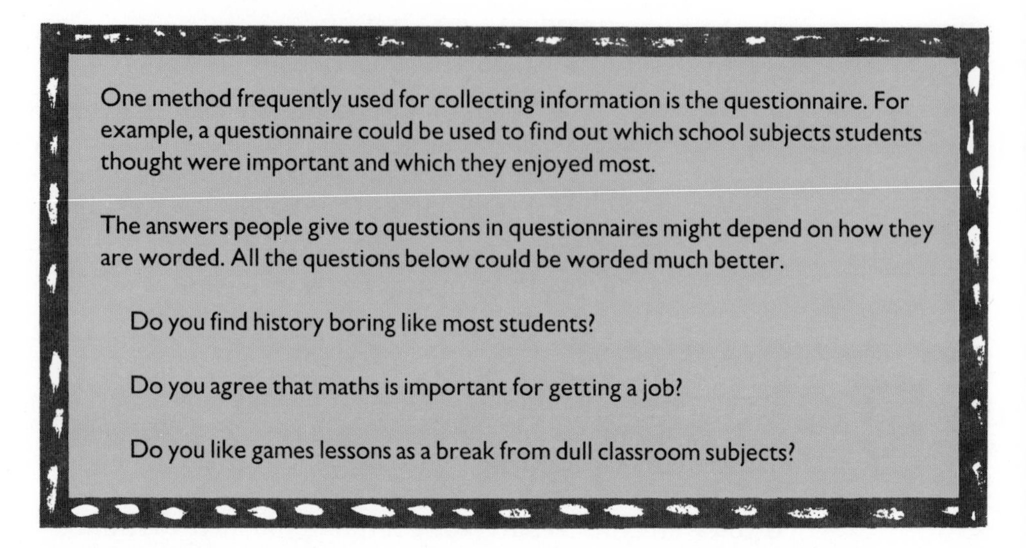

One method frequently used for collecting information is the questionnaire. For example, a questionnaire could be used to find out which school subjects students thought were important and which they enjoyed most.

The answers people give to questions in questionnaires might depend on how they are worded. All the questions below could be worded much better.

Do you find history boring like most students?

Do you agree that maths is important for getting a job?

Do you like games lessons as a break from dull classroom subjects?

5 Reword the questions in the box above so that people might be more likely to give their own opinions when they answer them.

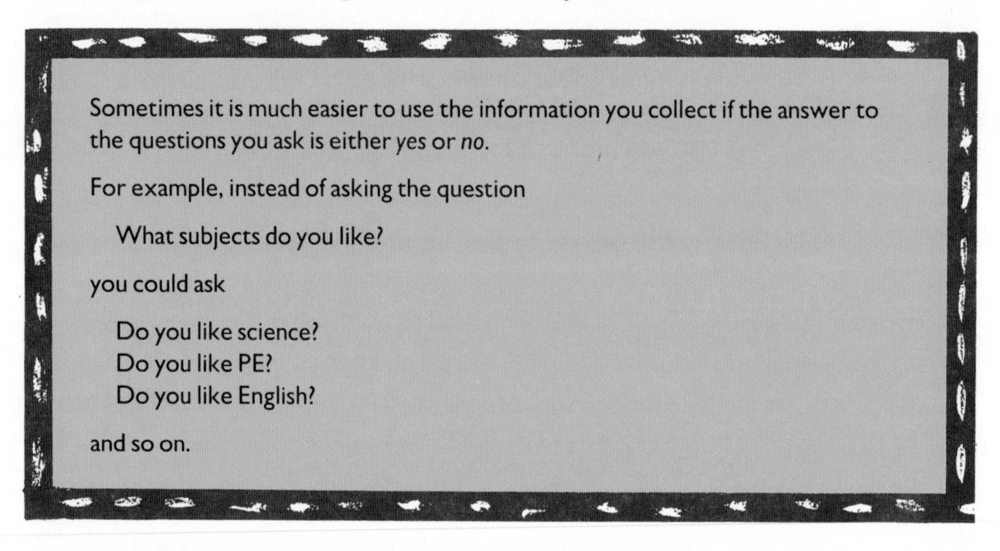

Sometimes it is much easier to use the information you collect if the answer to the questions you ask is either *yes* or *no*.

For example, instead of asking the question

What subjects do you like?

you could ask

Do you like science?
Do you like PE?
Do you like English?

and so on.

6 Suppose you want only *yes* or *no* answers in your questionnaire. What questions might you ask instead of each of the following questions?

(*a*) What sports do you like?

(*b*) What do you do on Saturdays?

(*c*) What are your views about smoking?

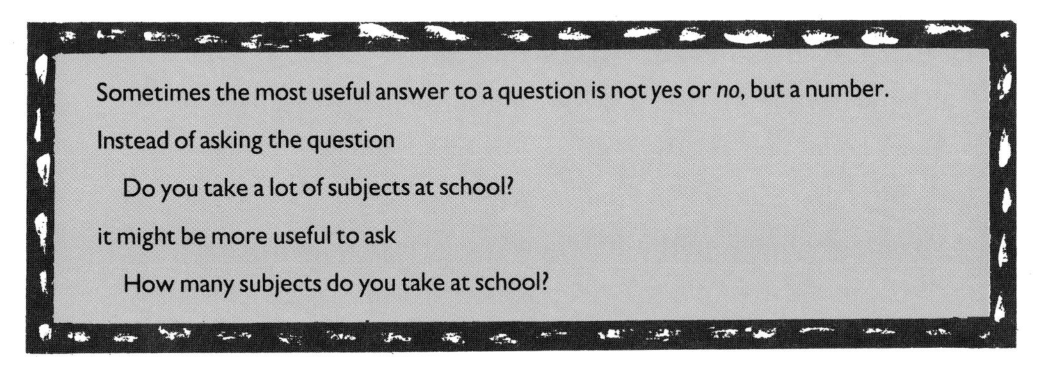

Sometimes the most useful answer to a question is not *yes* or *no*, but a number.

Instead of asking the question

Do you take a lot of subjects at school?

it might be more useful to ask

How many subjects do you take at school?

7 Rewrite each of the following questions so that the answer is a number.

(*a*) Are there a lot of people in your science class?

(*b*) Do you come from a large family?

(*c*) Do you often go for a bike ride?

When you have collected your information it helps you and other people to understand it if it is displayed clearly.

Remember that the information has been collected to help you answer a question. The method of display you choose should be the method which makes the answer as clear as possible. The questions in Section A provide examples of some of the ways in which information can be displayed.

A pie chart is an excellent way of displaying some types of information and a bad way of displaying others. A pie chart is an excellent way of displaying the percentages of people who are in different groups. For example, if you record the number of people who came to school today by bus, by bicycle, or on foot a pie chart would show this information clearly.

cycle
bus
walk

You can see at a glance that more than 50% of people came by bus.

But if the information collected was the number of people who sometimes walk, sometimes come by bus and sometimes cycle a pie chart should not be used to display it. This is because some people would be in *more than one* slice of the pie and this would mislead the reader of the chart.

Unless you deliberately want to mislead your reader you will choose a method which gives a fair impression. Questions 2(*a*) and 12(c) of Section A are about misleading ways of displaying information.

As well as displaying information you can usually calculate other results from the information. These calculated results often help you answer your starting question, and to draw sensible conclusions from your work. The remaining questions in this section give examples of this.

8 30 girls and 40 boys were asked whether they brought sandwiches for lunch. 10 girls and 12 boys said they did.

The person who collected this information concluded that

'more boys bring sandwiches for lunch than girls'.

(*a*) Why is this conclusion misleading?

(*b*) What percentage of the girls questioned bring sandwiches?

(*c*) What percentage of the boys questioned bring sandwiches?

(*d*) What conclusion might you draw?

9 In a survey to find out if the school library was more popular for boys or for girls, 30 people were asked how many times they had used it during one term. Here are the replies.

Girls: 12, 6, 0, 4, 4, 3, 8, 9, 11, 5, 8, 0.

Boys: 26, 0, 1, 2, 7, 9, 3, 18, 1, 2, 11, 1, 2, 4, 1, 5, 3, 12.

(*a*) 'One boy used the library 26 times, more than anyone else. So the library is more popular with boys.'

Do you agree with this statement? Give a reason?

(*b*) One way of answering the question is to calculate an 'average' of the girls' and the boys' use of the library. This 'average' could be the mode, the median or the mean.

(i) Which of mean, median and mode would be best 'average' to help answer the question? Give a reason for your choice.
(ii) Calculate the 'average' of your choice for the girls' and the boys' use of the library.
(iii) What conclusion might you come to?

10 A survey was conducted to discover whether swimming is more popular with first-year or fifth-year girls. 12 girls were asked how many times they had been swimming in the last month. Here are their replies.

First year: 3, 4, 4, 2, 5, 5

Fifth year: 1, 0, 7, 8, 0, 7

(*a*) Calculate the median number of times for both first-year and fifth-year girls.

(*b*) Calculate the mean number of times for both first-year and fifth-year girls.

(*c*) In spite of your answers to (*a*) and (*b*) the results for the first-year girls do look different from the results of the fifth-year girls. What other calculation could you make to demonstrate the difference?

(*d*) What explanation can you give for the difference in results for first-year and fifth-year girls?

1) When exploring one of the suggestions given below you might find it helpful to follow the advice given in Section B.

- First choose an appropriate set of starting questions to investigate. Word the questions so that you are clear about how you can collect data to help you answer them, and so that they help you to produce an interesting and worthwhile piece of work.

- If you need to collect a sample of information choose your sample carefully.

- If you use a questionnaire take care over the way you word questions. Decide what kind of answers you want.

- Display the information you collect clearly, and in a way which helps you, and other people, to draw conclusions from it. Do not mislead anyone. (You might want to include scattergrams, cumulative frequency graphs and other ideas from Chapter 7 in Book 4.)

- Calculate percentages, means, medians, modes, ranges, interquartile ranges, or standard deviations if these help you to draw conclusions from the results you collect.

- Look at newspapers, magazines, or books which provide similar information, so that you can compare what you find with what other people have found. You might find useful information on Teletext or Viewdata.

- Use a database or a statistical package on a computer if you think this will help you to organise your information, calculate results or display what you discover more clearly or more attractively.

- Draw conclusions which are justified by the results you have produced. Ensure that the conclusions you draw really are justified by your results.

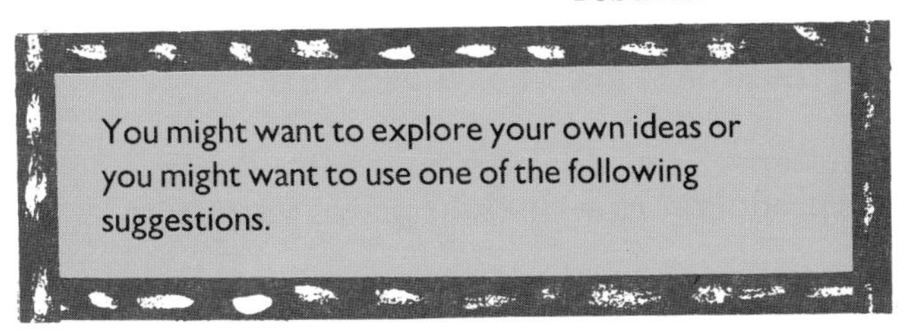

A What are typical television viewing habits for different groups in the population?

Which age groups watch most television? Do women watch more TV than men? What is the peak time for viewing? What kinds of programmes are most popular?

Compare the results you collect with published results (which you can sometimes find in newspapers or teletext).

B What are people's attitudes to smoking?

Which types of people are most likely to smoke? How much do people smoke? How easy do people find it to give up smoking?

What are people's opinions about smoking? Where should smoking be allowed? Who should be allowed to smoke? How much do people know about the diseases caused by smoking? How worried are they about these diseases?

C How do newspapers (or magazines) differ from one another? Look at their sizes, and at the percentage of space they give to different types of item, including advertisements.

Look at several papers on the same day to see whether they carry the same stories and how much space they give them.

Look at the language used in different newspapers (or magazines). Does one paper use longer words than another? Does it use longer sentences?

D How do different people spend their leisure time? How many people play sports? How many people go out to the cinema? For a drink? Elsewhere?

Do people of different ages spend their leisure time in different ways? Do women have more or less leisure time than men and do they spend it in different ways?

E Compare the cost of car transport with the cost of public transport. You can also compare the cost to the environment of car transport and public transport.

To do this find out, for example, whether more people use small or large cars, how many passengers there are in cars, which cars use unleaded petrol, whether there are good bus services or train services in your area, and whether there are good car parks near bus or railway stations, and how much they charge.

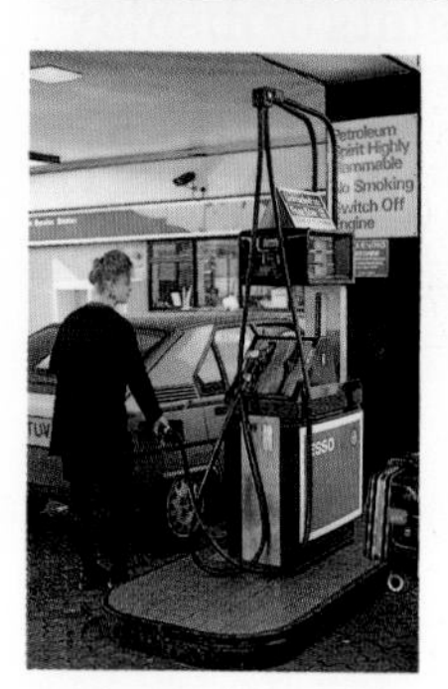

F Which jobs, or further education, do people want to do when they leave school? How much do people know about the jobs (or education) they want? Do they know what qualifications they need? Are the jobs people want to do available locally in sufficient numbers? Are people prepared to move away from the area to get what they want?

H How are the prices of certain items fixed? Do supermarkets charge different prices for the same products? How do their prices vary from week to week?

How much profit do shops make on different items? How much profit is made by the producers and wholesalers?

I Look at the way in which your school library is used.

At what time of day do most people use the library? What types of books do most users look at? What types of book do most users borrow?

Which types of staff and which types of students use the library most?

Suggest changes to the way in which the library is organised to improve the service to users.

J How long do people have to queue in different situations? How long are people prepared to queue for? How do the lengths of queues vary at different times? Are some types of people prepared to queue for longer than others? What do different people think about having to queue?

KNOWING WHERE YOU ARE

'I probably dropped it somewhere in the bedroom. Over near the window, I think.'

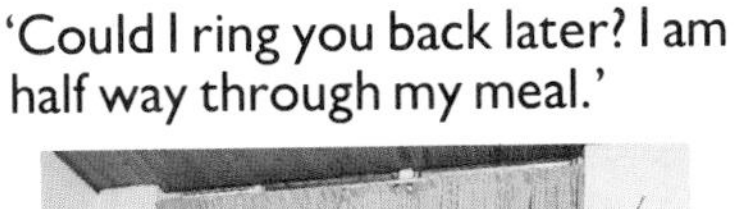

'Could I ring you back later? I am half way through my meal.'

'Where is Switzerland? Well, it is right in the middle of Europe.'

'Where we live is about half way down the road on the right-hand side.'

'Where I would like to spend my holiday is a long way from civilisation ...'

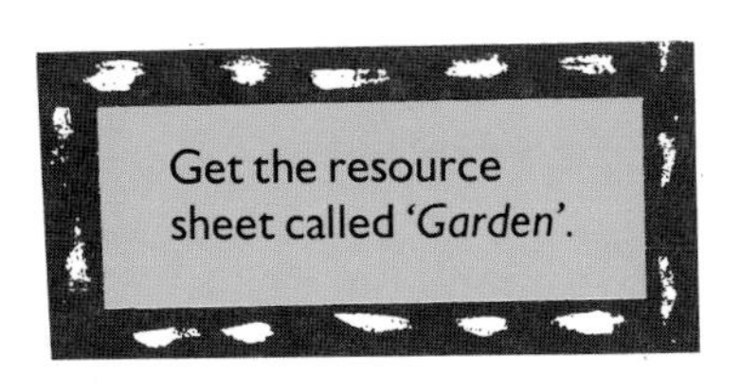

- You have left something in the garden shown on the resource sheet. It is exactly 5 metres from the post P. Show all the places where it could be.
- Something else is the same distance from fence F1 as it is from Fence F3. Show where it could be.
- Something else is one metre from the edge of the lawn. Show where it could be.
- Something is nearer to the power socket S than it is to the post P. Show where it could be.
- Something is 5 metres from the post P, and also the same distance from fence F1 as it is from fence F2. Show where it could be.
- Someone walks round the garden so that they are always 1 metre from the fence. Draw their path.
- The cable of a lawn mower is plugged in at socket S. It is just long enough for the whole of the lawn to be cut. What part of the lawn can *not* be cut if the cable is taken round the wrong side of post P?
- Now get another copy of the resource sheet *Garden*. Make up some rules of your own and show the results of your rules. If you want, you can put some other things in the garden and use these for your rules. Get other people to say what they think your rules were.

SECTION A

1 Look at the picture below.

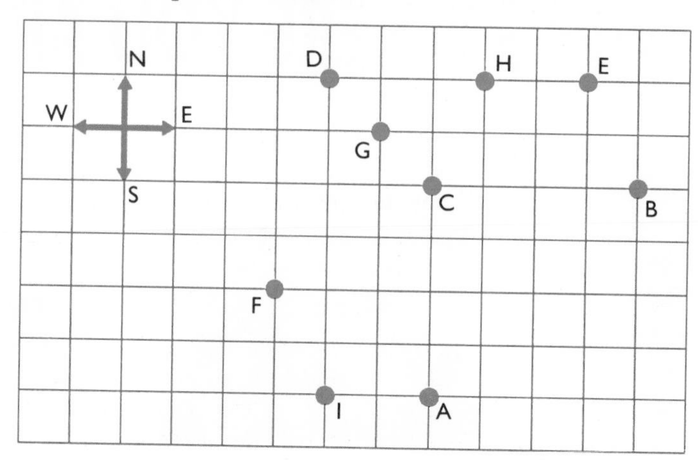

1 sq represents 1 km sq

(*a*) Which of the labelled points is North East of the point A?

(*b*) Which of the labelled points is less than 3 km from point B?

(*c*) Which of the labelled points is the same distance from point A and from point C?

(*d*) Which of the labelled points is North West of point C and also due West of point E?

2 The sheet shows a large field in which five goats are tied up.

Goats A, B, C and D are each tied to a different post. Goat A is tethered to post A, goat B is tethered to post B, and so on. The posts are not shown on the diagram. The grass each of these goats can reach is shaded.

(*a*) Mark on the diagram the positions of the posts to which goats A, B, C and D are tethered.

(*b*) A straight footpath runs across the field. All the points on the path are the same distance from post B as they are from post C. Draw the path.

(*c*) Goat A becomes aggressive and so the owner wants to shorten its tether so that it cannot get at any of the other goats. By how much should the tether be shortened?

(*d*) Goat E has a tether which is 4 m long. One end of the tether is attached to the goat's collar. On the other end of the tether is a ring which is free to slide up and down a bar fixed between the points X and Y. Shade the area of grass which goat E can reach.

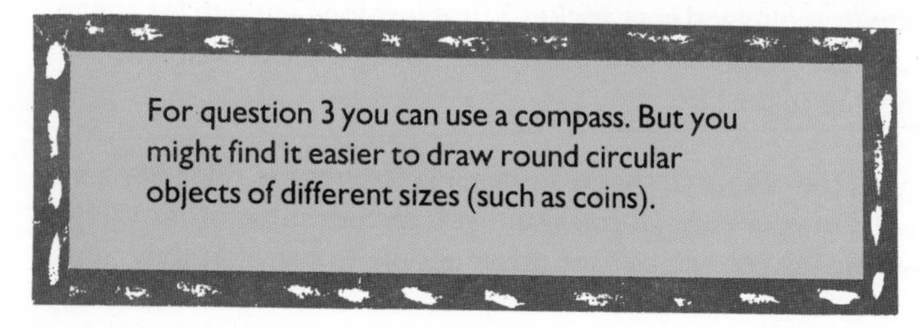

3 (*a*) (i) Mark a point on your paper.
(ii) Draw four circles with different radii, *all* of which pass through the point.

(*b*) (i) Mark two points, not too close together.
(ii) Draw four circles with different radii, *all* of which pass through *both* of these points.
(iii) Mark the centres of these circles. (If you have drawn round circular objects you might need to guess where the centres are.)
(iv) What pattern do the centres form?

(*c*) (i) Mark three points, not too close together.
(ii) Draw a circle whose circumference passes through all three points.
(*Hint:* You might find it easier to cheat and to draw the circle *before* you mark the three points.)
(iii) How many other circles can you draw which pass through these three points?

4

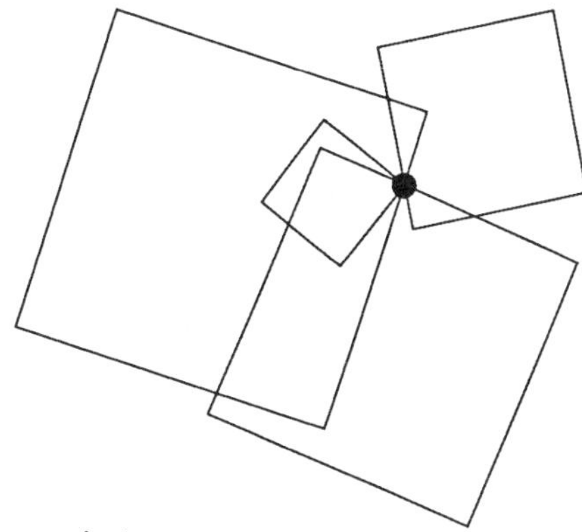

(*a*) (i) Mark a point on your paper.
(ii) Draw four squares of different sizes, *all* of which pass through the point.

(*b*) (i) Mark two points.
(ii) Draw four squares, *all* of which pass through *both* of these points.
(iii) Where are the centres of these four squares?

(*c*) (i) Mark three points.
(ii) Draw a square which passes through all three points.
(*Hint:* You might find it easier to cheat and to draw the square *before* you mark the three points.)
(iii) How many other squares can you draw which pass through these three points?

5 (*a*) Mark two points which are 6 cm apart. Label them A and B.

(*b*) Use your compass to draw all the points on your paper which are 4 cm from A.

(*c*) Use your compass to draw all the points on your paper which are 5 cm from B.

(*d*) Mark a point on your paper which is 4 cm from A and is also 5 cm from B.

(*e*) How many different points could you have chosen for (*d*)?

6 (*a*) Draw a line and label it l. Choose a point on the line and label it P.

(*b*) Draw all points on your paper which are 6 cm from the point P.

(*c*) Draw all points on your paper which are 4 cm from the line l.

(*d*) How many different points on your paper are 6 cm from P *and* 4 cm from l?

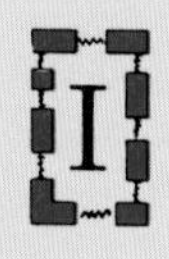

The diagram shows the ripples of a square.

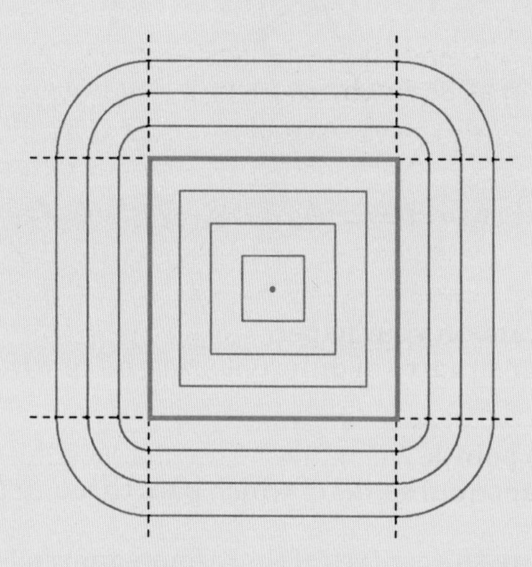

All the points on each ripple are the same distance from the square.

Each outside ripple is made up of four straight lines and four quarter-circles.

The dotted lines are not part of the ripple. They are drawn to help you see where the quarter-circles start and finish.

The inside ripples eventually disappear in a point. This could be called the *'last ripple'*.

7 (*a*) Draw a circle of radius 4 cm.

(*b*) Draw two ripples outside the circle, at a distance of 1 cm and 2 cm from the circle.

(*c*) Draw two ripples inside the circle at a distance of 1 cm and 2 cm from the circle.

(*d*) Mark the position of the last ripple.

8 (*a*) Draw a rectangle with sides of lengths 6 cm and 4 cm.

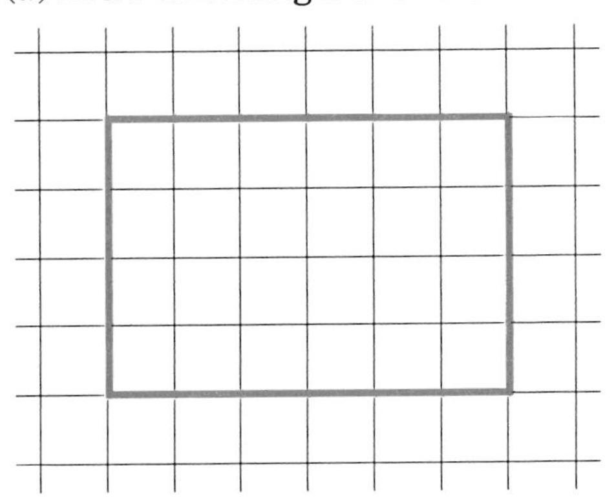

(*b*) Draw the locus of points which are 1 cm from the rectangle. (This consists of two ripples, one outside and one inside.)

(*c*) Draw the locus of points which are 2 cm from the rectangle.

(*d*) Mark the last ripple.

9 Draw ripples inside and ripples outside for each of the following shapes. In each case show the last ripple.

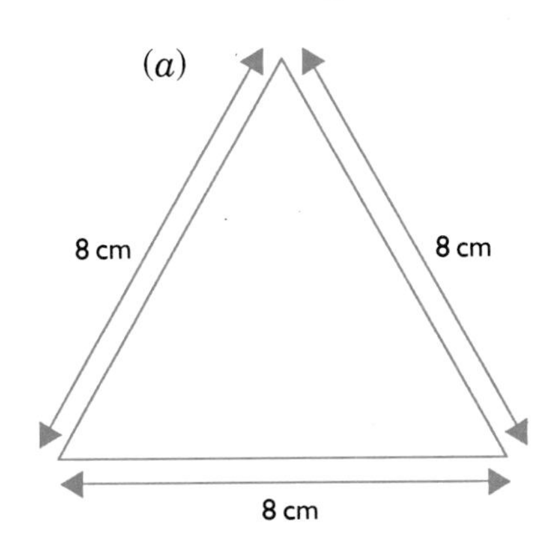

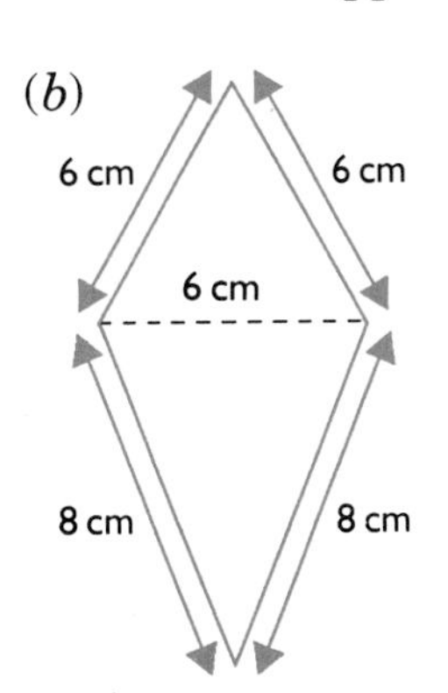

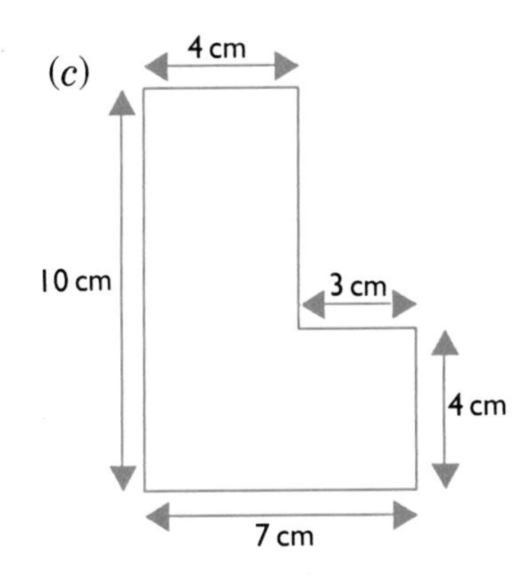

10 For each part of this question you will need a copy of the picture shown on the left.

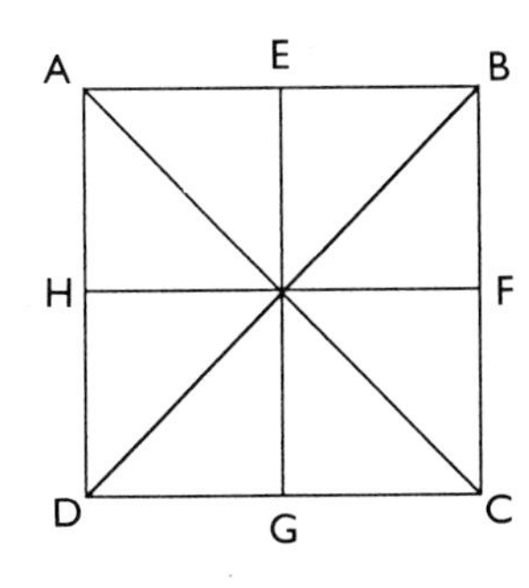

(*a*) P is a point in the square which is closer to H than F. Shade the region in which P must lie.

(*b*) P is a point in the square which is closer to H than F and closer to D than B. Shade the region in which P must lie.

(*c*) P is a point in the square which is closer to line DB than it is to line AC. Shade the region in which P must lie.

(*d*) P is a point in the square which is closer to B than it is to D *and* closer to E than it is to G. Shade the region in which P must lie.

11 (*a*) Draw a line and mark two points A and B on the line, 6 cm apart.

A B

P is a point on the line. AP means the distance from A to P.

(*b*) Mark the position of P on the line if $AP = BP$.

(*c*) Show all the places where P could be if

$AP < BP$.

12 Draw another line and mark two points A and B on the line, 6 cm apart.

A B

P is a point on the line.

(*a*) Mark *two* positions where P could be if

$AP = 2\,BP$.

(*Hint:* One position is between A and B. The other position is to the right of B.)

(*b*) Show all the places where P could be if

$AP < 2\,BP$.

13 The points A and B lie on a line l and are 10 cm apart. P is a point on the line l, and

$3\,AP = 2\,BP$

(*a*) Draw a sketch to show roughly the two positions where P can be.

(*b*) Calculate the distance of P from A in each of the positions.

14 (*a*) Mark two points A and B, 6 cm apart.

(*b*) P is a point on the paper and

$AP = 2BP$.

(i) Construct two points, each of which is 6 cm from A and 3 cm from B. (Each of these points is a possible position for P.)
(ii) Construct two points, each of which is 8 cm from A and 4 cm from B. (Each of these points is a possible position for P.)
(iii) Find four more possible positions for P.

(*c*) Draw your guess for the locus of P.

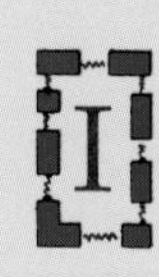

The picture below shows the locus of points which are 1.5 cm from a finite line.

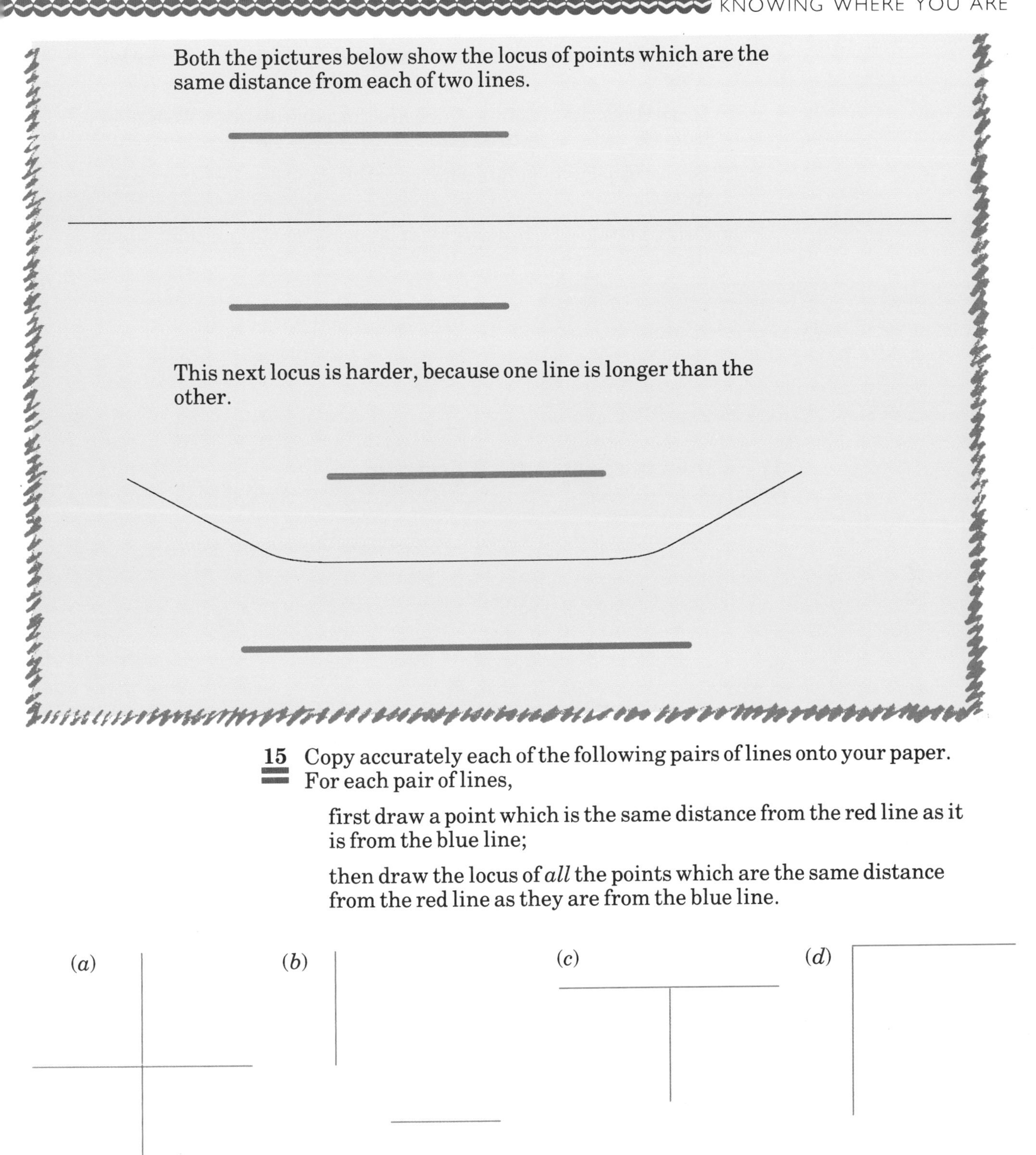

Both the pictures below show the locus of points which are the same distance from each of two lines.

This next locus is harder, because one line is longer than the other.

15 Copy accurately each of the following pairs of lines onto your paper. For each pair of lines,

first draw a point which is the same distance from the red line as it is from the blue line;

then draw the locus of *all* the points which are the same distance from the red line as they are from the blue line.

16 (*a*) Draw a triangle with sides of lengths 5 cm, 6 cm and 8 cm.

Label the vertices ABC, as in Figure 1.

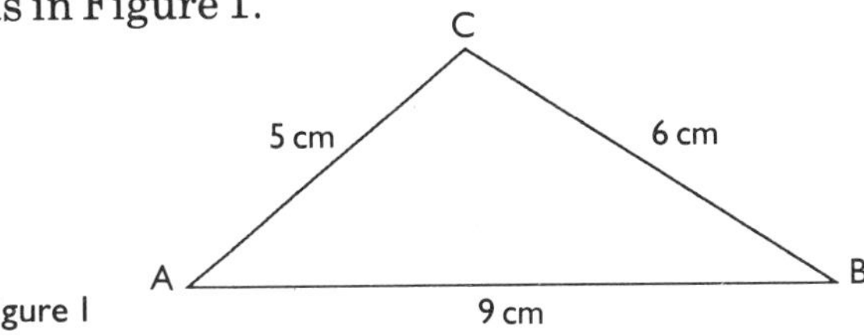

Figure 1

(*b*) Draw the locus of points which are the same distance from A as from B.

(*c*) Draw the locus of points which are the same distance from A as from C.

(*d*) Draw the locus of points which are the same distance from B as from C.

(*e*) Draw a circle which shows what is special about the point which lies on all three loci.

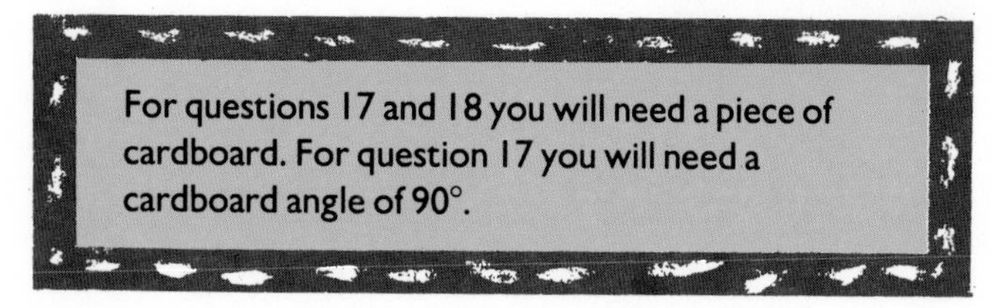

17 (*a*) Draw two points A and B, 6 cm apart.

(*b*) The point P is in a position such that the angle APB = 90°.

Use your cardboard to find several possible positions for P.

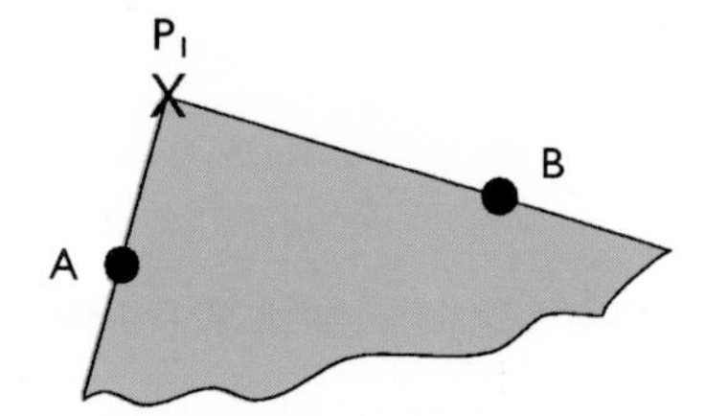

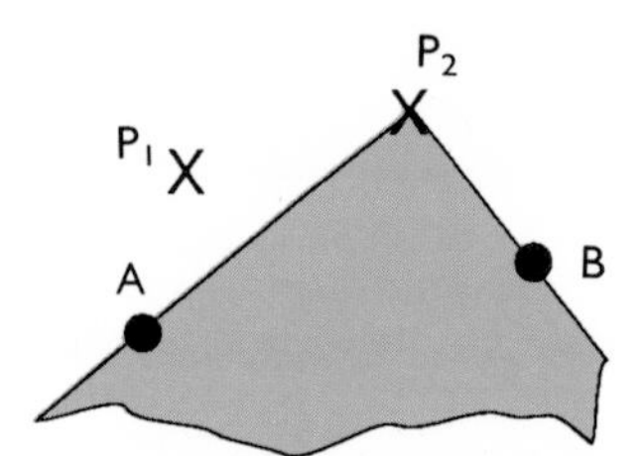

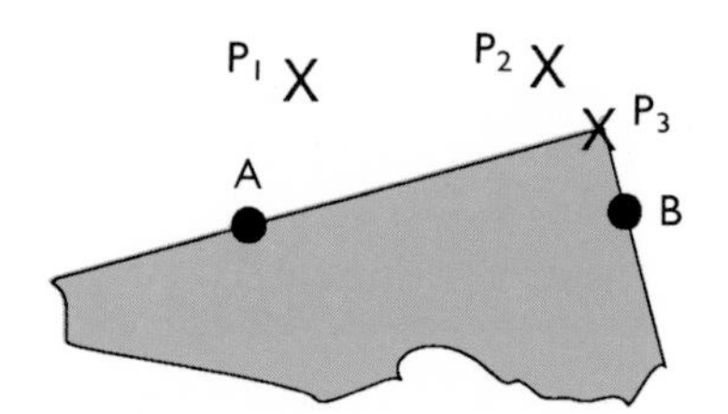

(*c*) Draw what you think is the locus of P.

(*d*) Describe the locus of P in words.

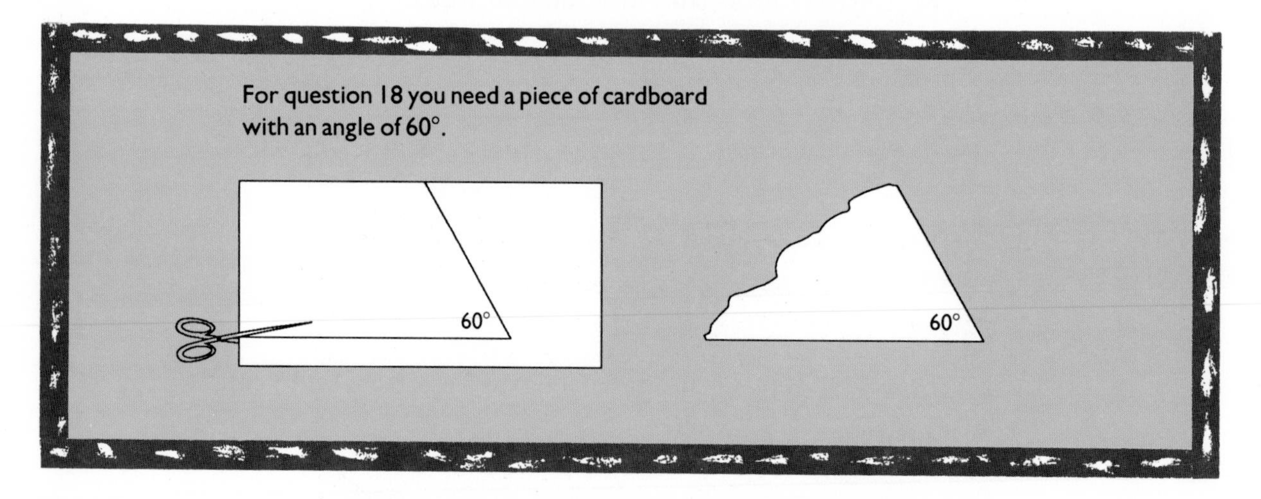

18 (*a*) Draw two points A and B, 6 cm apart.

(*b*) The point P is in a position such that the angle APB = 60°.

Use your cardboard to find several possible positions for P.

(*c*) Draw what you think is the locus of P.

(*d*) Describe the locus of P in words.

19 (*a*) Copy figure 2. O is the centre of the circle.

(*b*) AOP is an isosceles triangle because OP and OA are both radii of the circle. This is why the two angles marked x are equal.

There is another isosceles triangle in figure 2 and, therefore, two other angles are equal. Mark each of these angles y.

(*c*) Write down the sum of the angles of triangle APB in terms of x and y.

(*d*) What does this tell you about the value of $x+y$?

(*e*) Explain the connection between the answer to part (*d*) and the answer to 17(*d*).

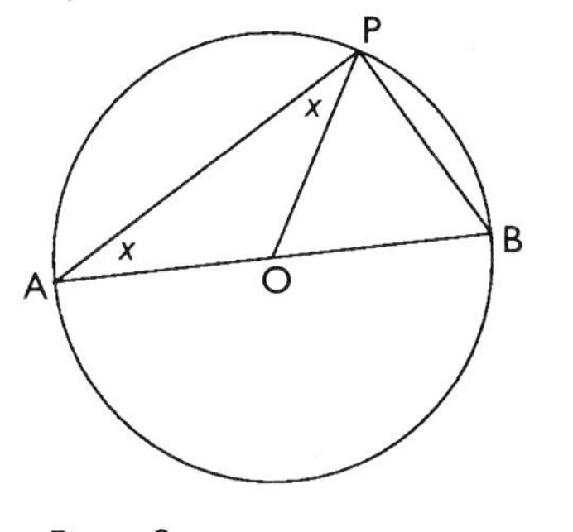

Figure 2

20 (*a*) Copy figure 3. O is the centre of the circle.

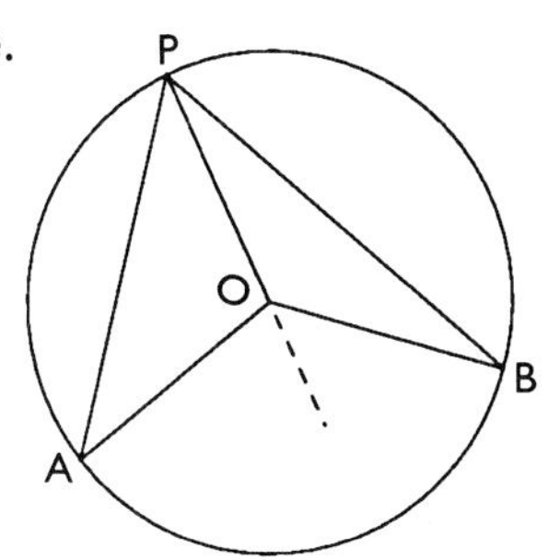

Figure 3

(*b*) Two of the triangles in figure 3 are isosceles and so there are two pairs of equal angles in figure 3. Mark the angles of one pair x and the angles of the other pair y.

(*c*) Work out the size of the angle AOB in terms of x and y.

(*d*) If angle APB is 70°, what is the size of angle AOB?

21 (*a*) The length of the side AB of the triangle ABC is 6 cm. Draw the side AB.

(*b*) The area of the triangle is 9 cm^2. Draw the locus of C.

(*c*) Angle ACB = 70°. Draw a circle on which C must lie.

(*d*) Find, by measuring, the two possible values for angle CAB.

SECTION B

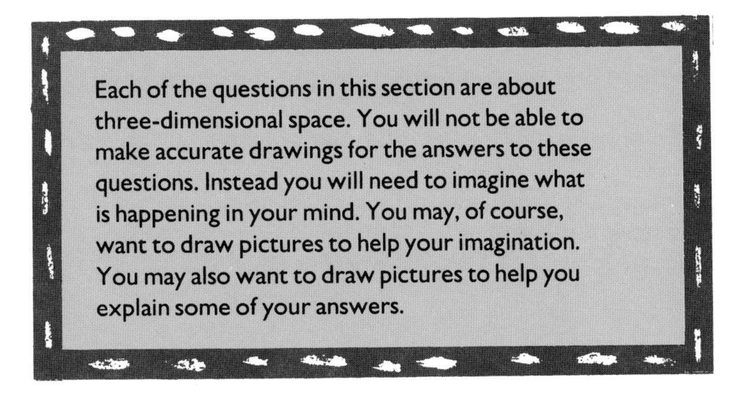

Each of the questions in this section are about three-dimensional space. You will not be able to make accurate drawings for the answers to these questions. Instead you will need to imagine what is happening in your mind. You may, of course, want to draw pictures to help your imagination. You may also want to draw pictures to help you explain some of your answers.

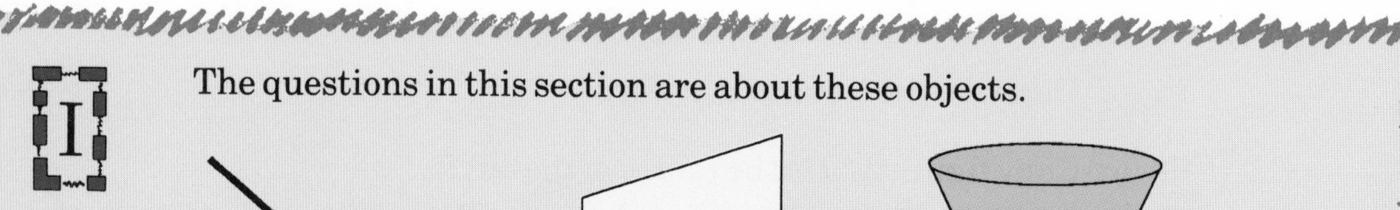

The questions in this section are about these objects.

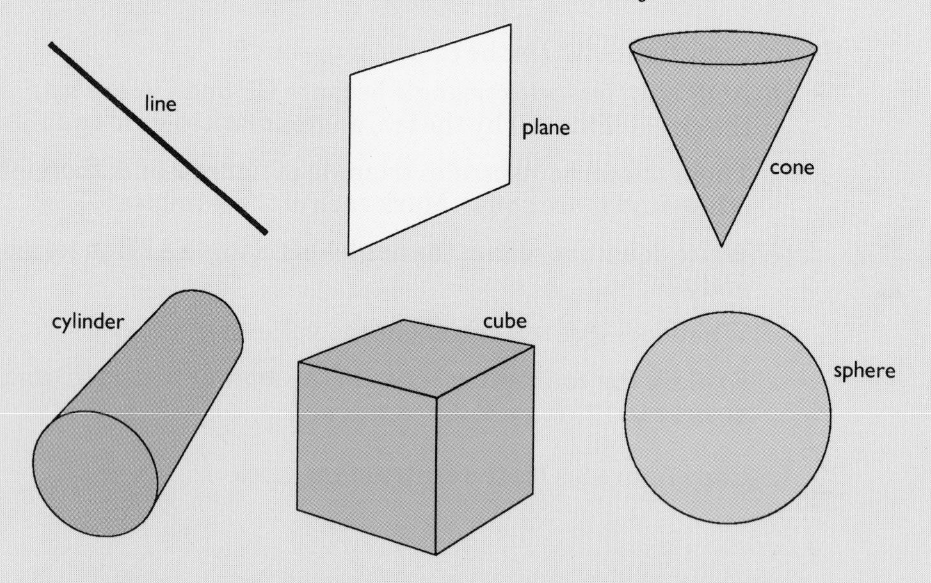

For most of the questions in this section assume that spheres, cylinders, cones and cubes are *hollow*. Also assume that lines, planes, cylinders and cones are *infinite*.

1 A is a point in 3-D space. What is the locus of points which are 1 m from A?

2 X is an infinite plane. What is the locus of points which are 1 m from X?

3 (*a*) l is an infinite line in space. Describe the locus of all points which are 1 m from l.

(*b*) What difference will there be to the locus if l is a *finite* line?

4 *S* is a hollow sphere. Describe the locus of all points which are 1 m from S.

5 A and B are two points in three-dimensional space. What is the locus of a point P if it is the same distance from A as it is from B?

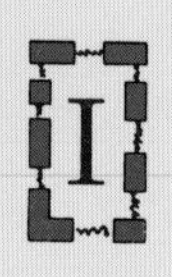

Two objects in 3-D space might or might not meet each other.

Consider a sphere and a plane. There are three possible cases.

In the first case the sphere and the plane *do not meet.*

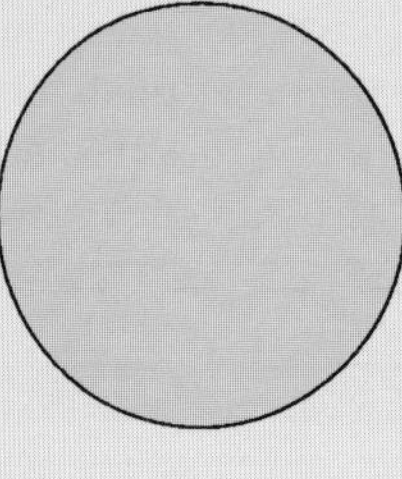

In the second case the sphere and plane meet in just *one point.*

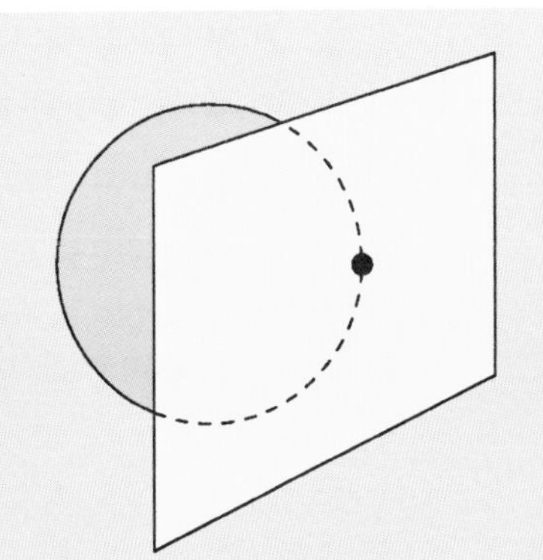

In the third case the sphere and the plane meet in *a circle*. (The size of the circle depends on how close the plane is to the centre of the sphere.)

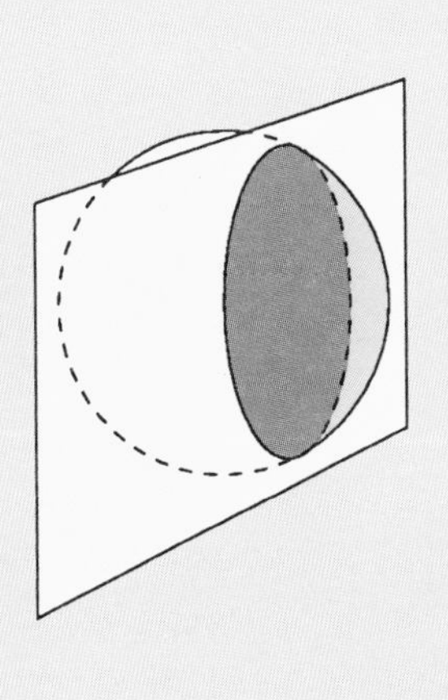

6 Which meetings are possible for each of the following pairs of objects? There is usually more than one answer. Wherever possible explain your answers, either in words or pictures.

(*a*) Two infinite planes.

(*b*) An infinite plane and an infinite line.

(*c*) Two infinite lines.

(*d*) An infinite line and a sphere.

(*e*) Two spheres.

(*f*) An infinite line and an infinite cylinder.

(*g*) An infinite plane and an infinite cylinder.

(*h*) A sphere and a cube.

(*i*) An infinite line and an infinite cone.

(*j*) An infinite plane and an infinite cone.

7 (*a*) l and m are two intersecting lines. What is the locus of a point P if its distance from l is equal to its distance from m?

(*b*) X and Y are two intersecting planes. What is the locus of a point if it is the same distance from *X* as it is from *Y*?

(*c*) X is a plane and l is a line which is perpendicular to this plane. What is the locus of a point which is the same distance from X as it is from l?

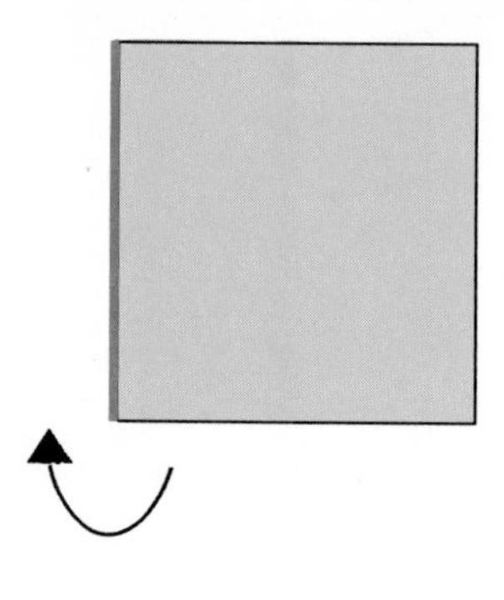

8 What shape is produced when:

(*a*) a square is rotated round one of its sides?

(*b*) a square is rotated round one of its diagonals?

(*c*) a circle is rotated round one of its diameters?

(*d*) a circle is rotated round a line in the same plane which does not meet the circle?

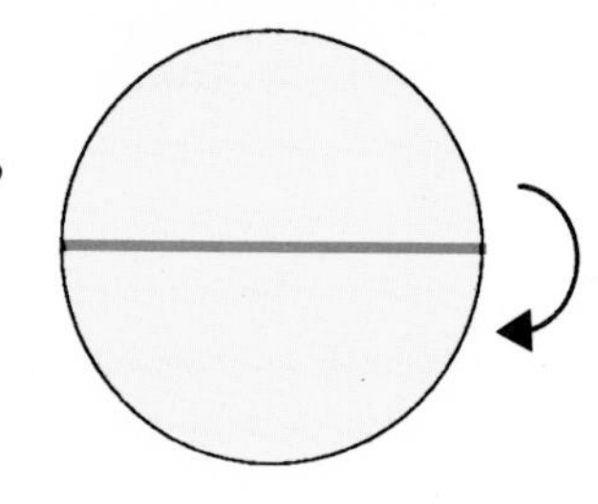

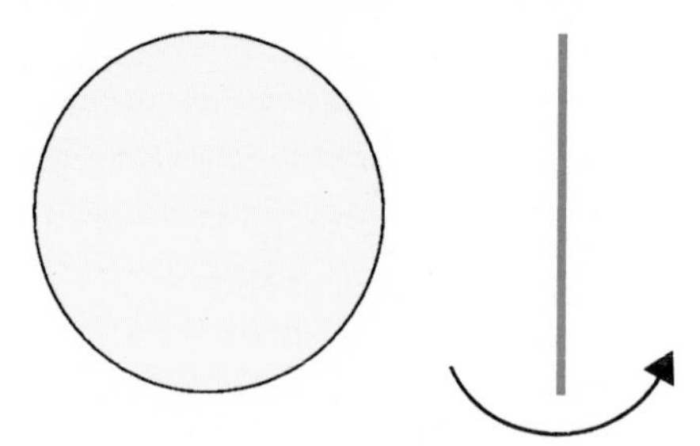

(*e*) a line is rotated about another line which is parallel to it?

(*f*) a line is rotated about another line which meets it?

(*g*) an obtuse-angled triangle is rotated about one of its sides? (There are two possibilities.)

(*h*) a line is rotated about another perpendicular line which does not meet it?

For some of the following questions you will need to know the formula for the volume of a solid. You will find the formula you need on page 282.

You might find Pythagoras' theorem helpful for some of the following questions. This is on page 281.

9 Find the volume of the solid produced when an isosceles triangle, whose sides are of length 10 cm, 13 cm and 13 cm, is rotated about its line of symmetry.

10 A is a point on a line l. What is the shape and size of the locus of a point which is 10 cm from A and 8 cm from l?

11 A and B are two points 10 m apart. What is the shape and size of the locus of a point P which is 8 m from A and 6 m from B?

12 A cube, with sides of length 1 m, is rotated about one of its edges. What is the area of the surface swept out by each of the other edges of the cube?

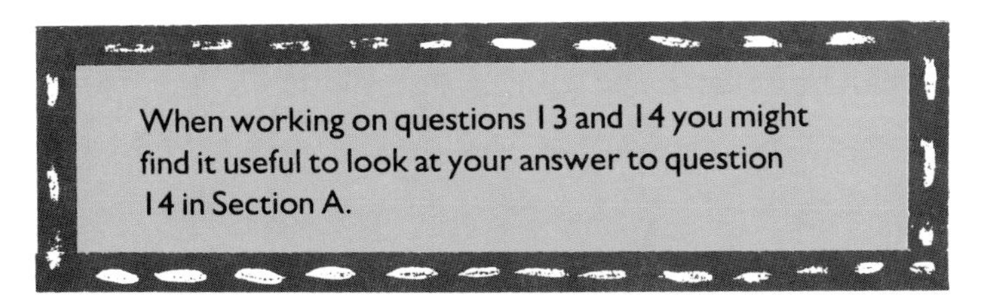
When working on questions 13 and 14 you might find it useful to look at your answer to question 14 in Section A.

13 l and m are two parallel lines. P is a point which is twice as far from l as it is from m. Describe the locus of P.

14 A and B are two points 1 m apart. P is a point such that the distance of P from A is twice the distance of P from B. What is the shape and size of the locus of P?

FURTHER COURSEWORK TASKS

1⟩ You have a field or a garden, in which you keep goats. All the goats are tethered in some way.

Make up a story about the goats which will give you some problems to solve. Here are some of the decisions you can make in your story.

What is the shape of the field or garden?

How are the goats tethered? The pictures below show some possibilities.

Are there buildings in the field around which the goats can move? These will affect the region of the field which the goats can reach.

How long are the tethers? Do they have to be short enough to prevent the goats eating vegetables in a vegetable plot, for example?

Are the goats replacing a lawn mower? In other words, is it important that all the grass can be reached by at least one goat?

The decisions you make will set you problems to solve.
How many goats do you need?
How should they be tethered?

You might want to find out what area of the field each goat can reach. And what area of grass can be eaten by two (or more) goats.

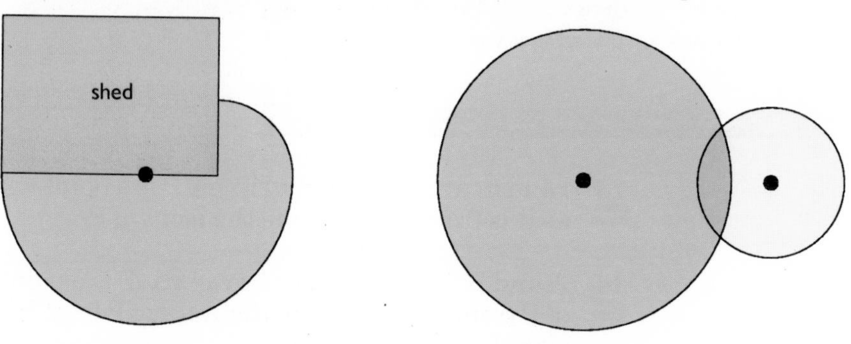

2⟩ Explore the shape of ripples obtained for different shapes. You might want to consider squares, rectangles, triangles, rhombuses, kites, semicircles, L shapes, T shapes, and so on.

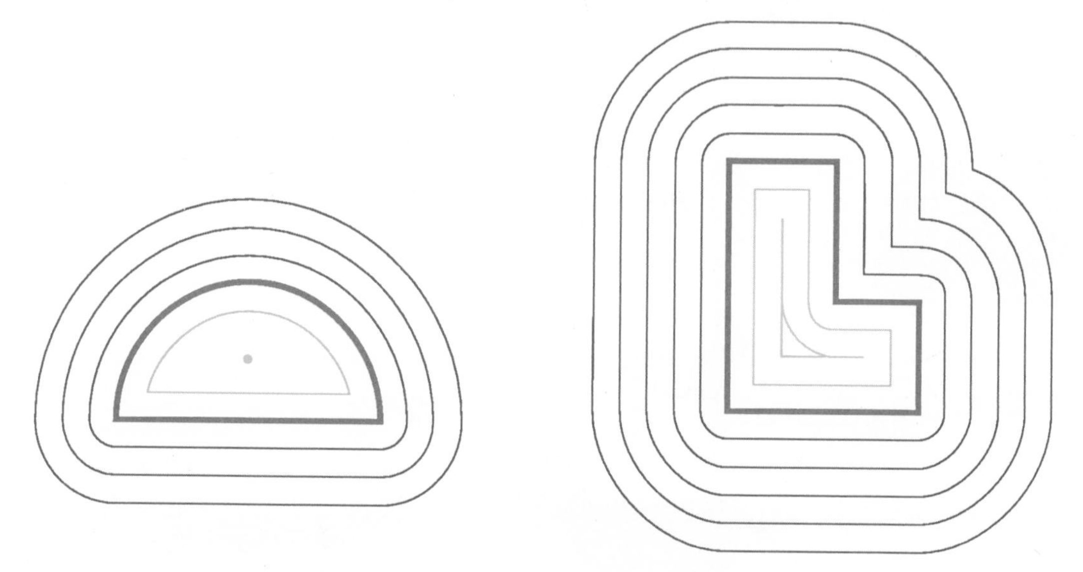

You might want to find the lengths of ripples. (This will involve finding the lengths of arcs of circles.) You might find how the length depends on the distance of the ripple from the shape. What is the last ripple for each shape?

3⟩ Figure 4 was drawn using three turtles.

Turtle 1 obeyed the normal *Logo* commands.

Turtle 2 moved at the same time as Turtle 1, but it moved *twice* the distance and it turned in the *opposite* direction (in other words, it turned *left* when Turtle 1 turned *right*.

Turtle 3 always stayed exactly half way between Turtle 1 and Turtle 2.

What does Turtle 3 draw if Turtle 1 draws a different shape?

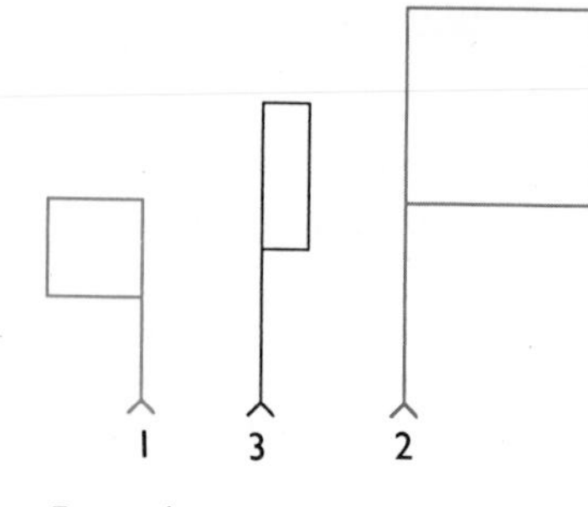

Figure 4

Figure 5 shows a different arrangement. In this figure Turtle 1 and Turtle 2 follow exactly the same instructions (but Turtle 2 is not facing the same direction as Turtle 1 to start with).

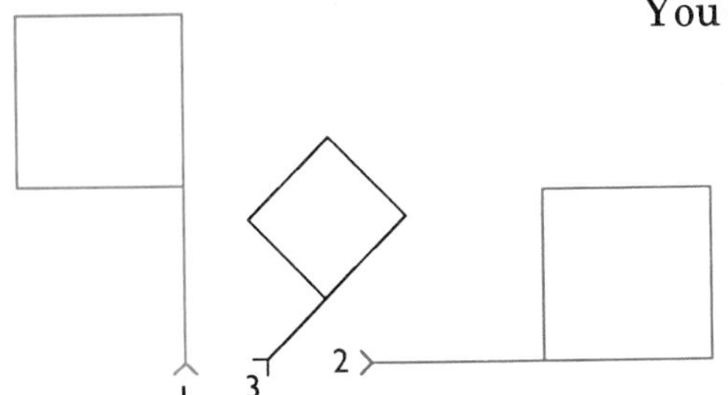

Figure 5

You can make up your own situations to explore.

A You can change the shape that Turtle 1 draws.

B You can change the rules which say how Turtle 2 should move.

Try to find rules that help you predict what Turtle 3 will draw when you make either change **A** or change **B**.

There is something else that can also be changed.

Turtle 3 can move so that it is a third of the way between Turtle 1 and Turtle 2. Or a quarter. Or ...

One way of exploring this idea is to use *Logo*. If you do not use *Logo* you will probably need to get people or objects to obey the turtle rules until the idea becomes clear to you.

4) A cube has a side of length 1 metre. Calculate the radius of a sphere which has the same volume as the cube.

The sphere is placed with its centre at the centre of the cube. What is the intersection of the sphere and the cube?

What happens if the centre of the sphere is not at the centre of the cube?

What happens if you use a cuboid instead of a cube?

This photograph is of a work of art created by Gary Woodley, using the ideas suggested above. The cuboid is an actual room. The photograph shows a drawing of an intersection of an imaginary sphere with a room.

5⟩ Draw a square. Choose three points on the square.

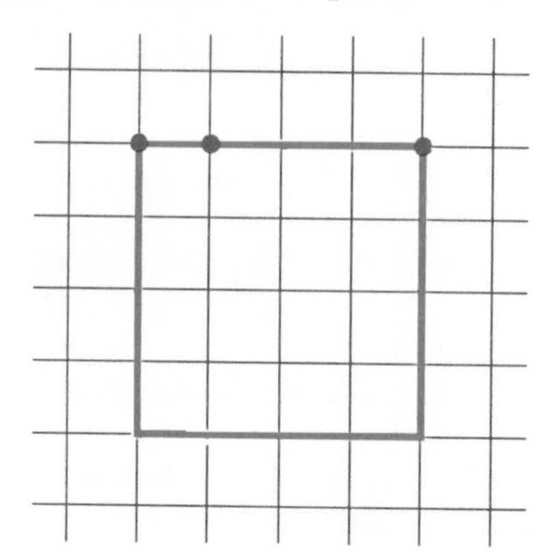

What other squares can be drawn through these three points?

The answer to this question will depend on where you choose the three points.

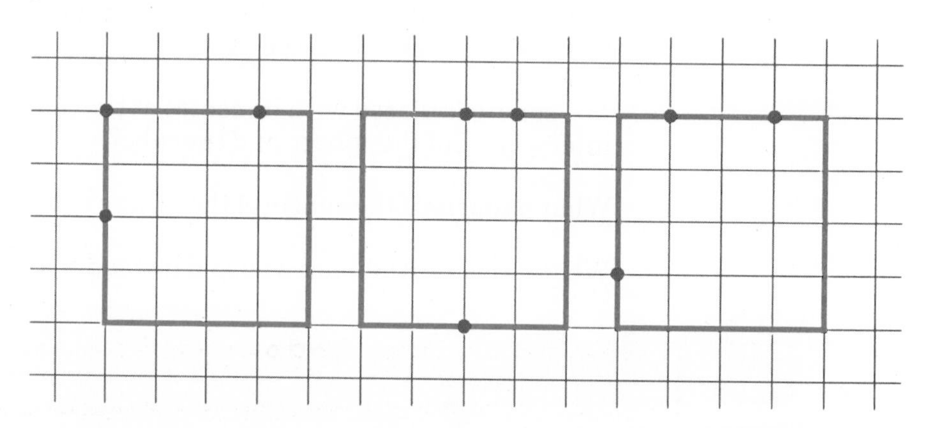

For any choice of three points explore *all* the positions for the *centres* of squares drawn through the three points.

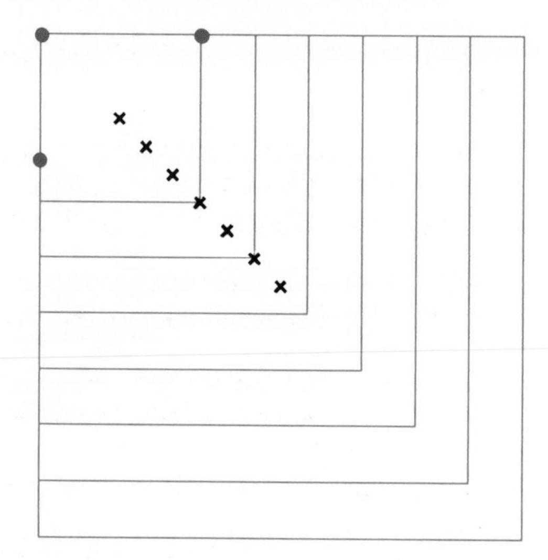

Now try the same idea but use only two points. Or use four points ...

23 WHAT DO YOU BELIEVE?

'A friend of mine saw a ghost when she was walking past the church last year.'

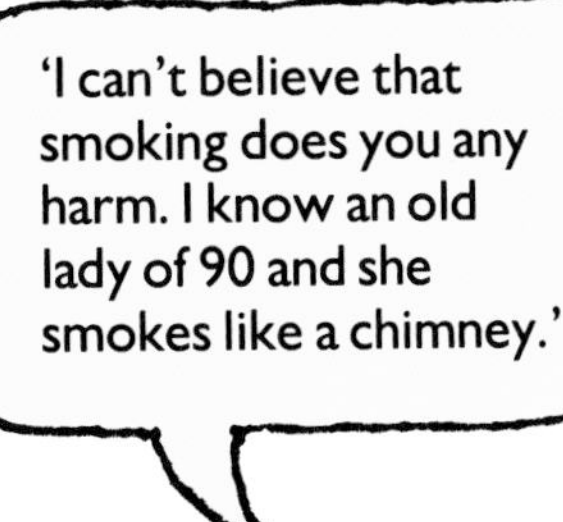

To win some games you have to make decisions based on what you believe other people will do.

Here is a game like that. Each player chooses one positive whole number and writes it on a piece of paper. When all the players have written down their numbers the numbers are collected.

The winner is the person who chose the *smallest* number that *no-one else chose.*

For example, if four people play and the numbers they choose are 2, 2, 3 and 5 the winner is the person who chooses 3.

- Play this game with everyone in your class.
- Play the game several times. Does everybody get better at the game with practice?
- If possible, play this game with a much larger group of people. Perhaps you could play it with several tutor groups during tutor time. Before you play it try to forecast approximately how large the winning number will be.
- Perhaps you could play this game with the whole school. You might want to have an entry fee to raise money for charity and offer a small prize to the winner.
- Does it help if people offer you advice about what they are going to choose? Suppose different people said the following things before playing.

  'I am going to choose 2, because no-one else will choose 2.'

  'Someone calculated that the best number to choose is 17.'

  'No-one who chooses less than 10 will win.'

  Would any of these influence what number you choose?

SECTION A

1 Three people play the game but they all agree they will only choose the numbers 1 or 2.

(*a*) List the eight different ways in which the three people can choose their numbers.

(*b*) How likely is it that *none* of them will win? Give a reason for your answer.

2 Three people play the game but they all agree that they will choose numbers between 1 and 3.

(*a*) Suppose one player chooses 3. List the nine different ways in which the other two players could choose their numbers.

(*b*) Is 3 a sensible number to choose? Give a reason for your answer.

3 Six people play the game of choosing numbers, but they all agree that they will only choose numbers between 1 and 6.

(*a*) Which number wins if everyone chooses 2 except one person, who chooses 3?

(*b*) Perhaps nobody wins. How could this happen?

(*c*) Would 6 be a sensible number to choose? Give a reason for your answer.

(*d*) What do you believe would be the best number to choose? Give a reason for your answer.

'If someone has a birthday, you should give them a chance to win.'

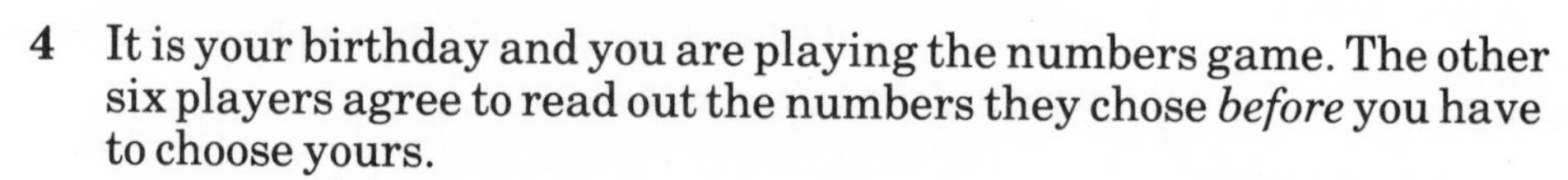

4 It is your birthday and you are playing the numbers game. The other six players agree to read out the numbers they chose *before* you have to choose yours.

(*a*) The first time you play, the other six players choose 4, 2, 1, 2, 5, 1. What would you choose? Explain your answer.

(*b*) The second time you play, the other six players choose 5, 1, 1, 2, 4, 5. What would you choose? Explain your answer.

5 In a pack of playing cards, 26 cards are red and 26 are black.

A pack of cards is shuffled well and you are given 10 cards.

(*a*) How many cards would you expect to be red?

(*b*) Would you be very surprised if you did not get this number of red cards? Explain your answer.

'Six is the hardest number on a die to get. It takes ages.'

6 In a normal pack of playing cards the Kings, Queens and Jacks are called picture cards.

Someone picks (without looking) a card from a pack of playing cards. She then throws a die.

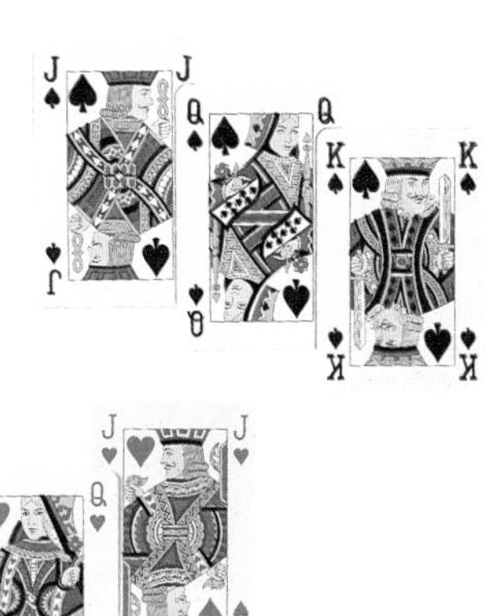

(*a*) Do you believe that she is more likely to pick a picture card or to throw a six?

(*b*) What is the probability of picking a picture card?

(*c*) What is the probability of throwing a six?

(*d*) Do you still believe your answer to part (*a*)?

7 In the Indonesian game of Conglak the two players decide who is to start by the following methods.

When someone says go, each of the two players raises either a thumb, a first finger or a little finger.

If one player raises a thumb and the other a first finger, the thumb wins and that player starts.

If one player raises a first finger and the other a little finger, the first finger wins.

If one player raises a little finger and the other a thumb, the little finger wins.

(*a*) If you were playing the game, what do you believe is the best way of trying to make sure that you start?

(*b*) List all the possible ways the two players can act.

(*c*) What is the probability that
(i) the thumb wins? (ii) the first finger wins?
(iii) the little finger wins? (iv) neither player wins?

(*d*) Do you still believe your answer to part (*a*)?

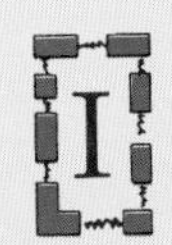

When answering questions 8, 9 and 10 you might find it helpful to use a sample space diagram. Here is a sample space diagram that might help with question 8(*a*).

		Second die					
		1	2	3	4	5	6
First die	1	2	3	4	5	6	7
	2	3	4	5	6	7	8
	3	4	5	6	7	8	9
	4	5	6	7	8	9	10
	5	6	7	8	9	10	11
	6	7	8	9	10	11	12

8 Julie and Thebender are betting on dice.

(*a*) Julie throws two dice. The two numbers thrown are added together and Julie agrees to pay Thebender 10p every time the answer is odd. Thebender is to pay Julie 10p every time the answer is even.

(i) Do you believe that this is fair?
(ii) Check whether it is fair.
(iii) If this is not fair suggest a way of adjusting the payments to make it fair.

(*b*) Julie throws two dice. The two numbers thrown are multiplied together and Julie agrees to pay Thebender 10p every time the answer is odd. Thebender is to pay Julie 10p every time the answer is even.

(i) Do you believe that this is fair?
(ii) Check whether it is fair.
(iii) If this is not fair suggest a way of adjusting the payments to make it fair.

9 Sanjay and Jason are playing a game.

Sanjay throws two dice, multiplies the two numbers obtained, and tells the answer to Jason. Jason has to guess what the two numbers were. If Sanjay tells Jason the answer is 25 Jason knows for certain what the two numbers were. If Sanjay says that the answer is 6 Jason cannot be sure.

(*a*) On one occasion Sanjay throws the dice and then he says to Jason:

> 'When I tell you the score you won't know what the two numbers were. But if I tell you that the two numbers were different then you will know.'

What two numbers must Sanjay have thrown?

(*b*) Each time Sanjay throws the two dice what is the probability that the answer he obtains will tell Jason exactly what the two numbers are?

(*c*) Suppose Sanjay gets his two numbers by picking one domino from a standard set of dominoes, instead of by throwing two dice.

How would your answer to parts (*a*) and (*b*) change?

'I am sure I shall get blue, because red is my favourite colour.'

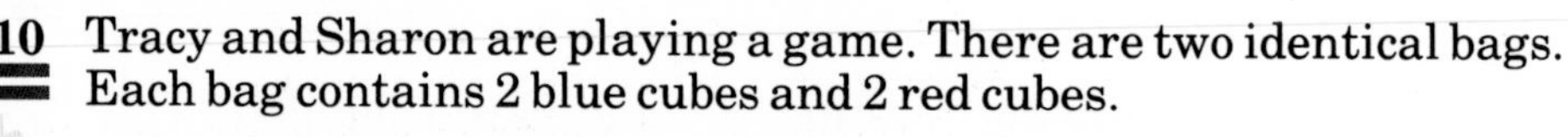

10 Tracy and Sharon are playing a game. There are two identical bags. Each bag contains 2 blue cubes and 2 red cubes.

Tracy has to close her eyes and pick one of the two bags at random. She then has to pick one of the cubes from that bag at random. Tracy wins if she picks a red cube.

(*a*) What is the probability that Tracy will win?

(*b*) Tracy says to Sharon,

> 'Before I pick the next cube, can I move the cubes around so that there are different numbers of cubes in the two bags?'

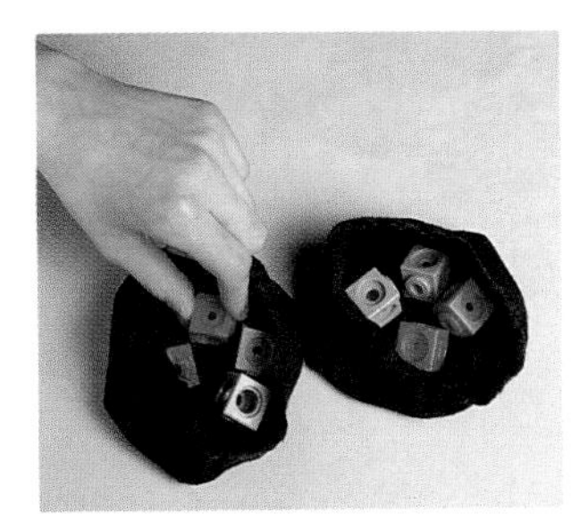

Sharon checks with Tracy that there will still be a total of 4 red cubes and 4 blue cubes in the two bags. Since the number of red cubes will still be the same as the number of blue cubes Sharon does not believe that a rearrangement will make any difference.

(i) How should Tracy rearrange the cubes between the two bags to give herself the best chance of winning?
(ii) When Tracy has done this, what will be the probability that she wins?

'It is not fair. You always go first.'

11 (*a*) Suppose you have a normal die, and your friend has another normal die. You both throw the dice at the same time. You win if the number on your die is larger than the number on your friend's die. Your friend wins if the number on his die is larger than the number on your die.

(i) What is the probability that you win?
(ii) What is the probability that neither you nor your friend wins?

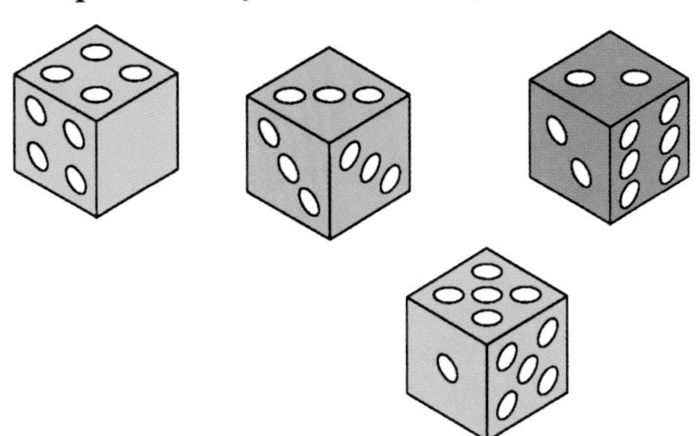

(*b*) Suppose now that you and your friend agree to use some dice which are not normal. There are four dice and the numbers on their faces are as follows.

First die	4	4	4	4	0	0
Second die	3	3	3	3	3	3
Third die	2	2	2	2	6	6
Fourth die	1	1	1	5	5	5

Your friend suggests that you can pick a die first and then he will pick a die. You then play with these two dice as in part (*a*).

(i) 'The person who chooses the die first should have the advantage, because she can pick the best die.'
Do you believe that this statement must be true?
(ii) If the first and second dice are used, which die has the advantage, and what is the probability that it will win?
(iii) If the second and third dice are used, which die has the advantage, and what is the probability that it will win?
(iv) If the third and fourth dice are used, which die has the advantage, and what is the probability that it will win?
(v) If the first and fourth dice are used, which die has the advantage, and what is the probability that it will win?
(vi) 'The person who chooses the die first should have the advantage, because she can pick the best die.'

Is this statement true?

SECTION B

Conjurers entertain us by getting us to believe that they have made the impossible happen.

Human beings are good at using science and technology to make 'impossible' things happen in real life. Some of those impossible things seem very useful; some seem very harmful.

In mathematics impossible things can sometimes seem to happen ...

The first version of a 'woman sawn in half'.

1 (*a*)

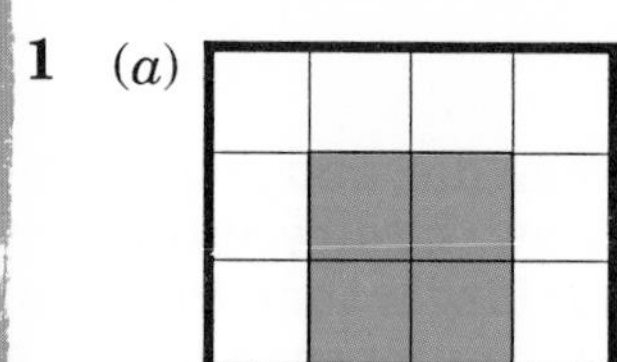

(*b*)

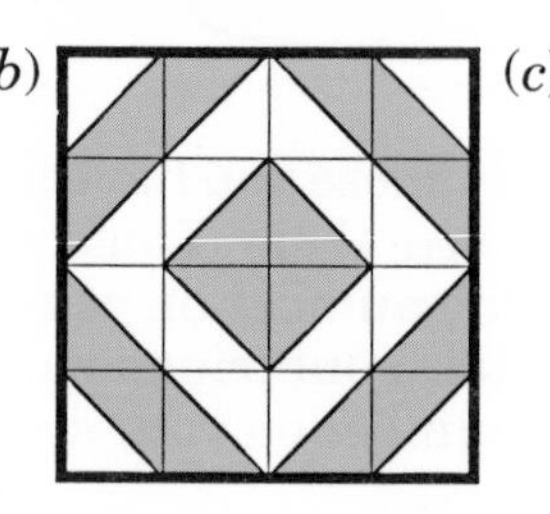

(*c*)

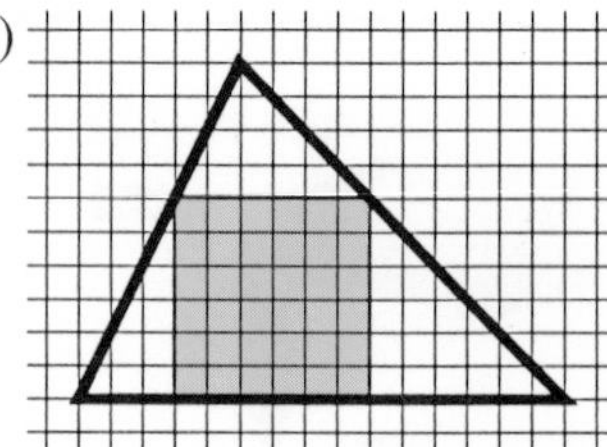

Just by looking at each picture say whether you believe

more than half
less than half
exactly half

of the picture is shaded.

Now work out exactly what fraction of each picture is shaded. Was your guess correct?

2 In the drawing, which of the three pieces do you believe has the biggest area?

When you have guessed, measure the drawing, and calculate the areas of the three pieces, to find out if you were right.

'I saw someone do a trick with coins once. He cheated. He said he was rolling the coins, but he must have slid them.'

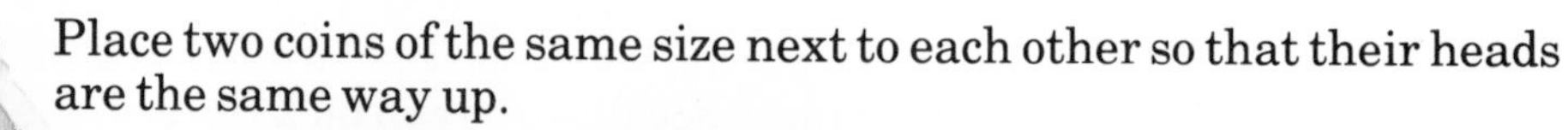

3 Place two coins of the same size next to each other so that their heads are the same way up.

Keep one coin fixed and roll the other one round it until it gets to the other side.

Will it end up like this, or like this?

Guess before you try it.

4 On squared paper draw a square as shown.

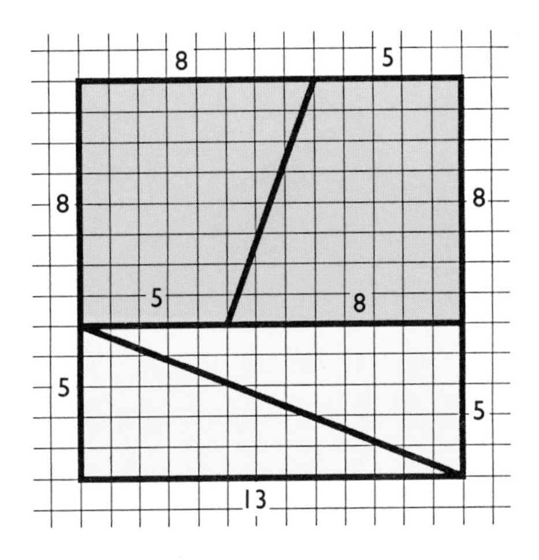

Cut out the four pieces and rearrange them to make the rectangle shown.

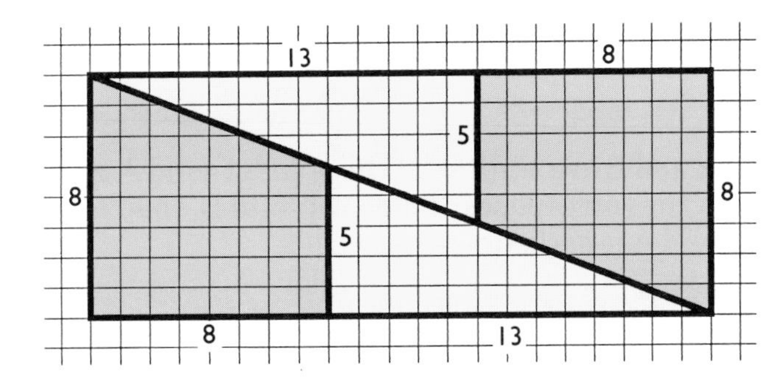

(*a*) What is the area of the square?

(*b*) What is the area of the rectangle?

(*c*) Explain why your answer to (*a*) is not the same as your answer to (*b*).

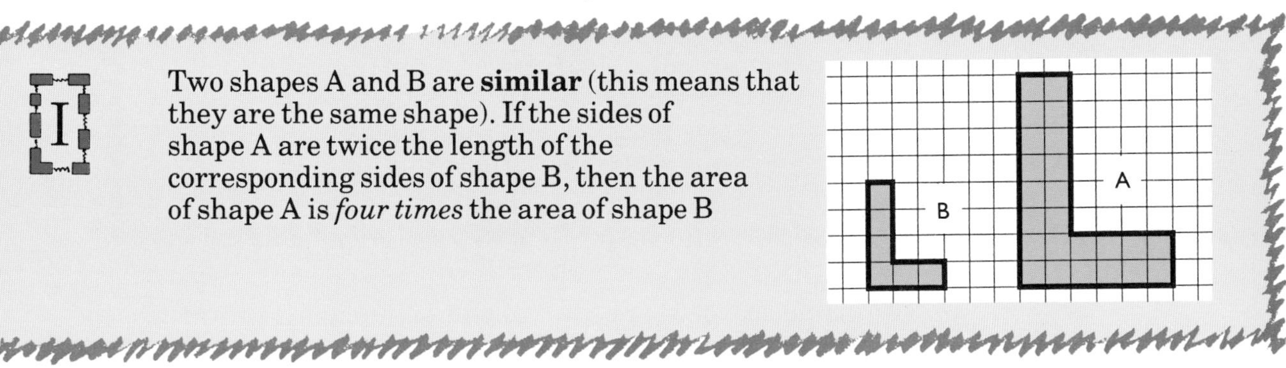

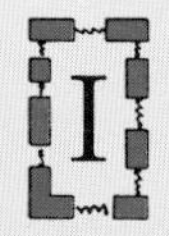

Two shapes A and B are **similar** (this means that they are the same shape). If the sides of shape A are twice the length of the corresponding sides of shape B, then the area of shape A is *four times* the area of shape B

5 (*a*) Do you believe the statement in the box on page 201.

(*b*) Verify the statement by drawing pictures when

(i) A and B are rectangles.
(ii) A and B are triangles.
(iii) A and B are regular hexagons.

6 (*a*) Look at the box on page 201.

(i) If the word 'twice' was changed to 'three times' what should the words in italics letters say?
(ii) If the word 'twice' was changed to 'seven times' what should the words in italics letters say?

(*b*) Triangle T is similar to triangle U.

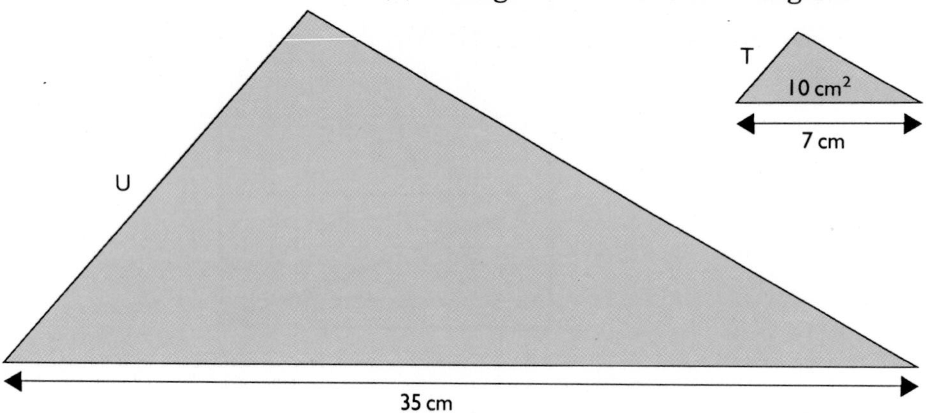

The longest side of triangle T is 7 cm and the longest side of triangle U is 35 cm. The area of triangle T is 10 cm^2. What is the area of triangle U?

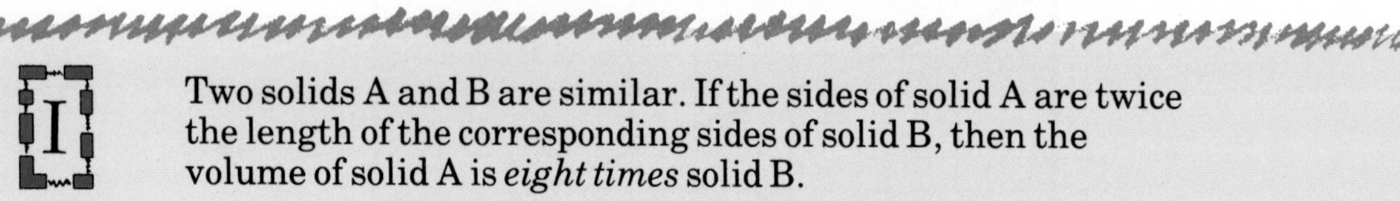

Two solids A and B are similar. If the sides of solid A are twice the length of the corresponding sides of solid B, then the volume of solid A is *eight times* solid B.

7 (*a*) Do you believe the statement in the box above?

(*b*) Verify the statement by drawing pictures when

(i) A and B are cubes.
(ii) A and B are triangular prisms.

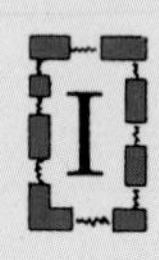

Two solids A and B are similar. If the sides of solid A are three times the length of the corresponding sides of solid B, then the volume of solid A is *twenty seven times* the volume of solid B. The surface area of solid A is *nine times* the surface area of solid B.

8 Two cylindrical cans are similar. One of the cans is three times the height of the other.

(*a*) If the volume of the larger can is 1 litre calculate, correct to the nearest millilitre, the volume of the smaller can.

(*b*) If the surface area of the smaller can is 150 cm^2, what is the surface area of the large can?

9 A tank is in the shape of a cube with a side of length 1 m. It is full of water.

How many two-litre bottles could be filled from the water in the tank? (1 litre = 1000 cm^3)

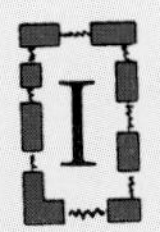

Solids A and B are similar. If the lengths for solid A are N times the corresponding lengths for solid B, then

- the volume of solid A is N^3 times the volume of solid B

and

- the surface area of solid A is N^2 times the surface area of solid B.

Judging from the number of mistakes made in examination questions about the volumes of similar solids, these results are probably extremely difficult for you to believe!

For questions providing practice in using these unbelievable results, see Review Exercise 47 on page 262.

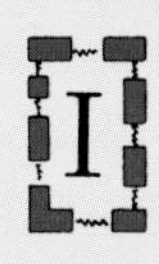

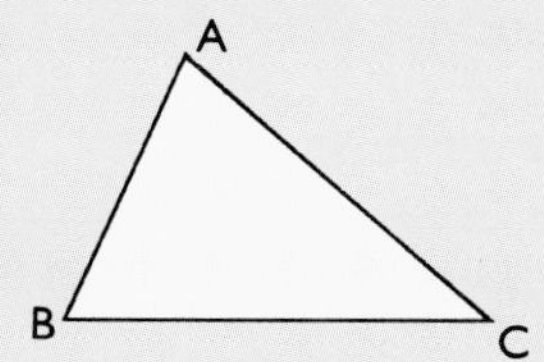

'What is the probability that a triangle is acute-angled?'

One way of answering this strange question is to draw a picture. Figure 1 shows a graph of all possible shapes of triangle, by plotting angle A against angle B.

Angle C does not need to be plotted, because knowing angles A and B means that you automatically know angle C.

The shaded region contains the points which represent possible triangles.

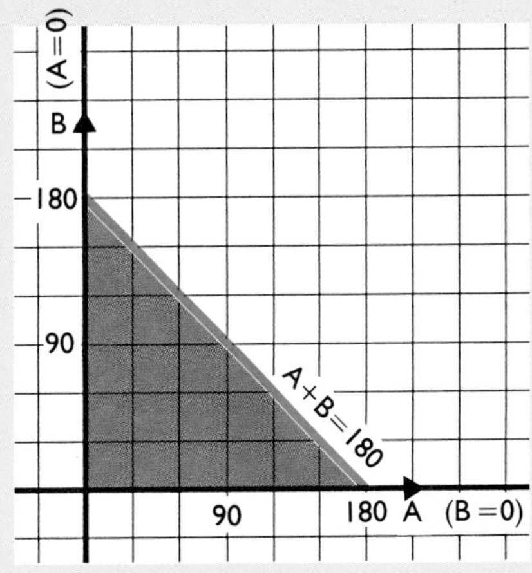

Figure 1

The line A = 0 is a boundary of this region because the angle of a triangle cannot be less than zero. For the same reason the line B = 0 is a boundary. The line A + B = 180° is a boundary because the sum of angles A and B must be less than 180°.

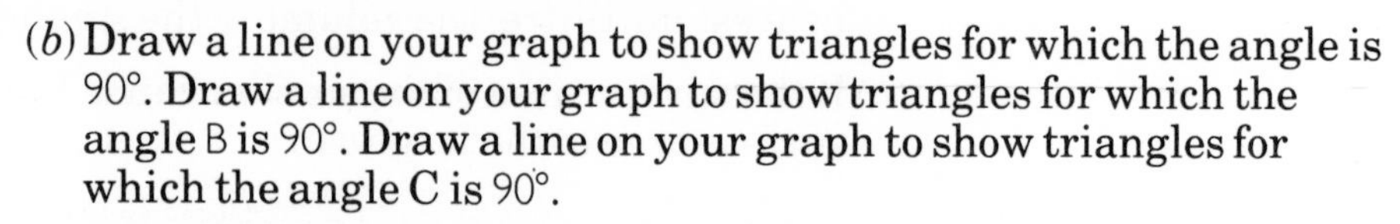

10 (*a*) Copy the graph in the box on page 203.

(*b*) Draw a line on your graph to show triangles for which the angle is 90°. Draw a line on your graph to show triangles for which the angle B is 90°. Draw a line on your graph to show triangles for which the angle C is 90°.

(*Hint:* What do you know about A and B when C = 90°?)

(*c*) Heavily shade in the region on your graph which represents acute-angled triangles.

(*d*) According to your graph, what is the probability that a triangle is acute-angled?

(*e*) Do you believe your answer to (*d*)?

11 Here is a different way of answering the question in the box. It is decided that A is to be the largest angle of the triangle, B the second largest angle and C the smallest angle.

This can be shown by a picture similar to the picture in question 10. It can be drawn as follows.

(*a*) First draw axes and label them as in the picture for question 10.

(*b*) Now draw the line $A + B = 180°$ on your graph.

(*c*) A is the largest angle, and so $A > B$. Draw the line $A = B$ on your graph.

(*d*) C is the smallest angle in the triangle and so $C < B$. Also $C = 180° - A - B$.

Use these facts to show that $B > 90 - \frac{1}{2}A$.

Draw the line $B = 90 - \frac{1}{2}A$ on your graph.

(*e*) Lightly shade in the region which represents triangles ABC, with angle A> angle B> angle C.

(*f*) Heavily shade in the region on your graph which represents acute-angled triangles.

(*Hint:* if the triangle is an obtuse-angled triangle, which angle has to be obtuse?)

(*g*) According to your graph, what is the probability that a triangle with angle A > angle B > angle C is acute-angled?

12

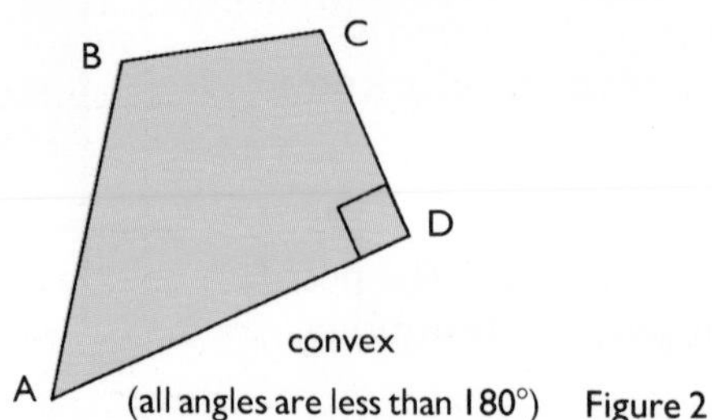

Figure 2

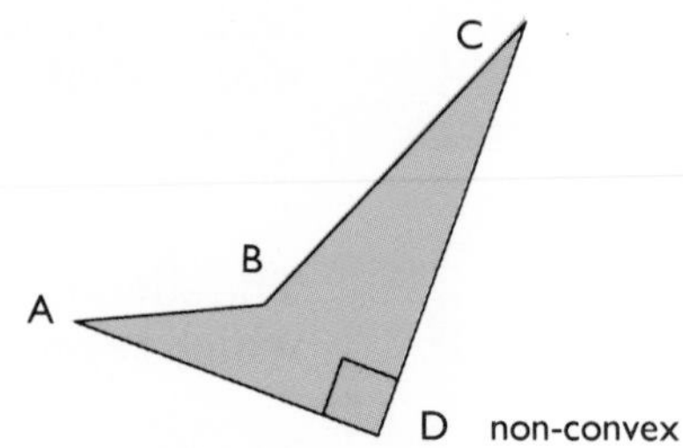

Figure 2 shows two right-angled quadrilaterals.

(*a*) ABCD is a right-angled quadrilateral with a right angle at D. Complete the following statements. The first is done for you.

(i) $A > 0$ (ii) $B >$ (iii) $A + B <$

(*b*) Draw a picture similar to the picture in question 10, to show the region which represents right-angled quadrilaterals ABCD.

(*c*) Heavily shade in the region which represents convex quadrilaterals.

(*d*) According to your graph, what is the probability that a right-angled quadrilateral is convex?

(*e*) Do you believe your answer to (*d*)?

13 A stick of length 100 cm is broken into three pieces. The length of one of the pieces is x cm, and another of the pieces is y cm.

(*a*) Explain why $x + y < 100$.

(*b*) Draw a picture similar to the picture in question 10, to show the region which represents all possible ways of breaking the stick into three.

(*c*) Show on your graph the ways of breaking the stick so that the three pieces can form a triangle.

(*Hint:* The three pieces of the stick will *not* form a triangle if one piece is longer than the other two put together.

Pieces of length 60 cm, 25 cm and 15 cm will *not* form a triangle.

Pieces of length 40 cm, 35 cm and 25 cm *will* form a triangle.)

(*d*) What is the probability that, if a stick is broken at random into three pieces, the pieces can form a triangle?

(*e*) Do you believe your answer to (*d*)?

SECTION C

1 40 students at a school in Leicestershire were asked to say which town they used most for clothes shopping.

36 of them said that they bought most of their clothes in Leicester.

(*a*) What percentage of the students bought their clothes in Leicester?

(*b*) Do you buy your clothes in Leicester?

(*c*) Does the survey show that most students using this book are likely to buy their clothes in Leicester? Give a reason for your answer.

Number of TV programmes	Males	Females	Total
0	11	10	21
1	7	4	11
2	11	14	25
3	19	8	27
4	9	14	23
5	8	5	13
6	2	5	7
7	2	3	5
8	3	1	4
Total	72	64	136

2 (*a*) How many television programmes did you watch last night?

(*b*) Do you believe you watch more or less television than most people?

The table on the left shows the number of television programmes watched by a number of fifteen-year-olds on a particular Tuesday evening.

(*c*) How many of the students watched more television programmes than you did?

(*d*) What percentage of the students in the survey watched more television programmes than you did?

(*e*) Do you still agree with your answer to part (*b*)?

3 In a survey of fifteen-year-old students the following results were obtained.

Do you hope to get married/have children?

	Yes	No	Don't know
Males	62	2	8
Females	59	0	5

(*a*) What percentage of the females definitely hope to get married/have children?

(*b*) What percentage of the males definitely hope to get married/have children?

(*c*) Do you believe that some of these students will change their minds? Give a reason for your answer.

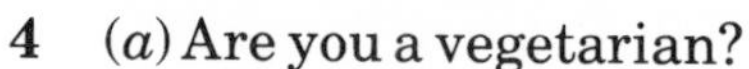

4 (*a*) Are you a vegetarian?

(*b*) Which of the following foods do you think are good for you?

apples	baked beans	bananas	beefburgers
bread	breakfast cereal	butter	carrots
cauliflower	cheese	chips	cream
crisps	curry	eggs	fried fish
lettuce	liver	margarine	oranges
pasta	peanuts	pork pie	sausages
rice	roast chicken	sardines	soup
spinach	sweetcorn	tomatoes	yoghurt

(*a*) In a survey a group of fifteen-year-olds were asked which foods they thought were good for them. The results are given below.

Food	Males	Females	Total
apples	31	19	50
oranges	15	10	25
yoghurt	13	9	22
bananas	16	5	21
lettuce	12	8	20
carrots	10	8	18
tomatoes	7	8	15
bread	13	1	14
cauliflower	7	5	12
cheese	7	5	12
baked beans	6	4	10

What surprises you most about the results of the survey?

5 (*a*) How much exercise have you taken during the last week?

Amount of exercise (hours per week)	Males	Females	Total
none	9	18	27
less than 1	4	6	10
between 1 and 2	8	9	17
between 2 and 3	12	6	18
between 3 and 4	7	5	12
between 4 and 5	5	5	10
between 5 and 6	6	0	6
between 6 and 7	5	4	9
between 7 and 8	8	3	11
between 8 and 9	4	4	8
between 9 and 10	1	1	2
between 10 and 11	2	2	4
between 11 and 12	1	0	1
more than 12	0	1	1
Total	72	64	136

(*b*) The table above shows the amount of exercise taken by a group of 136 fifteen-year-olds. Do you think you take more exercise or less exercise than most fifteen-year-olds? Explain your answer.

(*c*) Is length of time the best way to measure how much exercise someone takes? Explain your answer.

For question 6 you need a list of the TV programmes for one day. You can either get this from a paper or the TV Times or Radio Times, or you can use the resource sheet called *'Television times'*. **Do not look at the list until you have answered 6 (*a*).**

6 (*a*) What percentage of programmes on the television do you believe are

(i) films? (ii) news and current affairs?
(iii) sport? (iv) soaps?

(*b*) Use your list of TV programmes for one day to calculate the percentage which are

(i) films,
(ii) news and current affairs,
(iii) sport,
(iv) soaps.

(*c*) Explain whether or not you still believe your answer to part (*a*).

'Never eat pork unless there is a letter R in the month.'

7 Some people believe that Friday 13th is unlucky. If you are one of those people you might want to know when Friday 13th is about to happen.

(*a*) If the 13th is a Friday, what day of the week is the first of the month?

(*b*) One month the 13th was a Wednesday.

Would the 13th be a Friday in the following month if the following month was

(i) July? (ii) August? (iii) December?

(*c*) When was the next Friday 13th after Friday 13th April 1990?

(*d*) When is the next Friday 13th after today?

'I am not against eating animals, but I don't think anyone should be cruel to animals.'

8 Battery hens live in cages measuring 50 cm by 46 cm. Four hens live in a cage of this size.

(*a*) What is the area of the floor of the cage?

(*b*) What is the area of the sheet of paper you are writing on?

(*c*) How many times bigger is the floor of the cage than the sheet of paper you are writing on?

'Society is much more violent these days than it used to be. I blame the water.'

9

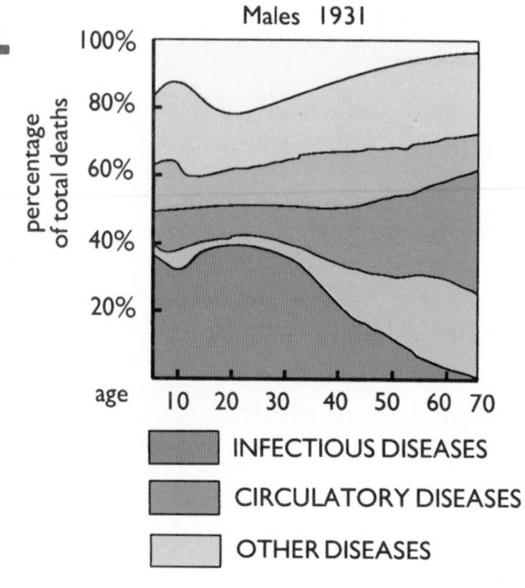

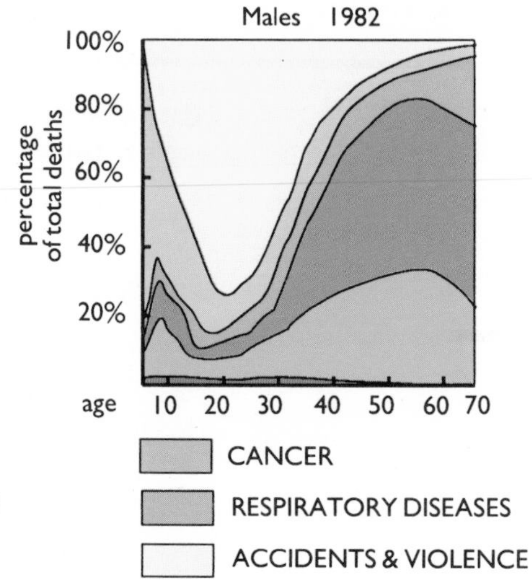

(*a*) What percentage of the deaths of 20-year-old males were accidental or violent deaths in

(i) 1931?
(ii) 1982?

(*b*) Were young males far more careless and violent in 1982 than they were in 1931, or is there a different explanation for your answer to (*a*)?

'Do you remember that rail disaster in the newspaper? I never travel on trains these days. It's much too dangerous.'

10

Risk of an individual dying in any one year from various causes	
Smoking 10 cigarettes a day:	one in 200
All natural causes, age 40:	one in 850
Any kind of violence or poisoning:	one in 3,300
Influenza:	one in 5,000
Accident on the road:	one in 8,000
Leukaemia:	one in 12,500
Playing soccer:	one in 25,000
Accident at home:	one in 26,000
Accident at work:	one in 43,500
Radiation working in radiation industry:	one in 57,000
Homicide:	one in 100,000
Accident on railway:	one in 500,000
Hit by lightning:	one in 10,000,000
Release of radiation from nearby nuclear power station:	one in 10,000,000

(*a*) Which is more dangerous: travelling by road, or travelling by railway? Explain your answer.

(*b*) A town has a population of 200 000 people.

(i) How many would you expect to die of influenza in an average year?
(ii) Would you expect more people to die of influenza in some years and fewer in other years? Give a reason for your answer.

(*c*) The population of the United Kingdom is about 50 million. On average, how many people in the United Kingdom would you expect to be killed by lightning each year?

11 Suppose that you live in London, near Heathrow Airport.

(*a*) On which of the following holidays do you believe you would be most likely to be killed during a journey? Choose an order for the four letters **A**, **B**, **C** and **D**, starting with the holiday you think is the most dangerous.

A Two weeks in Tenerife, travelling by air, lying on the beach when you get there.

B Two weeks cycling round Britain, assuming that you average 50 miles a day.

C Two weeks in Cornwall. You travel by train, and hire a car when you get there. You drive about 100 miles a day.

D A coach tour to Austria, crossing the Channel by sea.

The following statistics are taken from *'Social Trends 19'*.

Type of transport	Death rate per billion passenger kilometres
Air	0.3
Rail	0.3
Bus or coach	0.8
Car	5.9
Motor bike	156
Bicycle	68
Sea	1.8

(1 mile = 1.6 km approximately)
(1 billion = 10^9)

(*b*) Use the statistics and the maps to calculate the probability of being killed on each of these holidays.

Do you still believe your answer to part (*a*)?

12 A survey of fifteen-year-olds obtained the following information.

Latest time expected home in the evening	Boys	Girls
7.00 p.m.	1	0
↓	—	—
9.00 p.m.	7	5
9.30 p.m.	9	5
10.00 p.m.	20	9
10.30 p.m.	13	12
11.00 p.m.	8	12
11.30 p.m.	5	3
midnight	0	4
any time	8	7
never go out	1	6
when it gets dark	0	1
Total	72	64

The information in the table above is somewhat vague in some respects. State what assumptions you need to make when you answer each of the following.

(*a*) What is the median time at which boys are expected home?

(*b*) What is the median time at which girls are expected home?

(*c*) What makes it hard to calculate mean times at which boys and girls are expected home?

The survey asked students what time they thought most other boys and girls were expected home. Here are the results.

Boys' replies

other boys allowed out later	11	girls allowed out later	2
other boys have to be in earlier	6	girls have to be in earlier	24
don't know/same time	55	don't know/same time	46

Girls' replies

other girls allowed out later	9	boys allowed out later	30
other girls have to be in earlier	26	boys have to be in earlier	4
don't know/same time	29	don't know/same time	30

(*d*) Look at your answers to parts (*a*) and (*b*). Comment on the accuracy of the views expressed by the fifteen-year-olds in the survey.

'Lots of young people doing part-time jobs especially girls, are simply exploited as cheap labour.'

13 A survey of 136 fifteen-year-olds at school found that 75 of them had part-time jobs. 9 males and 7 females had jobs as shop assistants. Here is the information they provided.

Males

Hours per week	Wages per hour
10	£1.65
5	£1.40
16	£1.55
Variable	
9–16	£1.83
24	
7	£1.50
4	
8	£2.00

Females

Hours per week	Wages per hour
16	£1.44
7	£1.84
10	£1.00
8	£1.37
	£1.93
4	£1.46
6	£2.00

(*a*) From the information above, give the best possible estimate of the following. State any assumptions you need to make.

(i) The median hourly wage for the females.
(ii) The mean hourly wage for the females.
(iii) The median hourly wage for the males.
(iv) The mean hourly wage for the males.
(v) The mean number of hours worked per week by the females.
(vi) The mean number of hours worked per week by males.

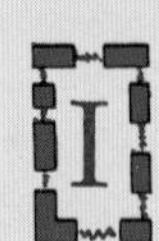

A different way of estimating the 'average' pay per hour is to find the *total amount earned* and divide by the *total number of hours worked*.

For example, consider the males in the survey who stated both how many hours they worked and how much they earned per hour.

The *total amount* earned by these males in a week is £$(7 \times 1.50 + 8 \times 2 + 12.5 \times 1.83 + 10 \times 1.65 + 5 \times 1.40 + 16 \times 1.55) =$ £97.675.

The *total number of hours* worked in a week by these males is $7 + 8 + 12.5 + 10 + 5 + 16 = 58.5$.

So the mean amount earned per hour, when calculated in this way, is $97.675 \div 58.5 =$ £1.67.

(*b*) Ignoring the female who provided incomplete information, what is the mean hourly wage for the females using the method in the box on page 212?

(*c*) Think of a way of including the female who provided incomplete information, in the mean when it is worked out in this way. Recalculate the mean taking her information into account.

(*d*) How strong is the evidence provided by this survey that males earn more than females as part-time shop assistants?

(*e*) If you conducted a similar survey in your school how do you think the averages you obtained might be different from these?

14 In tutor period a teacher asked four friends how many of them were vegetarians. Three of them said they were. The teacher knew there were 1000 pupils in the school and worked out that about 750 of them were probably vegetarians.

Do you think the teacher was right? Give reasons for your answer.

15 A national newspaper asked 21 schools in Lincolnshire whether they were experiencing problems with recruiting teachers. It reported that 61.9% of them said they were.

(*a*) How many schools said they were experiencing problems with recruiting teachers?

(*b*) Suppose the newspaper had asked an extra school as well as the 21 it did ask. What percentage of schools would have been experiencing problems if the extra school said

(i) it did have problems?
(ii) it did not have problems?

(*c*) Do you think that it was honest of the newspaper to quote the percentage correct to one decimal place? Give a reason for your answer.

There are some questions which statistics cannot help with. Here are examples.

- Are all people of equal importance?
- Are all people entitled to good health care, however rich or poor they are?
- Are all people entitled to good housing, however rich or poor they are?

Statistics can be collected about what kind of health care or housing people actually have. But statistics cannot tell you what people should have. This must be decided in other ways. *What do you believe?*

1) Some of the information used in Section C was collected from a survey of 136 fifteen-year-olds in a school in Leicestershire.

The questionnaire used is the resource sheet called *'What do you believe'*.

Use this questionnaire to find out what people in your school believe. Present your findings in the form of a report, with appropriate graphs and tables. You might want to compare some of your results with those for the Leicestershire school given in Section C.

You might find it useful to store your results in a database. You can then use the database to help you obtain your results.

2) Choose a topic about which you have strong opinions.

This topic might be to do with religion, or politics, or sport, or animal welfare, or the environment, or health, or something different.

Collect information about this topic which supports or contradicts your opinions.

This information might be the opinions of people in your school, or your family, or other people you know. To collect these opinions you can use a questionnaire.

Alternatively, this information might be obtained from books or magazines. It might be facts and figures about sporting records, or how animals are treated, or what is happening to the environment, and so on. It may include maps, diagrams and graphs.

Write a report in support of your opinions. Include in the report the statistics you have collected or the information you have discovered.

Make the best possible use of the information to support your case. On the other hand, your case will be made more strongly if you admit that some of the evidence you collect might *not* support your opinions.

You might find it useful to consider the advice given for the Further Coursework Tasks on page 177.

TELLING A COMPUTER WHAT TO DRAW

Telling a computer what to draw is a bit like telling a person what to draw.

If you want to get someone to draw a snowman:

you could show them the picture and tell them to copy it.

But you might want someone to draw their own idea of a snowman. In this case you could simply give the instruction

'Draw a snowman!'

Or you might say

'Draw a snowman, and make sure he has a nose, a scarf and a broom.'

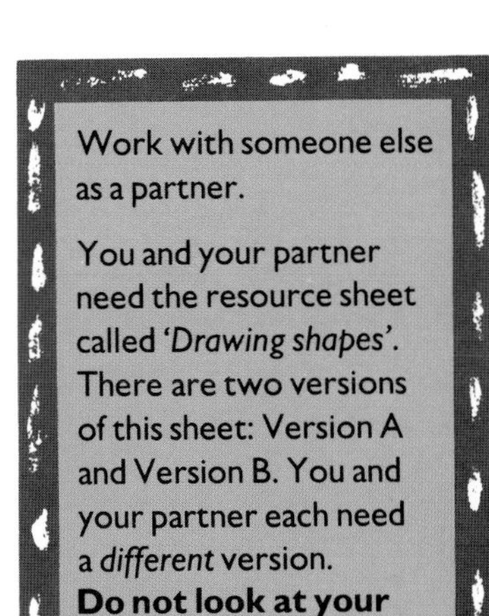

Work with someone else as a partner.

You and your partner need the resource sheet called '*Drawing shapes*'. There are two versions of this sheet: Version A and Version B. You and your partner each need a *different* version.
Do not look at your partner's worksheet.

If you told someone what to draw without showing them the picture, the snowman they produced would be different from the one shown in the picture above.

- At the top of your sheet is a picture of a square inside a circle. Do not show this to your partner. Describe the picture in words, so that your partner can draw it. Your partner will describe a similar picture for you to draw. Try to draw your picture as accurately as possible.
- Now describe in words the picture at the bottom of your resource sheet, so that your partner can draw it. Again, your partner will describe a similar picture for you to draw.
- When you have finished drawing your pictures look at your partner's resource sheet and compare what you have drawn with the pictures on the sheet. Discuss the differences.

When you want to tell a computer what to draw you can sometimes use a mouse with a drawing package. This is rather like showing the computer the picture.

But sometimes this does not produce accurate enough results. Or it might be too complicated. So instead you can give instructions to the computer by using words and numbers.

SECTION A

This section is about some of the ways in which you could describe a picture to a computer.

1 Coordinates are sometimes useful in describing pictures.

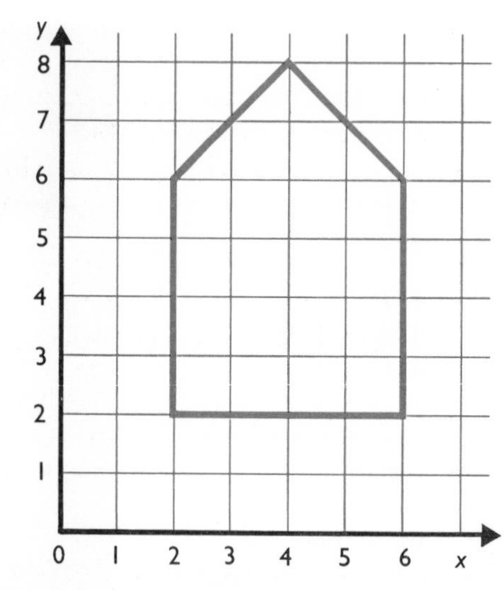

The pentagon shown above can be described using coordinates as follows

$$\begin{pmatrix} 2 & 6 & 6 & 4 & 2 \\ 2 & 2 & 6 & 8 & 6 \end{pmatrix}$$

Numbers put together in brackets like this are called a **matrix**.

Each of the matrices below describes a quadrilateral. Draw each quadrilateral. Then say what type of quadrilateral it is.

(*a*) $\begin{pmatrix} 3 & 4 & 3 & 2 \\ 1 & 3 & 5 & 3 \end{pmatrix}$ (*b*) $\begin{pmatrix} 0 & 6 & 4 & 2 \\ 0 & 0 & 3 & 3 \end{pmatrix}$ (*c*) $\begin{pmatrix} 3 & 5 & 4 & 2 \\ 1 & 2 & 4 & 3 \end{pmatrix}$

2 Replace the question marks with numbers so that the matrix gives the shape named.

(*a*) $\begin{pmatrix} 2 & 6 & 7 & ? \\ 4 & 6 & 4 & ? \end{pmatrix}$ kite

(*b*) $\begin{pmatrix} 2 & 4 & ? & 2 \\ 1 & 2 & 6 & ? \end{pmatrix}$ parallelogram

(*c*) $\begin{pmatrix} 3 & 5 & ? & 1 \\ 0 & ? & 5 & 4 \end{pmatrix}$ rectangle

3 Replace the question marks with numbers so that the matrix gives a triangle of the type shown.

(*a*) $\begin{pmatrix} -3 & 1 & ? \\ 1 & 1 & 6 \end{pmatrix}$ isosceles triangle (one answer)

(*b*) $\begin{pmatrix} 0 & 4 & 2 \\ 0 & 2 & ? \end{pmatrix}$ right-angled, isosceles triangle (two answers)

(*c*) $\begin{pmatrix} 0 & 4 & 1 \\ 0 & 2 & ? \end{pmatrix}$ right-angled, isosceles triangle (one answer)

(*d*) $\begin{pmatrix} 1 & 3 & ? \\ 1 & 5 & 2 \end{pmatrix}$ right-angled triangle (four answers)

4 Find a matrix which gives

(*a*) a rectangle with an area of 12 square units.

(*b*) a right-angled triangle with an area of 6 square units.

(*c*) a trapezium with an area of 18 square units.

5 (*a*) (i) Find a matrix which gives an acute-angled, isosceles triangle with an area of 8 square units.
(ii) By putting two triangles together, find a matrix which gives a rhombus with an area of 16 square units.

(*b*) Find a matrix which gives an obtuse-angled, isosceles triangle with an area of 8 square units.

(*c*) Find a matrix which gives a kite with an area of 6 square units.

6 Here is the matrix for a square.

$$\begin{pmatrix} -4 & -4 & 4 & 4 \\ -4 & 4 & 4 & -4 \end{pmatrix}$$

(*a*) The midpoints of the sides of this square are joined. What is the matrix for the shape shown?

(*b*) The midpoints are joined again. What is the matrix for the shape shown?

(*c*) Write down the matrices for the next four squares obtained in this way.

7 Here is the matrix for a triangle.

$$\begin{pmatrix} 1 & 13 & 7 \\ 1 & 7 & 19 \end{pmatrix}$$

(*a*) What is the matrix for the triangle obtained by joining the midpoints of the sides of this triangle?

(*b*) Use a calculator or a spreadsheet to find the matrix for the next six triangles obtained in this way.

(*c*) What happens eventually?

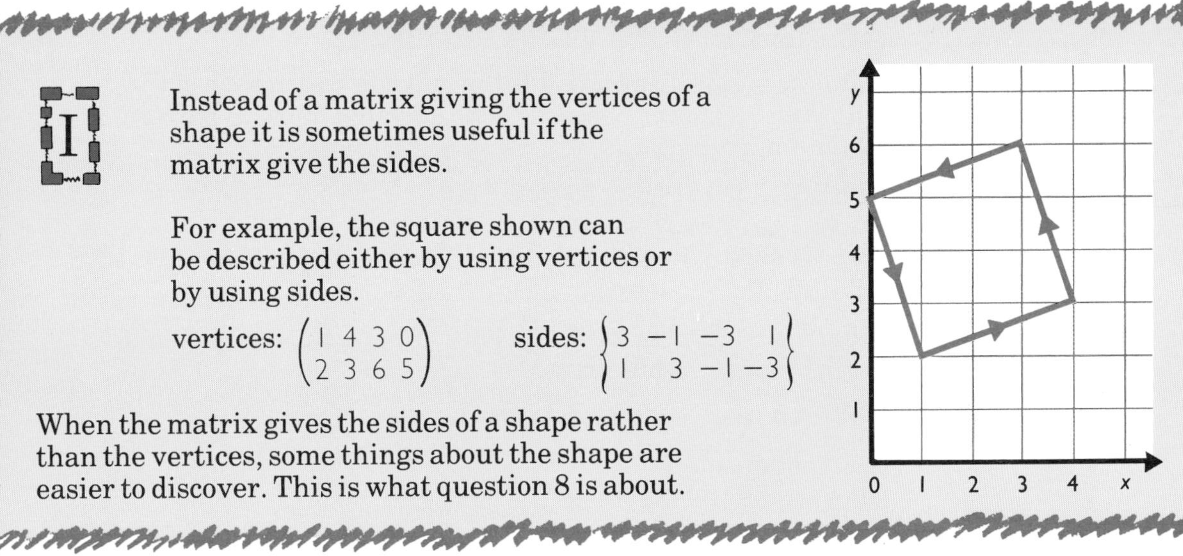

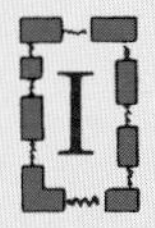

Instead of a matrix giving the vertices of a shape it is sometimes useful if the matrix give the sides.

For example, the square shown can be described either by using vertices or by using sides.

vertices: $\begin{pmatrix} 1 & 4 & 3 & 0 \\ 2 & 3 & 6 & 5 \end{pmatrix}$ sides: $\begin{Bmatrix} 3 & -1 & -3 & 1 \\ 1 & 3 & -1 & -3 \end{Bmatrix}$

When the matrix gives the sides of a shape rather than the vertices, some things about the shape are easier to discover. This is what question 8 is about.

You will need Pythagoras' theorem, which you can find on page 281.

8 (*a*) The square in the box has this matrix to describe its sides.

$$\begin{pmatrix} 3 & -1 & -3 & 1 \\ 1 & 3 & -1 & -3 \end{pmatrix}$$

(i) What is the length of one of the sides of the square?
(ii) What is the area of the square?

(*b*) This is the matrix which describes the sides of a triangle.

$$\begin{pmatrix} 3 & -5 & 2 \\ 4 & 0 & -4 \end{pmatrix}$$

What kind of triangle is this? Explain your answer.

(*c*) Which of the matrices below gives a rhombus, which gives a parallelogram, and which gives a trapezium? Explain your answer.

(i) $\begin{pmatrix} 3 & 5 & -3 & -5 \\ -1 & 0 & 1 & 0 \end{pmatrix}$ (ii) $\begin{pmatrix} 1 & 3 & -2 & -2 \\ 1 & 0 & -2 & 1 \end{pmatrix}$

(iii) $\begin{pmatrix} 2 & -3 & -2 & 3 \\ 3 & 2 & -3 & -2 \end{pmatrix}$ (iv) $\begin{pmatrix} 1 & 2 & -4 & 1 \\ 2 & -4 & 1 & 2 \end{pmatrix}$

Matrices such as those in question 8 are one way of telling a computer about the sides of a polygon.

Another way of describing a polygon's sides is to use *Logo* turtle commands.

The remaining questions in this section are about *Logo*. If possible use *Logo* on a computer for these questions.

9 (*a*) Name as precisely as possible the polygon which each of the following commands describe (the question mark in part (iii) stands for a number)

(i) REPEAT 3 [FD 100 RT 120]
(ii) REPEAT 2 [FD 100 LT 90 FD 50 LT 90]
(iii) FD 300 LT 120 FD 100 LT 60 FD ? LT 60 FD 100 LT 120

(*b*) What is the number which needs to replace the question mark in (*a*)(iii)? Explain your answer.

(*c*) Give *Logo* turtle commands for

(i) a rhombus,
(ii) a regular hexagon,
(iii) a non-regular hexagon.

10 The following procedure draws a rectangle of any size and shape

```
TO RECTANGLE "SIDE1 "SIDE2
REPEAT 2 [FD :SIDE1 RT 90 FD :SIDE2 RT 90]
END
```

(*a*) Write a procedure which draws a square of any size.

(*b*) Write a procedure which draws a rhombus of any size and shape.

(*c*) Write a procedure which draws a parallelogram of any size and shape.

> You will need to use trigonometry for parts (*b*) and (*c*) of question 11. You will find what you need on page 282.

11 The pattern below is produced by the procedures shown

```
TO PATTERN
REPEAT 4 [T RT 90]
END

TO T
FD 100
RT 90
FD 50 BK 100 FD 50
LT 90
BK 100
END
```

(*a*) How would you change the T procedure so that the Ts join up, as shown on the left?

(*b*) How would you change the procedures so that they draw the pattern shown on the right?

(*Hint:* You will need to calculate the lengths)

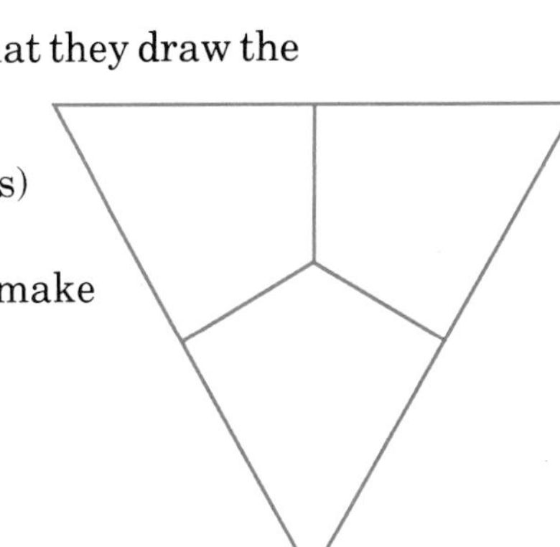

(*c*) One way of drawing a circle with *Logo* is to make a T pattern with a large number of Ts. The following procedures will draw a circle of radius 100.

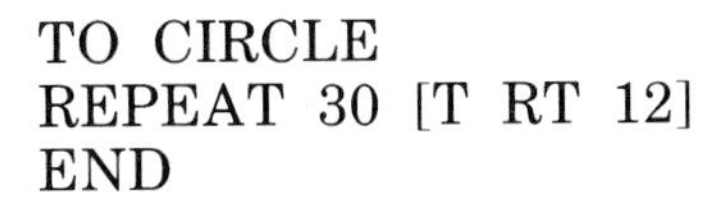

```
TO CIRCLE
REPEAT 30 [T RT 12]
END

TO T
PU FD 100
RT 90
PD FD ? BK ? FD ?
LT 90
PU BK 100
END
```

(N.B. PU means 'pen up' or LIFT: the turtle does not draw a line. PD means 'pen down' or DROP: the turtle draws a line.)

Calculate what should be used in place of the question marks in the T procedure.

Some shapes are easier to describe to a computer using *Logo*. Some shapes are easier to describe using matrices. Some shapes are difficult to describe by either method. Questions 12 to 16 are about this.

For these questions you will need to use Pythagoras' theorem and trigonometry. You will find what you need on page 281.

12 If you want to get a computer to draw the shapes shown below it is easier to use a *Logo* procedure than to use a sides matrix.

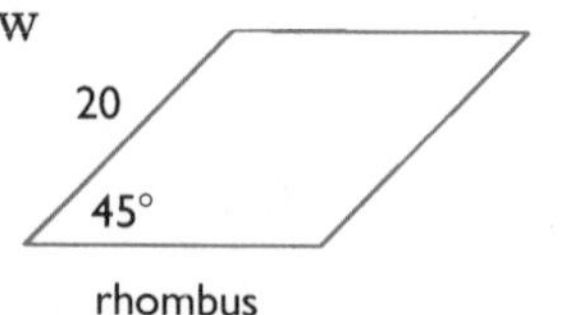

rhombus

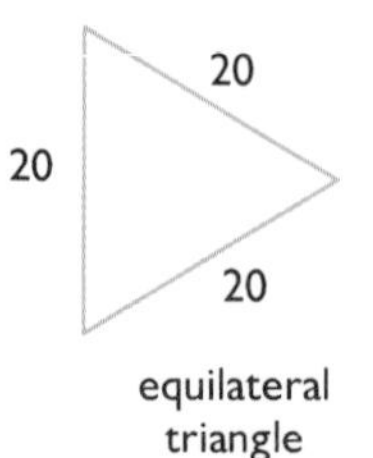

equilateral triangle

(i) Write *Logo* procedures for drawing each of these shapes.
(ii) Work out a sides matrix for each of these shapes.

13 If you want to get a computer to draw the shapes shown below it is easier to use a sides matrix than to use a *Logo* procedure.

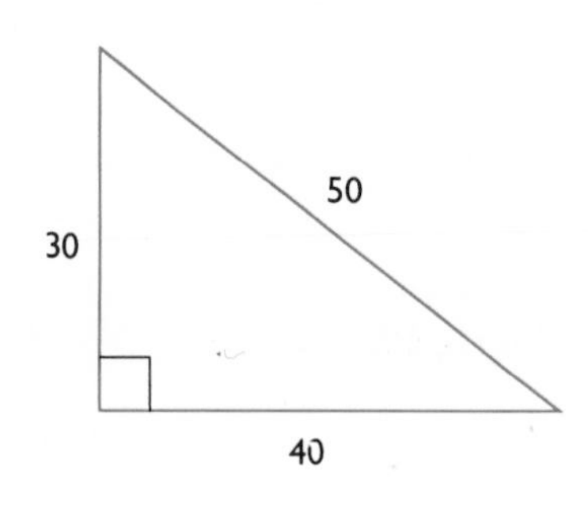

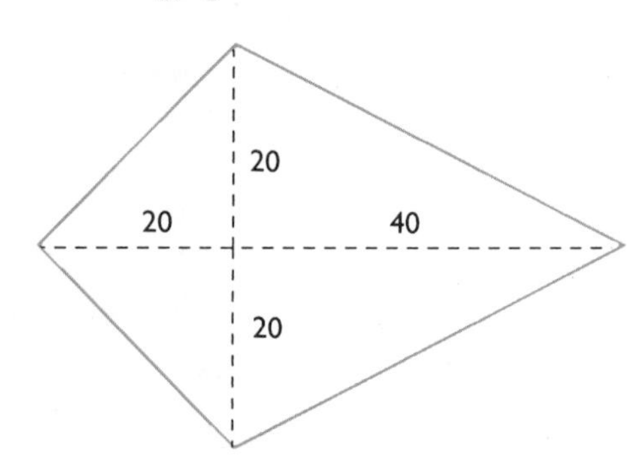

(i) Work out a sides matrix for each of these shapes.
(ii) Write *Logo* procedures for drawing each of these shapes.

14 Write *Logo* procedures for drawing each of these shapes. You will need to calculate either side lengths or angles before you can write the procedure.

The shapes in questions 14, 15 and 16 are not easy to draw using either *Logo* or a sides matrix.

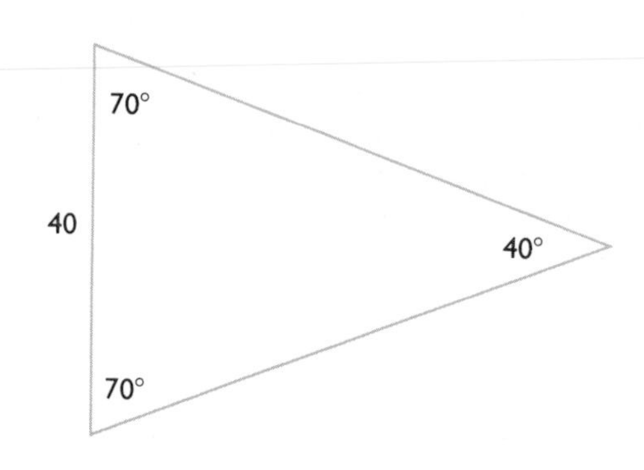

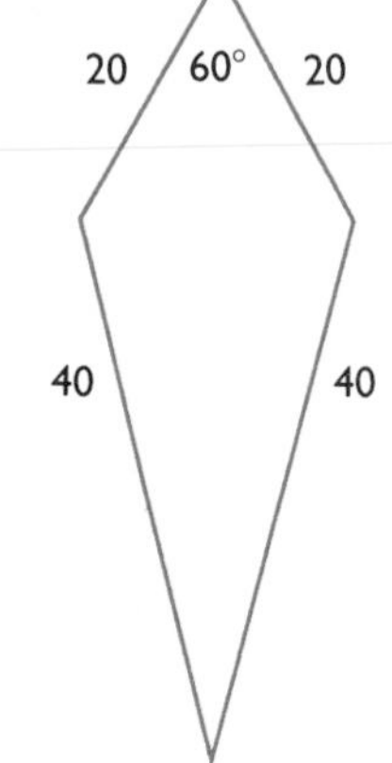

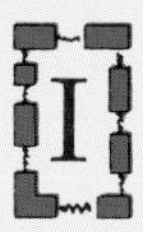

You need to calculate side lengths and angles before you can draw the shapes in question 15.

To find side lengths or angles in a triangle which is not right-angled you need to use the **cosine rule** and the **sine rule**.

The cosine rule is like Pythagoras' theorem, but there is an extra term to allow for the fact that the angle is not a right angle.

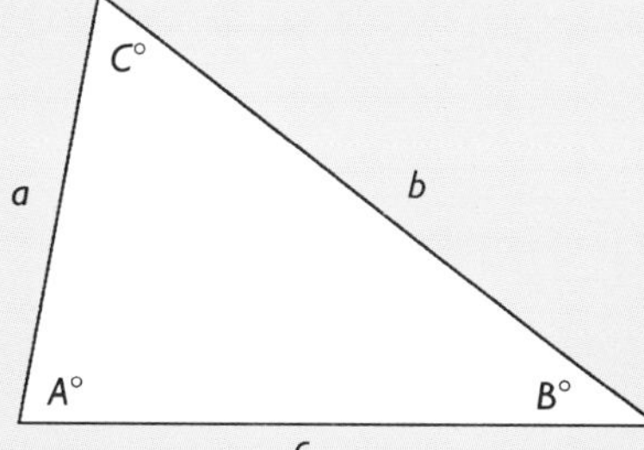

Cosine rule: $c^2 = a^2 + b^2 - 2ab\cos C$

Sine rule: $\frac{a}{\sin A} = \frac{b}{\sin B} = \frac{c}{\sin C}$

To write a *Logo* procedure for the triangle shown below you first need to calculate the length of the other side and the sizes of the other two angles.

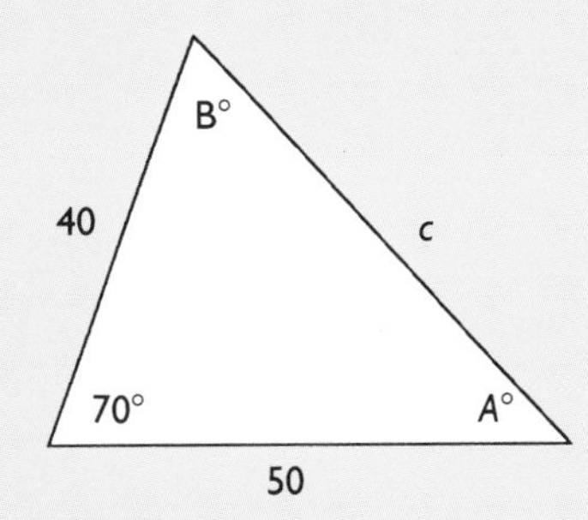

To find the missing side length, use the cosine rule.

$$c^2 = 40^2 + 50^2 - 2 \times 40 \times 50 \times \cos 70°$$
$$= 2732$$

Thus $c = 52.3$

To find one of the missing angles, use the sine rule.

$$\frac{40}{\sin A} = \frac{52.3}{\sin 70}$$

$$40 \times \sin 70 = 52.3 \times \sin A$$

$$\sin A = \frac{40 \times \sin 70}{52.3}$$

$$\sin A = 0.7187$$

$$A = 45.9°$$

You can find the third angle by using the fact that the sum of the angles of a triangle is 180°.

15 Write *Logo* procedures for drawing each of these shapes.

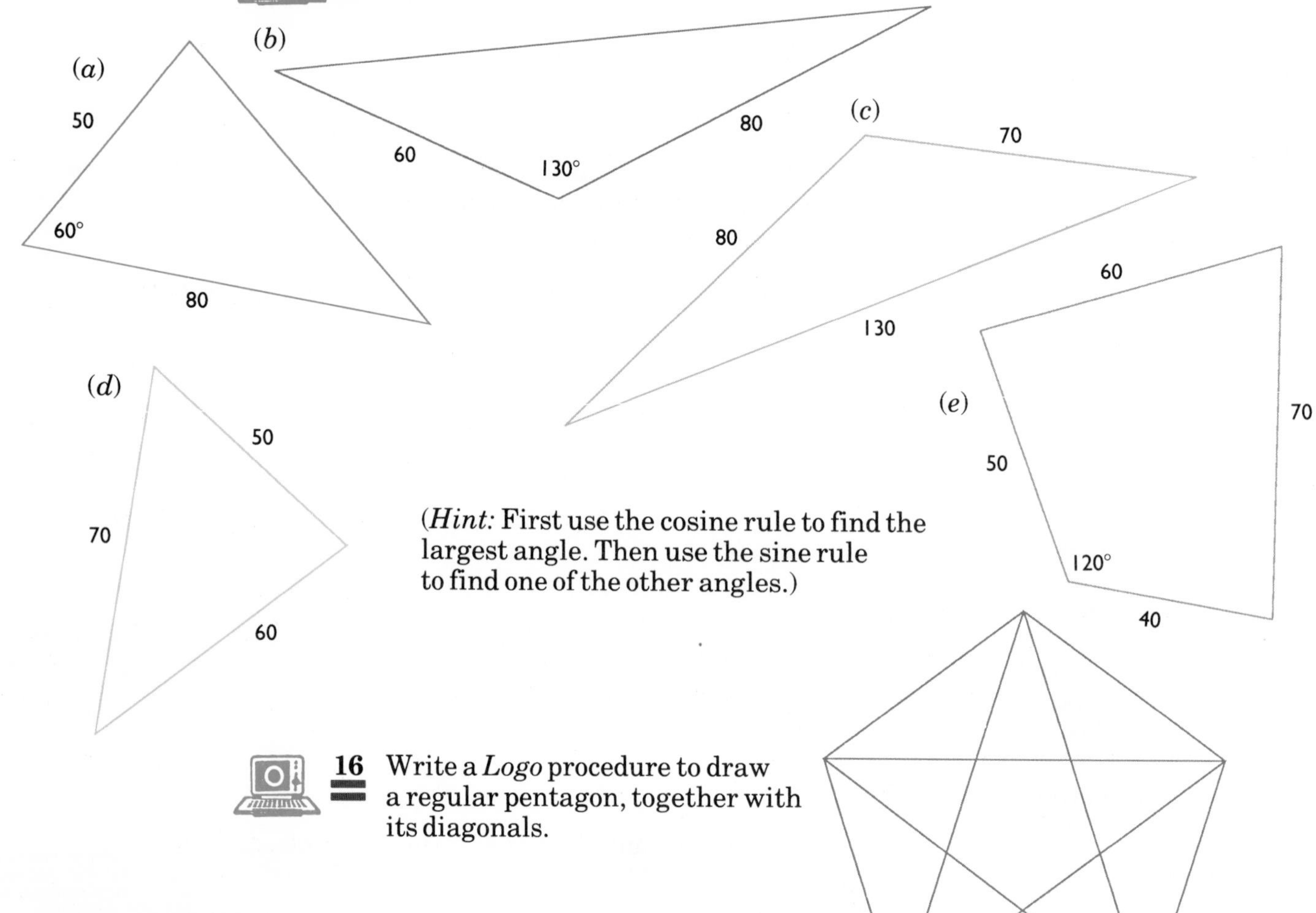

(*Hint:* First use the cosine rule to find the largest angle. Then use the sine rule to find one of the other angles.)

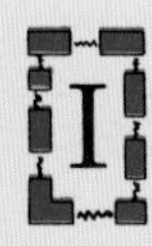

16 Write a *Logo* procedure to draw a regular pentagon, together with its diagonals.

SECTION B

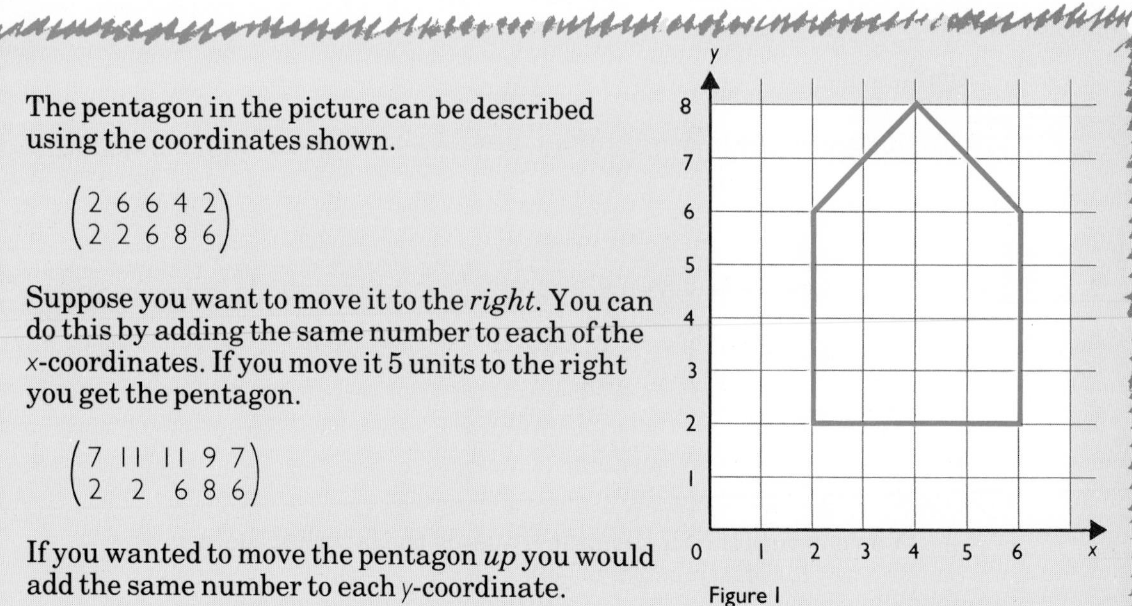

I The pentagon in the picture can be described using the coordinates shown.

$$\begin{pmatrix} 2 & 6 & 6 & 4 & 2 \\ 2 & 2 & 6 & 8 & 6 \end{pmatrix}$$

Suppose you want to move it to the *right*. You can do this by adding the same number to each of the x-coordinates. If you move it 5 units to the right you get the pentagon.

$$\begin{pmatrix} 7 & 11 & 11 & 9 & 7 \\ 2 & 2 & 6 & 8 & 6 \end{pmatrix}$$

If you wanted to move the pentagon *up* you would add the same number to each y-coordinate.

Figure 1

1 (*a*) The pentagon with coordinates matrix

$$\begin{pmatrix} 2 & 6 & 6 & 4 & 2 \\ 2 & 2 & 6 & 8 & 6 \end{pmatrix}$$

is moved *up* 3 units.

Write down its coordinates matrix.

(*b*) Having been moved up, the pentagon is moved 4 units to the *left*.

Write down its coordinates matrix.

(*c*) The pentagon has been moved somewhere else. The coordinates matrix is shown below.

$$\begin{pmatrix} ? & 10 & ? & ? & ? \\ ? & ? & ? & 2 & ? \end{pmatrix}$$

Only two of the numbers are shown.

Copy the coordinates matrix, replacing the question marks with the correct numbers.

2 On a particular computer screen the x-coordinates go from 0 to 1279 and the y-coordinates go from 0 to 1023.

On the screen is a rhombus with coordinates matrix

$$\begin{pmatrix} 300 & 400 & 300 & 200 \\ 100 & 300 & 500 & 300 \end{pmatrix}.$$

The rhombus is moved until it is close to the top right-hand corner of the screen without any of it disappearing.

Find the coordinates matrix for the rhombus in this new position.

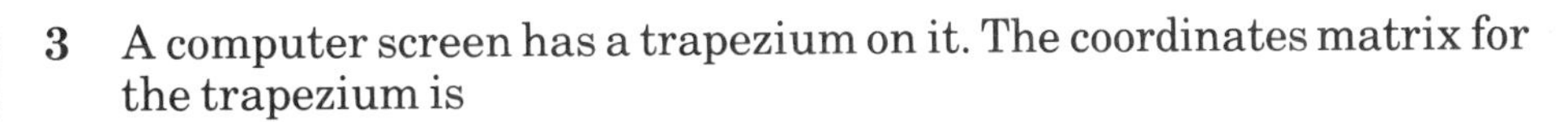

3 A computer screen has a trapezium on it. The coordinates matrix for the trapezium is

$$\begin{pmatrix} 200 & 500 & 400 & 200 \\ 100 & 100 & 300 & 300 \end{pmatrix}.$$

A larger trapezium is required. It is to be the same shape, but all its sides are to be twice as long.

Find a possible coordinates matrix for the larger trapezium.

(*Hint:* Use squared paper, with 1 square representing 10 units.)

4 A computer screen has a pentagon on it. The coordinates matrix for the pentagon is

$$\begin{pmatrix} 2 & 6 & 6 & 4 & 2 \\ 2 & 2 & 6 & 8 & 6 \end{pmatrix}.$$

The pentagon is to be turned upside down.

Find a possible coordinates matrix for the new pentagon.

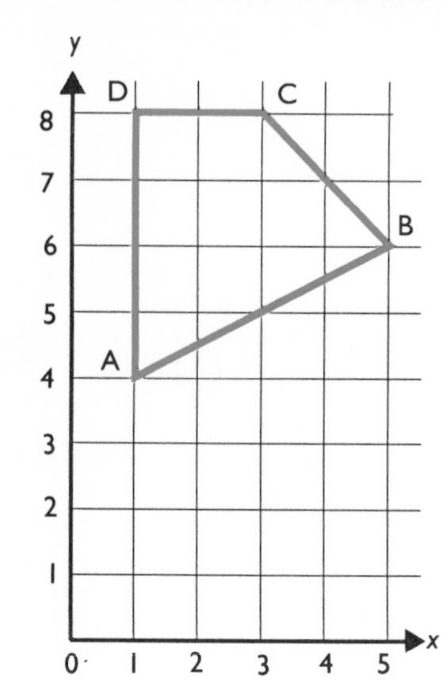

5 This is the coordinates matrix of the quadrilateral ABCD.

$$\begin{array}{cccc} A & B & C & D \end{array}$$
$$\begin{pmatrix} 1 & 5 & 3 & 1 \\ 4 & 6 & 8 & 8 \end{pmatrix}$$

The letters show how the vertices of the quadrilateral are labelled.

(*a*) Find the coordinates matrix of the shape obtained by reflecting the quadrilateral in the line CD.

(*b*) Find the coordinates matrix of the shape obtained by reflecting the quadrilateral in the line AD.

(*c*) Find the coordinates matrix of the shape obtained by reflecting the quadrilateral in the line BC.

6 The same quadrilateral ABCD is to be enlarged with scale factor 3.

Find the coordinates matrix of the new quadrilateral if

(*a*) the point A is the centre of the enlargement.

(*b*) the point B is the centre of the enlargement.

7 The same quadrilateral ABCD is to be rotated.

Find the coordinates matrix of the new quadrilateral obtained by

(*a*) rotating it through 180° about the point B.

(*b*) rotating it anticlockwise through 90° about the point A.

8 (*a*) The same quadrilateral ABCD is rotated through half a turn about the midpoint of side BC.

Find the coordinates matrix of the quadrilateral obtained.

(*b*) The original quadrilateral, together with the quadrilateral obtained in part (*a*), can be joined together to make a hexagon.

(i) Write down the coordinates matrix for this hexagon.
(ii) This hexagon tessellates the plane. Find the coordinates matrices of two other hexagons in the tessellation.

9 (*a*) Write a *Logo* procedure to draw a L shape.

(*b*) Change the procedure so that it draws a reflection of the L shape of part (*a*).

(*c*) Change the procedure so that it draws an enlargement of the L shape with scale factor 3.

10 Suppose that you have written a *Logo* procedure which draws a flag.

State for which of the following you can use your *Logo* procedure *without changing it*. Explain your answers.

(*a*) To draw a rotation of the flag.

(*b*) To draw a reflection of the flag.

(*c*) To draw a translation of the flag.

(*d*) To draw an enlargement of the flag.

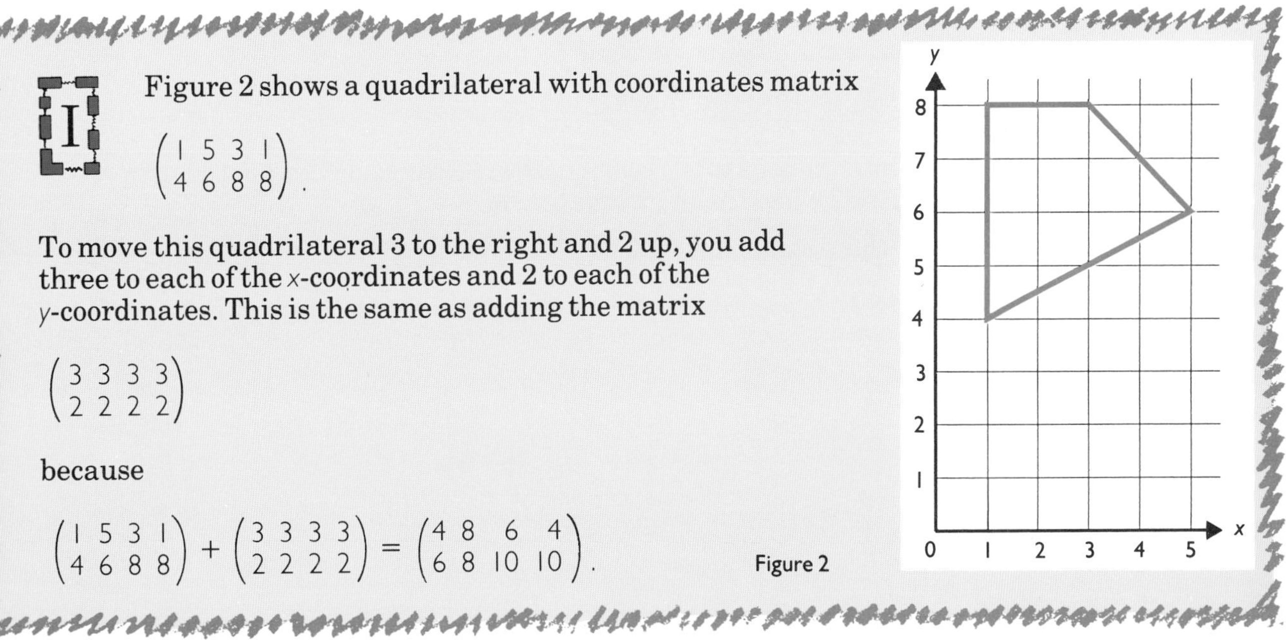

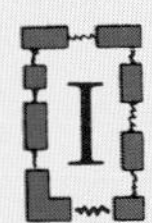

Figure 2 shows a quadrilateral with coordinates matrix

$$\begin{pmatrix} 1 & 5 & 3 & 1 \\ 4 & 6 & 8 & 8 \end{pmatrix}.$$

To move this quadrilateral 3 to the right and 2 up, you add three to each of the x-coordinates and 2 to each of the y-coordinates. This is the same as adding the matrix

$$\begin{pmatrix} 3 & 3 & 3 & 3 \\ 2 & 2 & 2 & 2 \end{pmatrix}$$

because

$$\begin{pmatrix} 1 & 5 & 3 & 1 \\ 4 & 6 & 8 & 8 \end{pmatrix} + \begin{pmatrix} 3 & 3 & 3 & 3 \\ 2 & 2 & 2 & 2 \end{pmatrix} = \begin{pmatrix} 4 & 8 & 6 & 4 \\ 6 & 8 & 10 & 10 \end{pmatrix}.$$

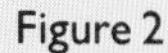

Figure 2

11 (*a*) The triangle with coordinates matrix

$$\begin{pmatrix} 2 & 5 & 4 \\ 3 & 3 & 6 \end{pmatrix}$$

is to be translated 4 units to the left and 2 units up.

What matrix should be added to the coordinates matrix to translate the triangle?

(*b*) Would your answer to part (*a*) be changed if the same translation was applied to a different triangle? Explain your answer.

(*c*) Would your answer to part (*a*) be changed if the same translation was applied to a hexagon? Explain your answer.

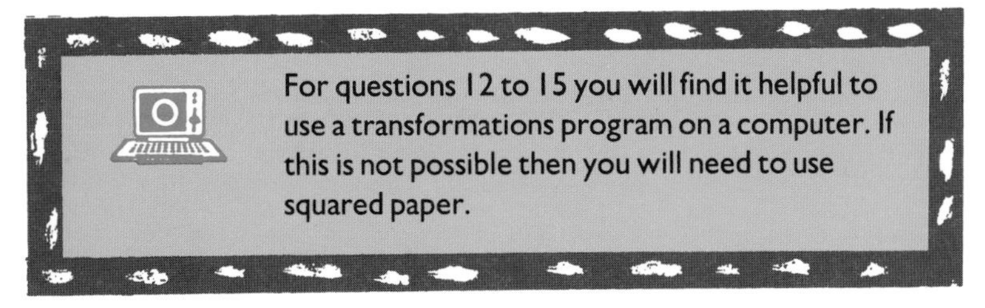

For questions 12 to 15 you will find it helpful to use a transformations program on a computer. If this is not possible then you will need to use squared paper.

12 What happens to the coordinates of points when the points are reflected in

(*a*) the x-axis?

(*b*) the y-axis?

(*c*) the line $y = x$?

(*d*) the line $y = -x$?

13 What happens to the coordinates of points when the points are rotated about the origin through

(*a*) 180°? (*b*) 90° anticlockwise? (*c*) 90° clockwise?

14 What happens to the coordinates of a shape if it is enlarged with centre the origin with scale factor

(*a*) 2? (*b*) -3? (*c*) k?

15 What happens to the coordinates of a shape if it is sheared with a factor 2 when the invariant line is

(*a*) the x-axis? (*b*) the y-axis?

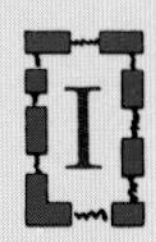

Here is the answer to 15(*a*).

The point $\begin{pmatrix} x \\ y \end{pmatrix}$ goes to the point $\begin{pmatrix} x+2y \\ y \end{pmatrix}$

This can be written as

$$\begin{pmatrix} x \\ y \end{pmatrix} \rightarrow \begin{pmatrix} 1x + 2y \\ 0x + 1y \end{pmatrix} \qquad \text{(A)}$$

The reason for putting in the 0 and the 1s is that the numbers

$$\begin{pmatrix} 1 & 2 \\ 0 & 1 \end{pmatrix}$$

can be separated out as a matrix. It is this matrix which tells you, or a computer, what transformation is required (in this case, a shear).

Mathematicians write

$$\begin{pmatrix} x \\ y \end{pmatrix} \rightarrow \begin{pmatrix} 1 & 2 \\ 0 & 1 \end{pmatrix} \begin{pmatrix} x \\ y \end{pmatrix} \qquad \text{(B)}$$

to mean the same as (A) above.

If instead, the matrix

$$\begin{pmatrix} 2 & 0 \\ 0 & 2 \end{pmatrix}$$

is used, the transformation is

$$\begin{pmatrix} x \\ y \end{pmatrix} \rightarrow \begin{pmatrix} 2x + 0y \\ 0x + 2y \end{pmatrix}$$

or, in other words

$$\begin{pmatrix} x \\ y \end{pmatrix} \rightarrow \begin{pmatrix} 2x \\ 2y \end{pmatrix}$$

This is an enlargement with centre the origin and scale factor 2.

16 Describe geometrically the transformations represented by each of the following matrices.

(*a*) $\begin{pmatrix} 3 & 0 \\ 0 & 3 \end{pmatrix}$ (*b*) $\begin{pmatrix} -1 & 0 \\ 0 & -1 \end{pmatrix}$ (*c*) $\begin{pmatrix} 0 & -1 \\ 1 & 0 \end{pmatrix}$ (*d*) $\begin{pmatrix} 1 & 0 \\ 3 & 1 \end{pmatrix}$

(*e*) $\begin{pmatrix} 1 & 0 \\ 0 & -1 \end{pmatrix}$ (*f*) $\begin{pmatrix} 0 & 1 \\ 1 & 0 \end{pmatrix}$ (*g*) $\begin{pmatrix} 2 & 0 \\ 0 & 1 \end{pmatrix}$

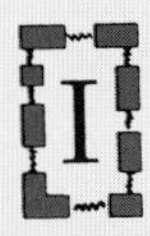

If you start with a transformation, you can find the matrix to describe it by seeing what happens to the points with position vectors $\begin{pmatrix} 1 \\ 0 \end{pmatrix}$ and $\begin{pmatrix} 0 \\ 1 \end{pmatrix}$.

If the matrix is

$$\begin{pmatrix} a & b \\ c & d \end{pmatrix}$$

then

$$\begin{pmatrix} a & b \\ c & d \end{pmatrix}\begin{pmatrix} 1 \\ 0 \end{pmatrix} = \begin{pmatrix} a \\ c \end{pmatrix} \text{ and } \begin{pmatrix} a & b \\ c & d \end{pmatrix}\begin{pmatrix} 0 \\ 1 \end{pmatrix} = \begin{pmatrix} b \\ d \end{pmatrix}$$

Thus, the image of $\begin{pmatrix} 1 \\ 0 \end{pmatrix}$ is the first column of the matrix and the image of $\begin{pmatrix} 0 \\ 1 \end{pmatrix}$ is the second column of the matrix.

For example, suppose you want the matrix of the rotation about the origin clockwise through 90°.

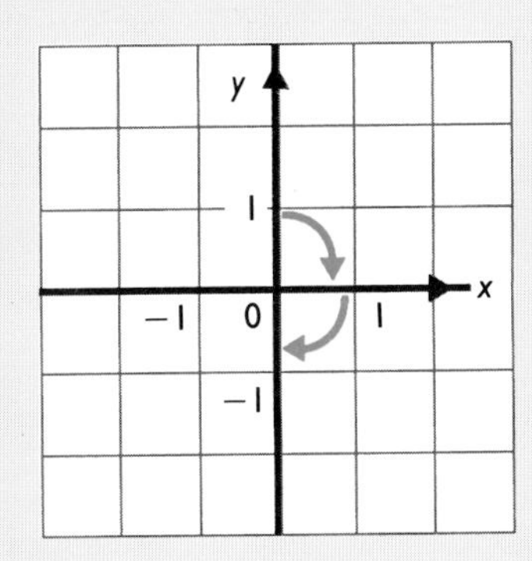

The point $\begin{pmatrix} 1 \\ 0 \end{pmatrix}$ maps to the point $\begin{pmatrix} 0 \\ -1 \end{pmatrix}$ and the point $\begin{pmatrix} 0 \\ 1 \end{pmatrix}$ maps to the point $\begin{pmatrix} 1 \\ 0 \end{pmatrix}$. So the matrix for this reflection is

$$\begin{pmatrix} 0 & 1 \\ -1 & 0 \end{pmatrix}$$

Note that the only transformations which can be represented by matrices in this way are those where the point $\begin{pmatrix} 0 \\ 0 \end{pmatrix}$ maps to itself.

So you could not use a matrix to represent a reflection in the line $x = 1$, for example.

17 Find the matrices which represent each of the following transformations:

(*a*) a reflection in the line $y = -x$,

(*b*) a stretch with scale factor 4 and the y-axis as the invariant line,

(*c*) an enlargement with scale factor -2,

(*d*) a rotation about the origin anticlockwise through 60°,

(*e*) a rotational enlargement where the rotation and the enlargement are centred on the origin, the rotation is anticlockwise through 90°, and the enlargement has scale factor 2.

18 For each of the transformations below, describe the transformation which reverses its effect. (For example, if the transformation given moves shape S to shape T, describe the transformation which moves T back to S).

(*a*) Reflection in a line AB.

(*b*) Translation with vector $\begin{pmatrix} 3 \\ -4 \end{pmatrix}$.

(*c*). Rotation through 60° anticlockwise about a point C.

(*d*) Enlargement with centre D and scale factor -2.

(*e*) Shear with scale factor 2 and invariant line EF.

19 For each *pair* of transformations given below, describe the *single* transformation which has the same effect as the first transformation in the pair *followed by* the second transformation.

(*a*) A translation of $\begin{pmatrix} 3 \\ -2 \end{pmatrix}$, followed by a translation of $\begin{pmatrix} -4 \\ -5 \end{pmatrix}$.

(*b*) A reflection in the line AB, followed by a reflection in the line BC, when angle ABC is a right angle.

(*c*) An anticlockwise rotation about D through 90°, followed by a clockwise rotation about D through 150°.

(*d*) An anticlockwise rotation about E through 90°, followed by a clockwise rotation about F through 90°.

(*e*) A reflection in line GH, followed by an anticlockwise rotation about G through 90°.

(*f*) An enlargement with centre J and scale factor 2, followed by an enlargement centre K and scale factor 3.

There are some easier questions about combined transformations in Review Exercise 49 on page 268.

A wider exploration of the effect of combining two or more transformations would make a suitable Further Coursework Task.

FURTHER COURSEWORK TASKS

1⟩ Use *Logo* to make some symmetrical designs on the computer screen

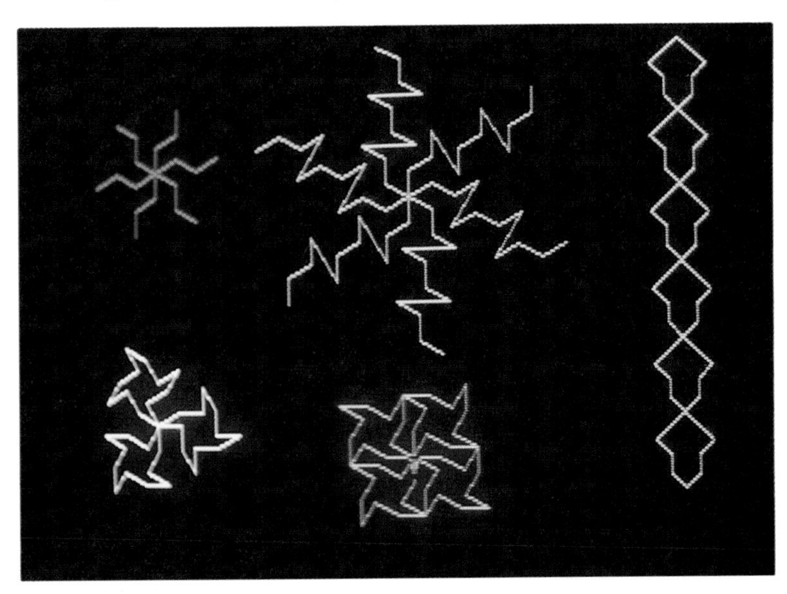

The *Logo* you are using might allow you to use several turtles at once. If so, you might want to use several turtles to create your design.

2⟩ Investigate how to draw tessellations of various kinds on the computer's screen.

You can use *Logo* or *BASIC*. Alternatively, you can use *Tilekit* or another tiling package.

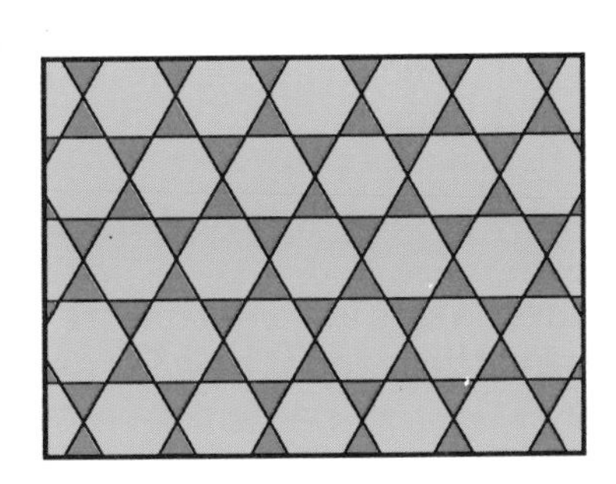

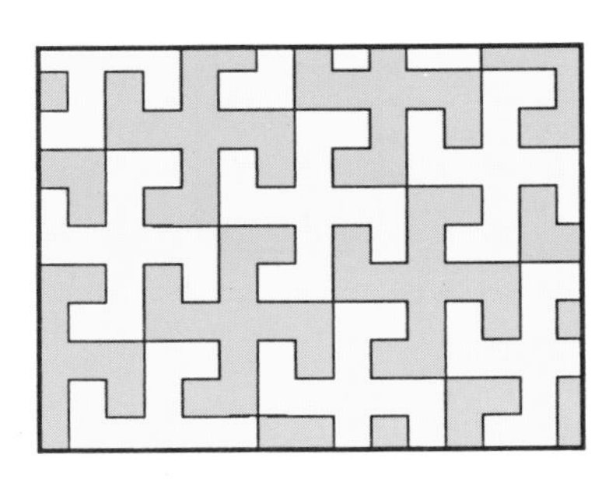

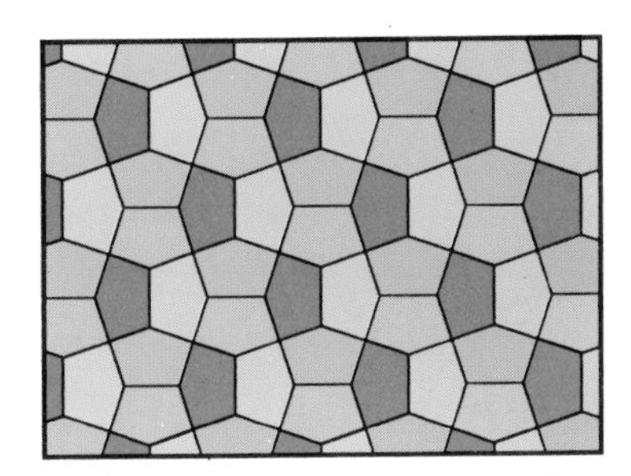

3⟩ The matrix

$$\begin{pmatrix} 2 & 0 \\ 0 & 2 \end{pmatrix}$$

produces an enlargement with scale factor 2, and the matrix

$$\begin{pmatrix} 1 & 2 \\ 0 & 1 \end{pmatrix}$$

produces a shear with the x-axis as the invariant line.

Use a transformations program on a computer to investigate the transformations produced by different matrices.

You might want to start by restricting yourself to matrices of a particular type. For example, you could look at matrices where all four numbers are either 1 or 0. Or where all four numbers are either 1, −1 or 0.

4) When you draw a polygon with *Logo* you usually start from a corner. This makes it hard to create patterns like these:

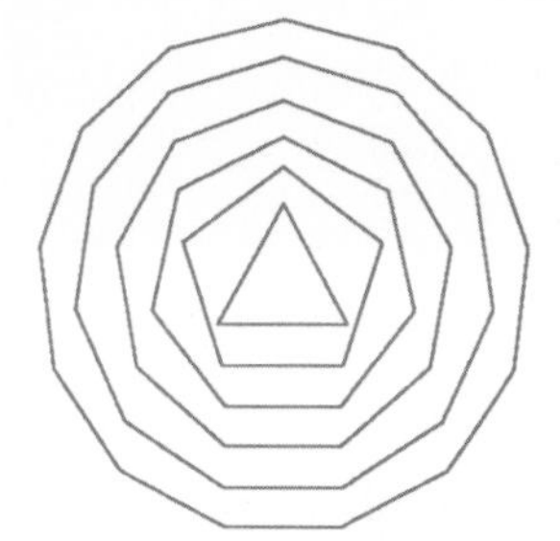

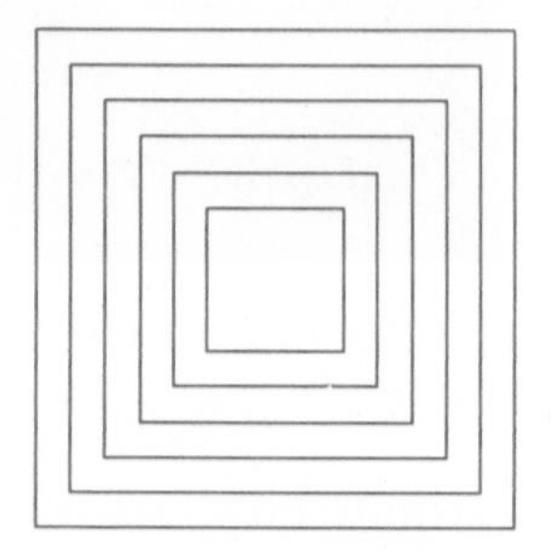

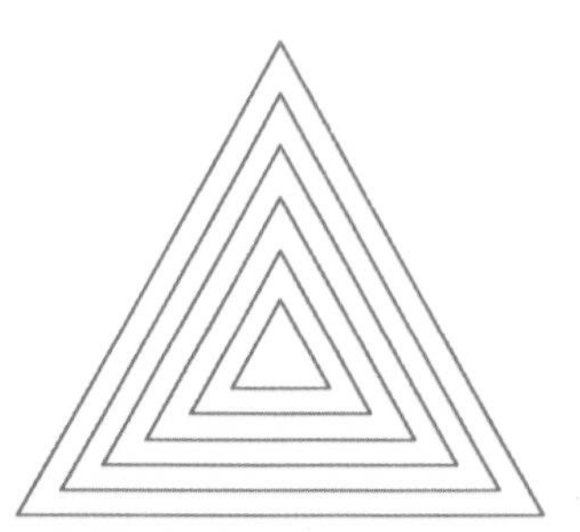

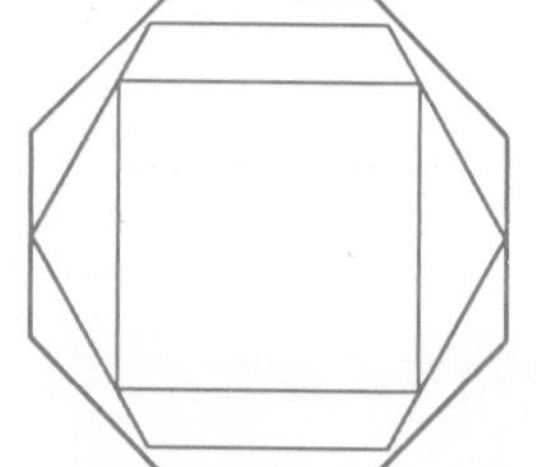

You might also want to explore other issues. When do different shapes in the pattern overlap? Can you make a pattern in which the shapes touch each other?

5) Some computer robots can recognise the shapes of objects. Here is one way they can do this.

Figure 3 shows a robot 'looking' at a cube 'face on'.

The robot fires lasers at 1 centimetre intervals horizontally and vertically, and these tell it how far away different points on the cube's surface are

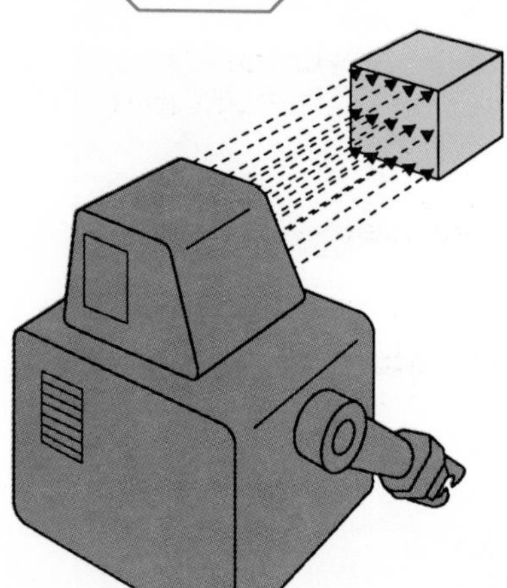

Figure 3

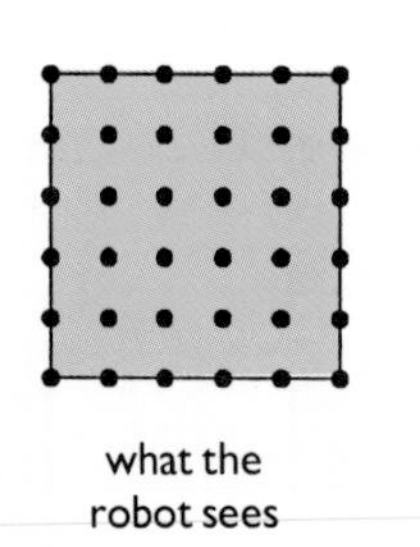

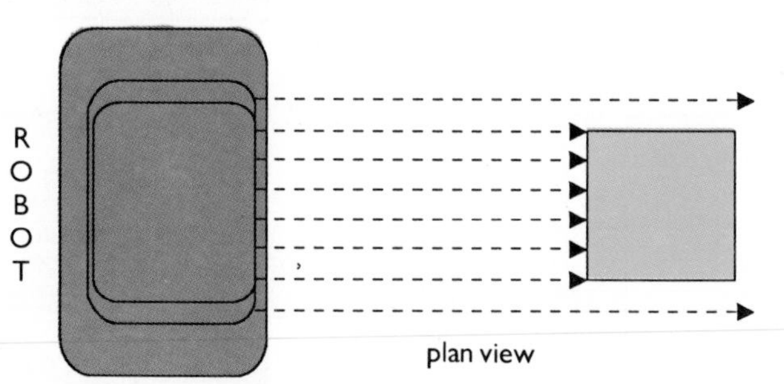

Because the cube is 'face on', all the points are the same distance (10 cm) from the robot's front. So the robot records what it sees like this.

$$\begin{pmatrix} 10 & 10 & 10 & 10 & 10 & 10 \\ 10 & 10 & 10 & 10 & 10 & 10 \\ 10 & 10 & 10 & 10 & 10 & 10 \\ 10 & 10 & 10 & 10 & 10 & 10 \\ 10 & 10 & 10 & 10 & 10 & 10 \\ 10 & 10 & 10 & 10 & 10 & 10 \end{pmatrix}$$

Figure 4

Figure 4 shows the robot looking at the cube after it has been rotated a bit about a vertical axis.

The front edge of the cube is still 10 cm from the robot.

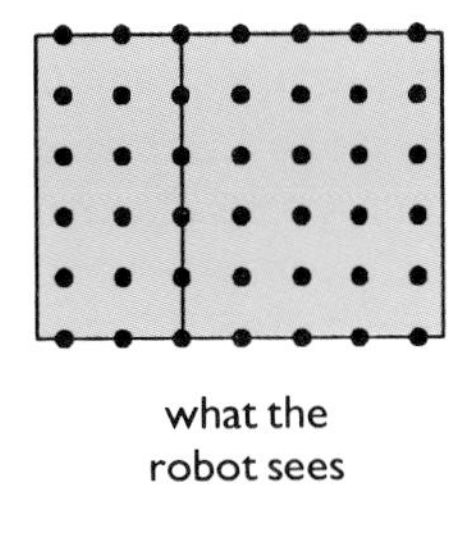

what the robot sees

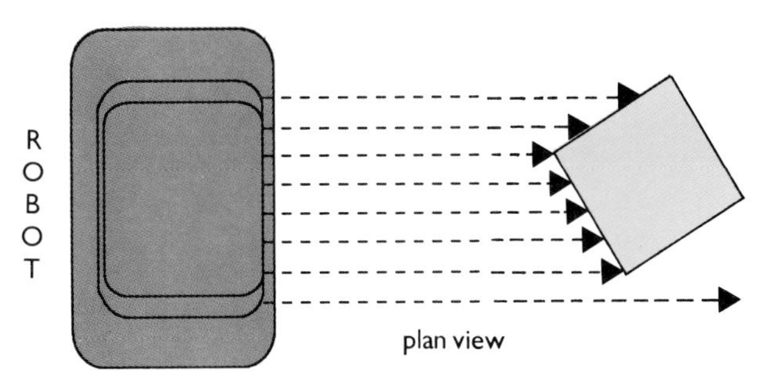

plan view

This time the robot records what it sees like this.

$$\begin{pmatrix} 14 & 12 & 10 & 10.5 & 11 & 11.5 & 12 \\ 14 & 12 & 10 & 10.5 & 11 & 11.5 & 12 \\ 14 & 12 & 10 & 10.5 & 11 & 11.5 & 12 \\ 14 & 12 & 10 & 10.5 & 11 & 11.5 & 12 \\ 14 & 12 & 10 & 10.5 & 11 & 11.5 & 12 \\ 14 & 12 & 10 & 10.5 & 11 & 11.5 & 12 \end{pmatrix}$$

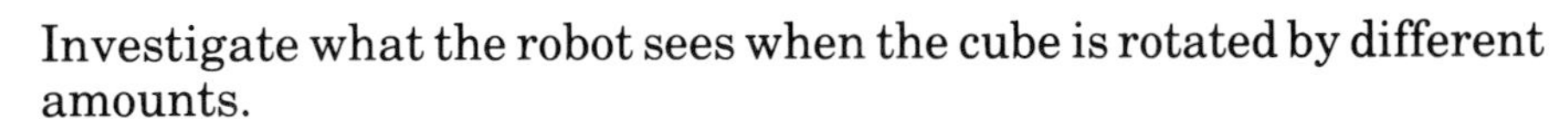

Investigate what the robot sees when the cube is rotated by different amounts.

You might find it helpful to make plan views on squared paper, or to use trigonometry.

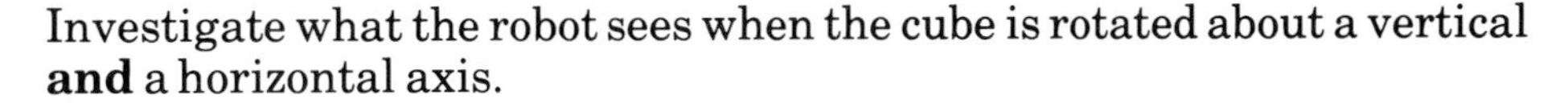

Investigate what the robot sees when the cube is rotated about a vertical **and** a horizontal axis.

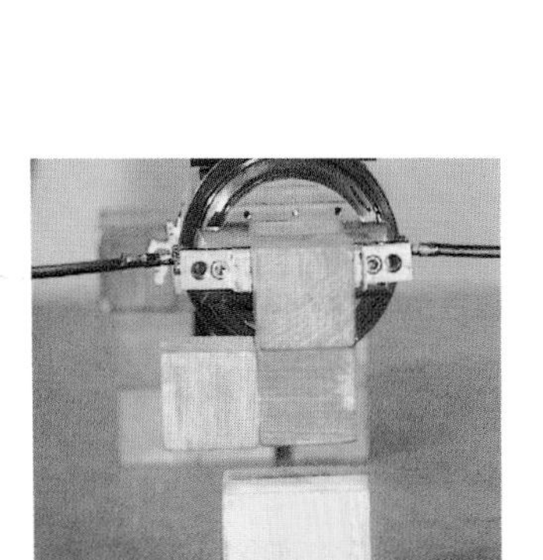

A robot that recognises cubes, solving a cube puzzle.

6) Equilateral triangles are easy to draw using *Logo*. This is because you can use whole numbers for all six of the quantities: the three sides **and** the three angles.

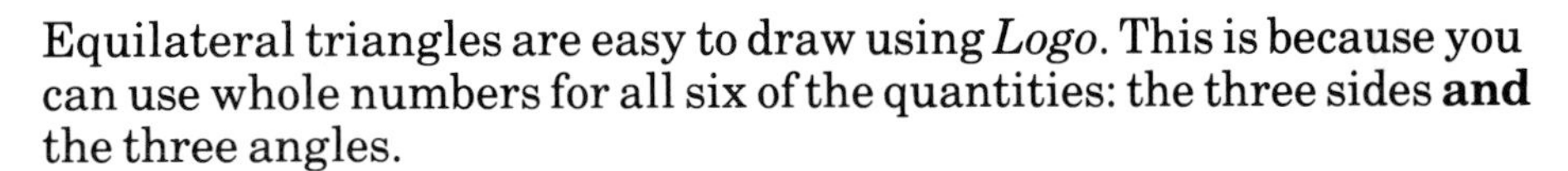

There are **no** other triangles for which all three sides and all three angles are whole numbers.

Investigate ways in which four or more of the quantities can be whole numbers.

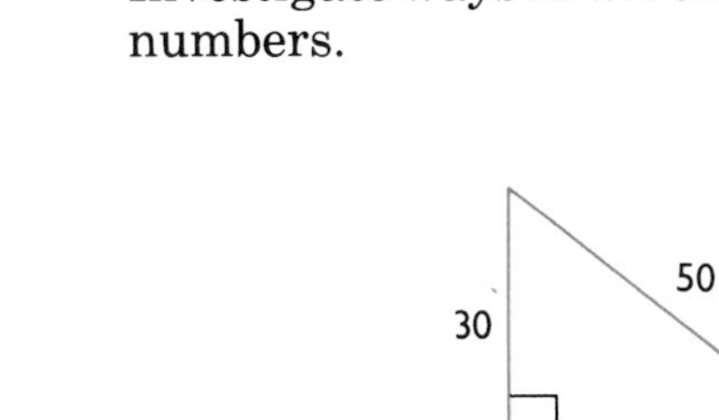

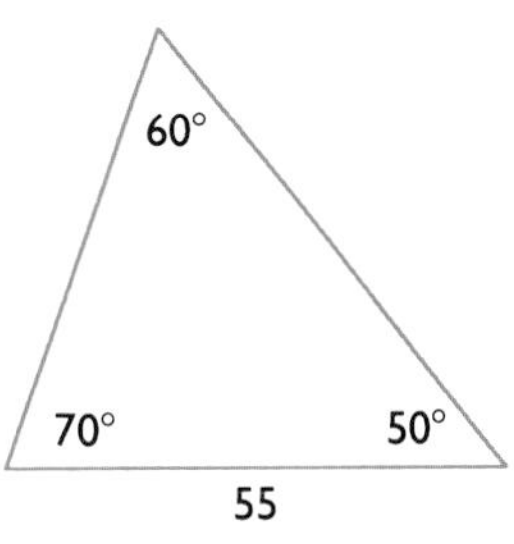

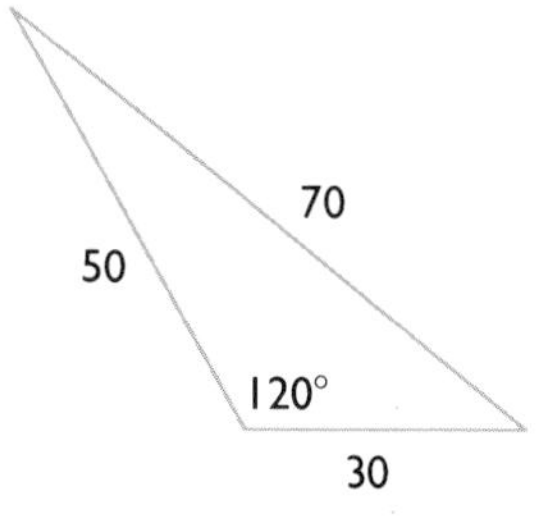

One way in which this can happen is for one angle of the triangle to be 60° or 120°, and for the sides all to be integers. You could use the cosine rule with a spreadsheet to help you find triangles of this type.

You might find it helpful to refer to question 11 on page 153 of Book 4 of this series.

25 GETTING THE MOST OUT OF LIFE

Getting the most out of life might mean having as much money, or friends, or holidays as possible. Or as fast a car as possible. Or going to as many discos as possible. Or it might mean being nice to as many people as possible. Or helping as many people as possible. Or it might mean enjoying yourself as much as possible, and this might be difficult to measure.

There are many things which limit how much you can get out of life. The amount of money you have is one. Your physical strength, or health or where you live are others. Or your age. You can change some of these things; other things are much harder or impossible to change.

Mathematicians are often concerned with deciding how to get the most from a fixed amount of something.

- For this task you have limited resources: one sheet of A4 paper and some adhesive tape. What is the largest container you can make? Largest means that its capacity is as big as possible.
- Your container could be in the shape of a box, or a cylinder or a cone, or any other shape, but it must be made entirely out of one sheet of A4 paper.
- You could find the capacity of your container by using a measuring cylinder and something to fill the container, such as rice or dried peas. Or you could choose to calculate its capacity.
- When you have made your container explain why you chose the particular shape you did. Do you think that your container really is the largest that it is possible to make out of a sheet of A4 paper?

SECTION A

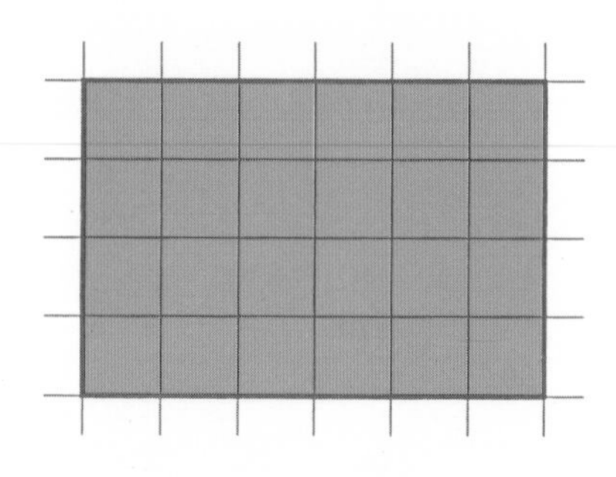

1 (*a*) Using squared paper, draw different rectangles with a perimeter of 20 cm and find their areas.

(*b*) What is the largest possible area for a rectangle with a perimeter of 20 cm?

2 (*a*) Using squared paper draw different rectangles with an area of 36 cm^2.

(*b*) What is the smallest possible perimeter for a rectangle with an area of 36 cm^2?

3 A rectangular area is to be fenced off with fencing of total length 40 m. What is the largest area that can be enclosed?

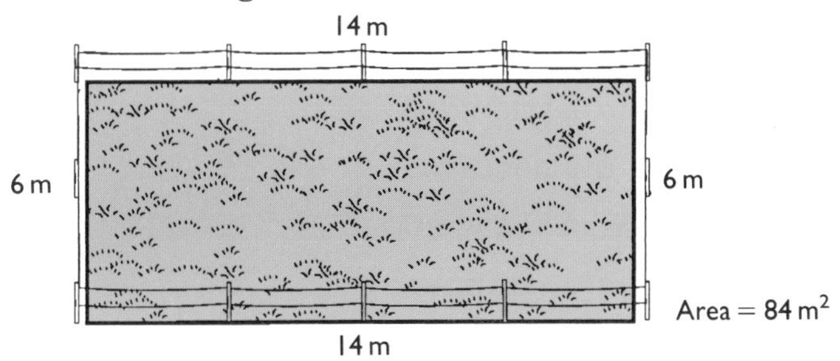

4 A rectangular area is to be fenced off with fencing of total length 96 m. Enough fencing must be left to divide the rectangle into two rectangular parts with the same area.

One way of doing this is shown below.

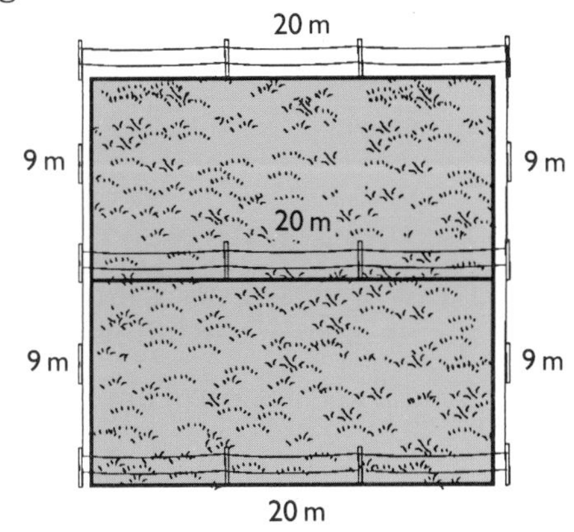

(*a*) Draw diagrams to show other ways of doing this.

(*b*) Find the largest total area which you can enclose.

(*c*) Suppose the two parts do not have to have the same area. What difference does this make to your answer to part (*b*)?

5 A rectangular enclosure is to be fenced off with fencing of total length 96 m. This time the enclosure is to be divided into three rectangular parts of equal area.

(*a*) The drawing below shows one method of arranging the parts.

(i) Draw diagrams to show ways of making three parts of equal area, using this method.
(ii) Find the largest total area which you can enclose, using this method.

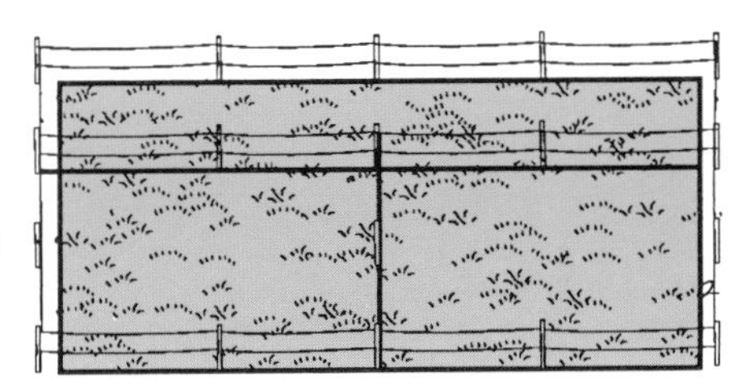

(*b*) The drawing on the right shows the other method of arranging the parts.

(i) Draw diagrams to show ways of making three parts of equal area, using this second method.
(ii) Find the largest total area which you can enclose using this method.

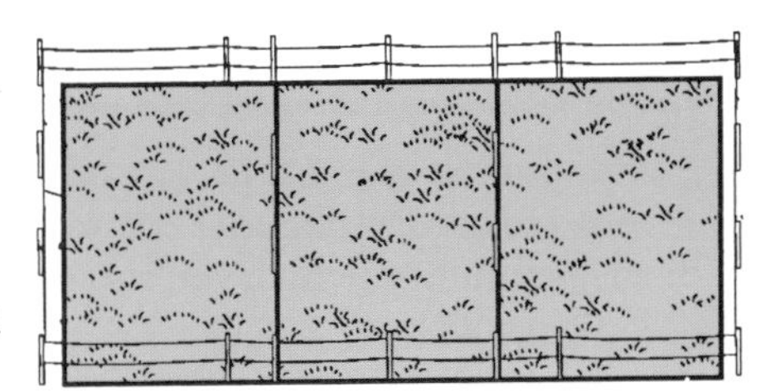

6 The greatest number of right angles a quadrilateral can have is 4.

What is the greatest number of right angles each of the following shapes can have?

(*a*) a triangle?

(*b*) a pentagon?

(*c*) a hexagon?

(*d*) a septagon?

(*e*) an octagon?

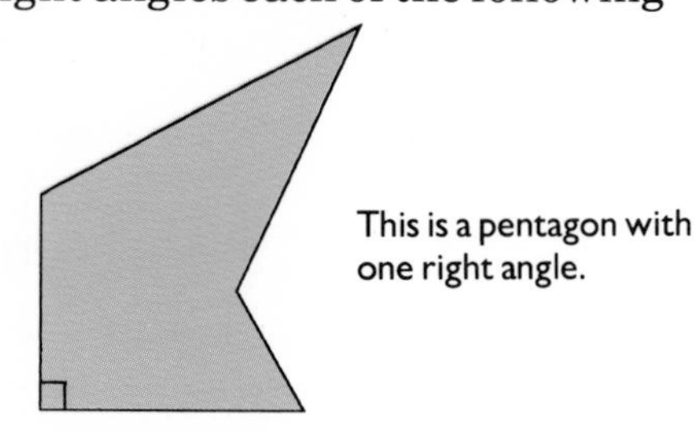
This is a pentagon with one right angle.

7

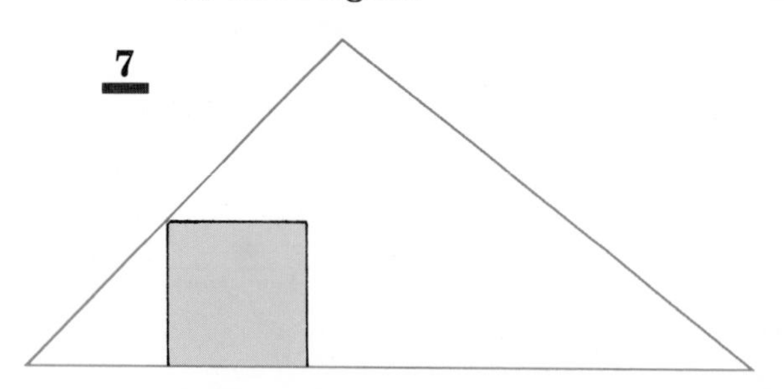

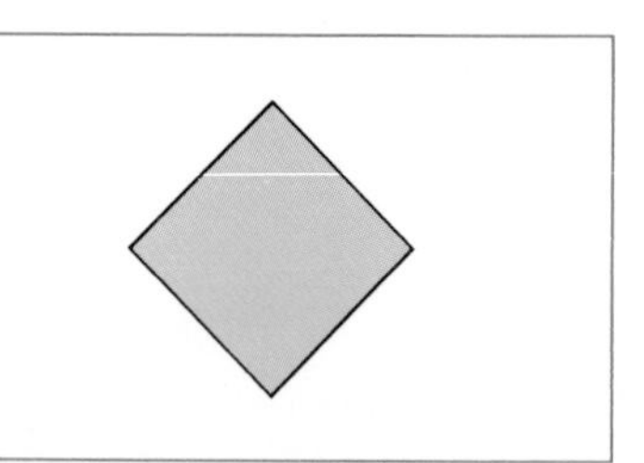

The pictures above show shapes containing a square.

Draw a picture showing the *largest* square which can be placed inside each of the following shapes.

Find the fraction of each shape which is filled by the square.

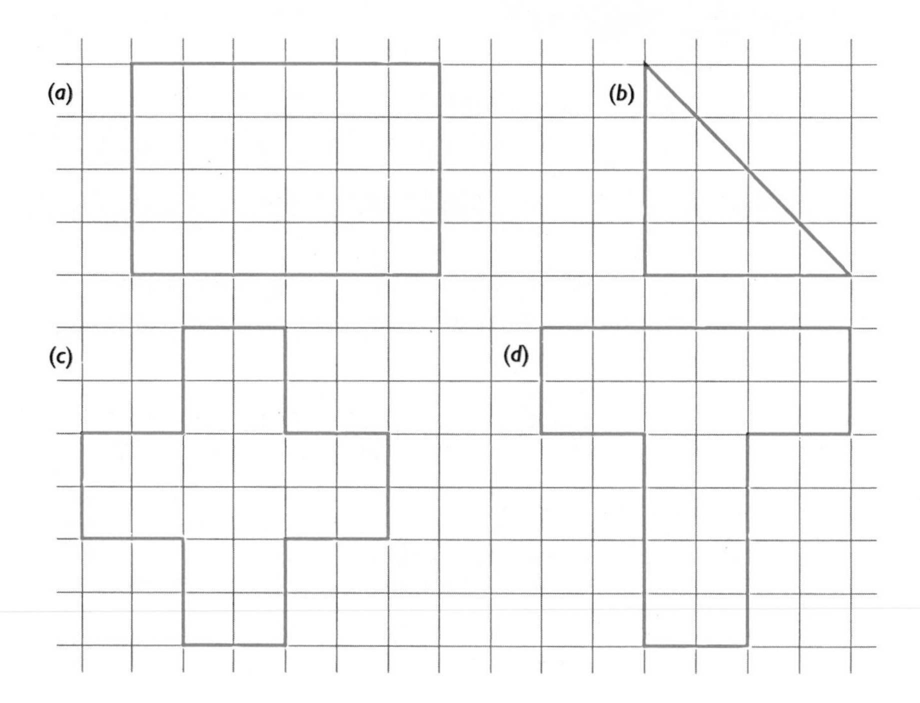

For questions 8, 11, 12, 13 and 14 you will need to use Pythagoras' theorem and trigonometry, which you can read about on page 281.

8 A square with sides of length 4 cm can cover two dots, provided that the dots are not more than 5.6 cm apart.

(*a*) Explain the above statement about the square.

(*b*) Calculate the greatest distance between two points if both of them can be covered by:

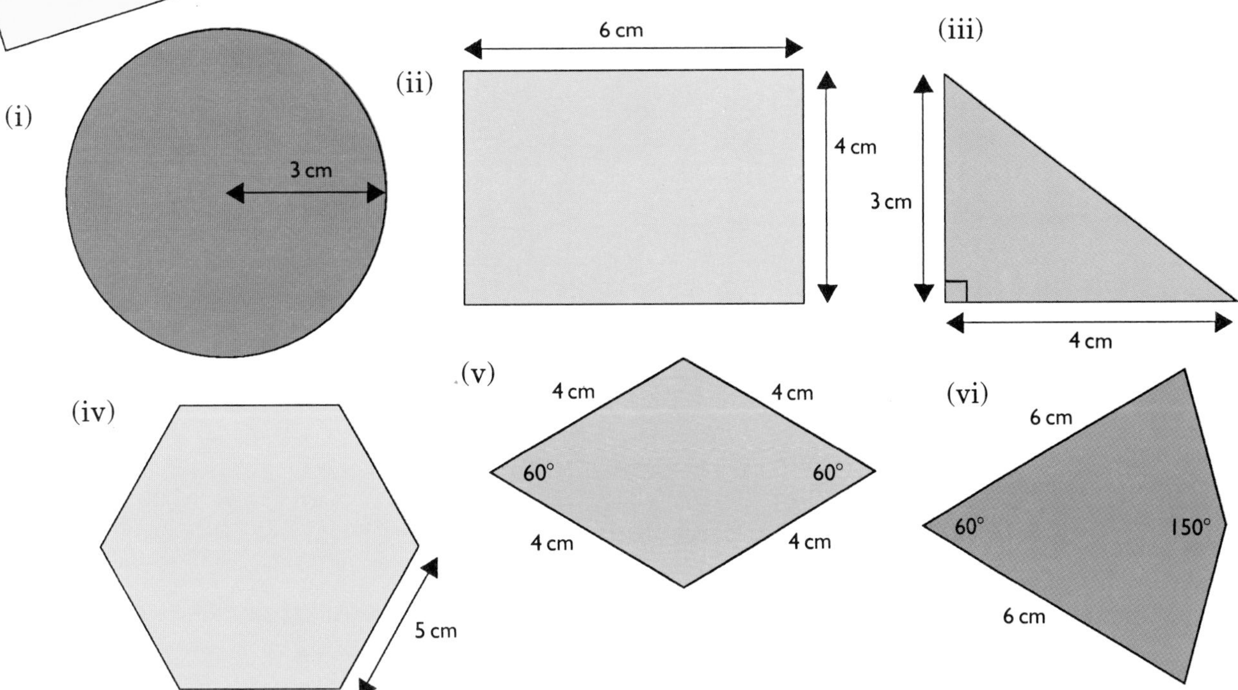

9 A container in the shape of a cuboid without a lid is to have a square base, and a volume of 108 cm^3.

(*a*) If the length of one side of the base is x cm, what is

(i) the height of the container?
(ii) the surface area of the container?

(*b*) Use a spreadsheet, a computer program or a calculator to find the value of x which makes the surface area as small as possible.

(*c*) The net for the container is made from a rectangular sheet of card. Find the least possible area of the sheet of card.

For question 10 you need the formulae for the volume and surface area of a cylinder, which you will find on page 282.

10 A cylindrical can (with both ends closed) is to have a volume of 170 cm^3.

(*a*) If the radius of the base of the can is r cm, what is

(i) the height of the can?
(ii) the surface area of the can?

(*b*) Use a spreadsheet, a computer program or a calculator to find the value of r, which makes the surface area of the can as small as possible.

(*c*) What is the area of the smallest rectangle of metal from which the can could be sensibly made?

11 A circle has a diameter of 10 cm.

(*a*) Find the dimensions of three different rectangles whose corners are on the circumference of the circle.

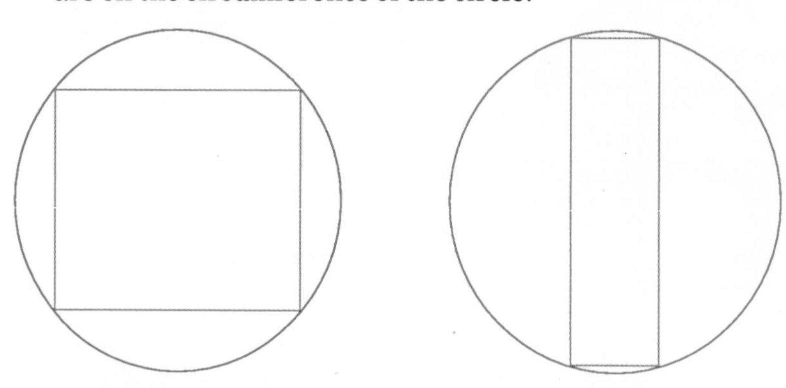

(*b*) (i) What is the largest rectangle which can be put inside the circle?
(ii) What percentage of the area of the circle does this largest rectangle fill?

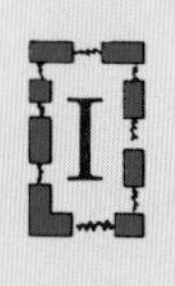

Figure 1 shows a formula which is sometimes useful to help calculate the area of a triangle.

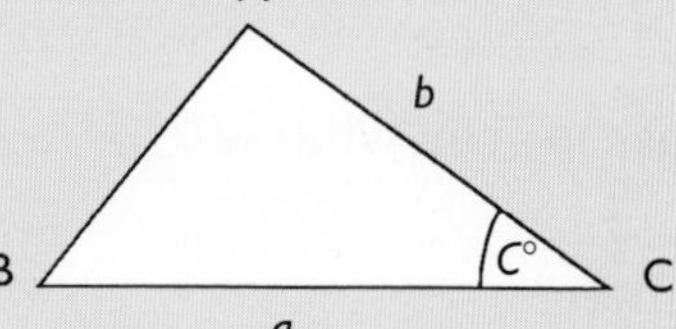

Figure 1

Area of triangle $= \frac{1}{2}\, ab \sin C$

Figure 2 explains why this formula works.

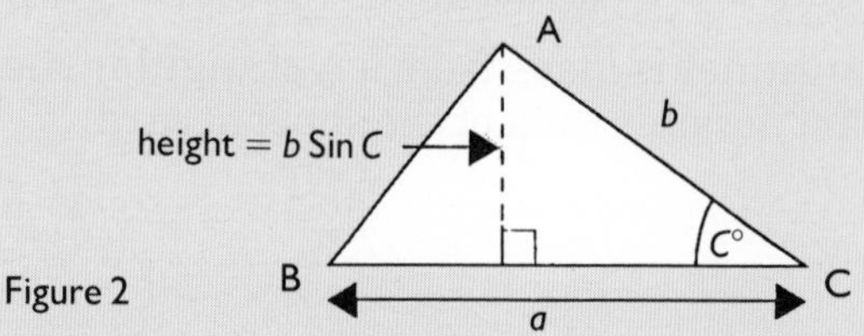

Figure 2

Here is an example of how the formula is used.

Area of triangle $= \frac{1}{2} \times 4 \times 5 \times \sin 70°$
$= 9.4 \text{ cm}^2$

4 cm
70°
5 cm

You might want to use this formula in connection with question 12.

12 (*a*) Three rods, each of which is of length 6 cm, are jointed together to form a triangle. What is the area of the triangle?

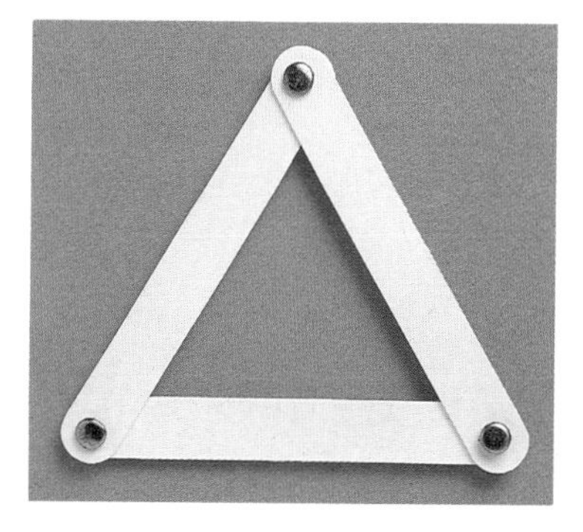

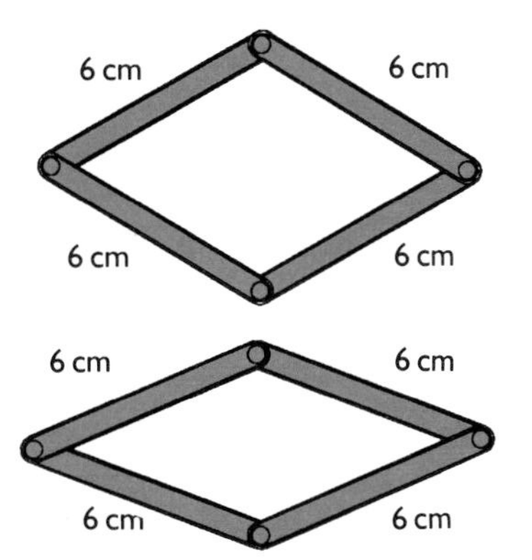

Figure 3

(*b*) Four rods, each of which is of length 6 cm are jointed together to form a quadrilateral. The quadrilateral is not rigid. Figure 3 shows two possible quadrilaterals which can be made.

(i) What is the area of the quadrilateral if one of its angles is 60°?
(ii) What is the area of the quadrilateral if one of its angles is 90°?
(iii) What is the greatest possible area for the quadrilateral? Explain your answer.

(*c*) Four rods, two of which are of length 6 cm and two of length 4 cm, are jointed together to form a quadrilateral. As in part (*b*) the quadrilateral is not rigid.

(i) What is the greatest possible area of the quadrilateral if the two rods of length 6 cm are not next to each other? Explain your answer.

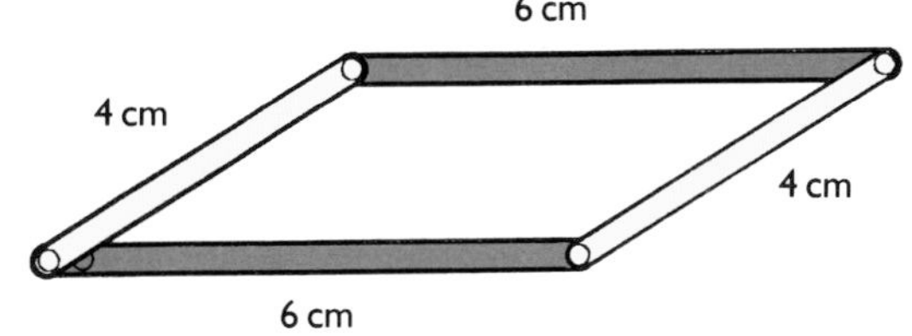

(ii) What is the greatest possible area of the quadrilateral if the two rods of length 6 cm are next to each other? Explain your answer.

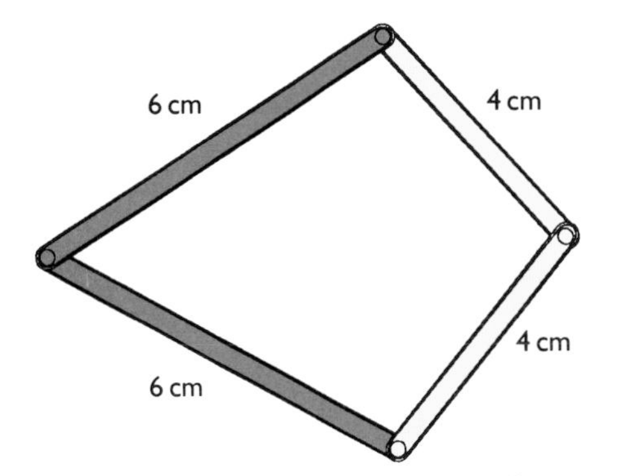

For question 13 you need the formula for the volume of a cone, which you will find on page 282.

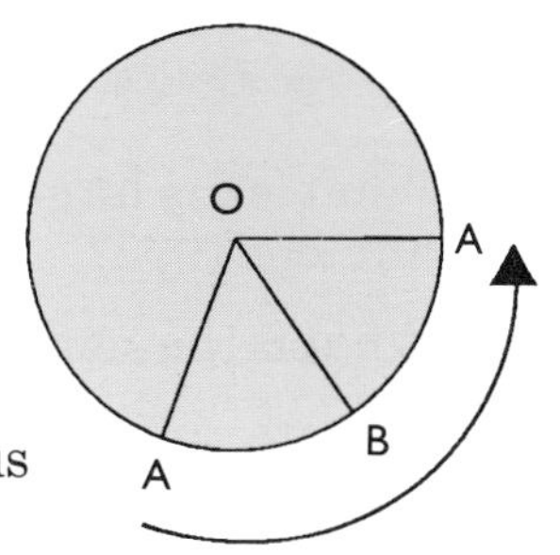

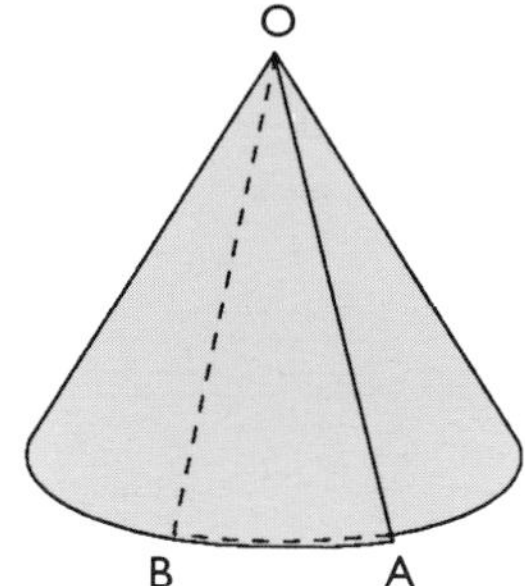

13 A circle of paper of radius 5 cm is folded so as to make a cone.

(*a*) If the radius of the base of the cone is r find

(i) the height of the cone in terms of r,
(ii) the volume of the cone in terms of r.

(*b*) Use a calculator or a spreadsheet to find the greatest possible volume of the cone.

14 A channel for water is to be made from a strip of metal 12 inches wide, which is to be bent into the shape of a trapezium.

(*a*) In the first instance, the strip is bent so that the width of each part is 4 inches.

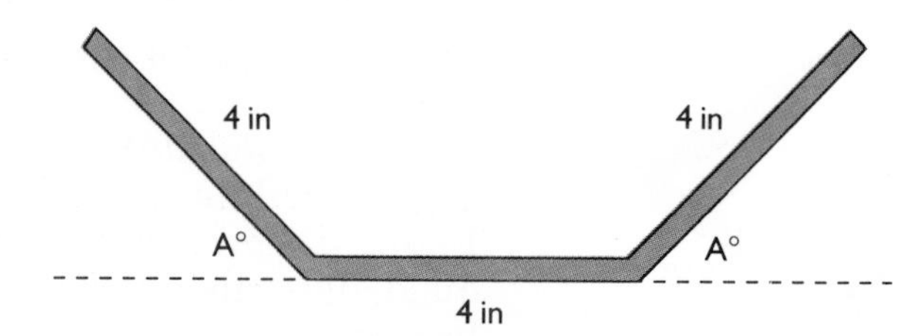

(i) Find, in terms of A, the area of the cross-section of the channel.

(ii) Use a calculator or spreadsheet to find the value of A, which maximises the flow of water down the channel.

(*b*) Someone suggests that it might be better if the middle of the channel was 6 inches long.

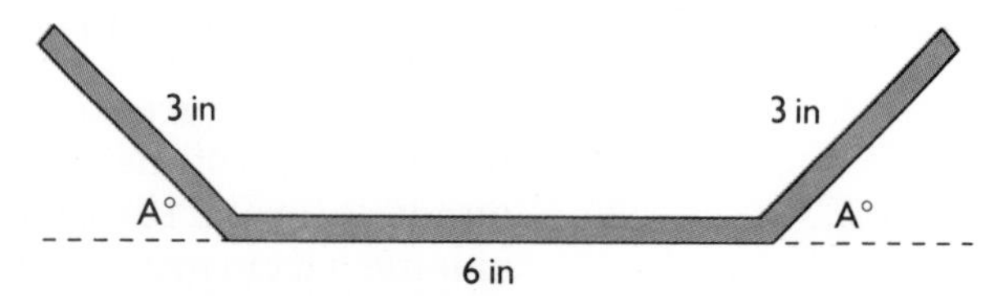

(i) Find, in terms of A, the area of the cross-section of the channel in this case.

(ii) Find the value of A which maximises the flow through the channel in this case.

(*c*) Which out of (*a*) and (*b*) is the better method of maximising the flow through the channel?

SECTION B

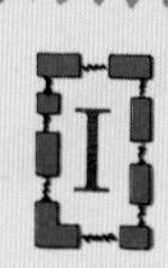

The largest number which has the same digits as 372 is 732.

The smallest number which has the same digits as 372 is 237.

1 (*a*) What is the largest number which has the same digits as the number 1993?

(*b*) What is the smallest number which has the same digits as 1993?

(*c*) You are given three different digits. You make the smallest number possible using all these three digits and you also make the largest number possible. You add these two numbers together and the answer is 848. What are the three digits?

2 (*a*) What is the smallest square number with four digits?

(*b*) What is the largest square number with four digits?

3 Look at the set of numbers below.

2.6, 4, 1.13, 17, 0.27, −1.9, 7.12, 1.7

What is the largest number that can be made by

(*a*) choosing *two* of these numbers and adding them?

(*b*) choosing *two* of these numbers and subtracting one from the other?

(*c*) choosing *two* of these numbers and multiplying them?

(*d*) choosing *two* of these numbers and dividing one by the other?

4 (*a*) The digits of a number add to 9 and the number does not have a zero in it. What is the largest number it could be?

(*b*) The digits of a number add to 9 and the digits are all different. What is the largest number it could be?

5 (*a*) The sum of two numbers is 8. The numbers are multiplied together.

Here are two possible ways of doing this.

$3 \times 5 = 15$
$2.5 \times 5.5 = 13.75$

The first way gives a larger answer than the second way.

Find by trial and improvement the largest possible answer.

(*b*) The sum of two numbers is 15. The numbers are multiplied together.

Find by trial and improvement the largest possible answer.

(*c*) The sum of two numbers is N. The numbers are multiplied together.

What is the largest possible answer?

6 (*a*) The sum of three numbers is 15. The numbers are multiplied together.

Find by trial and improvement the largest possible answer.

(*b*) The sum of three numbers is 20. The numbers are multiplied together.

Find by trial and improvement the largest possible answer.

(*c*) The sum of three numbers is N. The numbers are multiplied together.

What is the largest possible answer?

7 (*a*) The sum of four numbers is 30. The numbers are multiplied together.

What is the largest possible answer?

(*b*) The sum of four numbers is N. The numbers are multiplied together.

What is the largest possible answer?

8 The sum of p numbers is N. The numbers are multiplied together.

What is the largest possible answer?

9 (*a*) The sum of several numbers is 12. The numbers are all multiplied together.

Here are some ways of doing this.

$5 \times 7 = 35$
$2 \times 2 \times 2 \times 2 \times 2 \times 2 = 64$
$2.4 \times 4 \times 5.6 = 53.76$
$1 \times 1 \times 1 \times 2.5 \times 6.5 = 16.25$

Find by trial and improvement the largest possible answer.

(*b*) The sum of several numbers is 5.

Find by trial and improvement the largest possible answer.

(*c*) The sum of several numbers is 14.

Find by trial and improvement the largest possible answer.

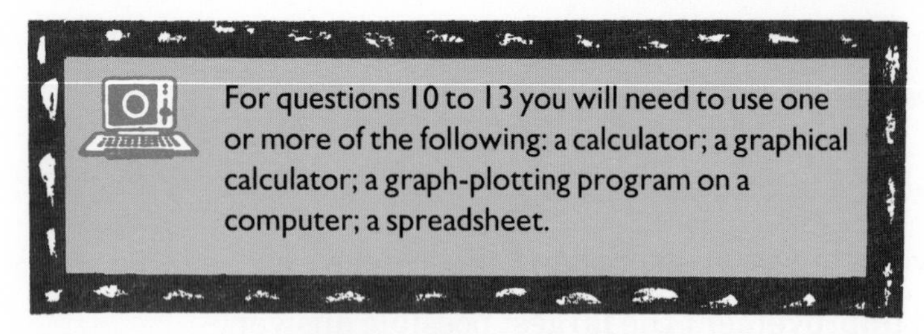
For questions 10 to 13 you will need to use one or more of the following: a calculator; a graphical calculator; a graph-plotting program on a computer; a spreadsheet.

10 (*a*) Use a graphical calculator or graph-plotting program to draw the graph of $y = x(x-1)$.

(*b*) Describe the symmetry of this graph.

(*c*) Use the fact that the graph is symmetrical to find the minimum value of $x(x-1)$.

11 (*a*) Draw the graph of $y = x(x-1)(x-2)$.

(*b*) Describe the symmetry of this graph.

(*c*) Find, correct to 1 decimal place, the maximum value of $x(x-1)(x-2)$ between 0 and 1.

(*d*) Does the answer to part (*b*) help with the answer to part (*c*)? Explain.

12 (*a*) Draw the graph of $y = x(x-1)(x-2)(x-3)$.

(*b*) Describe the symmetry of this graph.

(*c*) Find, correct to 1 decimal place, the minimum value of $x(x-1)(x-2)(x-3)$ between 0 and 1.

(*d*) Find, correct to 1 decimal place, the maximum value of $x(x-1)(x-2)(x-3)$ between 1 and 2.

(*e*) Does the answer to part (*b*) help with the answers to part (*c*) or (*d*)? Explain.

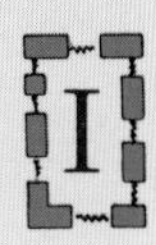

Suppose you want to find the minimum value of a quadratic expression such as

$x^2 + 6x + 11.$

One way of doing this is as follows.

You make part of the expression into a square. The diagram below shows how this can be done.

From the diagram,

	x	3
x	x^2	$3x$
3	$3x$	9

$$\begin{aligned} & x^2 + 6x + 11 \\ = \; & x^2 + 6x + 9 + 2 \\ = \; & (x+3)^2 + 2 \end{aligned}$$

The last line says that $x^2 + 6x + 11$ is '**square** + 2'. **Square** is always positive or zero, and so you get the minimum value by making **square** equal to zero. This means that you make x equal to -3 and the minimum value is 2.

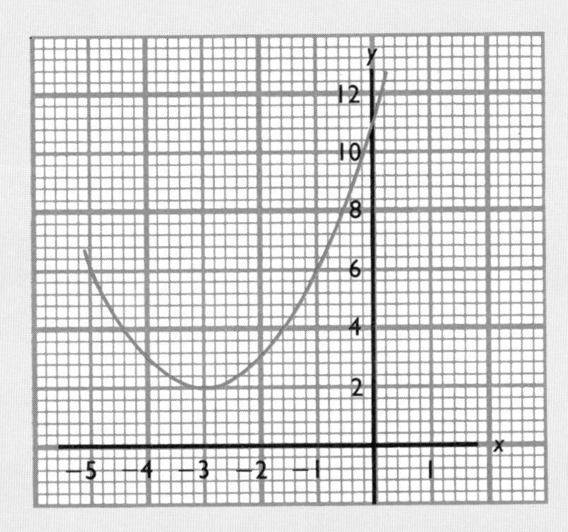

13 (*a*) Find the minimum values of each of the following:

(i) $x^2 + 4x + 7$ (ii) $x^2 + 2x + 17$ (iii) $x^2 - 8x + 11$
(iv) $x^2 + 5x + 10$ (v) $x^2 - 6x + 14$

(*b*) Draw graphs for each of the expressions in part (*a*).

Use the graphs to check your answers to part (*a*).

14 A ray of light always follows a path so that the time taken to travel between any two points is as small as possible.

The speed of light depends on the material it is travelling through. It is different for glass, air and water.

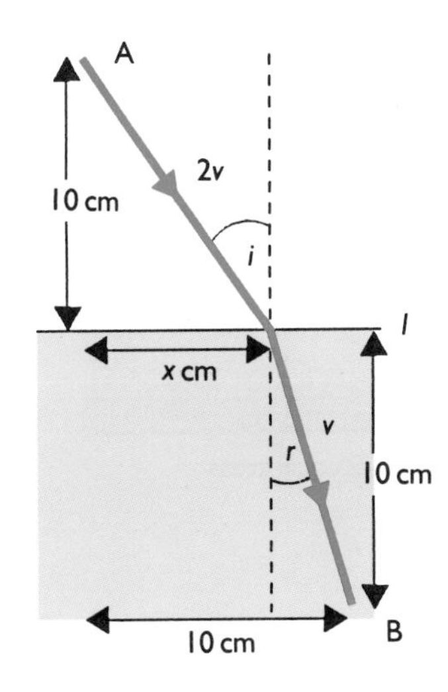

The picture shows two different materials which meet along the line l. The speed of light through the unshaded region is $2v$, and its speed through the shaded region is v.

The picture shows the path a ray of light takes between point A and point B, but it is not drawn accurately.

(*a*) Find, in terms of x and v, the time taken for the light to travel between point A and point B.

(*b*) Using a spreadsheet or a computer program, find the value of x which makes this time as small as possible. (This gives the path taken by the light ray.)

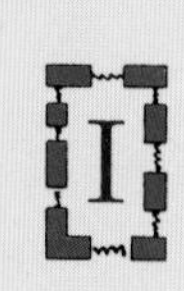

Snell's law of refraction states that, when light passes from one material to another,

$$\frac{\sin i}{\sin r} = n, \text{ where } n \text{ is a constant.}$$

i is usually called the angle of incidence, and r is the angle of refraction.

The value of n is called the refractive index, and is equal to the **ratio** of the speed of light through the two materials.

(*c*) By calculating $\sin i$ and $\sin r$, check that your answer to part (*b*) satisfies Snell's law.

15 (*a*) What are the smallest three numbers which have exactly

(i) 2 factors? (ii) 3 factors? (iii) 4 factors? (iv) 5 factors?

(*b*) Write each of your answers to part (*a*) as the product of prime factors.

(*c*) What is the largest number less than 1000 which has exactly

(i) 2 factors? (ii) 3 factors? (iii) 4 factors? (iv) 5 factors?

1⟩ Questions 4 and 5 of Section A were about enclosing equal rectangular areas with a fixed length of fencing.

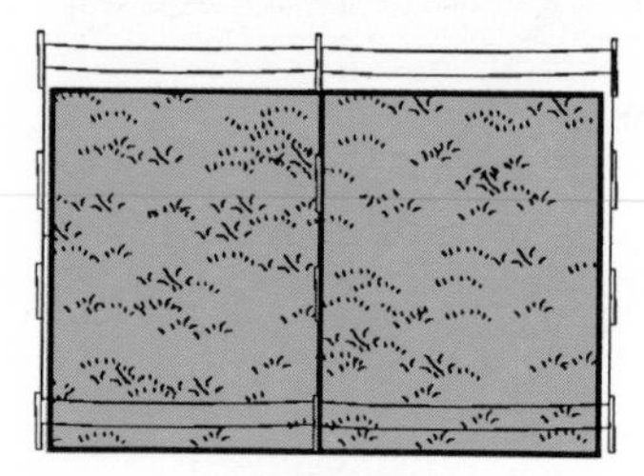

2 equal areas

3 equal areas

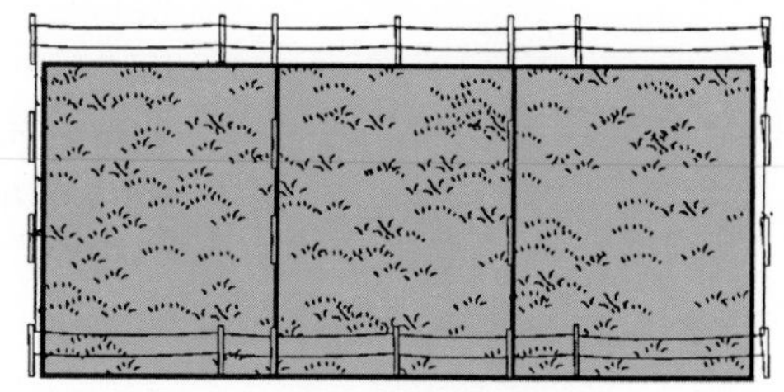

3 equal areas

Explore the situations described in these questions more fully.

If the rectangular area is to be divided into *four* pieces of equal area, several different arrangements are possible. Here are two of them.

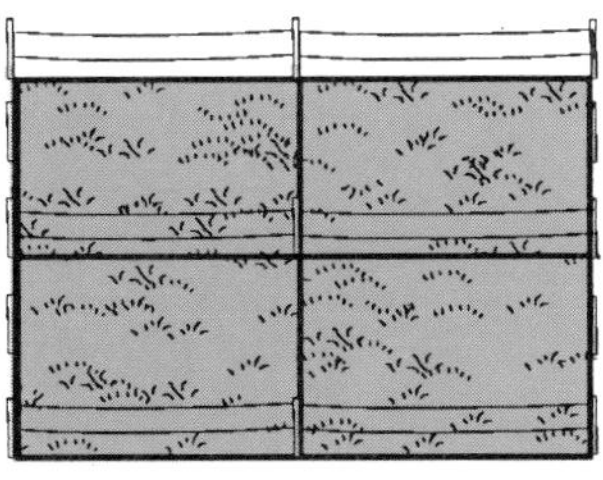

4 equal areas

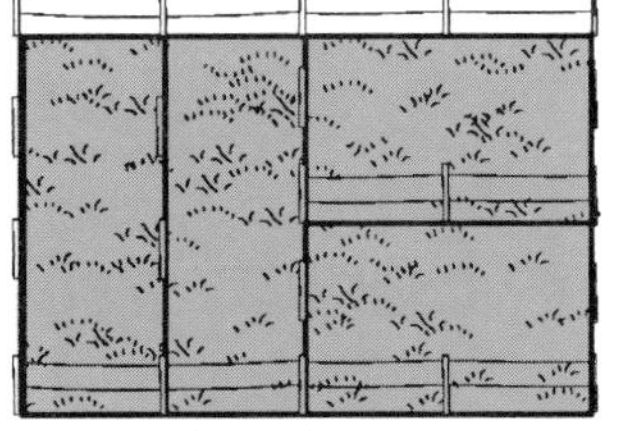

4 equal areas

Explore the possibilities for each arrangement. What is the maximum total area which can be enclosed for a fixed length of fencing?

What if a different arrangement of four pieces is used? What if there are five pieces? Six pieces? ...

2⟩ Four equal squares are cut from the four corners of a rectangle 24 cm long and 15 cm wide.

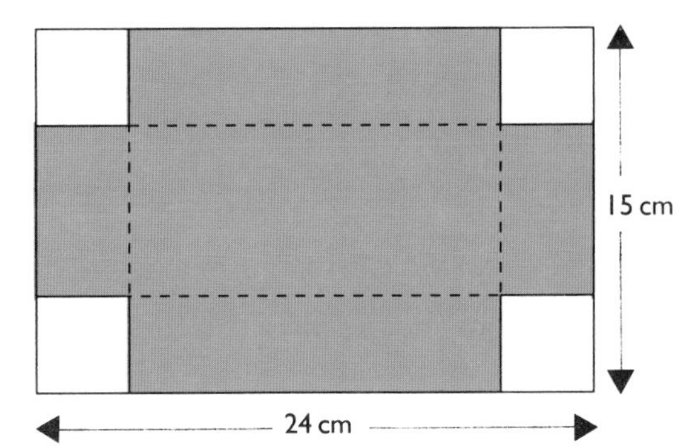

The rectangle is then folded to make a box.

Find, by trial and improvement, what size the square should be so that the volume of the box is as large as possible.

Do the same task for rectangles of other sizes.

What is the largest box that can be made from a sheet of A4 paper?

3⟩ Design a container which will hold 4 tennis balls. Make the surface area of the container as small as possible.

Try the same task for different numbers of tennis balls.

4⟩ Figure 4 shows 7 circles fitted into a rectangle. Each circle has a radius of 3 cm and the circles do not overlap.

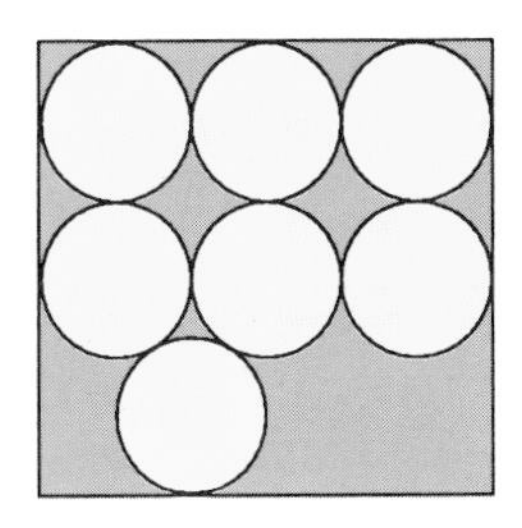

Figure 4

What is the *smallest* possible area for a rectangle into which you can fit 2 circles? 3 circles? 4 circles? ...

5⟩ Question 14 of Section A was about a channel made by bending a strip of metal 12 inches wide.

Investigate different ways of bending the metal to make a channel. Compare the cross-sections of several channels.

Try to make the cross-section of the channel as large as possible.

Review Exercises D

EXERCISE 42 Everyday graphs

1

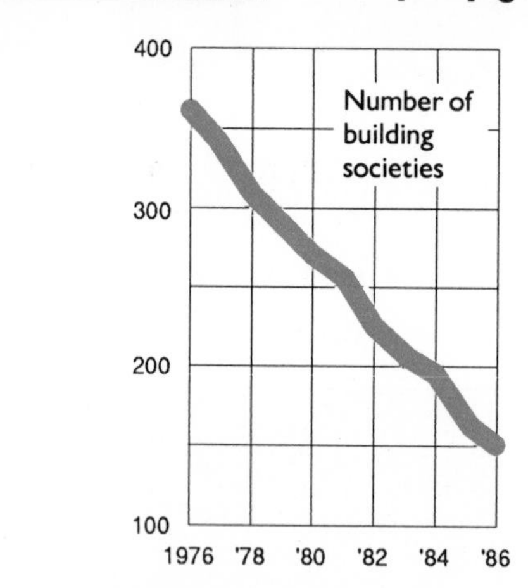

(*a*) Give two criticisms of this graph.

(*b*) From the graph, estimate the number of building societies in 1980.

(*MEG* May 1988, Paper 1)

2

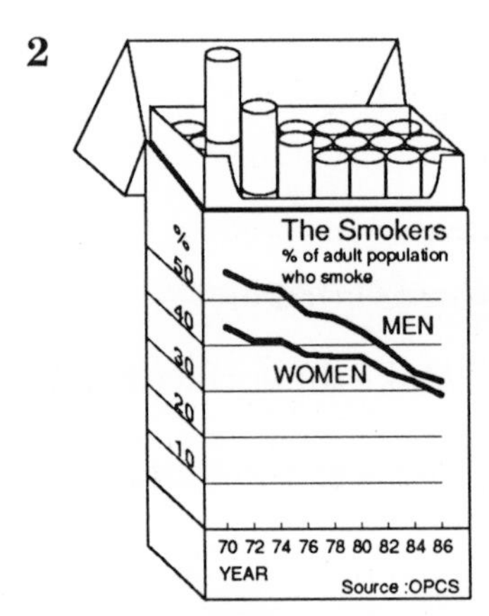

MILLIONS TO PACK UP CIGARETTES

NATIONAL NO SMOKING Day was launched on Wednesday this week with hundreds of walk-in clinics for smokers around the country.

Around three million people are expected to try to give up smoking this week, said campaign co-ordinator Peter Firth. 'We estimate a change in smoking behaviour — of either giving up or reducing — by about 400 000 people by the end of three months,' he added.

Nursing Times, March 11, 1987

(*a*) (i) What percentage of the male adult population smoked in 1982?
(ii) During which two-year period did the percentage of women smokers remain constant?
(iii) State the year in which exactly half of the male population was recorded as being smokers.

(*b*) (i) How many people are estimated to change their smoking behaviour as a result of the campaign?
(ii) Write your estimate to (i) as a fraction of the three million expected to try to give up smoking. Put this fraction into its simplest terms.

(*NEA* May 1989, Syllabus C Paper 2)

3 The graph below shows how many miles per gallon a car will do at various speeds.

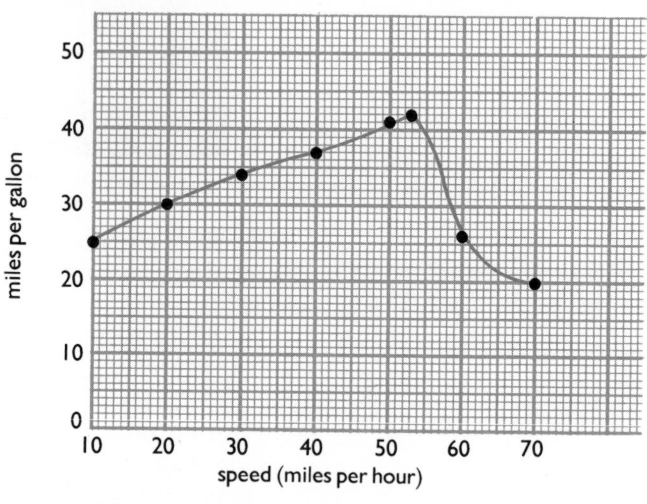

(*a*) How many miles to the gallon will the car do at 20 miles per hour?

(*b*) The car is used for a journey of 200 miles. It travels along a motorway at a speed of 60 miles per hour. How many complete gallons of petrol are needed?

(*c*) Use the graph to estimate the speed at which you get most miles per gallon.

(*SEG* Summer 1989, Mathematics C Paper 2)

4 The stopping distance for a car making a sudden stop is found by adding the thinking distance to the braking distance.

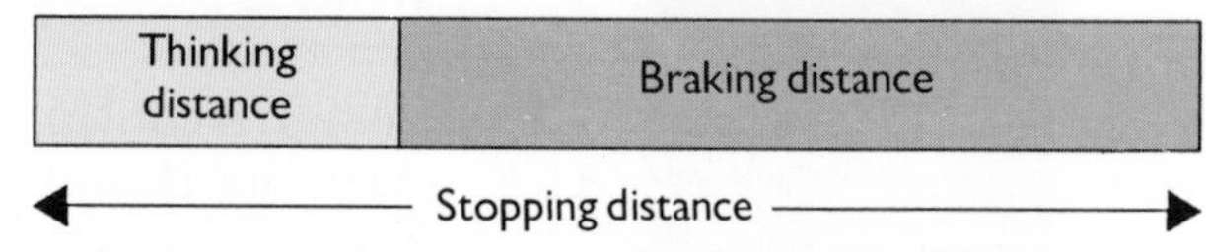

The chart below shows the stopping distance for cars travelling at different speeds in kilometres per hour.

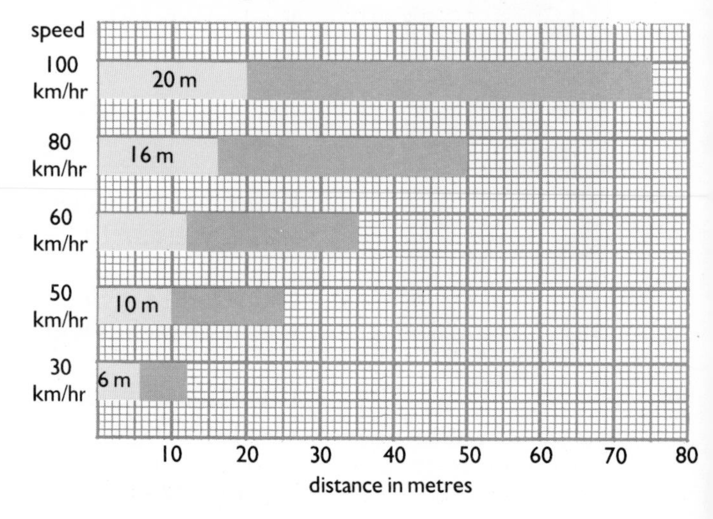

Use the above chart to answer the following questions.

(*a*) Complete the following statement:

To make a sudden stop when travelling at 60 km/hr, the thinking distance is ___ m.

(*b*) On a motorway Julie is travelling at 100 km/hr. She makes a sudden stop.

Find
(i) her stopping distance,
(ii) her braking distance.

(*c*) Estimate what the thinking distance is when a car travelling at 160 km/hr makes a sudden stop. Explain how you arrive at your answer.

(*Welsh* May 1988, Paper 1)

5

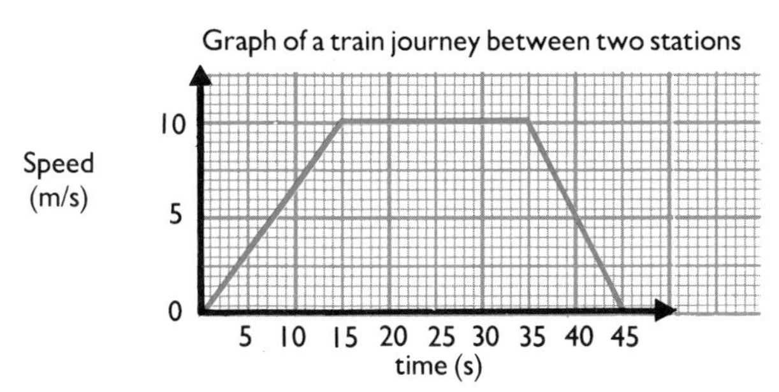

The graph shows the speed of a train travelling between two stations. From the graph write down

(*a*) the greatest speed of the train,

(*b*) the length of time for which the train travelled at constant speed.

(*LEAG* January 1989, Paper 2)

6

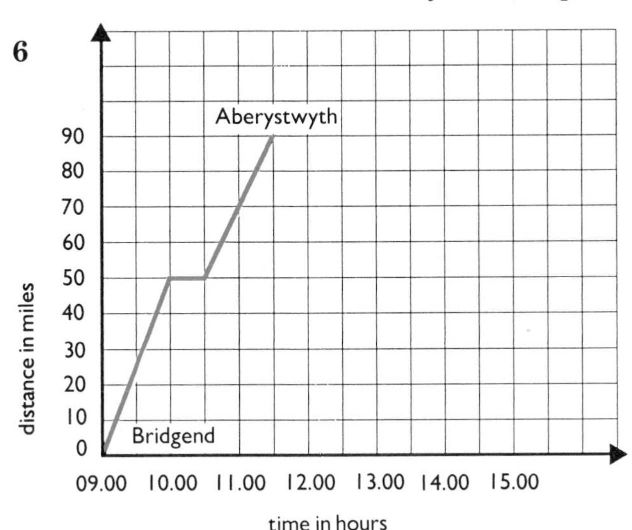

The above graph represents part of the journey of a motorist travelling from Bridgend to Aberystwyth and back to Bridgend.

(*a*) Describe fully the section of the journey shown on the graph.

(*b*) The motorist stays in Aberystwyth for $1\frac{1}{2}$ hours.

He then drives back to Bridgend without stopping, arriving at 1500.

Copy the graph, and complete it to show that return section of the journey.

(*Welsh* May 1988, Paper 2)

7

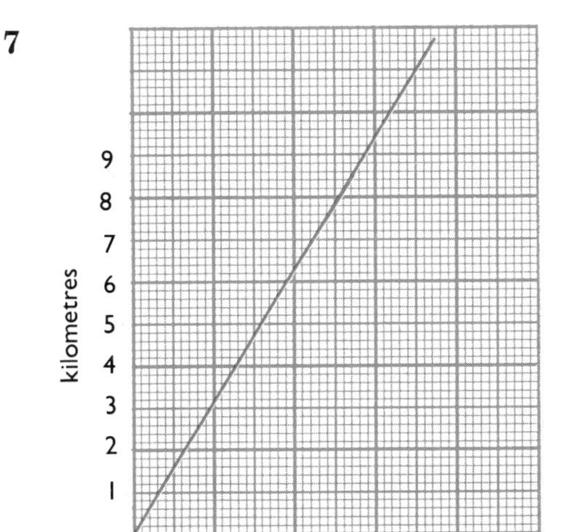

(*a*) Change 4 miles into kilometres.

(*b*) Change 5.6 kilometres into miles.

(*c*) A runner who completes a marathon runs 26.2 miles. How many kilometres is this?

(*SEG* Winter 1988, Mathematics B Paper 1)

8 In 1987, the rate of exchange was 9.80 French francs to the £.

(*a*) Complete the table below.

£	0	50	100	150	200	250
French francs	0				1960	2450

(*b*) Draw axes using a scale of 2 cm to represent £50 across the page and 2 cm to represent 500 francs up the page.

Use the figures in the table and draw a graph on the axes you have drawn for converting £ to French francs.

(*c*) Show by drawing lines on your graph how you would use the graph to convert

(i) £175 to French francs,
(ii) 800 French francs to pounds.

(*LEAG* May 1989, Paper 1)

9 Some packets and jars have both ounces and grams written on them.

Draw axes using a scale of 2 cm to represent 2 ounces across the page and 2 cm to represent 50 grams up the page.

Using these figures as coordinates, plot them on the axes you have drawn and join them up to make a conversion graph between ounces and grams.

Use your graph to estimate

(*a*) the weight in grams of 4 ounces of salt,

(*b*) the weight in ounces of 265 grams of flour.

(*NEA* November 1988, Syllabus C Paper 2)

10 The electricity bill for each quarter is made up of two parts, A and B.

A is a fixed charge. B is a charge for each unit of electricity used.

Mr Watt's electricity bills for the last summer and winter quarters are shown below.

	Number of units used	Total cost
Summer	350	£27.50
Winter	750	£51.50

(*a*) Draw axes using a scale of 2 cm to 100 units across the page and 2 cm to £5 up the page.

(*b*) Plot on your graph the two points for the summer and winter bills.

(*c*) Draw a straight line through the two points.

(*d*) Use your graph to find

(i) the total cost of electricity for a quarter in which 550 units of electricity were used.
(ii) the number of units used in a quarter when the total cost was £42.50.
(iii) the fixed charge.

(*MEG SMP* May 1988, Paper 2)

11

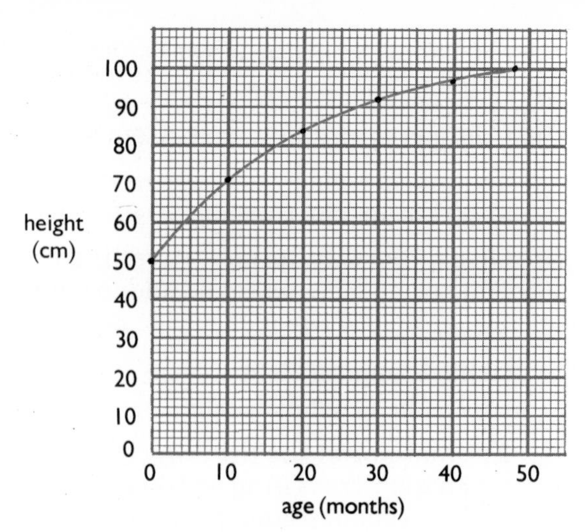

The graph above shows how the height of an average male child changes during the first four years of life.

Use the graph to answer the following questions.

(*a*) What is the height of the child at the age of 18 months?

(*b*) At what age is the child 85 cm in height?

(*c*) At the age of 2 years, a male child is normally one half its adult height. Estimate the child's adult height.

(*MEG* November 1988, Paper 2)

12

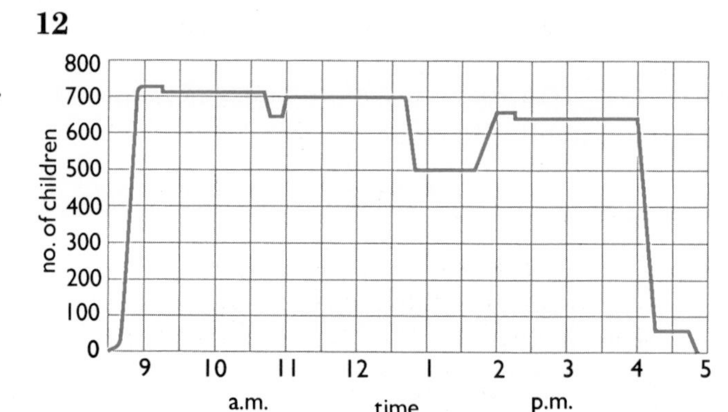

The graph shows the number of children on the premises of a school at different times during one day.

Describe what the graph tells you about what happens during the day.

(*NEA* May 1989, Syllabus B Paper 3)

13 The picture shows a children's paddling pool in the shape of a cylinder of height 20 cm and base radius 80 cm. The base and side of the pool are lined with blue plastic.

(*a*) Calculate the area of blue plastic required to line the base and side of the pool.

(*b*) The price of the plastic is 94p per m^2.

Calculate the cost, in pounds, of the plastic needed to make the lining of the pool.

(*c*) The pool is filled to a depth of 25 cm. How many litres of water are needed? Give your answer to the nearest 10 litres.

(*d*) Which of the graphs (i) to (iv) below, shows how the volume (V) of water used varies with the height (h) of the water in the pool as the pool is filling with water?

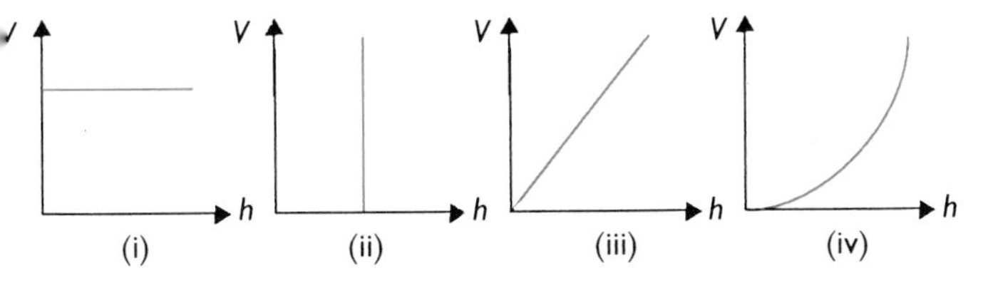

(*Welsh* May 1988, Paper 3)

14 For the family saloon car, the petrol consumption, c mpg, is given for various steady speeds, v mph, in the following table.

v	30	40	56	75
c	62	58	46	37

(*a*) On graph paper draw axes with $0 \leqslant v \leqslant 90$ and $0 \leqslant c \leqslant 70$ and plot the above values.

(*b*) For $30 \leqslant v \leqslant 75$ draw the best straight line you can to represent the relationship between v and c.

(*c*) From your graph, estimate the petrol consumption at

(i) 45 mph, (ii) 65 mph.

(*d*) If extended, your straight line would cross both axes. Explain why it is inappropriate to extend the graph in this way.

(*NEA* November 1988, Syllabus C Paper 3)

15 A car pulls away from the kerb and travels down a busy road. The table below shows the distance, s metres, it has gone after t seconds.

t	0	2	4	6	8	10	12
s	0	3	10	24	50	62	71

(*a*) Using a scale of 1 centimetre to represent 1 second on the horizontal (t) axis and a scale of 2 centimetres to represent 10 metres on the vertical (s) axis, draw the graph of s for values of t from 0 to 12.

(*b*) Use your graph to find

(i) how far the car has gone after 5 seconds,
(ii) how long it takes the car to travel 30 metres.

(*c*) Describe, as fully as possible, how the car's speed changes during the 12 seconds.

(*d*) A pedestrian is standing on the pavement 35 metres in front of the car. When the car starts to move, the pedestrian starts to walk at a constant speed of 2 metres per second in the same direction as the car.

(i) Draw, on the same axes, the graph illustrating the pedestrian's movement.
(ii) When does the car overtake the pedestrian?
(iii) Estimate, by drawing an appropriate tangent, the speed of the car at the moment it overtakes the pedestrian.

(*MEG* November 1988, Paper 5)

16 The table below shows the depth of water, in metres, at the mouth of Sheringport harbour at various times of a day.

Time (number of hours after midnight)	0	1	2	3	4	5	6
Depth of water (metres)	12.0	11.7	11.0	10.0	9.0	8.3	8.0

(*a*) (i) Draw an axis across the page to represent time (hours after midnight),

labelled from 0 to 6, and an axis up the page to represent depth of water (metres), labelled from 8 to 12.
(ii) Plot the points representing the information in the table.
(iii) Join these points to form a smooth curve.

(*b*) From your graph, estimate the depth of water at 4.15 a.m.

(*c*) A ship needs at least 9.2 metres of water to be able to leave the harbour. What is the latest time before 6.00 a.m. that the ship could leave?

(*d*) The formula for finding the depth of water is

$$D = 10 + k\cos(30t)^\circ$$

where D is the depth of water in metres, t is the number of hours after midnight and k is a constant. Using the values $t = 0$ and $D = 12.0$, find the value of k.

(*LEAG SMP* June 1988, Paper 3)

17

The table shows the temperature, θ °C, of a mug of coffee after it had been cooling for time t minutes.

t	0	5	10	15	20	25	30	35	40	45	50	55	60
θ	81	70	63	57	52	48	44	41.5	39	37	35.5	34	32.5

(*a*) Plot a graph to show this information. Use a scale of 2 cm to 10 minutes across the page (with $t = 0$ at the left hand edge) and 2 cm to 10 °C up the page.

(*b*) From your graph estimate

(i) the temperature after 38 minutes,
(ii) the time at which the temperature would be 28 °C.

(*c*) Explain why your answer to (*b*) (ii) must be treated with caution.

(*d*) Estimate the rate at which the mug of coffee was cooling after 20 minutes had elapsed.

(*e*) Estimate the room temperature giving a clear indication of how you arrive at your answer.

(*MEG SMP* June 1988, Paper 4)

18 Water is sucked at a constant rate into the pipette shown on the right. Draw a sketch graph showing how the water level increases with time as the water is sucked to the level indicated on the drawing.

(*NEA* November 1988, Syllabus A Paper 4)

19 The diagram, which is drawn to a scale of 1 cm to represent 1 m, shows a rod of length 3 m, which is pivoted at a point O on a horizontal table so that it can rotate in a vertical plane. A light is positioned at L, 5 m vertically above O, as a result of which the rod casts a shadow OP on the table.

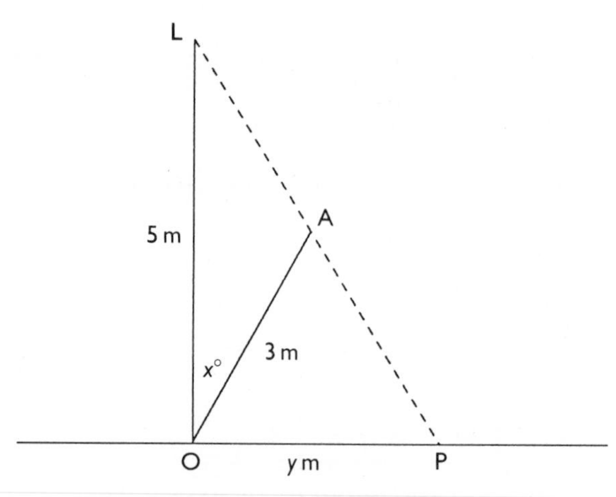

When the size of angle LOA is $x°$, the length of the shadow OP is y metres.

By drawing different positions of OA and measuring, construct a table of possible values of y against x for $0° \leqslant x \leqslant 90°$. Draw a graph to show how y varies as x increases from 0 to 90 and hence determine the greatest possible value of y.

(*NEA* May 1988, Syllabus C Paper 4)

EXERCISE 43 Graphs of functions

1 The equations of four straight lines are given below:

$y = 4x + 5$ $\quad$ $y = 5x + 2$
$y = 2x + 2$ $\quad$ $y = 2x + 5$

(*a*) Which two of these lines pass through the point (0, 5)?

(*b*) Which two of these lines are parallel?

(*SEG* Summer 1989, Mathematics A Paper 4)

2 A farmer has 16 m of fencing which he is going to use to make a rectangular pen PQRS in which to keep chickens.

He has been advised that he should allow 1 m^2 for each chicken. The pen is to be built using a barn wall as one side, as shown in the diagram.

He wants to design the pen in such a way that he can keep the maximum number of chickens in it.

Let the length of PS be x metres.

(*a*) Write down, in terms of x, the expression for the length of the side PQ.

(*b*) Show that the area, A square metres, of the pen is given by $A = 2x(8-x)$.

(*c*) Complete the table below, which gives the value of A for different possible values of x.

x	0	1	2	3	3.5	4	4.5	5	6	7	8
A		14	24	30	31.5			30	24	14	0

(*d*) Draw the graph of A against x. Use your graph to find the maximum number of chickens that the farmer may keep in his pen and write down the dimensions of the pen that he should use.

(*NEA* November 1988, Syllabus A Paper 4)

3 (*a*) Complete the table for values of $x^2 + 3x + 1$.

x	−5	−4	−3	−2	−1	0	1	2
x^2+3x+1	11		1		−1		5	

(*b*) Draw the graph of $y = x^2 + 3x + 1$ for values of x from −5 to 2.

(*c*) Use your graph to find approximate solutions to $x^2 + 3x + 1 = 4$.

(*NEA* May 1988, Syllabus B Paper 3)

4 An estate agent charges a fee to sell a house.

His fee is either £145 or $\frac{1}{2}$% of the house price, which ever is the greater.

(*a*) A house is sold for £40 000. Calculate the fee.

(*b*) Find the largest house price for which the fee will be £145.

(*c*) Draw a sketch graph to show the fees for house prices up to £40 000.

(*MEG SMP* November 1988, Paper 3)

5 (*a*) Plot the following points on graph paper and connect them with a smooth curve.

(−3, 18), (−2, 8), (−1, 2), (0, 0)
(1, 2), (2, 8), (3, 18).

(*b*) Write the equation which is satisfied by these points in form $y =$

(*c*) (i) Mark the point D on the curve whose x-coordinate is $-2\frac{1}{2}$.
(ii) Mark the point E on the curve whose y-coordinate is 7 and whose x-coordinate is positive.

(*d*) (i) Write down the coordinates of any three points which are on the graph paper and also on the line $y = x + 3$.
(ii) Plot these three points on the graph paper and draw a straight line through them.
(iii) Write down the coordinates of the two points where the line meets the curve. Label these two points A and B.

(*e*) (i) Draw a straight line joining (2, 8) to (0, 0). State the gradient of this line.
(ii) Draw a straight line joining (−2, 8) to (0, 0). State the gradient of this line.

(*SEG* Summer 1989, Mathematics B Paper 3)

6

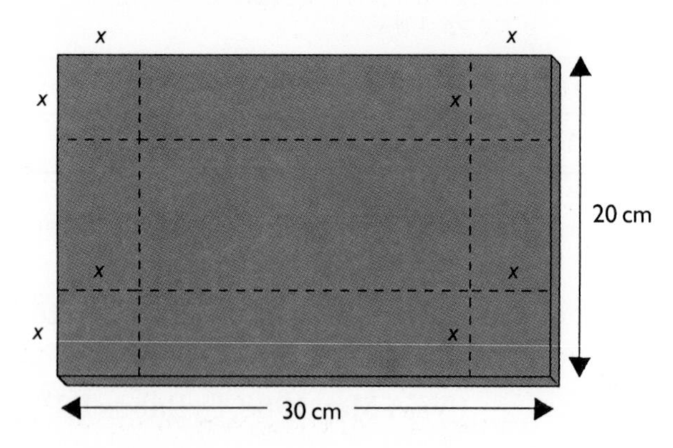

A box without a lid is to be made from a sheet of thin metal. The sheet measures 20 cm by 30 cm.

Squares of side x cm are cut from each corner and the sides folded up.

(*a*) V cm^3 is the volume enclosed by the box when it is made up.

Explain why $V = 4x(10 - x)(15 - x)$.

(*b*) Complete the table for these values of x.

x	4x	10−x	15−x	V
1	4	9	14	504
2	8	8	13	832
3				
4				
5				
6				
7				
8				
9				

(*c*) Draw a horizontal axis for values of x from 0 to 10, and a vertical axis for values of V from 0 to 1200 going up in steps of 100.

Draw the graph of (x, V).

(*d*) From your graph find

(i) the largest value of V,
(ii) the corresponding value of x, to the nearest whole number.

(*MEG SMP* 11–16 June 1988, Paper 3)

7 A trolley consists of a frame of four wheels. The size of the wheels varies with the size of the frame.

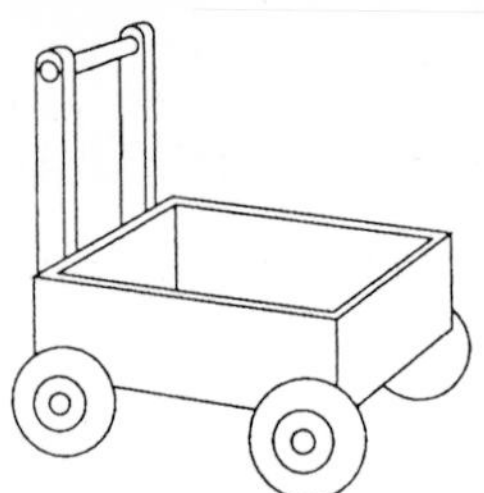

When the radius of a wheel is $x$cm, the total weight of the 4 wheels is y grams where $y = 80x^2$.

Some values of x and y which fit this relationship are shown in the table.

Radius (cm)	x	0	1	2	3	4	5
weight (g)	y	0	80	320	720	1280	2000

(*a*) Using a scale of 2 cm to represent 1 cm on the x-axis, and 2 cm to represent 200 g on the y-axis, plot these values and draw the graph of y against x.

(*b*) The weight of the frame is given by the formula $y = 300x + 200$. Copy and complete the following table of values for the weight of the frame.

Radius (cm)	x	1	2	3	4	5
Weight of frame (g)	y	500			1400	

(*c*) On the graph drawn in part (*a*), draw a further graph showing the weight of the frame.

(*d*) A trolley is to be made so that the weight of the wheels is equal to the weight of the frame. Use the intersection of the two graphs to decide the radius of the wheels which should be used.

(*SEG* Winter 1988, Mathematics A Paper 3)

8 Huw observes a bird flying directly away from a bird box.

He starts his watch and finds out how far the bird is from the box at different times.

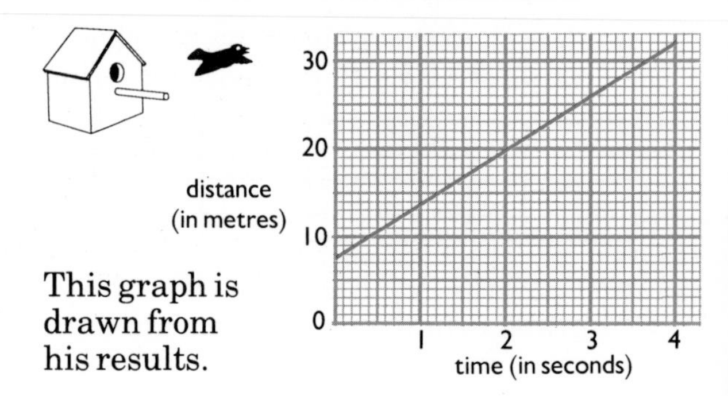

This graph is drawn from his results.

(*a*) How far is the bird from the box when Huw starts his watch?

(*b*) How fast is the bird flying?

(*c*) Write down a formula for the distance, d, the bird is from the box in terms of time, t.

(*Welsh* May 1988, Paper 4)

9

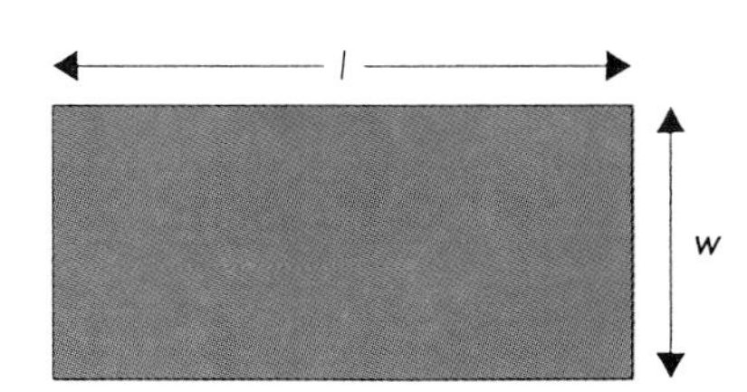

(*a*) A rectangle is drawn with length l and width w (as shown in the diagram), such that the perimeter is equal to 1 unit in length.

(*b*) Express this fact mathematically.

(*c*) Express w in terms of l.

(*d*) Express the area A of the rectangle in terms of l.

(*e*) Sketch the graph of A against l as l varies.

(*f*) For what value of l is A a maximum?

(*g*) What is the maximum possible value of A?

(*NEA* November 1988, Syllabus B Paper 4)

10

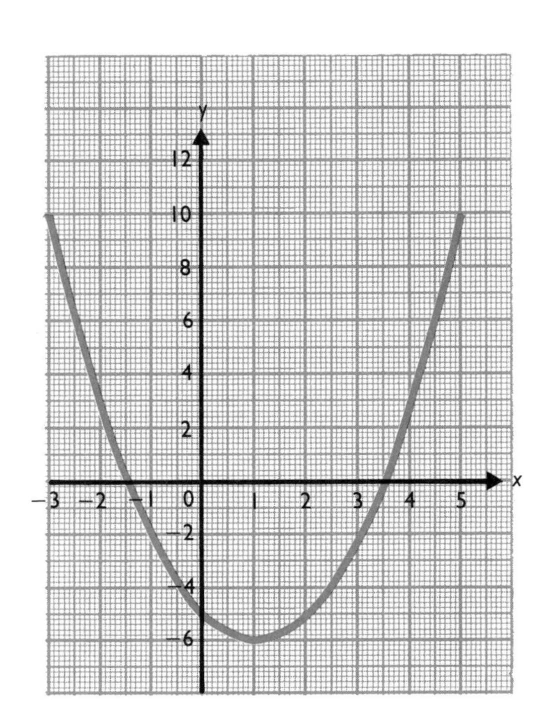

The equation of the graph above is $y = x^2 - 2x - 5$.

(*a*) Copy this graph. On the same set of axes draw the line whose equation is $y = x - 1$.

(*b*) Write down the solution set to $x^2 - 2x - 5 = x - 1$.

(*c*) Show that $x^2 - 2x - 5 = x - 1$ can be written as $x^2 - 3x - 4 = 0$.

(*d*) By drawing a suitable line, using the same axes, solve the equation $x^2 - x - 11 = 0$.

(*Welsh* May 1988, Paper 4)

11 (*a*) (i) Either by copying and completing the following table, or otherwise, find the values of y, for the given values of x from 1 to 6, when

$$y = 4x^2 - 28x + 41.$$

x	1	2	3	4	5	6
$4x^2$	4			64		144
$-28x$	−28			−112		−168
$+41$	+41			+41		+41
y	17			−7		17

(ii) Using a scale of 2 centimetres to represent 1 unit on the x-axis and a scale of 2 centimetres to represent 5 units on the y-axis, draw the graph of $y = 4x^2 - 28x + 41$ for values of x from 1 to 6.
(iii) Draw in the line of symmetry on your graph and calculate the minimum value of y.

(*b*) (i) Show how the equation $4x^3 - 28x^2 + 41x - 12 = 0$ may be transformed into the form $4x^2 - 28x + 41 = \frac{12}{x}$ $(x \neq 0)$.

(ii) By drawing, on the same axes, an appropriate graph, find the two solutions of $4x^3 - 28x^2 + 41x - 12 = 0$ which lie between 1 and 6.

(*MEG* November 1988, Paper 6)

12 For values of t in the range $0 \leqslant t \leqslant 12\frac{1}{2}$, a function v is defined by

$$v = \begin{cases} \frac{1}{2}t^2 & \text{for } 0 \leqslant t < 4 \\ -t^2 + 12t - 24 & \text{for } 4 \leqslant t < 7 \\ -2t + 25 & \text{for } 7 \leqslant t < 12\frac{1}{2} \end{cases}$$

(*a*) Complete the following table which gives the values of v corresponding to values of t for the given function.

t	0	1	2	3	4	5	6	7	9	11	$12\frac{1}{2}$
v	0				8			11			

(*b*) Draw a graph of the given function for values of t in the range $0 \leqslant t \leqslant 12\frac{1}{2}$.

The relationship between the velocity v metres per second of a car and the time t seconds, during which the car has been travelling, may be represented by the mathematical model given below.

$$v = \begin{cases} \frac{1}{2}t^2 & \text{for } 0 \leqslant t < 4 \\ -t^2 + 12t - 24 & \text{for } 4 \leqslant t < 7 \\ -2t + 25 & \text{for } 7 \leqslant t < 12\frac{1}{2} \end{cases}$$

(*c*) Use the graph drawn in part (*b*) of this question to answer each of the following questions:

(i) by drawing a tangent to the curve, estimate the acceleration of the car when $t = 2$,
(ii) estimate the deceleration of the car, due to application of the brakes, when $t = 7$,
(iii) estimate the distance travelled by the car from the moment the brakes are applied ($t = 7$) to the moment the car stops.

(*NEA* May 1989, Syllabus C Paper 4)

13 A grandfather clock has a long pendulum. As it moves, the distance x cm of the bob of the pendulum from its vertical position is given by the formula

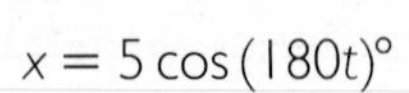

$$x = 5\cos(180t)°$$

where t is the time in seconds.

(*a*) Use this formula to complete the table below, giving values of x correct to one decimal place.

t	0	0.2	0.4	0.6	0.8	1.0	1.2	1.4	1.6	1.8	2.0
x			1.5				−4.0				

(*b*) What does it mean when x is negative?

(*c*) Plot these results on a graph, and join your points with a smooth curve.

Use your graph to answer the following.

(*d*) What is the greatest distance of the bob from the vertical during the motion?

(*e*) What is the value of t when the pendulum is first vertical?

(*MEG SMP* 11–16 November 1988, Paper 4)

14

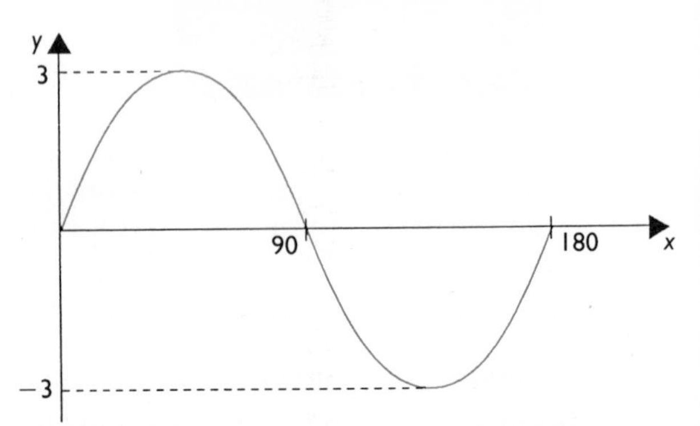

The curve shown in the diagram has the equation $y = p\sin(qx)$. State the values of p and q.

(*MEG SMP* November 1988, Paper 4)

15 (*a*) Draw the graph of $x + y = 1$.

(*b*) On separate axes plot the points $((\sin x)^2, (\cos x)^2)$, for $x = 0°, 10°, 20°, \ldots, 80°, 90°$.

(*c*) By joining the points with a suitable graph, suggest a relationship between $(\sin x)^2$ and $(\cos x)^2$.

(*d*) Use your relationship to find the exact value of $\cos x$ when $\sin x = \frac{9}{41}$.

(*NEA* November 1988, Syllabus B Paper 4)

16 (*a*) At a certain location in the British Isles, the number of hours sunlight per day, t months after the Spring equinox (21 March), is given approximately by the formula

$$y = 12 + 4\sin(30t)°.$$

What are the greatest and least amounts of daylight per day, during the year?

(*b*) At a certain location in Greenland, the number of hours daylight per day, t months after the Spring equinox, is given approximately by the formula

$y = 12 + 24\sin(30t)°$,

but this formula is valid only at certain times of the year.

Why is this formula not valid when $t = 3$?

(*SEG* 1990 Specimen, Extension Paper)

EXERCISE 44 Bearings and loci

1 The diagram below is a map of the village of Treforlan.

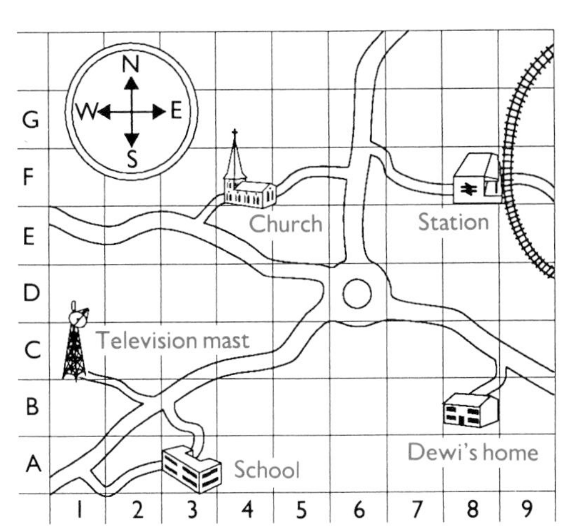

In the village of Treforlan, the station is to the East of the church.

(*a*) Complete the following statements.

(i) Dewi's home is to the __________ of the station.
(ii) The television mast is North West of __________.
(iii) The station is to the __________ of the school.

(*b*) Dewi's home is shown in square B8.

(i) In what square is the church?
(ii) What is in square D6?

(*Welsh* May 1988, Paper 1)

2

N
Fishguard
$z°$ $x°$ $y°$
Haverfordwest
Whitland
Broad Haven

In Pembrokeshire, Fishguard is due North of Haverfordwest, Whitland is due East of Haverfordwest and Broad Haven is on a bearing of 260° from Haverfordwest.

The diagram is a sketch of their relative positions.

Find the values of x, y and z.

(*LEAG SMP* January 1989, Paper 1)

3 Newark is 56 kilometres from Sheffield on a bearing of 128°.

Grimsby is 77 kilometres from Newark on a bearing of 042° from Newark.

Copy the diagram shown. Using a scale of 1 centimetre to represent 10 kilometres, draw accurately on your diagram the positions of Newark and Grimsby.

North
Sheffield

Use a protractor to measure the angles and a ruler to measure the distances.

Use your diagram to find the distance, in kilometres, between Sheffield and Grimsby.

(*NEA* May 1989, Syllabuses A and B Paper 1)

4

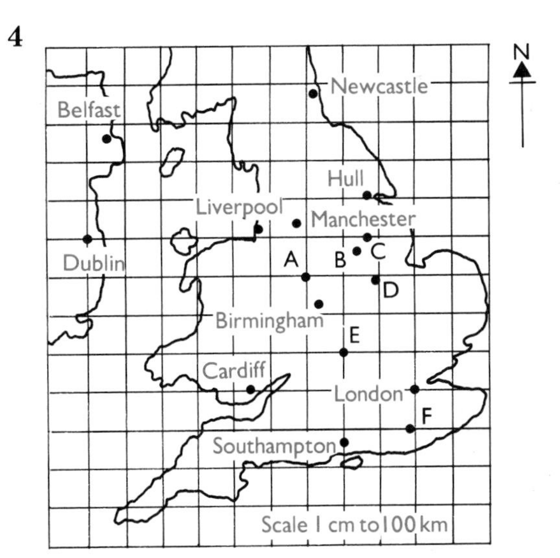

The diagram shows part of a map of the British Isles, drawn to a scale of 1 cm to 100 km.

(*a*) Give the straight line distance, in km, between

(i) Cardiff and Southampton,
(ii) London and Birmingham.

(*b*) With the help of a protractor, find

(i) the bearing of Newcastle from Dublin,
(ii) the bearing of Liverpool from Birmingham.

The bearing of Nottingham from Cardiff is 040°. The straight line distance of Nottingham from Cardiff is 225 km.

(*c*) Which of the points A, B, C, D, E or F represents Nottingham?

(*LEAG* May 1989, Paper 2)

5 A square field has sides of length 10 m. A goat is tied by a rope of length 8 m to a post in one corner of the field.

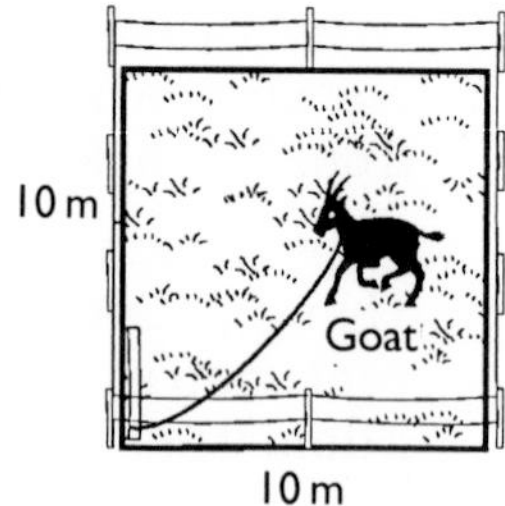

(*a*) What is the area of the field the goat can graze?

(*b*) What percentage of the field can the goat graze?

(*SEG* Summer 1988, Mathematics A Paper 3)

6

Position I
Position II
20cm
40 cm
50 cm

The diagram, which is not drawn to scale, represents a garden roller of radius 20 cm which is moved from position I, over a step of height 20 cm, to position II. The roller is always in contact with the ground.

(*a*) Draw the diagram accurately to a scale of 1 cm to represent 10 cm and draw accurately the path of the centre O of the roller as it is moved from position I to position II.

(*b*) Taking π as 3.14, calculate the length, in centimetres, of this path.

(*MEG* November 1987, Paper 2)

7

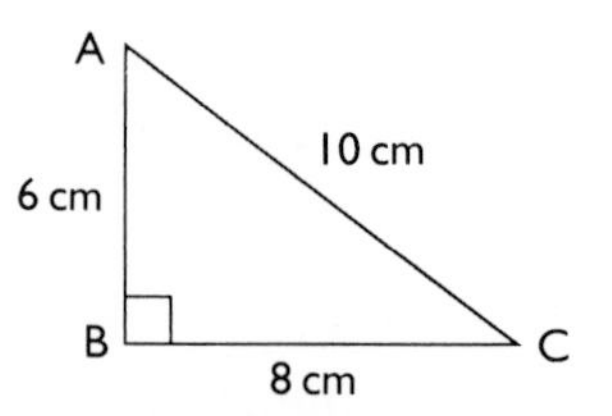

(*a*) Draw triangle ABC accurately. Construct the bisector of angle BAC. Make sure the bisector is drawn long enough to meet BC and label this intersection X.

(*b*) Measure the lengths of BX and XC, and hence write down the ratio BX:XC.

(*c*) Show that this ratio is approximately the same ratio as AB:AC.

(*NEA* November 1988, Syllabus A Paper 3)

8 The diagram shows the centre circle and part of the half-way line on a football pitch. Ahmed at A passes the ball to Brian at B who then passes to Carl at C.

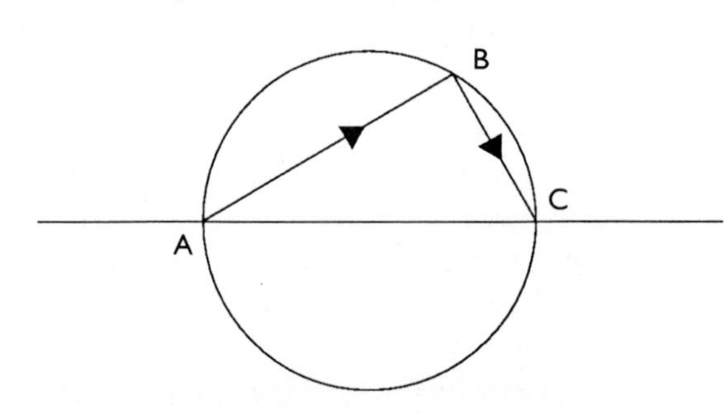

(*a*) Without measuring, write down the size of the angle ABC. Give a reason for your answer.

(*b*) Brian moves around the circumference of the centre circle. Explain what happens to the angle ABC.

(*SEG* Summer 1989, Mathematics A Paper 3)

9 Mr K. Perbility-Brown's lawn is a rectangle DEFG with

DE = 18 m
DG = 12 m.

He cuts the lawn with an electric 'Bovvermo' connected to a power point P which is on the edge DG and one third of the way from D to G. The cable is long enough for him to mow up to 16 m from P.

(*a*) Using a scale of 1 cm to 2 m draw a scale diagram of DEFG.

(*b*) On your diagram shade the area which Mr Brown can reach with his Bovvermo.

(*c*) Mr Brown wants to be able to reach the whole lawn with his mower and so decides to buy a new cable. By measuring, find the shortest length of cable which he will need. Mark on your diagram any length which you measure.

(*d*) The cable costs 48p per metre. An exact number of metres must be bought. How much will the new cable cost?

(*e*) The original cable would allow him to mow the whole lawn if he moved the power point. On your diagram mark a point Q on the edge of the lawn which would be a suitable position to fix the power point.

(*MEG SMP* November 1988, Paper 3)

10

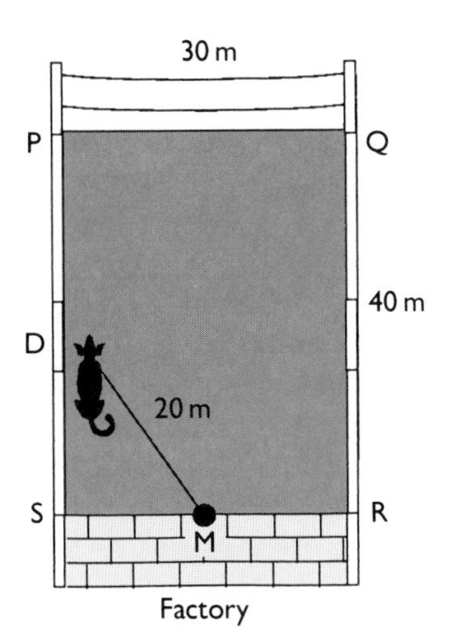

The diagram represents a rectangular yard adjacent to a factory, which is patrolled by a guard dog D, tethered by a chain 20 m long attached at the midpoint, M, of the factory wall, SR.

(*a*) Copy the diagram.

(*b*) Assuming the dog keeps the chain taut, sketch on your diagram the locus of the dog's path as it moves from one side of the yard to the other.

(*c*) Calculate the distance PM.

(*d*) An intruder climbs into the yard at P. Mark on your diagram the point N at which the dog is closest to the intruder. Calculate the distance PN.

(*NEA* November 1988, Syllabus C Paper 3)

11

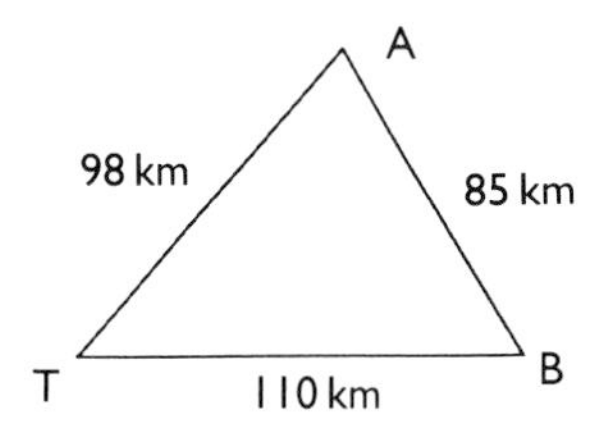

The diagram shows the location of a television transmitter (T) in relation to two towns Amburg (A) and Beetown (B).

(*a*) Using a scale of 1 cm to represent 10 km, draw an accurate scale diagram of the triangle TAB.

The transmitter has a range of 80 km.

(*b*) Draw accurately, on your scale drawing, the curve which represents the limiting range of the transmitter.

It is planned to build a repeater station (R), which is an equal distance from both Amburg and Beetown.

(*c*) On your drawing, construct accurately the line on which the repeater station must be built.

The repeater station is to be built at the maximum range of the transmitter.

(*d*) (i) Mark, with the letter R, the position of the repeater station on your diagram.
(ii) Find the minimum transmitting range of the repeater station so that programmes can be received in Amburg. Give your answer in km, to the nearest km.

(*LEAG* June 1988, Paper 3)

12 In a garden there is a lawn which is in the shape of a rectangle and a semicircle, as shown in the diagram.

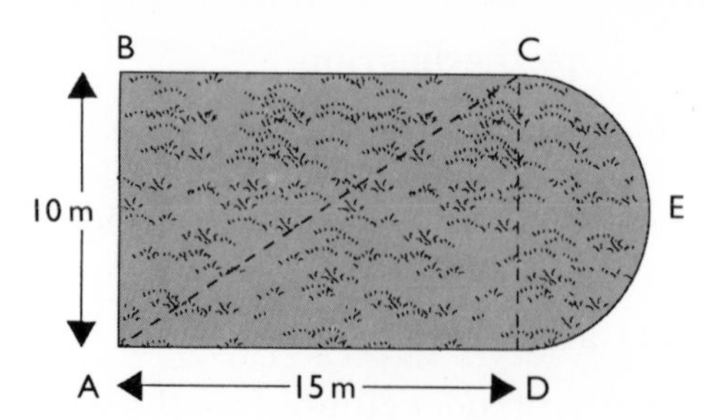

The rectangle is 15 m long and 10 m wide.

The radius of the semicircle is 5 m.

(*a*) Calculate the area of the lawn.

Lawn fertilizer is to be spread evenly over the lawn at the rate of 50 g per m^2.

(*b*) Find how much fertilizer is needed, correct to the nearest 100 g.

The fertilizer is sold in 1 kg packets, which cost £1.20 each plus 15% VAT.

(*c*) Find the total cost of the fertilizer which must be bought.

A water sprinkler can be placed at any point on the line AC.

(*d*) Find, by drawing or calculation, the radius of the smallest spraying circle so that all points of the lawn may be watered without moving the sprinkler.

(*LEAG SMP* January 1989, Paper 4)

13

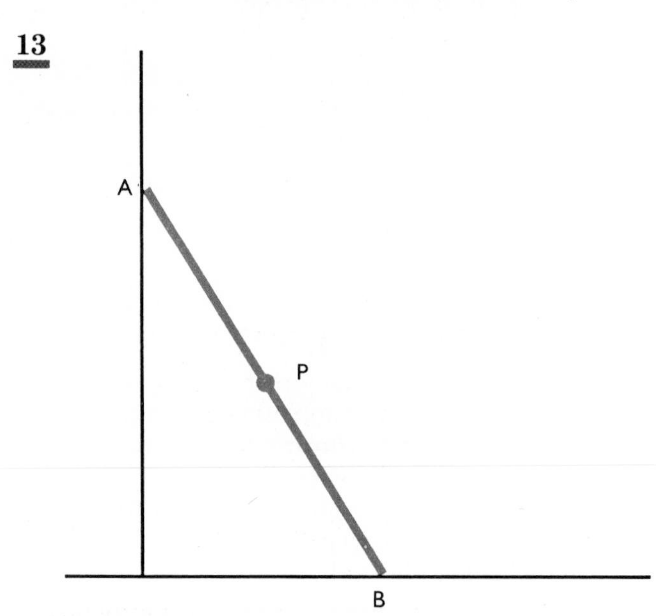

The diagram, which is drawn to a scale of 1 cm to represent 0.5 m, shows a rod AB, of length 3 m, resting in a vertical plane with A against a vertical wall and B resting on horizontal ground.

Measure the diagram and make a copy of it. Draw the locus of P, the midpoint of AB, as A moves vertically up and down the wall and B moves along the ground.

(*NEA* November 1988, Syllabus C Paper 4)

14 A 30 m square sports arena is lit by powerful floodlights positioned at each corner. Each floodlight lights up a circular area on the ground of radius 20 m, the centre of the circle being directly below the light.

(*a*) Make a scale drawing of the arena, using 1 cm to represent 4 m, and shade the region *not* lit.

(*b*) How many more lights of the same kind would be needed to make sure the whole arena is lit, assuming that lights can only be placed at the edge of the arena? Use as few lights as possible and mark the position of any extra lights on your scale drawing.

(*c*) Starting with the same arena, but no lights already there, try to find a way of lighting up the whole arena using as few lights as possible. The same kind of lights must be used and they must be placed around the edge of the arena. State clearly what is the least number of lights and show a possible way of arranging them by making a second scale drawing of the arena.

(*MEG SMP* 11–16 November 1988, Paper 4)

15

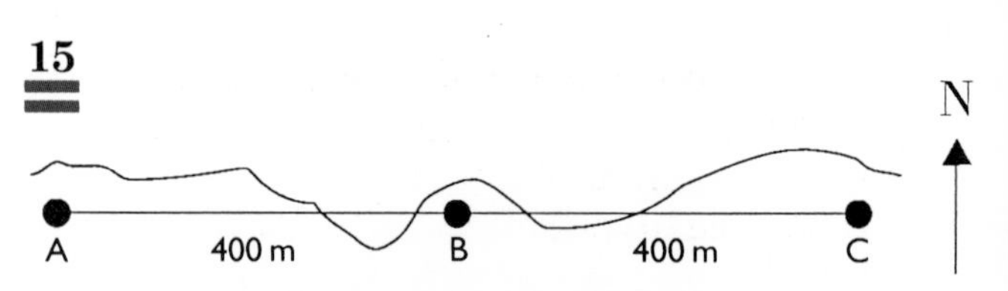

A, B and C are three posts on a North-facing coastline (see the above figure). C is 800 m due East of A, and B is half-way between A and C. In order to avoid the danger of sunken rocks near the coast, instructions are given that a boat, P, should never be in a position where either angle APB or angle BPC is more than 60°.

(*a*) Copy the figure on a suitable scale, and sketch the boundary of the region from which boats are excluded by the instruction. Shade this region and shade doubly the region in which angles APB and BPC are *both* more than 60°.

(*b*) O is the point on the boundary which is nearest to B. Write down the size of angle AOC, and calculate the distances OA and OB.

(*c*) If B is removed, suggest an instruction, involving A and C only, which will keep boats out of the dangerous area, even if it will keep them out of some additional area as well.

(*MEG* 1990 and 1991 Specimens, Extension Paper)

16 (i) Mark two points A and B on your paper, 8 cm apart. By choosing various pairs of numbers (not necessarily both whole numbers) which multiply together to give 20, plot a number of points P on your paper with the property that

$$PA \times PB = 20$$

(where both PA and PB are measured in centimetres). Hence draw, as accurately as you can, the locus of points with this property.
(ii) Starting again with a new pair of points A and B, still 8 cm apart, draw the locus of points with the property

$$PA \times PB = 16.$$

(iii) Repeat with the property

$$PA \times PB = 15.$$

(iv) The three loci which you have drawn should all look different, but they all have the same kinds of symmetry. Name, with reference to the points A and B,

(*a*) any lines of reflection symmetry,

(*b*) the centre and angle of rotational symmetry,

for all three loci. Describe a simple shape which has the same symmetry as these loci.
(v) All the loci in (i), (ii) and (iii) have a property of the form

$$PA \times PB = k,$$

where k is a number. For some values of k, there are points where the locus cuts the line between A and B. Suppose that it does this at a point P where

$PA = x$ cm.

(*a*) What is the length PB in terms of x?

(*b*) Show that x satisfies the quadratic equation

$$x^2 - 8x + k = 0.$$

(*c*) For the value $k = 16$ and $k = 15$, solve this equation for x.

(*d*) Show that, if $k = 20$, the equation has no solutions for x.

(*e*) Use these results to explain why the loci have different forms for these three values of k.

(*LEAG SMP* 11–16 June 1987, Extension Paper)

EXERCISE 45 Statistics 2

1 Each symbol (sun) represents 2 hours of sunshine during a particular day in Bournemouth.

How many hours of sunshine were there on the day represented below?

(*NEA* May 1989, Syllabuses A and B Paper 1)

2

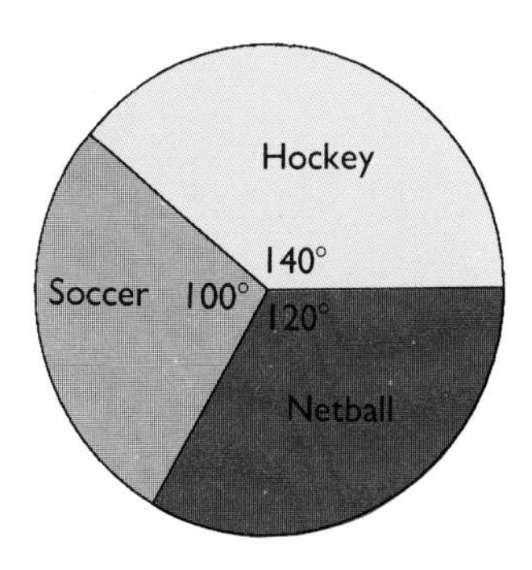

The pie chart shows the games played by 36 pupils in a class.

(*a*) Use the pie chart to find how many pupils did each of the three games.

(*b*) Draw a *pictogram* to show the above information.

(*SEG* Winter 1988, Mathematics B Paper 1)

3 Of the people in Great Britain,

45% have blood group O
40% have blood group A,
10% have blood group B and
5% have blood group AB.

(*a*) Part of a pie chart to represent this information is drawn below.

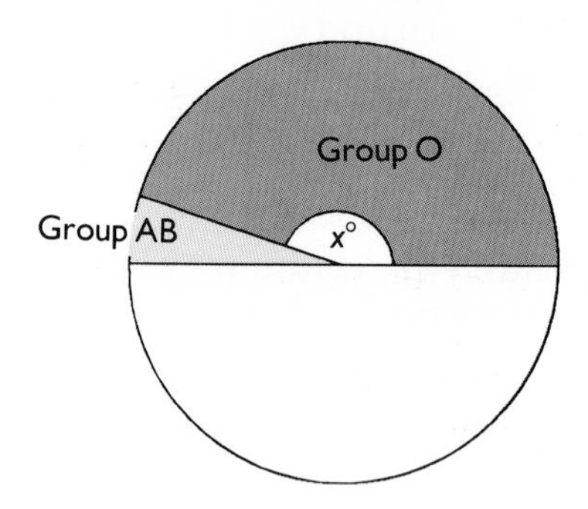

(i) Measure and write down the size of the angle marked $x°$ in the pie chart.
(ii) Complete the pie chart accurately.

(*b*) One of the people in Great Britain is chosen at random. What is the probability that this person has blood group O? Give your answer as a fraction.

(*MEG* November 1988, Paper 1)

4 The pie chart shows the percentage of different fuels used by households in Britain during 1985.

Study the chart and write down two facts about the use of fuels in that year.

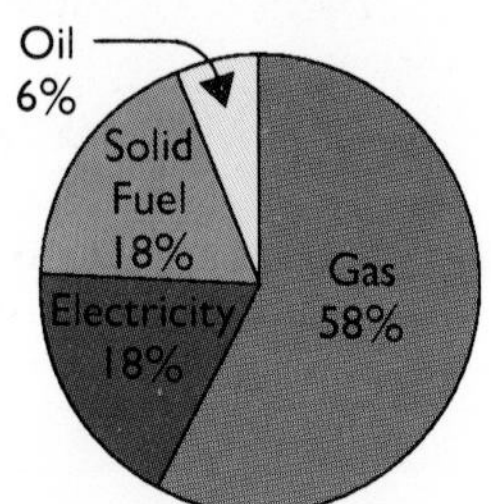

(*MEG SMP* November 1988, Paper 1)

5 A knitted jumper costs £30. The pie chart shows how the cost of the jumper is made up.

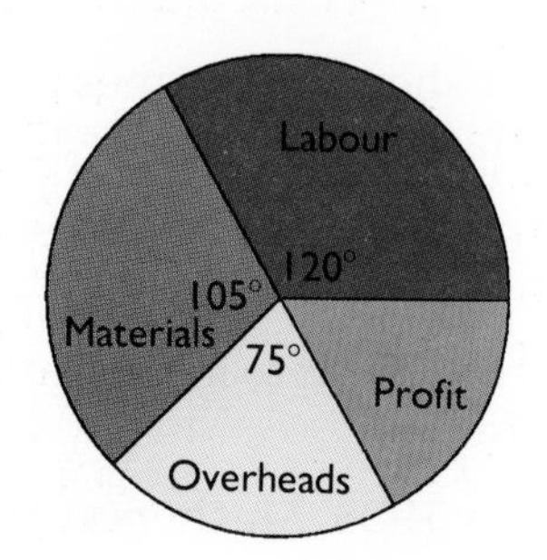

(*a*) (i) What fraction represents 'profit'?
(ii) What is the labour cost of producing the jumper?

(*b*) The profit is increased to £6, but the total cost of the article is still £30. A new pie chart is drawn. What is the angle representing 'profit'?

(*SEG* Summer 1989, Mathematics C Paper 2)

6 These are the marks scored by class 4E in an English test. The test was marked out of 50.

36	15	17	37	37	10	30	50
42	24	12	5	50	7	16	37
29	32	44	23	35			

(*a*) How many people took the test?

(*b*) How many people scored full marks?

(*c*) Put all the marks in order, starting with the lowest.

(*d*) What is the middle mark?

(*e*) Which mark was scored by most people?

(*f*) What was the average (mean) mark for the class?

(*g*) Wynn scored 29. He said 'I did better than most of the class.' Was he right? Give a reason for your answer.

(*Welsh* May 1989, Paper 2)

7 A survey was carried out during part of one day to see how long it took nurses to weigh and assess babies. The recorded times, to the nearest minute, were as follows:

6	24	11	12	7
18	13	16	17	13
17	19	23	8	19
18	9	17	17	13
16	16	12	12	21.

(*a*) (i) Calculate the mean time taken by the nurses to weigh and assess a baby on this day at the clinic.
(ii) On average, how many babies could be assessed and weighed by one nurse during a three-hour session?

(*b*) The clinic usually has around 80 babies to weigh and assess each day in a morning session between 9 a.m. and 12 noon. Using your answers to part (*a*), calculate the number of nurses needed for each morning session.

(*c*) Draw a fully labelled histogram to illustrate the recorded data above.

Use class intervals of 5–10 minutes, 10–15 minutes, etc.

(*NEA* November 1988, Syllabus A Paper 3)

8 Two dice were thrown together 125 times. The scores are shown in this frequency table.

Score	Frequency
2	4
3	7
4	9
5	11
6	7
7	5
8	17
9	19
10	24
11	12
12	10

Use this information to find

(*a*) the mode of the scores,

(*b*) the median score,

(*c*) the mean score.

(*NEA* November 1988, Syllabus B Paper 3)

9 Ten people were asked to estimate the dimensions of a room. Their estimates (in metres) are shown in the table.

Person	Width	Length	Height
A	2.7	4.4	1.9
B	3.3	4.4	1.7
C	3.3	4.2	2.2
D	3.2	4.1	2.1
E	3.0	4.0	2.0
F	3.1	4.1	1.8
G	2.9	3.7	1.9
H	3.1	3.7	2.1
J	3.0	3.9	2.1
K	3.0	4.1	2.2

(*a*) (i) Which person's estimate produced the least volume?
(ii) What is the least volume?

(*b*) (i) Which person's estimate produced the greatest volume?
(ii) What is the greatest volume?

(*c*) (i) State the modal width.
(ii) State the median length.
(iii) State the mean height.

(*d*) The correct volume was 24 m^3.

(i) Which person's estimate was furthest from this volume?

(ii) What percentage error did that person make?

(*SEG* Summer 1989, Mathematics B Paper 3)

10 Gemma calculates that from her monthly salary after deductions for Income Tax and National Insurance she spends

25% on household bills,
20% on transport,
40% on food.

She saves the remainder of her salary.

(*a*) Draw a circle of radius 5 cm and illustrate this information on a pie chart. Label each sector clearly.

(*b*) Gemma's monthly income after deduction is £540. How much does she save?

(*SEG* Summer 1989, Mathematics A Paper 3)

11 This pie chart shows the proportion of body length taken up by the head, body and legs of a new born baby.

(*a*) What percentage of its total body length is the head of the baby?

(*b*) The baby's legs measure 14 cm. What is the baby's total length?

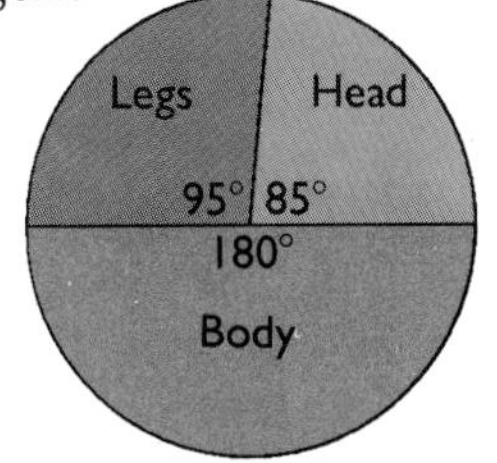

(*Welsh* May 1989, Paper 4)

12 (*a*) The pie chart, which is not drawn to scale, shows the distribution of types of land on an island A near the Arctic Circle.

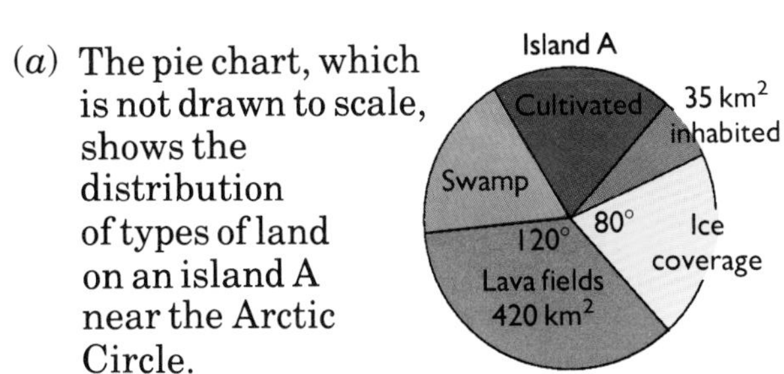

The area covered by ice is 1.6 times the cultivated area.

Calculate

(i) the angle of the inhabited sector,
(ii) the area which is cultivated,
(iii) the percentage of land covered by swamp.

(*b*) A neighbouring island B, when surveyed, was found to have half the area of island A. A pie chart is to be drawn for island B in order that the distribution of types of land on the two islands can be compared. Explain why the radius of the chart should be approximately $\frac{7}{10}$ that for island A.

(*NEA* May 1989, Syllabus B Paper 4)

13 A poultry farmer recorded the weight (***w*** kg) of 50 chickens at the age of 7 weeks.

The results are shown in the table below.

Weight (*w* kg)	Number of chickens
$1 \leqslant w < 1.2$	12
$1.2 \leqslant w < 1.4$	14
$1.4 \leqslant w < 1.6$	5
$1.6 \leqslant w < 1.8$	15
$1.8 \leqslant w < 2.0$	4

(*a*) What is the modal class?

(*b*) In which class does the median weight lie?

(*c*) Calculate an estimate of the mean weight of these 50 chickens.

(*MEG* November 1988, Paper 3)

14

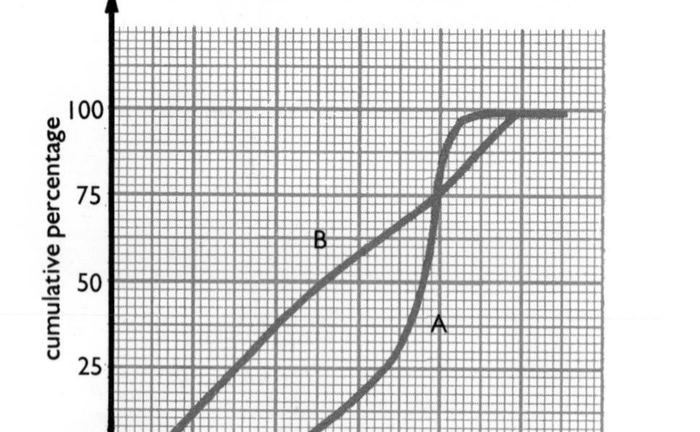

The graph illustrates the cumulative frequency distributions for the heights of two different types of mature (fully grown) corn, type A and type B.

(*a*) Copy and complete the table below for the two types of corn.

	Median height (cm)	Upper quartile (cm)	Lower quartile (cm)	Inter-quartile range (cm)
Type A				
Type B				

(*b*) Comment briefly on the distributions of the height of the two types of corn.

(*c*) A mature corn plant is measured and found to have a height of 28 cm. State, with a reason, which of the two types of corn you think it is.

(*NEA* November 1988, Syllabus A Paper 4)

15 The following information shows the percentage distributions by age of teachers of mathematics and physical education in schools in 1984.

	Aged under 30	Aged 30–39	Aged 40–49	Aged 50 and over
Mathematics	17	36	29	18
Physical education	28	39	21	12

(*a*) Using the same axes and scales, draw cumulative frequency diagrams to represent this information. (You can assume that there were no teachers aged under 21 or aged 65 or over.)

(*b*) Estimate the difference between the median age of the mathematics teachers and the median age of the physical education teachers.

(*c*) Estimate the interquartile range for each distribution.

(*d*) What do you notice about your answer to parts (*b*) and (*c*)?

(*e*) Given that there were 47 900 mathematics teachers, estimate the number aged 45 or over.

(*NEA* November 1988, Syllabus C Paper 4)

EXERCISE 46 Properties of circles

1

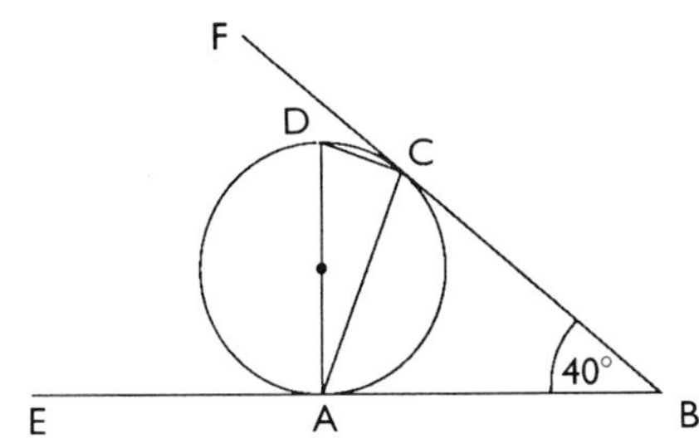

In the diagram, BCF and BAE are tangents to the circle, of which AD is a diameter. Angle ABC = 40°.

(*a*) Explain why triangle ABC is isosceles.

(*b*) Calculate the size of

(i) angle CAB,
(ii) angle DAC
(iii) angle ADC.

(*MEG* November 1988, Paper 5)

2 (*a*) ABC is an isosceles triangle, with AB = 14 cm and BC = 10 cm.

Calculate

(i) the perpendicular height AD,
(ii) the size of A$\hat{B}$D.

(*b*) O is the centre of the circle that touches the three sides of the triangle ABC. OB bisects ABD. Calculate OD, the radius of the circle.

(*Welsh* May 1989, Paper 3)

3 The diagram shows a regular pentagon inscribed in a circle of centre O.

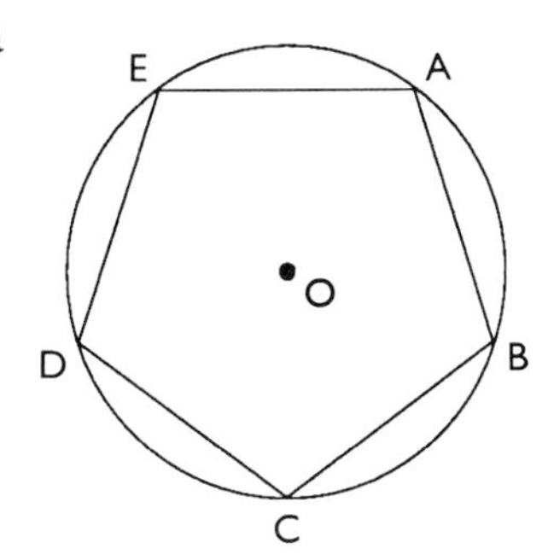

(*a*) Prove that the total of all the interior angles of the pentagon (at A, B, C, D and E) is 540°. Explain your reasoning.

(*b*) Calculate the size of angle ADB.

(*NEA* November 1988, Syllabus A Paper 4)

4 

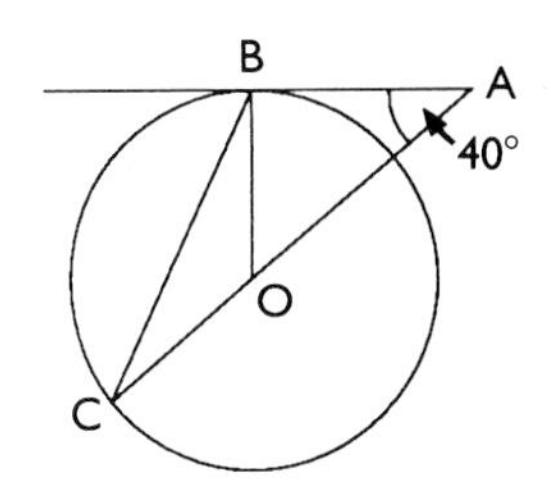

The diagram shows a circle with centre O. AB is the tangent to the circle at B, angle OAB = 40° and COA is a straight line.

(*a*) State the size of angle ABO.

(*b*) Find the sizes of

(i) angle AOB,
(ii) angle ACB,
(iii) angle CBO.

(*NEA* May 1989, Syllabus A Paper 4)

5 A straight plank rests on a circular roller with centre O, as shown in the diagram, with angle APT = 30°.

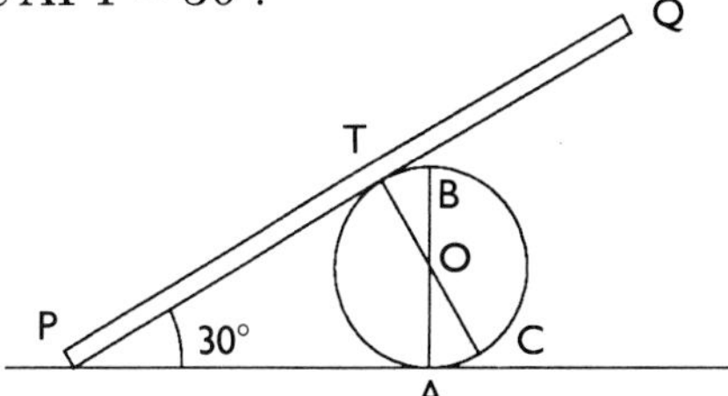

Find

(*a*) angle TOB,

(*b*) angle TCB.

(*SEG* Summer 1989, Mathematics B Paper 4)

6 A space station, S, is in orbit at a height of 4000 km above the Earth's surface. The Earth may be assumed to be a sphere of radius 6400 km, with centre O.

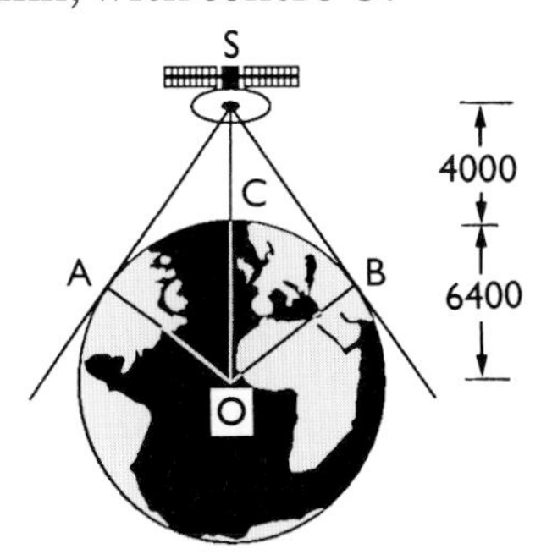

A and B are the ends of an arc on the surface of the Earth, just visible from the satellite.

(*a*) Calculate angle AOS.

(*b*) Calculate the length of the arc ACB.

(*SEG* Summer 1989, Mathematics A Paper 4)

7 ABCD is a cyclic quadrilateral drawn in a circle centre O. Angle ABC = 45°, AO = 7 cm. The diagram is not drawn to scale.

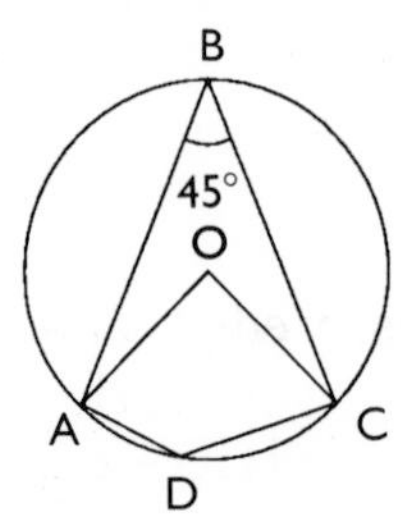

(*a*) Find

(i) the size of angle ADC,
(ii) the size of reflex angle AOC.

(*b*) Explain why a circle could be drawn through the points AOC with AC as diameter.

(*c*) Calculate the length of the circular arc ADC.

(*SEG* Winter 1988, Mathematics A Paper 4)

8

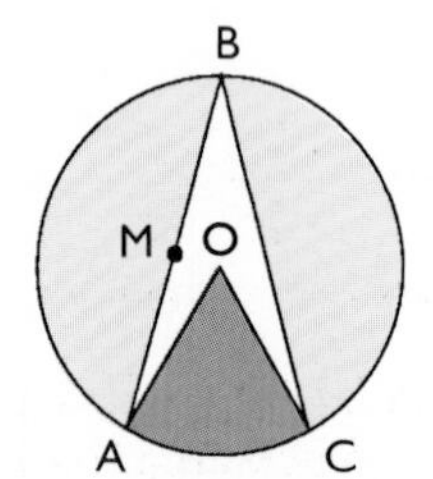

The diagram shows a design which is painted on the lorries of a certain firm.

The circle has centre O and radius 50 cm. Angle AOC = 80°. Lengths AB and CB are equal. M is the midpoint of AB.

(*a*) Calculate (do not measure)

(i) angle ABC, (ii) angle ABO.

(*b*) Calculate the length of

(i) OM, (ii) AM.

(*c*) Calculate the area of triangle AOB.

(*d*) Calculate the area painted pink.

(*SEG* Winter 1988, Mathematics B Paper 4)

9 (*a*) The diagram shows a circle, centre O. AB is a tangent to the circle and ABC = x°.

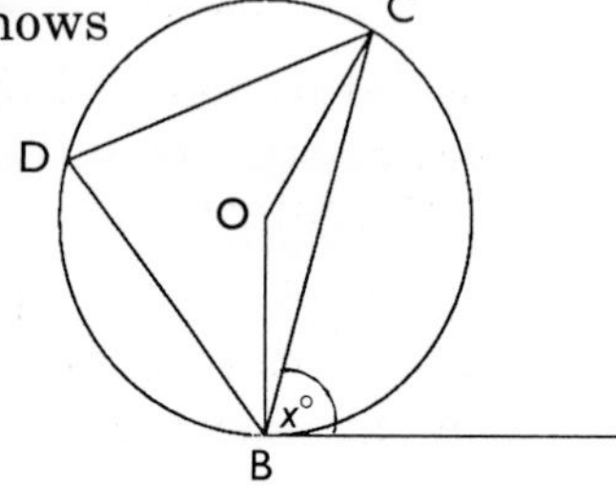

Giving a valid reason in each case, write down in terms of x

(i) $O\hat{B}C$,
(ii) $B\hat{O}C$,
(iii) $B\hat{D}C$.

(*b*) Q, R and S are points on the circumference of a circle with SQ = SR and SQR = 70°.

PQ is a tangent to the circle with RQP acute.

Draw a clear diagram and hence find RQP.

(*Welsh* May 1989, Paper 4)

10

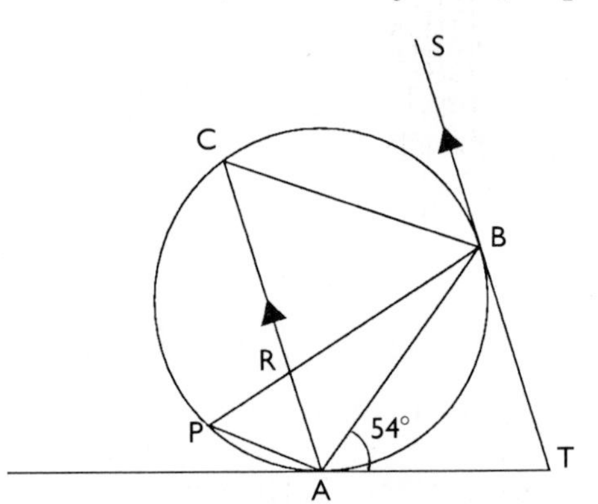

The figure shows a circle with a chord AB. The lines AT and SBT are tangents to the circle at A and B respectively. The chord CA is parallel to the tangent SBT. The angle BAT = 54°.

(*a*) Giving reasons, find the size of

(i) angle ACB,
(ii) angle CBS.

(*b*) Show that triangle ABC is isosceles.

The chord BP cuts AC at R.

(*c*) Give reasons why the triangles PBA and ABR are similar.

(*d*) State two more pairs of similar triangles shown in the figure.

(*LEAG* June 1989, Paper 4)

EXERCISE 47 Enlargement and similarity

1 Peta has a photograph which she wants to enlarge. The photograph is a rectangle with height 8 cm and width 6 cm. The enlargement will have a height of 12 cm.

(*a*) What is the scale factor of the enlargement?

(*b*) What will be the width of the enlargement?

(*MEG* November 1988, Paper 1)

2 It is possible to produce poster-size enlargements of photographic prints. The length and the width of the rectangular shaped print are each increased by the same scale factor.

Here is an example.

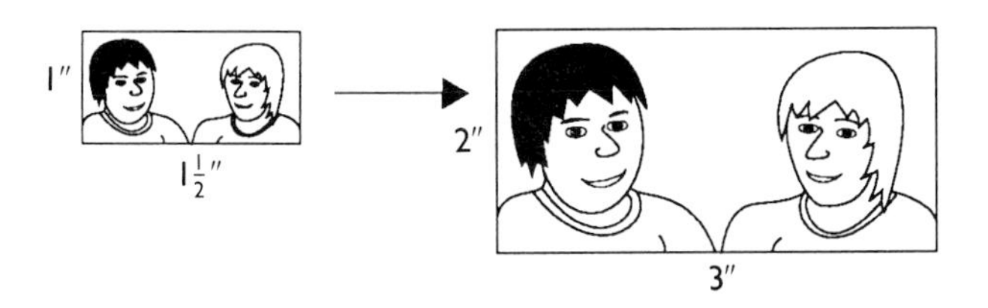

The scale factor is 2 in this example.

(*a*) From an original print size 3″ by 4″ a scale factor of 4 produced a poster. Give the dimensions of the poster.

(*b*) From a print of size 3″ by 5″ a poster of size 18″ by 30″ was produced. How many times larger is the area of the poster compared with the area of the print?

(*NEA* November 1988, Syllabus A and B Paper 1)

3

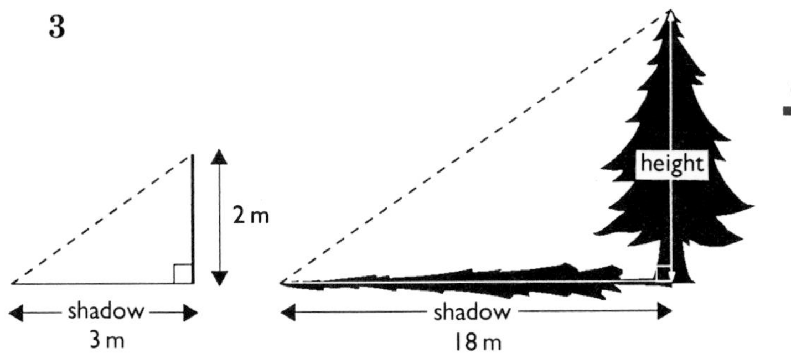

A pole of height 2 m casts a shadow 3 m long. At the same time a tree casts a shadow 18 m long.

Calculate the height of the tree.

(*Welsh* May 1989, Paper 1)

4 The following diagram shows two boxes A and B. The dimensions of box B are twice those of box A.

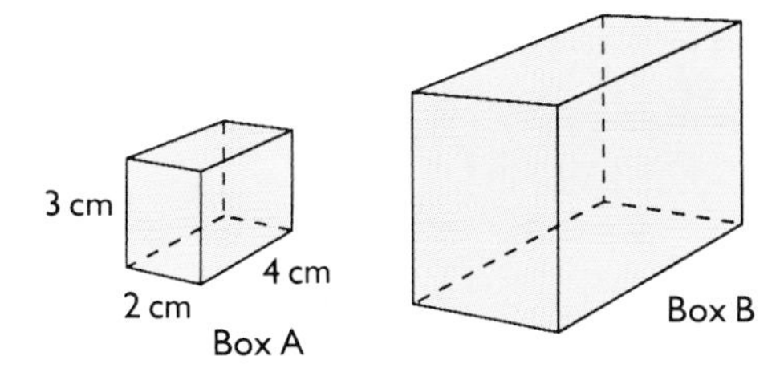

(*a*) How many edges has box A?

(*b*) The dimensions of box A are 2 cm, 3 cm and 4 cm. What are the dimensions of box B?

(*c*) Calculate the volume of box A.

(*d*) 'The volume of box B is twice the volume of box A.' Show why this statement is incorrect.

(*NEA* May 1988, Syllabus A and B, Paper 2)

5

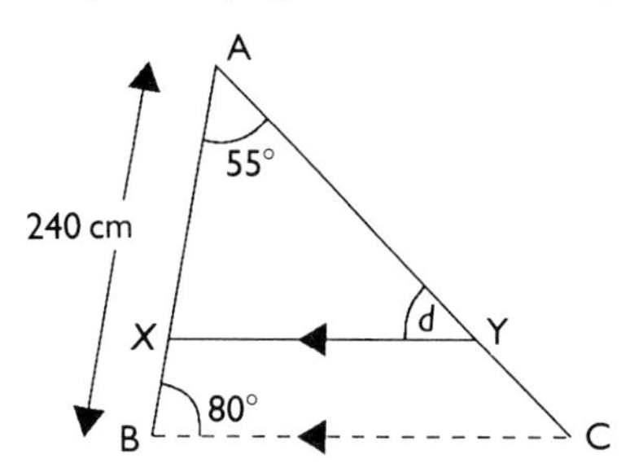

In the diagram above the line XY is parallel to BC. The length of AY is twice the length of YC.

(*a*) What is the length of XB?

(*b*) Find the size of angle *d*.

(*NEA* November 1988, Syllabus C Paper 2)

6

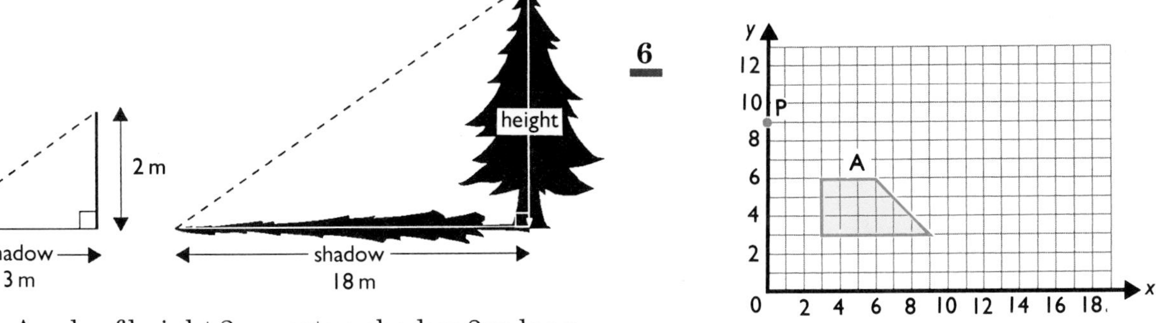

(*a*) Copy the diagram onto centimetre squared paper.

(*b*) Enlarge the quadrilateral A with centre O and scale factor 2. Label the enlargement B.

(*c*) Enlarge the quadrilateral A with centre P and scale factor $\frac{1}{3}$. Label this enlargement C.

(*d*) Find the areas of B and of C.

(*e*) How many times is the area of B bigger than the area of C?

7

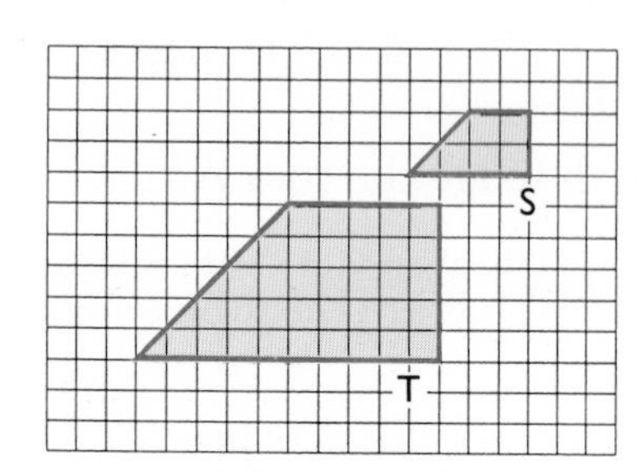

The shape labelled S has been enlarged to give the shape labelled T.

(*a*) Copy the diagram onto centimetre squared paper.

(*b*) Mark on your diagram the centre of enlargement.

(*c*) What is the scale factor of the enlargement?

8

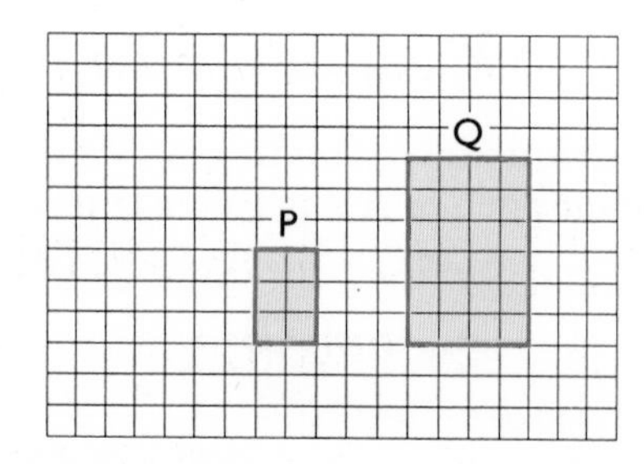

There are two different ways in which the rectangle P can be enlarged to give the rectangle Q.

(*a*) Copy the diagram onto centimetre squared paper.

(*b*) There are two possible centres of enlargement. Mark both of them and label them A and B.

(*c*) State the scale factor for the enlargement with centre A and the scale factor for the enlargement with centre B.

9

The 'old' lid

The 'new' lid

These illustrations show the lid from cylindrical boxes of cheese.

The 'new' box was made to have a volume 10% bigger than that of the 'old' box.

(*a*) Calculate 10% of 84 g.

(*b*) Why is the statement '94 g for the price of 84 g' made on the 'new' cheese box lid wrong?

(*c*) The 'old' box had a radius of 5 cm and a height of 1 cm.

Describe two different ways in which the box could be increased in volume by 10%, giving the new dimensions of the box in each case.

(*NEA* May 1989, Syllabus A Paper 3)

10 The points A, B and C are on the circumference of a circle, centre O, with a radius of 5 cm. AB is the diameter.

(*a*) State the size of angle C.

(*b*) Given that length AC = 8 cm, calculate the lengths of

(i) AD,
(ii) BC.

(*SEG* Summer 1989, Mathematics B Paper 3)

11

Ace soap powder is sold in cubical boxes. The small size has a side of 10 cm and contains 600 grams. The large size has a side of length 15 cm. Calculate the weight of powder contained in the large size.

(*SEG* Summer 1989, Mathematics A Paper 4)

12

The small box contains 6 kg of sugar.

Estimate the weight, in kg, of the sugar in the large box.

(*SEG* Winter 1988, Mathematics B Paper 4)

13 The scale of a map was 1:2000. The map is reduced in size so that it uses a quarter of the original area of paper. What is the scale of the new map?

(*SEG* Summer 1989, Mathematics B Paper 4)

14 The most commonly available Ordnance Survey maps are drawn to a scale of 1:50 000.

Write down the ratio *area on map:area on ground* using standard form.

(*Welsh* May 1989, Paper 4)

15 When a new car came onto the market recently, a scale model of it, similar in every respect to the actual car, was made for sale in toy shops.

The table below compares certain details of the actual car with the scale model.

	Car	Model
Length	420 cm	12 cm
Width	x cm	5 cm
Area of windscreen	8330 cm^2	y cm^2
Capacity of boot	z cm^3	19.2 cm^3

(*a*) Calculate the linear scale factor.

(*b*) Calculate the value of x.

(*c*) Calculate the value of y.

(*d*) Calculate the value of z.

(*NEA* May 1989, Syllabus C Paper 4)

16 (*a*) A lead ball of radius 4 cm is melted and cast into small balls each of radius 0.25 cm.

(i) Calculate the volume, in cm^3, of the large lead ball.
(ii) Calculate the volume, in cm^3, of a single small lead ball.
(iii) How many small lead balls can be cast from the large lead ball?

(*b*) A cylindrical can of radius 5 cm contains water to a depth of 6 cm. Four thousand lead balls, each of radius 0.25 cm, are dropped into the can. Calculate the rise, in cm, of the water level.

(*c*) Lead in water is believed to poison water birds.

A fisherman has 8 small lead balls on his line. He considers an alternative arrangement of the same volume of lead using a single lead ball in order to reduce the surface area.

(i) Find the radius of this alternative lead ball.
(ii) Find the surface area of this alternative lead ball.
(iii) Calculate the surface area of a small lead ball of radius 0.25 cm.
(iv) Copy and complete the following table to display all the evidence about the alternative balls.

	One small lead ball	8 small lead balls	One alternative lead ball
Radius	0.25 cm	0.25 cm	
Surface area			
Volume			

(*LEAG* January 1989, Paper 4)

EXERCISE 48 Inequalities and linear programming

1 Given that $x < 2$ and $x \geqslant -3$ list the possible values of x when

(*a*) x is an integer,

(*b*) x is a natural number.

(*SEG* Winter 1988, Mathematics B Paper 3)

2 Given that $3x > 2$ and $\frac{1}{2}x \leqslant 1\frac{1}{2}$ list the possible integral values of x.

(*SEG* Summer 1989, Mathematics B Paper 3)

3 Given that $-6 \leqslant x \leqslant 3$ and $-4 \leqslant y \leqslant 5$, find

(*a*) the largest possible value of x^2,

(*b*) the smallest possible value of xy.

(*c*) the value of x if $x^2 = 25$.

(*NEA* May 1989, Syllabus C Paper 4)

4 (*a*) Draw a graph of $y = 6 + x - x^2$ for values of x from -4 to 4.

(*b*) For what values of x is $6 + x - x^2$ positive?

5 Solve the inequality $2 - x < 1 + 2x$.

6 In the English football league, 3 points are awarded for each match won, 1 point for each match drawn, and no points for matches lost.

(*a*) Complete the table below.

	Played	Wins	Draws	Losses	Points
Team A	10	7	1	2	
Team B	10	5			18
Team C	10			3	13

(*b*) Find two solutions of the pair of relations

$$3x + y = 20, x + y \leqslant 10$$

where x and y are positive integers.

(*c*) There is a connection between parts (*a*) and (*b*). Explain what it is.

(*MEG* November 1988, Paper 3)

7 Give the three inequalities satisfied by all the points in the shaded region (including its boundaries) and by no other points.

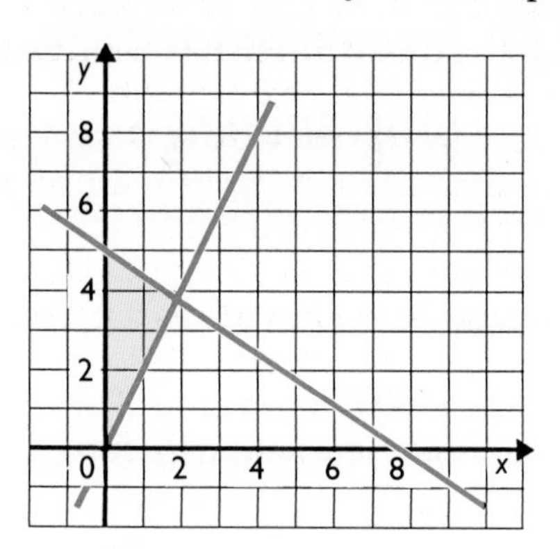

(*MEG SMP* November 1988, Paper 4)

8 (*a*) Draw axes to show values of x and values of y from -4 to 4.

(*b*) Draw the graphs of $y = x - 2$ and $y = 4 - 2x$.

(*c*) On your graph, shade the region where both $y > x - 2$ and $y < 4 - 2x$ are true.

9 On the same axes and using the same scales, draw the graphs of $y = \frac{6}{x}$ and $x + y = 9$ for $1 \leqslant x \leqslant 7$.

Hence find all pairs of positive integers whose product is greater than 6 and whose sum is less than 9.

(*NEA* November 1988, Syllabus C Paper 4)

10 (*a*) Expand $(x + y)^2$.

(*b*) If $x + y = 2$ and $x^2 + y^2 = 9$, calculate the value of xy.

(*c*) (i) Draw axes to show values of x and values of y from -4 to 4. Use a scale of 1 cm for 1 unit on each axis.
(ii) On your axes draw the circle with centre the origin and radius 3 cm.
(iii) Explain why, for any point (x, y) on the circumference of this circle, $x^2 + y^2 = 9$.
(iv) On the same axes, draw the line $x + y = 2$.
(v) Mark clearly a point R with coordinates (x, y) such that $(x + y)$ is greater than 2, x is less than zero, and $(x^2 + y^2)$ is less than 9.

(*NEA* November 1988, Syllabus B Paper 4)

11 A couple on holiday in Greece decide to bring back some 'duty free' drinks to England. They decide on two types of drink:

Wine, sold in $\frac{3}{4}$ litre bottles, costing 500 drachmas and spirits, sold in 1 litre bottles, costing 900 drachmas.

They are allowed to bring back only 6 litres between them, and have only 4500 drachmas to spend. They want to bring back at least one bottle of wine and at least one bottle of spirits.

Suppose that they bring back x bottles of wine and y bottles of spirits.

(*a*) Show that, because they have only 4500 drachmas between them, this leads to the inequality

$$5x + 9y \leqslant 45$$

(*b*) Write down three other inequalities which must be satisfied.

(*c*) On graph paper, draw the necessary graphs and indicate the region in which all four inequalities are satisfied.

(*d*) State a combination of bottles of wine and spirits which the couple could bring back.

(*NEA* May 1989, Syllabus A Paper 4)

12 (*a*) Draw axes to show values of x from 0 to 10 and values of y from -4 to 8.

(*b*) On these axes, draw the graphs of

$$y = 3x - 3$$
$$\text{and } x + 2y = 8$$

(*c*) A is the point (3, 6) and B is the point (6, 1). Find the equation of the line AB.

(*d*) C is the point of intersection of the lines $y = 3x - 3$ and $x + 2y = 8$.

Draw and label the triangle ABC.

(*e*) S is the set of points inside, or on the boundary of, triangle ABC.

Write down three inequalities which together define the set S.

(*f*) Find the minimum value of $x + y$ within the set S.

13 (*a*) Solve this pair of simultaneous equations to find the point of intersection of the lines they represent:

$$2x + y = 500,$$
$$2x - 3y = 0.$$

A transport company owns 250 double-decker buses and 250 single-decker buses. A double-decker seats 60 passengers and a single-decker seats 30 passengers. One Saturday the company needs to provide buses to transport 15 000 people to a football match.

Let x be the number of double-decker buses used and y the number of single-decker buses used to transport the people.

(*b*) From the above information write down three inequalities other than $x \geqslant 0$ and $y \geqslant 0$, and show that one of them reduces to $2x + y \geqslant 500$.

Owing to low bridges near the football ground the number of single-decker buses run cannot be less than $\frac{2}{3}$ the number of double-decker buses run.

(*c*) Using this information write down a fourth inequality.

(*d*) Represent these four inequalities on squared paper, using a scale of 2 cm to represent 50 buses and shading the *unwanted* regions.

(*e*) What is the minimum number of buses which the company can use to transport these people?

(*AEB* O level, June 1986, General C Paper 3)

14 (i) XYZ is a triangle. Here is a statement about the lengths of the sides with one symbol missing:

$$XY + XZ \square YZ.$$

Which of the symbols

$$<, = \text{ or } >$$

should go into the box to make the statement true, whatever the shape of the triangle?

(ii)

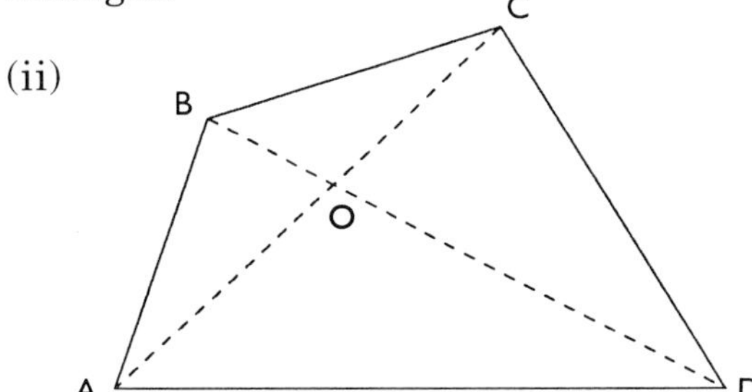

The quadrilateral in the diagram has diagonals AC and BD which meet at O. The perimeter of the quadrilateral is written as p. Use the result of (i) for each of the triangles which have a vertex at O, and by adding show that the sum of the lengths of the diagonals is greater than $\frac{1}{2}p$.

(iii) In the same diagram there are four triangles, which do *not* have O as a vertex. Use the result of (i) for each of these triangles, and show that the sum of the lengths of the diagonals is less than p.

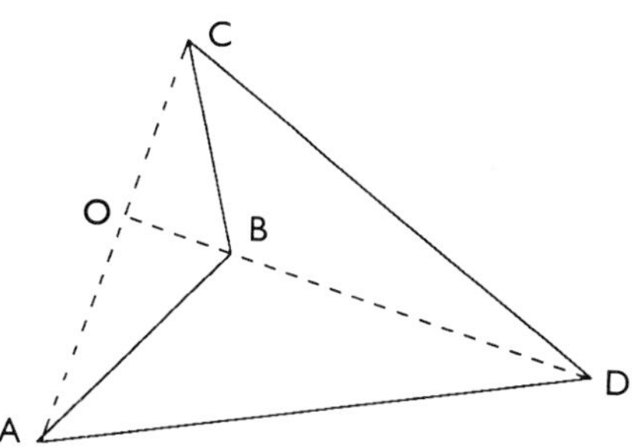

One of the results in (ii) and (iii) is still true if the quadrilateral has the shape of this second diagram. State which one it is, and give a reason for your answer.

(*LEAG SMP* 11–16 June 1987, Extension Paper)

EXERCISE 49 Transformations and matrices

1

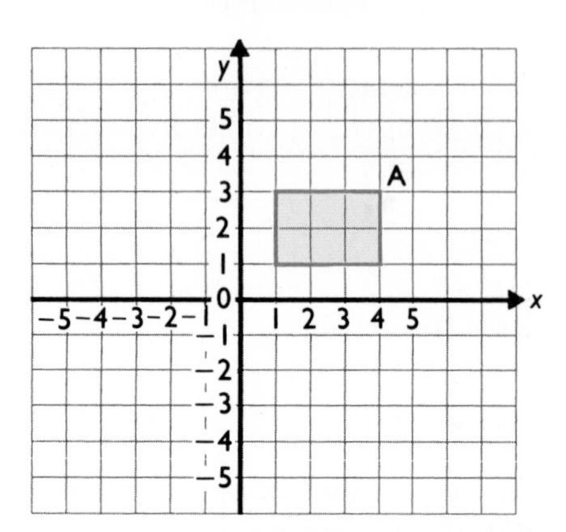

(*a*) Copy the diagram above onto centimetre squared paper.

(*b*) Shape A is reflected in the x-axis.

Draw this reflection and label it B.

(*c*) Shape A is rotated a quarter-turn anticlockwise about O.

Draw the result and label it C.

(*LEAG* January 1989, Paper 1)

2

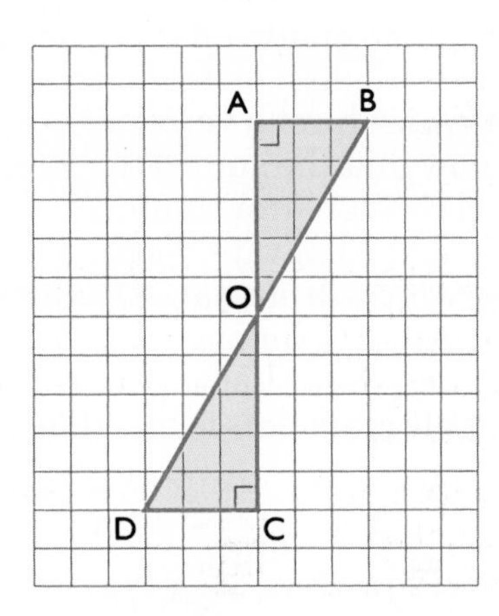

(*a*) Copy the diagram above onto centimetre squared paper.

(*b*) What single transformation moves triangle ABO onto triangle CDO?

(*c*) Draw on your diagram the reflection of triangle CDO in the line AC.

(*d*) What single transformation moves triangle ABO onto the triangle you drew for part (*c*)?

3

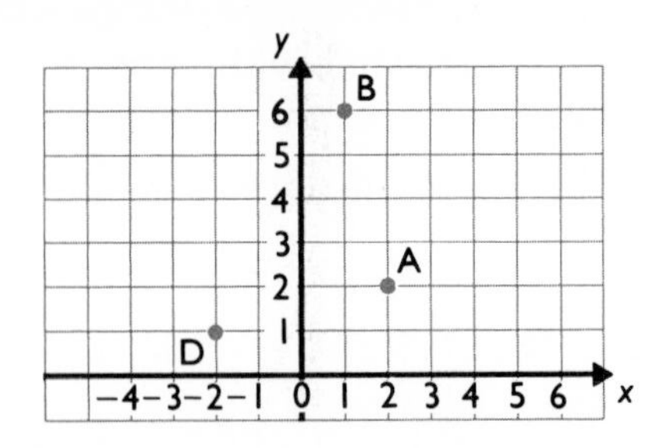

(*a*) Write down the coordinates of points A, B and D.

(*b*) The three points shown are three corners of a square. The fourth corner is C. What are the coordinates of C?

(*c*) The square is moved so that A becomes (4, 1) and D becomes (0, 0). What are the new coordinates of B and C?

(*Welsh* May 1989, Paper 2)

4 The diagram below shows a plot of land with a house (shaded in the diagram) built on it. The builder wants to build two more houses. One house is to be the reflection of the existing house in the fence XY and the other is to be the reflection of the existing house in the fence XZ.

(*a*) Copy or trace the diagram and show the positions of the two new houses.

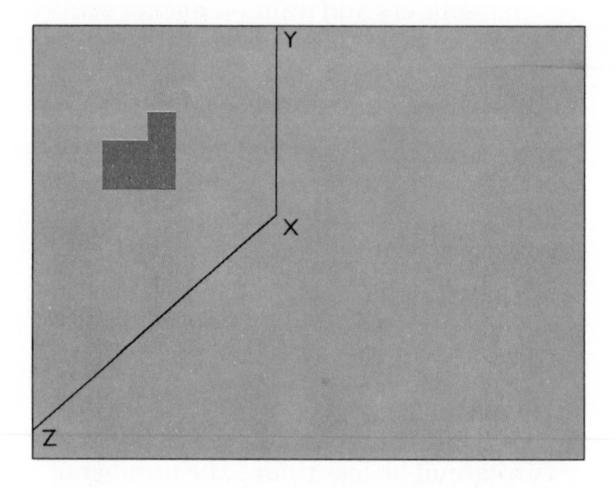

(*b*) What type of transformation would map the two reflections onto each other?

(*NEA* November 1988, Syllabus A Paper 3)

5

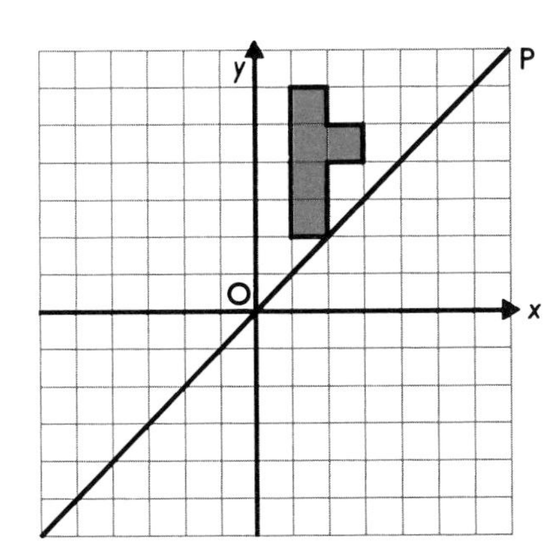

(*a*) Copy the diagram onto centimetre squared paper.

(*b*) Draw the image of the shaded shape after reflection in the line OP.

Label this image A.

(*c*) Draw the image of the shaded shape after a rotation through 90° anticlockwise about O.

Label this image B.

(*d*) Draw the image of the shaded shape after reflection in the x-axis.

Label this image C.

(*e*) Describe fully the single transformation that will transform shape C directly to the shape A.

(*NEA* May 1989, Syllabus A Paper 3)

6

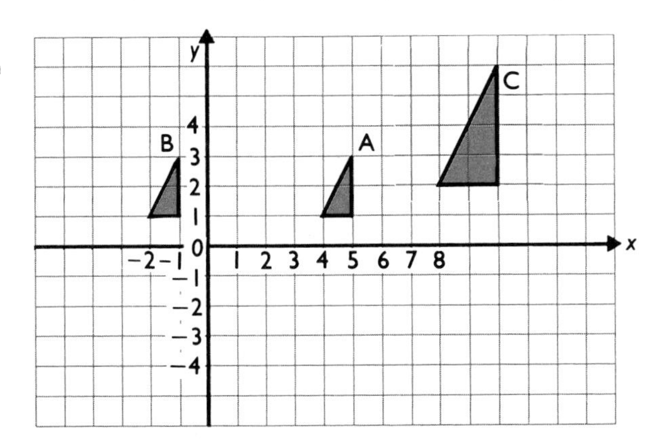

(*a*) Copy the diagram above onto centimetre squared paper.

(*b*) Triangle B is the image of triangle A after a certain transformation. Describe this transformation fully.

(*c*) Triangle C is the image of triangle A after a certain transformation. Describe this transformation fully.

(*d*) Draw the image of triangle A after reflection in the x-axis, and label it D.

(*e*) Draw the image of triangle B after a quarter turn clockwise about O, and label it E.

(*f*) Describe the single transformation which moves triangle A onto triangle E.

7

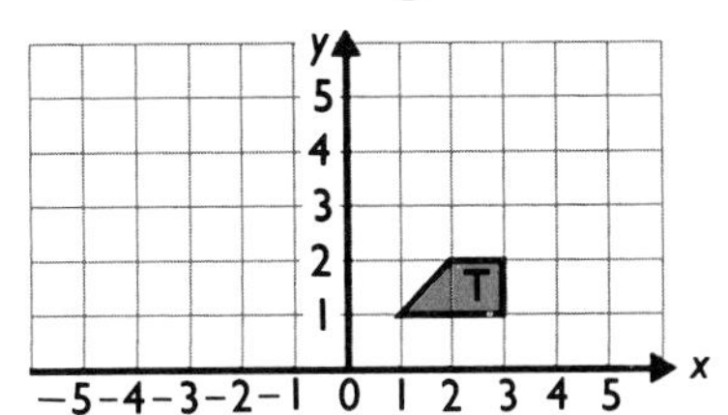

Trapezium T is reflected in the line $y = 3$ to give trapezium T_1.

Trapezium T_1 is then rotated 90° anticlockwise about (0, 0) to give trapezium T_2.

Trapezium T_2 is then translated $\begin{pmatrix} 6 \\ 0 \end{pmatrix}$ to give trapezium T_3.

(*a*) Copy the diagram onto centimetre squared paper.

(*b*) Show the position of T_1, T_2 and T_3 on your diagram.

(*c*) Describe the single transformation that would take T to T_3.

(*NEA* November 1988, Syllabus B Paper 3)

8

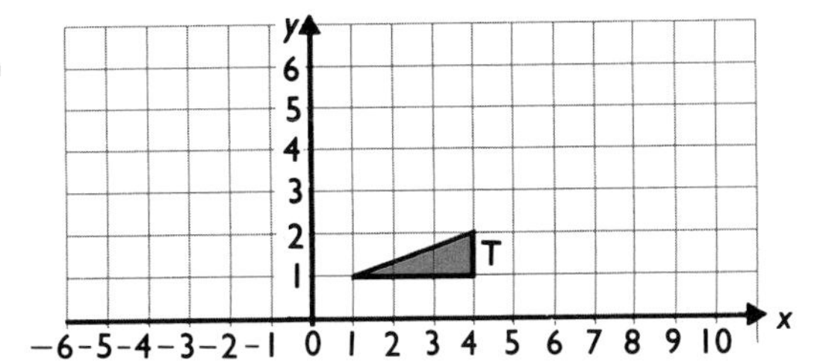

(*a*) Copy the diagram shown above onto centimetre squared paper.

Triangle T has vertices (1, 1), (4, 1), (4, 2) as shown in the diagram.

Triangle T is translated using the vector $\begin{pmatrix} 4 \\ 2 \end{pmatrix}$ to triangle T_1.

(*b*) Show T_1 on your diagram.

Triangle T_1 is reflected in the line $x = 5$ to triangle T_2.

(*c*) Show T_2 on your diagram.

Triangle T_2 is reflected in the line $x = 0$ to triangle T_3.

(*c*) Show T_3 on your diagram.

(*d*) What is the vector of the translation that will take triangle T_3 to triangle T?

(*NEA* May 1989, Syllabus B Paper 3)

9 The diagram represents the movement of a car which has turned a corner from the position ABCD to A′B′C′D′. This movement from ABCD to A′B′C′D′ is a rotation.

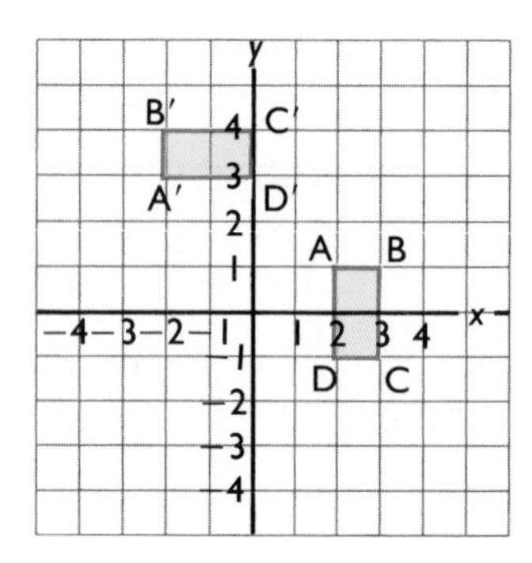

Find

(*a*) the centre of the roation,

(*b*) the angle of the rotation.

(*SEG* Winter 1988, Mathematics A Paper 3)

10 (*a*) Draw axes showing values of x and values of y from -3 to 8. On your axes plot and label the points A (6, 0) and B (0, 4).

(*b*) Find the gradient of the line AB.

(*c*) AB is the diameter of a circle. Draw this circle.

(*d*) Two points C and D lie on this circle and are also equidistant from A and B. Plot and label C and D and write down their coordinates.

(*e*) Describe fully the transformation which will map triangle BCA onto triangle BDA.

(*LEAG SMP* June 1989, Paper 3)

11 Here are four different ways in which the shape A may be transformed to the shape B.

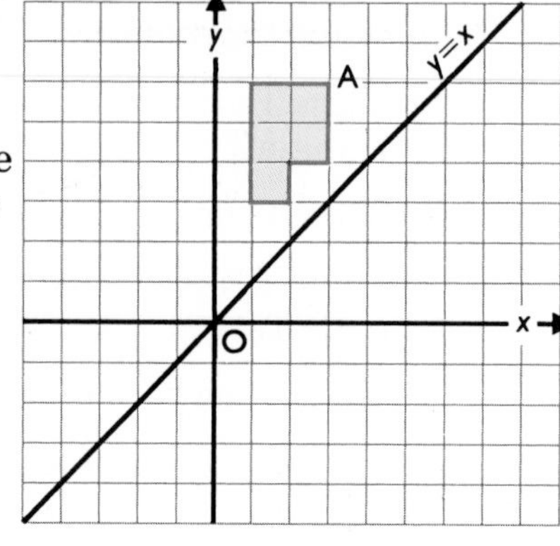

(*a*) A can be translated using the vector $\begin{pmatrix} 1 \\ -2 \end{pmatrix}$.

(*b*) A can be rotated anticlockwise through 90° about O.

(*c*) A can be reflected in the line $y = x$.

(*d*) A can be enlarged with centre O and scale factor 1.5.

For each of (*a*), (*b*), (*c*) and (*d*) describe the transformation which transforms B back to A.

12 The four vertices of a square S are (1, 2), (3, 2), (3, 4) and (1, 4).

(*a*) Using a scale of 2 cm to 1 unit draw axes showing values of x from -4 to $+4$ and values of y from 0 to 6.

(*b*) Draw the square S on your diagram.

(*c*) The image of S under reflection in the y-axis is the square S′. Draw the image S′ on your diagram.

(*d*) Describe the translation which maps S onto S′.

(*e*) There is a rotation with angle +90° which maps S onto S′. Give the coordinates of the centre of this rotation.

(*f*) Write down two other rotations each of which maps S onto S′. Describe them in full.

(*MEG SMP* November 1988, Paper 3)

13 (*a*) Draw axes showing values of x from -3 to 3 and values of y from -4 to 4.

Draw and label a triangle T with coordinates $(-1, 1)$, $(-2, 1)$ and $(-1, 4)$.

(*b*) Using the same axes draw the image of the triangle T after

(i) a reflection in the x-axis; label this image A,
(ii) a translation $\begin{pmatrix} 4 \\ -2 \end{pmatrix}$; label this image B.

(*c*) The triangle A can be transformed onto triangle B by a rotation about the point $(-1, q)$ followed by a reflection in the line $x = 1$. Find

(i) the value of q,

(ii) the angle through which A is rotated.

(*SEG* Winter 1988, Mathematics A Paper 4)

14 S is the transformation represented by the matrix

$$\begin{pmatrix} 1 & 2 \\ -2 & 3 \end{pmatrix}.$$

T is the translation $\begin{pmatrix} 1 \\ 4 \end{pmatrix}$.

(*a*) Calculate the image of the point (0, 0) under the transformation

(i) S, (ii) T.

(*b*) Give one reason why a translation cannot be represented by a 2 by 2 matrix.

(*SEG* Winter 1988, Mathematics B Paper 4)

15 The transformation T is defined by the matrix A where $A = \begin{pmatrix} -4 & 0 \\ 0 & -4 \end{pmatrix}$.

(*a*) Write down the images of $\begin{pmatrix} 1 \\ 0 \end{pmatrix}$ and $\begin{pmatrix} 0 \\ 1 \end{pmatrix}$ under T.

(*b*) Describe fully, in words, the transformation T.

The transformation U is a clockwise rotation through 90° about the origin.

(*c*) Find the matrix B which defines the transformation U.

(*LEAG* June 1989, Mathematics A Paper 4)

16 The corners A, B, C and D of the square ABCD have position vectors $\begin{pmatrix} 1 \\ 1 \end{pmatrix}$, $\begin{pmatrix} 2 \\ 1 \end{pmatrix}$, $\begin{pmatrix} 2 \\ 2 \end{pmatrix}$ and $\begin{pmatrix} 1 \\ 2 \end{pmatrix}$ respectively.

(*a*) Draw axes showing values of x and values of y from -3 to 3. Draw the square ABCD on your diagram.

(*b*) A transformation, X, is represented by the matrix

$$\begin{pmatrix} -1 & 0 \\ 0 & -1 \end{pmatrix}$$

and it maps A, B, C and D onto E, F, G and H respectively.

(i) Calculate the position vectors of E, F, G and H.
(ii) Draw EFGH on your diagram.
(iii) Describe geometrically the transformation X.

(*c*) A transformation, Y, reflects the square ABCD in the x-axis to form the square PQRS.

(i) Write down the position vectors of P, Q, R and S.
(ii) Write down the matrix which represents the transformation Y.

(*d*) Describe the transformation that maps P, Q, R and S onto E, F, G and H respectively. Write down the matrix of this transformation.

(*SEG* Summer 1989, Mathematics B Paper 4)

17 The line segment OP joins O (0, 0) to P (1, 1). Find the matrix of a transformation which

(*a*) doubles the length of OP,

(*b*) rotates OP clockwise about O through 90°,

(*c*) doubles the length of OP and rotates OP through 90° clockwise about O.

(*NEA* November 1988, Syllabus B Paper 4)

18 (*a*) Describe, in geometrical terms, the transformation given by

$$\begin{pmatrix} x \\ y \end{pmatrix} \to \begin{pmatrix} 0 & 1 \\ 1 & 0 \end{pmatrix}\begin{pmatrix} x \\ y \end{pmatrix}.$$

(*b*) (i) A rectangle has vertices A (1, −1), B (3, −1), C (3, −2) and D (1, −2). Find the coordinates of the images A′, B′, C′ and D′ respectively of the vertices under the transformation given in part (*a*).
(ii) Draw axes showing values of x from −3 to 5 and values of y from −4 to 4.

Draw and label the rectangles ABCD and A′B′C′D′ on your axes.

Also draw the lines $y = x$ and $y = x + 2$.

(*c*) (i) What translation, following the transformation described in (*a*), results in the rectangle ABCD being reflected in the line $y = x + 2$?
(ii) Hence, or otherwise, find the coordinates of the vertices of A″B″C″D″, the reflection of ABCD in the line $y = x + 2$.

(*NEA* May 1989, Syllabus B Paper 4)

EXERCISE 50 Trigonometry and triangles

1 The diagram on the right shows two stages of a cable car route.

Safety experts have decided that a cable car is only safe if the angle of elevation is less than 68° and greater than 30°.

(*a*) Calculate the angles of elevation, x and y, indicated on the diagram.

(*b*) Based on the information given, is each stage of this route safe? Give reasons for your answers.

(*NEA* November 1988, Syllabus A Paper 3)

2

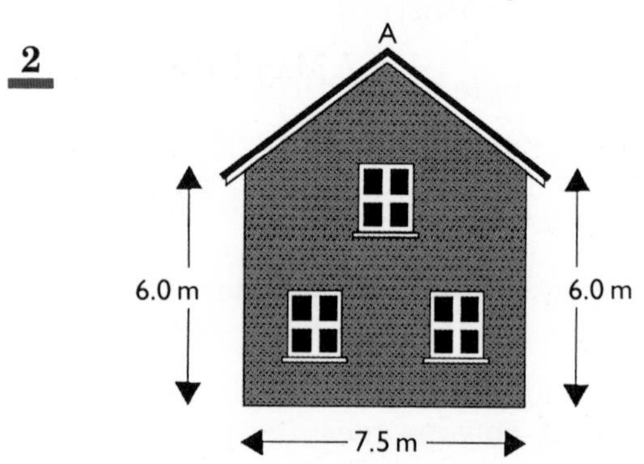

The diagram shows the gable end of a house. The pitch of the roof is the angle which the roof makes with the horizontal. In order to comply with building regulations, the pitch of the roof must be at least 23°.

Calculate the minimum height above ground level of the apex A of the roof.

(*NEA* November 1988, Syllabus C Paper 3)

3

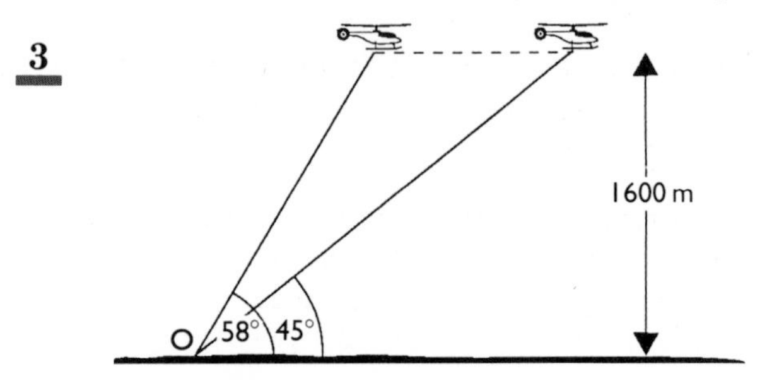

The diagram shows two sightings made from a point O of a helicopter flying at a height of 1600 metres. At the first sighting, the helicopter was due East of O and the angle of elevation was 58°. One minute later it was still due East of O, but the angle of elevation was 45°.

Calculate the speed of the helicopter in kilometres per hour.

(*NEA* May 1989, Syllabus C Paper 4)

4 Veena is taking part in an orienteering event. In the first leg she travels 700 m on a bearing of 128°. The second leg is 500 m due East.

(*a*) How far is Veena East and South of her starting point

(i) after the first leg?
(ii) after the second leg?

The third leg is to follow a straight course back to the starting point.

(*b*) (i) What is the length of the third leg?
(ii) What is the bearing of the third leg?

5

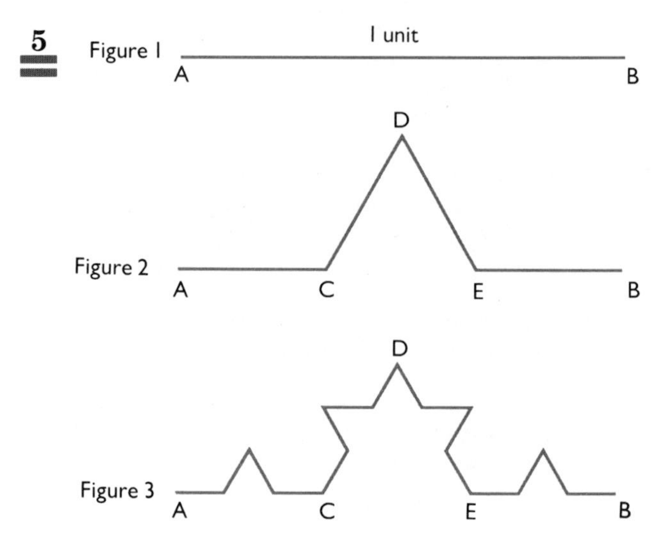

Figure 2 is produced from figure 1 by dividing the straight line AB into three equal parts and replacing the middle section by the other two sides of an equilateral triangle drawn on it.

Thus, in figure 2, AC = CE = EB and CDE, if drawn, would be an equilateral triangle.

A similar construction is carried out on AC, CD, DE and EB to give figure 3.

In figure 1, AB is of length one unit.

(*a*) (i) What is the length of the path from A to B along the solid line in figure 2?
(ii) What is the length of the path from A to B along the solid line in figure 3?

(*b*) If the straight line AB is drawn in figure 2, find the area of the triangle CDE.

(*c*) If the straight line AB is drawn in figure 3, find the total area of the regions enclosed.

(*NEA* November 1988, Syllabus B Paper 4)

6 Calculate the sizes of the angles of an isosceles triangle given that each of the equal sides is twice the length of the third side.

(*NEA* May 1989, Syllabus B Paper 4)

7 

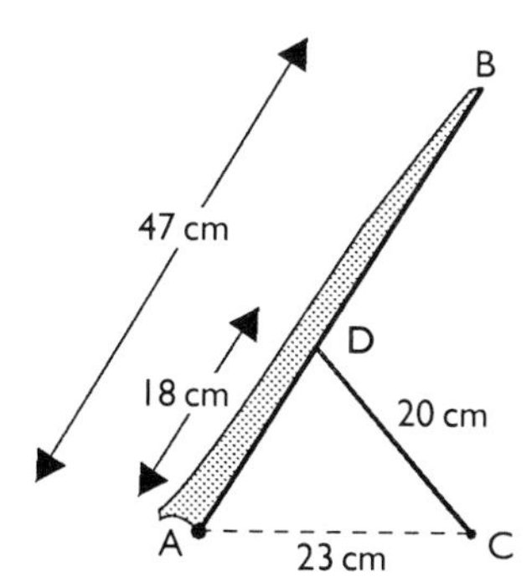

The diagram represents a car bonnet, AB, hinged at A and propped open by a stay, CD. AC = 23 cm, AB = 47 cm, AD = 18 cm and CD = 20 cm.

(*a*) Calculate the size of angle CAD, correct to the nearest degree.

(*b*) Find the height of B above the level of AC, giving your answer correct to the nearest centimetre.

(*MEG* November 1988, Paper 3)

8

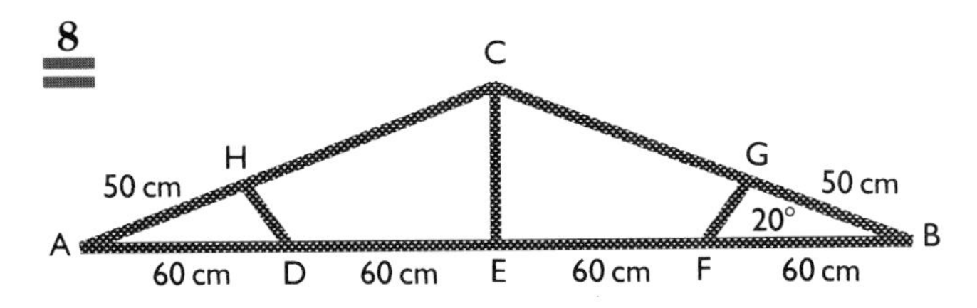

The diagram shows part of the wooden framework of the roof of a shed. In triangle ABC, the sides AC and BC are equal and AD = DE = EF = FB = 60 cm. Angle ABC = 20° and AH = BG = 50 cm.

Calculate

(*a*) the length of FG,

(*b*) the total length of wood required to make the framework shown in the diagram.

(*MEG* November 1988, Paper 6)

9  This sketch shows the flight paths between three airports at Appleton (A), Berriton (B) and Cherriton (C). Berriton is 60 km from Appleton on a bearing of 060°. Cherriton is 80 km from Appleton on a bearing of 170°.

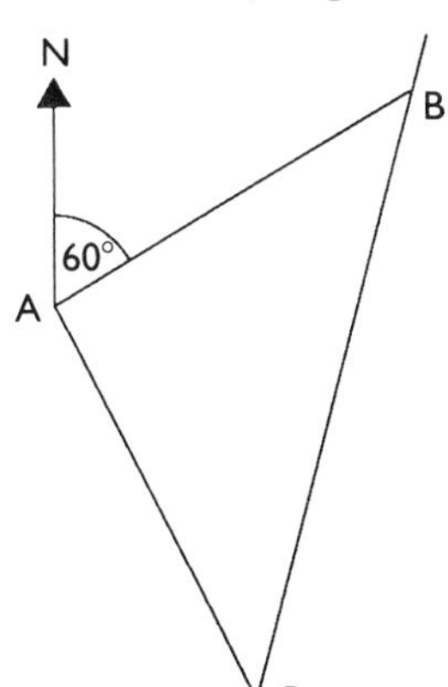

(*a*) (i) What is the size of B$\hat{A}$C?
(ii) Calculate the distance from Berriton to Cherriton.
(iii) By finding A$\hat{C}$B, find the bearing of Berriton from Cherriton.

(*b*) Find the area of land enclosed by the three flight paths.

(*Welsh* May 1988, Paper 4)

10  Two fences of length 10 m and 20 m are placed so that, together with a straight wall, they enclose an area.

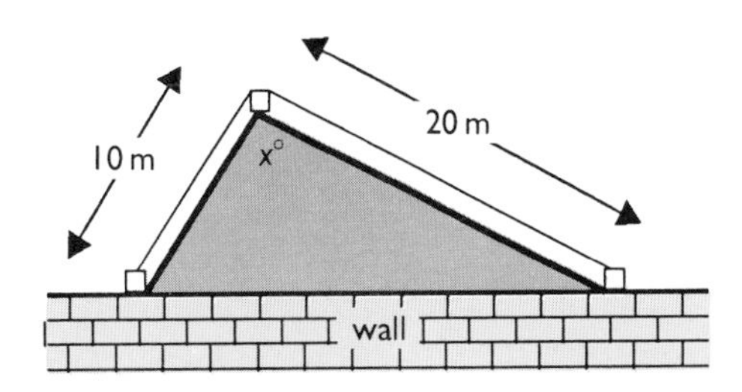

(*a*) Find a formula for the area enclosed when the angle between the fences is $x°$.

(*b*) What should the value of x be so that the fences enclose the maximum possible area?

(*c*) What should the value of x be so that the fences enclose half the maximum possible area?

11 Experiments have shown that dogs are able to distinguish between two sound sources when they are 11° apart, but for humans the angle must be considerably greater.

Two sound sources are placed at X and Y, and a man and his dog stand at A, where $X\hat{A}Y = 6°$. They walk 100 m directly towards Y, to the point B, where the dog is just able to distinguish the sound sources (Thus $X\hat{B}Y = 11°$).

(*a*) Calculate the distance BX, between the dog and the sound source at X.

They then walk a further 100 m directly towards Y, to the point C, where the man is just able to distinguish the sound sources.

(*b*) Calculate the distance CX, between the man and the sound source at X.

(*c*) Calculate the angle XCY at which the man is just able to distinguish between the two sound sources.

(*Welsh* May 1989, Paper 4)

12 A corner of a cube is sliced off as shown in the picture below. The shape of the face created (the section) is a triangle.

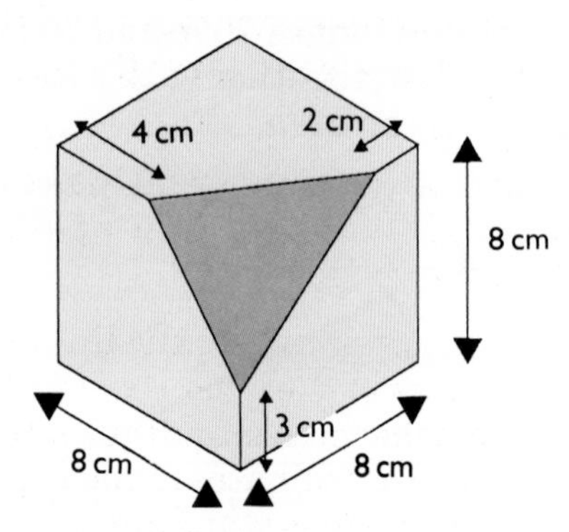

(*a*) Calculate the lengths of the sides of this triangle.

(*b*) Calculate the largest angle of this triangle.

(*c*) Calculate the area of this triangle.

(*d*) Calculate the volume of the corner piece which has been cut off.

(*e*) The corner piece cut off is placed on a table with the section triangle in contact with the table. Using your answers to (*c*) and (*d*), or otherwise, calculate the height of the corner piece in this position.

EXERCISE 51 Coordinates and vectors

1 Draw axes showing values of x and values of y from -5 to 5.

(*a*) Mark the points P $(-2, 3)$, Q $(1, -3)$ and R $(2, 2)$ on your axes.

(*b*) Draw a line which is parallel to PQ and which goes through R.

(*c*) Draw a line which is perpendicular to PQ and which goes through R.

2 The diagram illustrates three vectors, AB, CD and XY.

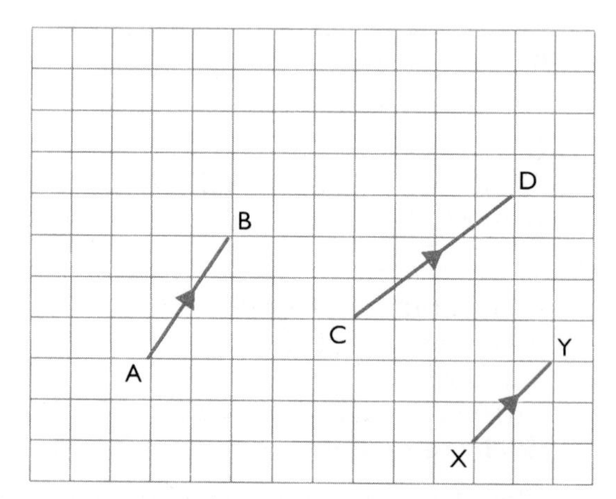

(*a*) Draw and label on squared paper a representation of

(i) $\vec{AB} + \vec{CD}$,

(ii) $\vec{AB} - \vec{CD}$.

(*b*) What connection is there between the vector $\vec{AB} + \vec{CD}$ and the vector $\vec{XY}$?

(*NEA* November 1988, Syllabus A Paper 3)

3

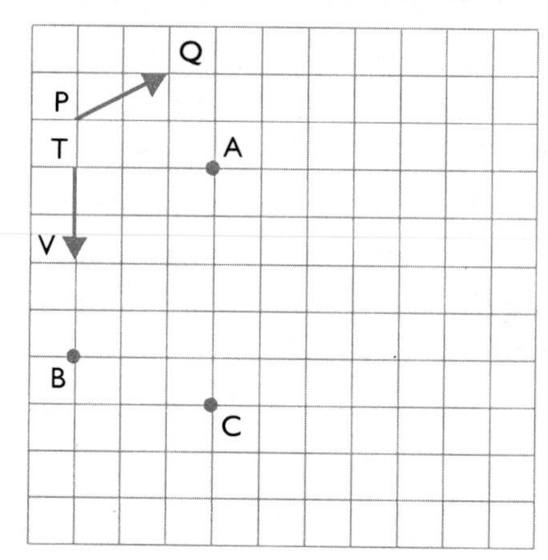

Draw clearly on squared paper vectors which represent

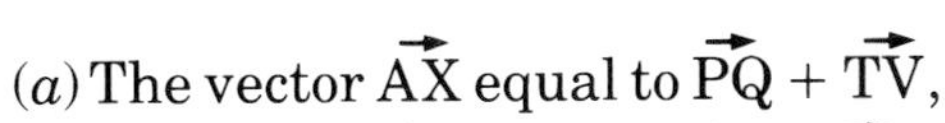

(a) The vector $\overrightarrow{AX}$ equal to $\overrightarrow{PQ} + \overrightarrow{TV}$,

(b) the vector $\overrightarrow{BY}$ equal to $\overrightarrow{PQ} - \overrightarrow{TV}$,

(c) the vector $\overrightarrow{CZ}$ equal to $3\,\overrightarrow{PQ}$.

(*NEA* May 1989, Syllabus A Paper 3)

4

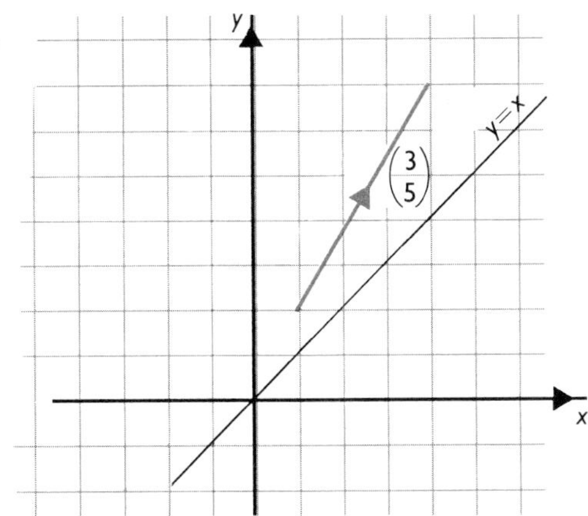

(a) What vector do you obtain from the vector $\begin{pmatrix} 3 \\ 5 \end{pmatrix}$

(i) by rotating it through 180°?
(ii) by rotating it through 90° anticlockwise?
(iii) by reflecting it in the y-axis?
(iv) by reflecting it in the line $y = x$?

(b) Would any of your answers to part (a) be changed if the vector $\begin{pmatrix} 3 \\ 5 \end{pmatrix}$ was drawn in a different position?

5 The three dimensions of a cuboid are 1, 2 and 3. The cuboid is placed on a coordinate grid so that one of its vertices is at (4, 5, 6).

There are several possible ways of doing this. Find the coordinates of all the vertices of the cuboid for *one* of these ways.

6 Each edge of a cuboid is parallel to one of the coordinate axes. The opposite vertices of the cuboid are at (2, 3, −2) and (−4, 1, 2).

(a) Find the coordinates of one other vertex of the cuboid.

(b) Find the coordinates of the centre of the cuboid.

(c) What is the volume of the cuboid?

7

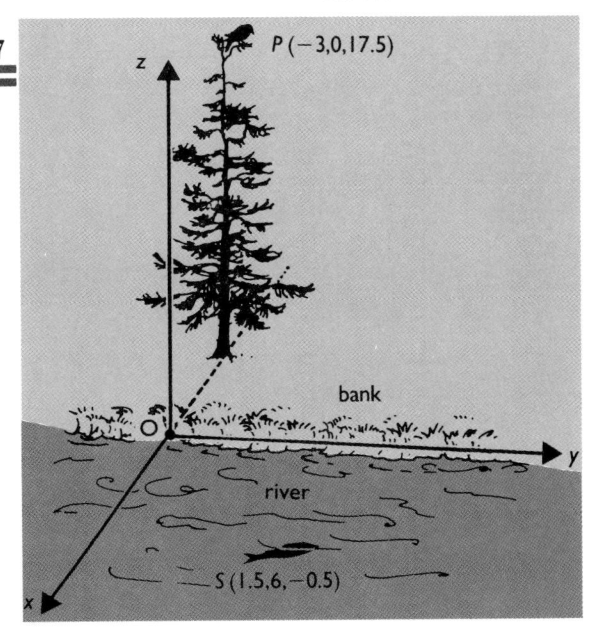

The units throughout this question are metres.

An osprey is in its nest at the point, P, (−3, 0, 17.5). The osprey sights a salmon, S, in the river at (1.5, 6, −0.5).

(a) Find the vector PS.

(b) Calculate the distance the osprey has to travel to catch the salmon. (Assume that the salmon does not move and that the osprey travels in a straight line.)

(c) State the height lost by the osprey in catching the salmon and hence calculate the angle that the osprey's path makes with the vertical.

(d) As the osprey crosses the line of the (y-axis) bank of the river it passes directly over a fisherman standing on the bank. State the coordinates of the point where the fisherman is standing.

(*MEG SMP* November 1988, Paper 4)

8 (a) Find the length of the vector $\begin{pmatrix} 2 \\ 2 \\ 1 \end{pmatrix}$.

The side of a cube is 3 units long. One vertex of the cube is at (3, 4, −5).

(b) Suppose that each edge of the cube is parallel to one of the coordinate axes. Find the eight possible positions for the opposite vertex of the cube.

(c) Now suppose that none of the edges of the cube is parallel to a coordinate axis.

Using your answer to (a), or otherwise, find one possible position for the opposite vertex of the cube.

9

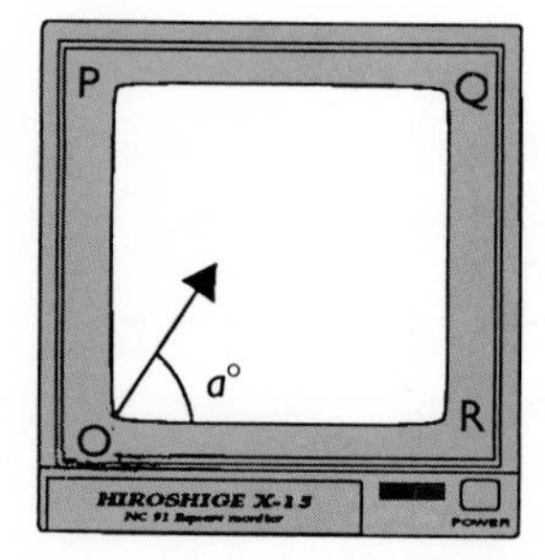

In a video game, the screen is 100 units by 100 units.

The player has to enter a vector to give the direction the 'ball' will travel.

The ball starts at O (0, 0).

John enters the vector $\begin{pmatrix} 1 \\ 2 \end{pmatrix}$ and the ball moves making an angle $a°$ with OR.

(a) What is the value of a?

(b) The position of the ball as it moves to the top of the screen PQ can be written as $k\begin{pmatrix} 1 \\ 2 \end{pmatrix}$.

What is the value of k when the ball reaches PQ?

(c) What are the coordinates of the point where the ball hits PQ?

(d) When the ball hits PQ it rebounds so that the 'new' path is 90° to the 'old' path.

Which vector describes the ball's direction after it rebounds from PQ?

(e) What are the coordinates of the point where the ball hits QR?

(*Welsh* May 1988, Paper 4)

10 A river has parallel sides 40 metres apart. A boat is taken in a straight line across the river to a point k metres downstream of its starting point.

The direction taken by the boat is given by the vector $\begin{pmatrix} 1 \\ 5 \end{pmatrix}$

(where the first number represents movement along the river and the second represents movement across the river at right angles to the bank).

(a) Find k.

(b) At what angle to the bank is the boat moving?

(c) Write down a vector representing the direction the boat would need to travel in order to return to its starting point.

In fact on its journey back across the river the boat travels in a direction given by $\begin{pmatrix} 1 \\ -4 \end{pmatrix}$

(d) How far away from its original starting point would the boat land?

(*Welsh* May 1989, Paper 4)

The example below illustrates the methods to use when answering some of the remaining questions in this exercise.

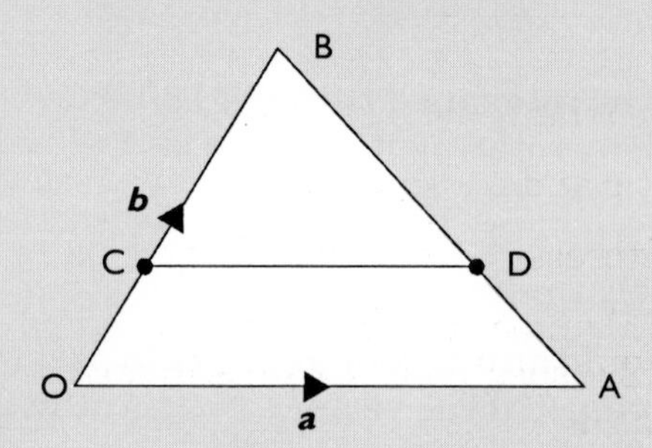

OAB is a triangle. The point C divides OB in the ratio of 1:2. The point D divides AB in the ratio 1:2. $\overrightarrow{OA} = \mathbf{a}$ and $\overrightarrow{OB} = \mathbf{b}$.

(a) Express in terms of **a** or **b** or both

(i) $\overrightarrow{OC}$,

(ii) $\overrightarrow{AB}$,

(iii) $\overrightarrow{AD}$,

(iv) $\overrightarrow{OD}$.

(b) Express $\overrightarrow{CD}$ in terms of **a** or **b** or both.

(c) Deduce from (b) two geometrical facts relating $\overrightarrow{CD}$ to $\overrightarrow{OA}$.

Solution

(a) (i) $\overrightarrow{OC}$ is in the same direction as $\overrightarrow{OB}$ and $\frac{1}{3}$ of its length.

So $\overrightarrow{OC} = \frac{1}{3}\mathbf{b}$

(ii) $\overrightarrow{AB} = \overrightarrow{AO} + \overrightarrow{OB} = -\mathbf{a} + \mathbf{b} = \mathbf{b} - \mathbf{a}$

(iii) $\overrightarrow{AD}$ is in the same direction as $\overrightarrow{AB}$ and $\frac{1}{3}$ of its length.

So $\overrightarrow{AD} = \frac{1}{3}(\mathbf{b} - \mathbf{a}) = \frac{1}{3}\mathbf{b} - \frac{1}{3}\mathbf{a}$

(iv) $\overrightarrow{OD} = \overrightarrow{OA} + \overrightarrow{AD} = \mathbf{a} + \frac{1}{3}\mathbf{b} - \frac{1}{3}\mathbf{a} = \frac{2}{3}\mathbf{a} + \frac{1}{3}\mathbf{b}$

(*b*) $\overrightarrow{CD} = \overrightarrow{CO} + \overrightarrow{OD} = -\frac{1}{3}\mathbf{b} + \frac{2}{3}\mathbf{a} + \frac{1}{3}\mathbf{b} = \frac{2}{3}\mathbf{a}$

(*c*) $\overrightarrow{OA} = \mathbf{a}$ and $\overrightarrow{CD} = \frac{2}{3}\mathbf{a}$. This means that $\overrightarrow{OA}$ and $\overrightarrow{CD}$ are in the same direction. In other words $\overrightarrow{CD}$ is parallel to $\overrightarrow{OA}$.

Also the length of $\overrightarrow{CD}$ is $\frac{2}{3}$ of the length of $\overrightarrow{OA}$.

11

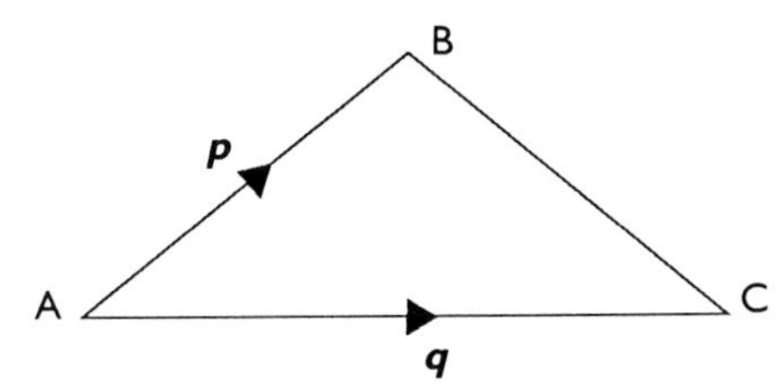

In the triangle shown, $\overrightarrow{AB} = \mathbf{p}$ and $\overrightarrow{AC} = \mathbf{q}$.

(*a*) Express $\overrightarrow{BC}$ in terms of $\mathbf{p}$ and $\mathbf{q}$.

(*b*) If M and N are the midpoints of AB and AC respectively, express in terms of $\mathbf{p}$ and $\mathbf{q}$

(i) $\overrightarrow{MB}$,

(ii) $\overrightarrow{MN}$.

(*c*) What two facts can you deduce about the line MN from the result obtained in (*b*) part (ii)?

(*NEA* November 1988, Syllabus B Paper 4)

12

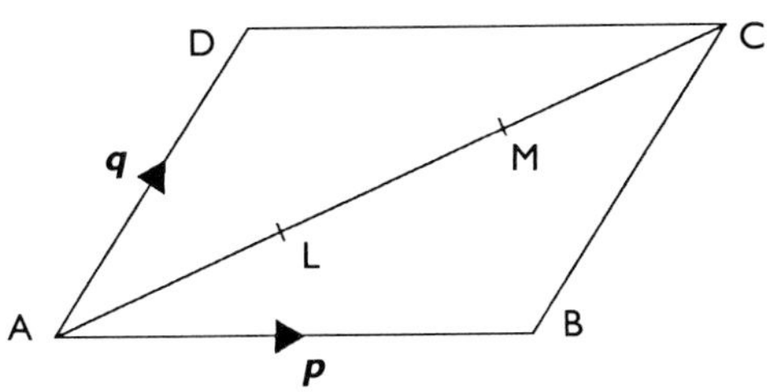

The diagram shows the parallelogram ABCD. Points L and M are taken on the diagonal AC so that AL = LM = MC.

(*a*) Given that $\overrightarrow{AB} = \mathbf{p}$ and $\overrightarrow{AD} = \mathbf{q}$, express each of the vectors $\overrightarrow{AC}$, $\overrightarrow{AL}$, $\overrightarrow{DL}$ and $\overrightarrow{MB}$ in terms of $\mathbf{p}$ and $\mathbf{q}$, simplifying your answers where possible.

(*b*) Hence prove that DLBM is a parallelogram.

(*NEA* November 1988, Syllabus C Paper 4)

13 The point O is the centre of the regular hexagon ABCDEF. $\overrightarrow{FA} = \mathbf{x}$ and $\overrightarrow{FE} = \mathbf{y}$.

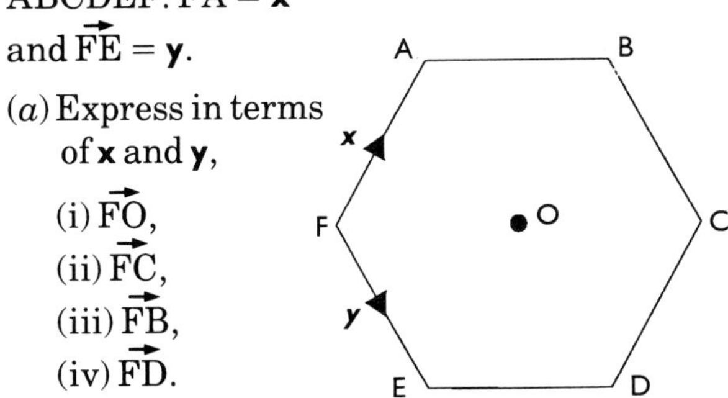

(*a*) Express in terms of $\mathbf{x}$ and $\mathbf{y}$,

(i) $\overrightarrow{FO}$,

(ii) $\overrightarrow{FC}$,

(iii) $\overrightarrow{FB}$,

(iv) $\overrightarrow{FD}$.

(*b*) If M is the midpoint of CD and N is the point which divides BE in the ratio 5:3, express in terms of $\mathbf{x}$ and $\mathbf{y}$,

(i) $\overrightarrow{FM}$, (ii) $\overrightarrow{FN}$.

(*c*) What conclusions can you draw about the points M and N?

(*MEG* November 1988, Paper 6)

14 OABC is a parallelogram. M and N are the midpoints of the sides OC and CB respectively. $\overrightarrow{OA} = \mathbf{a}$ and $\overrightarrow{OC} = \mathbf{c}$.

(*a*) Write down $\overrightarrow{ON}$ and $\overrightarrow{AM}$ in terms of $\mathbf{a}$ and $\mathbf{c}$.

(*b*) AM meets ON at P. Denoting $\overrightarrow{OP}$ by $\lambda\,\overrightarrow{ON}$ and $\overrightarrow{AP}$ by $\mu\,\overrightarrow{AM}$, use the fact that $\overrightarrow{OA} + \overrightarrow{AP} = \overrightarrow{OP}$ to find the values of λ and μ.

(*c*) Hence express the area of triangle OAP as a fraction of the area of the parallelogram OABC.

(*NEA* May 1989, Syllabus B Paper 4)

EXERCISE 52 Algebraic fractions and dimensional analysis

1 The positive numbers R, R_1 and R_2 are such that

$$\frac{1}{R} = \frac{1}{R_1} + \frac{1}{R_2}$$

(*a*) Calculate R when $R_1 = 125$ and $R_2 = 200$.

(b) It is required that $R = 100$. If $R_1 = 250$, calculate the value of R_2, giving your answer to 2 significant figures.

(*NEA* November 1988, Syllabus A Paper 4)

2 Maria is investigating number patterns on a calculator. She discovers that 2 divided by a number is the same as the number minus 1. What are the two possible numbers she could have found?

(*SEG* 1991 Specimen, Paper 4)

3 Solve the equation

$$\frac{2x-1}{3} - \frac{x-2}{5} = \frac{x}{2}$$

4 (a) Factorise $4x^2 + 17x + 4$.

(b) Hence, or otherwise, solve the equation

$$\frac{4}{y^2} + \frac{17}{y} + 4 = 0.$$

5 (a) A man runs 50 metres in 12 seconds. What is his average speed in m/s?

(b) A woman runs 50 metres in $\frac{25}{x}$ seconds.

What is her average speed in m/s in terms of x?

(*SEG* Winter 1988, Mathematics B Paper 4)

6 Solve

$$\frac{3}{x-5} = 2.$$

7 (a) Factorise

(i) $2x - 8$,
(ii) $x^2 - 3x - 4$.

(b) Find the exact value of $\frac{x^2 - 3x - 4}{2x - 8}$ when $x = -5.32$.

(c) Sketch the graph of $y = x^2 - 3x - 4$, clearly stating the coordinates of the points at which it cuts the axes.

(*MEG* November 1988, Paper 3)

8 The area of a rectangle is 24 square metres. The length of the rectangle is x metres.

(a) Show that the perimeter of the rectangle is given by the formula

$$\frac{48}{x} + 2x.$$

(b) If the perimeter is 35 metres write down an equation satisfied by x. Hence, or otherwise, find the two possible values of x.

9

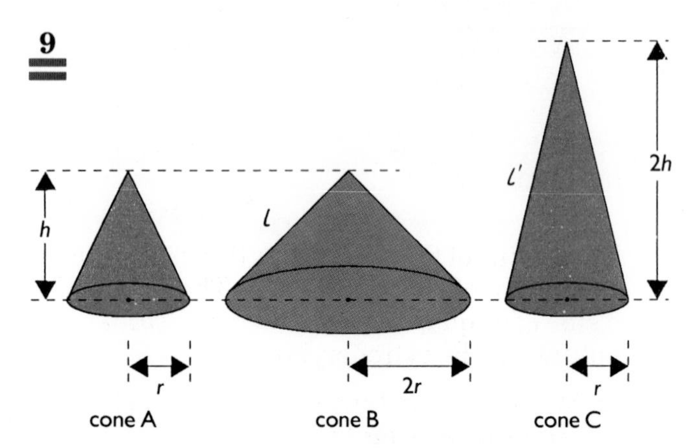

Three cones are constructed with the dimensions as shown above.

(a) Express each of the following in its simplest form.

(i) $\frac{\text{Volume of cone A}}{\text{Volume of cone B}}$

(ii) $\frac{\text{Volume of cone A}}{\text{Volume of cone C}}$

(b) If $h = \sqrt{2}r$, and l and l' are the slant heights of cone B and cone C respectively, calculate the value of $\frac{l}{l'}$.

(*NEA* November 1988, Syllabus B Paper 4)

10

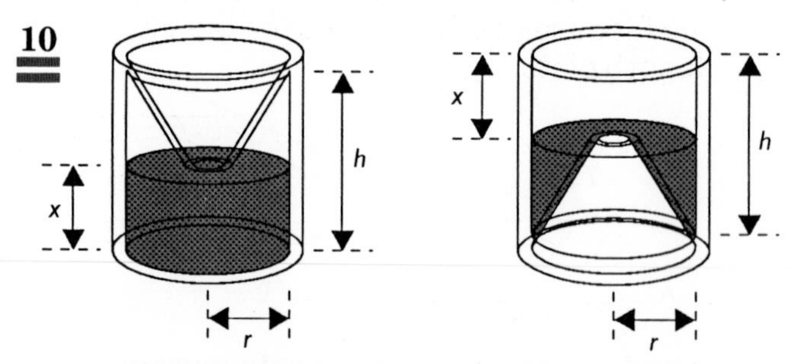

An old-fashioned ink pot, as shown in the diagram, was constructed so that, if it was filled to the bottom of the inverted cone, it was impossible to spill any ink even if the pot was turned upside down.

If h is the height of the pot, r is the radius of the cylinder and x is the height of the vertex of the cone from the base, calculate the value of x as a fraction of h.

(Assume conical part is a perfect cone.)

(*NEA* May 1989, Syllabus B Paper 4)

11 

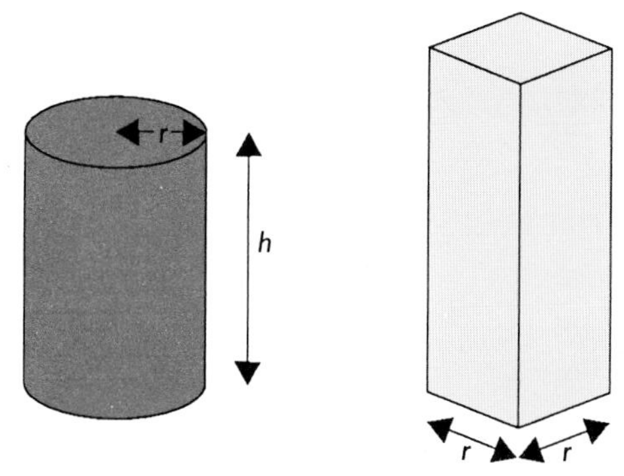

The radius of the base of a cylinder is r and the height of the cylinder is h. The length of a side of a square-based prism, the same volume as the cylinder, is r.

(*a*) Write down in terms of r and h, and then simplify, a formula for

$$\frac{\text{Volume of cylinder}}{\text{Area of base of square-based prism}}.$$

(*b*) Explain how you know that your answer to (*a*) is a formula for a length (rather than an area or a volume).

(*c*) Which edges of one of the models does your formula give the length of?

12  A solid is formed by putting together different common solid shapes. The variables x and z are used to represent different *lengths* on the solid.

Among the formulae below is a formula for the volume of the solid, a formula for its surface area and a formula for the total length of its edges.

$24x + z^2$ $\quad \frac{4x^2z}{3} + 8x^3$ $\quad 4\sqrt{2x^2+z^2} + 24x^2$

$4\sqrt{2x^2+z^2} + 24x^2$ $\quad 24x^2 + 4x\sqrt{2x^2+z^2}$

$\frac{4x^2z}{3} + 8\sqrt{x^3+z^3}$

(*a*) Which formula gives the volume of the solid?

(*b*) Which formula gives the surface area of the solid?

(*c*) Which formula gives the edge length of the solid?

INFORMATION

Units

Abbreviations

m metre
km kilometre
mm millimetre
cm centimetre

in inch
ft foot
yd yard

l litre
cl centilitre
ml millilitre

fl oz fluid ounce

g gram
kg kilogram

oz ounce
lb pound

kj kilojoule
kcal kilocalorie
(also called calorie)

Equivalents of Units

1000 m = 1 km
1000 mm = 1 m
100 cm = 1 m
10 mm = 1 cm

12 in = 1 ft
3 ft = 1 yd

1 l = 1000 cm^3

20 fl oz = 1 pint
8 pints = 1 gallon

1 cubic centimetre
= 1 millilitre

16 oz = 1 lb

1000 g = 1 kg
1000 kg = 1 tonne

1 cubic centimetre
of water weighs
1 gram

Rough metric equivalents

1 m is approximately 1.09 yd
1 in is approximately 2.54 cm

1 kg is approximately 2.2 lb

1 l is approximately 1.75 pints
1 gallon is approximately 5 l

Triangles, quadrilaterals and circles

(*a*)

Angle sum of
triangle
$a + b + c = 180°$

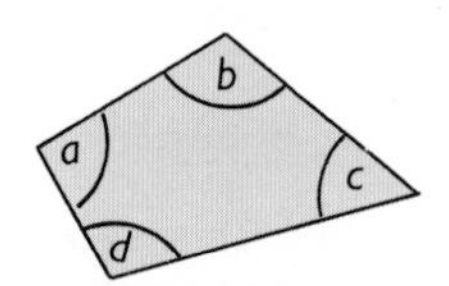

Angle sum of
quadrilateral
$a + b + c + d = 360°$

(*b*)

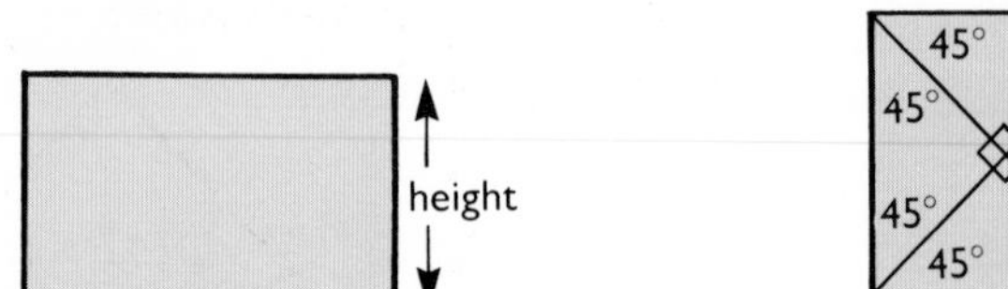

Rectangle:
four right angles;
diagonals are of equal length

Area of rectangle
= base × height

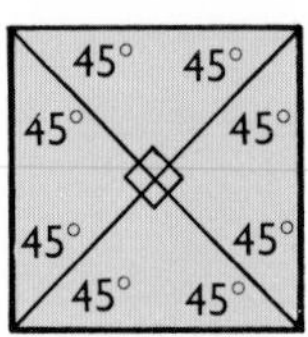

Square:
four right angles;
all sides of equal length;
diagonals of equal length
and meet at right angles;
diagonals bisect angles at
corners (bisect means cut in half)

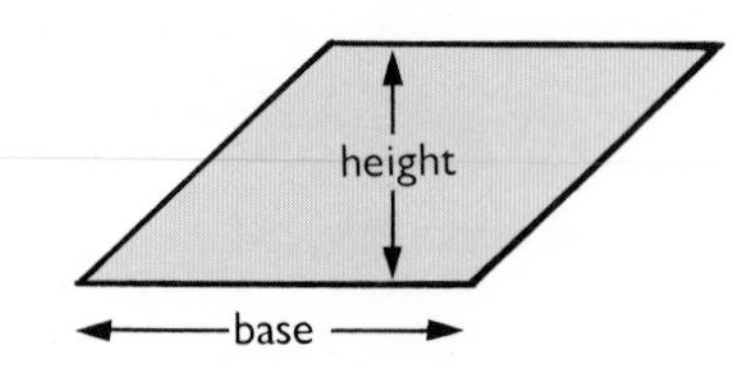

Parallelogram:
opposite sides parallel
and of equal length

Area of parallelogram
= base × height

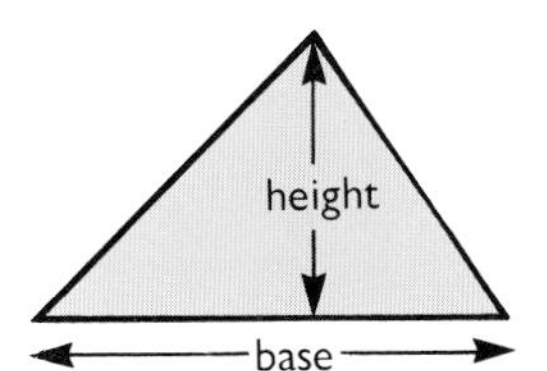

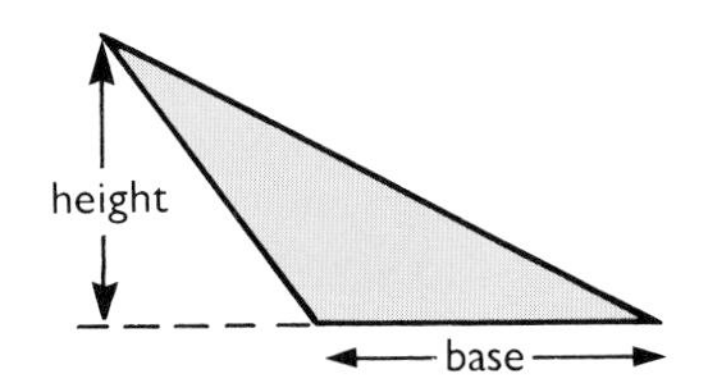

Triangle: Area of triangle = $\frac{\text{base} \times \text{height}}{2}$

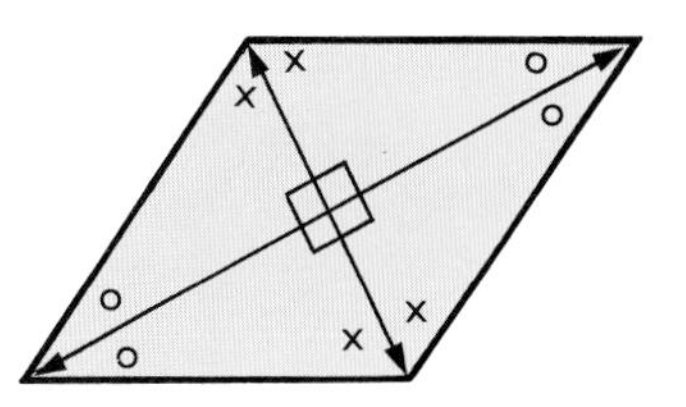

Rhombus:
all sides of equal length;
diagonals meet at right-angles;
diagonals bisect angles at corners

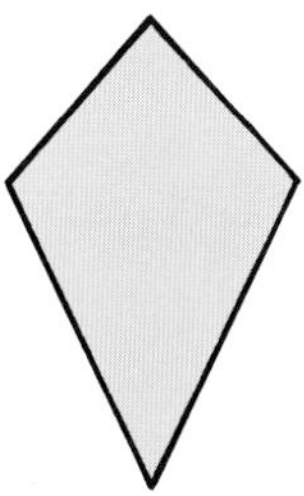

Kite:
two pairs of sides of equal length

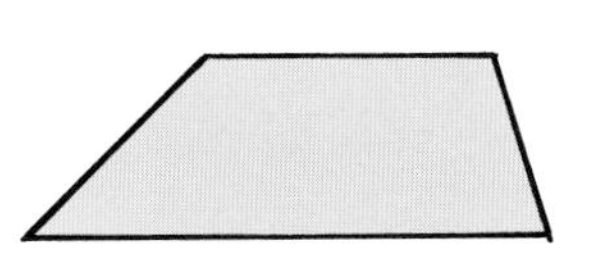

Trapezium:
one pair of sides parallel

Area of trapezium = height × average of parallel sides

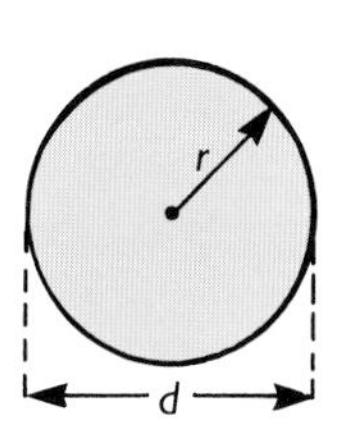

Circle

Circumference of circle = π × diameter = πd

Area of circle = π × radius × radius = πr^2

(*c*)

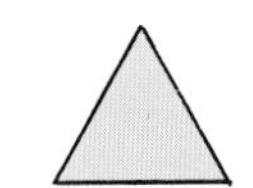

Equilateral triangle:
three sides of equal length;
three angles equal

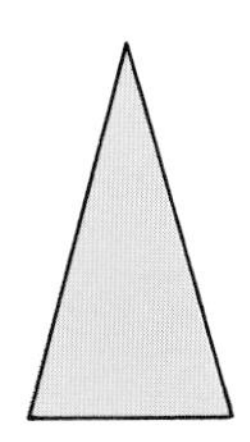

Isosceles triangle:
two sides of equal length;
two angles equal

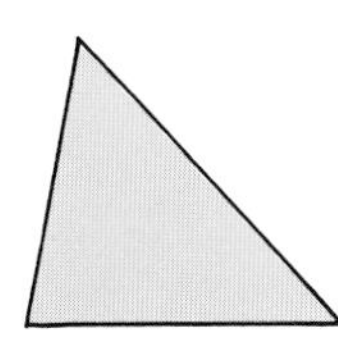

Scalene triangle:
three sides of different lengths

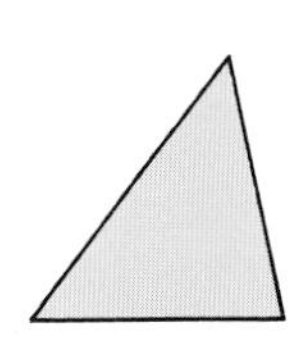

Acute-angled triangle:
all angles acute

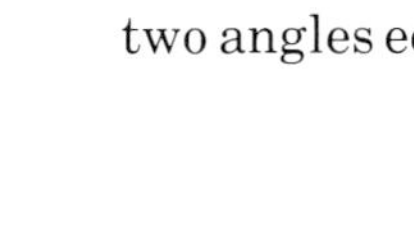

Right-angled triangle:
one angle a right angle

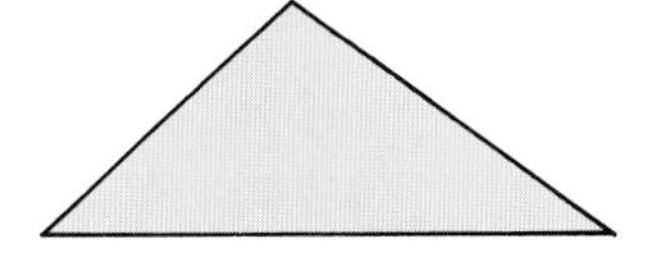

Obtuse-angled triangle:
one angle obtuse

(*d*) **Pythagoras' theorem**

Version 1

Area of R = area of X + area of Y

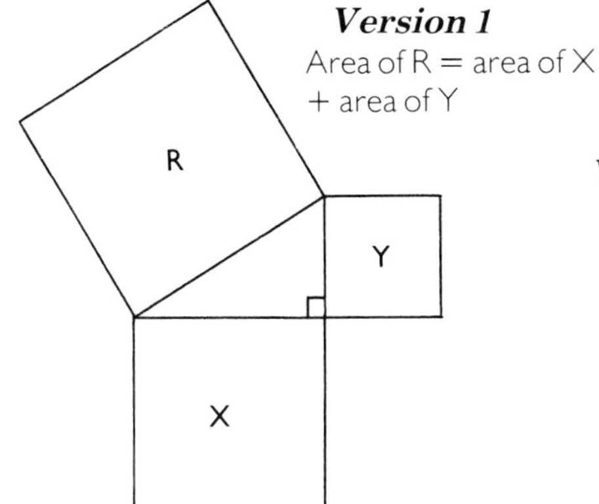

Version 2

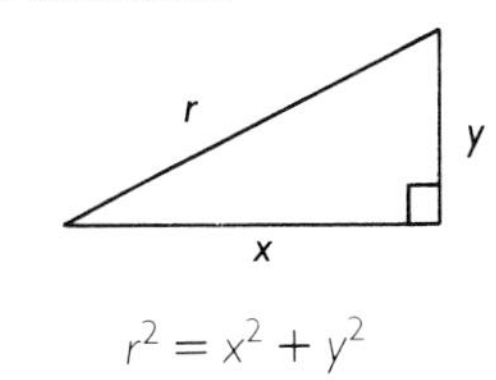

$r^2 = x^2 + y^2$

Version 3

This version is useful when calculating areas of squares on dotty paper.

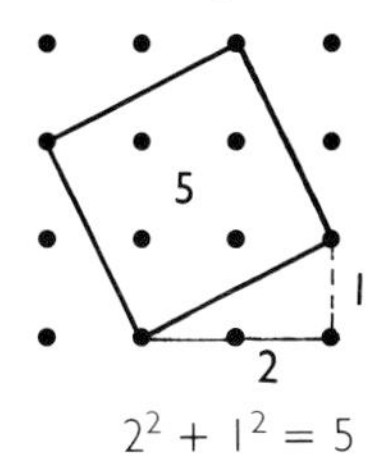

$2^2 + 1^2 = 5$

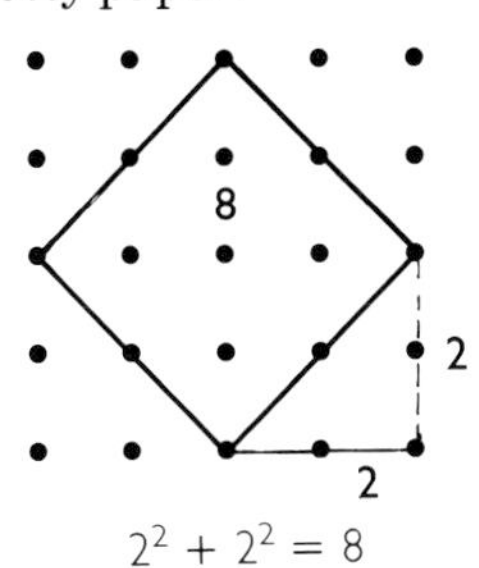

$2^2 + 2^2 = 8$

To find the area of an $\binom{a}{b}$ square you square a and square b and add the answers.

(*e*) **Trigonometry**

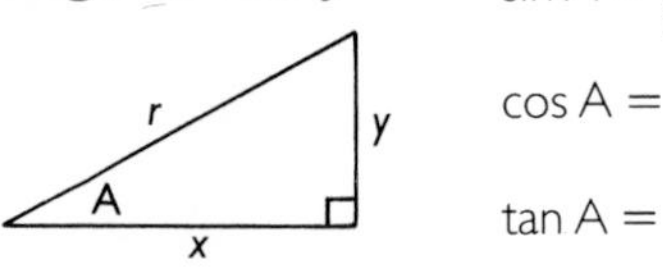

$\sin A = \frac{y}{r}$

$\cos A = \frac{x}{r}$

$\tan A = \frac{y}{x}$

$x = r \cos A$ (Note that x is *next to* A)
$y = r \sin A$ (Note that y is *opposite* A)
$y = x \tan A$ (Note that y is *opposite* A)

The following formulae are for triangles which are not right-angled.

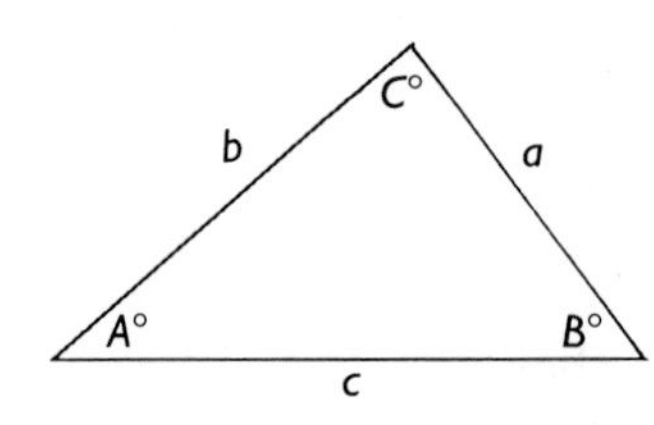

Cosine rule: $c^2 = a^2 + b^2 - 2ab \cos C$

Sine rule: $\frac{a}{\sin A} = \frac{b}{\sin B} = \frac{c}{\sin C}$

Area rule: Area of triangle is $= \frac{1}{2} ab \sin C$

Three-dimensional shapes

Cuboid;
all faces rectangles

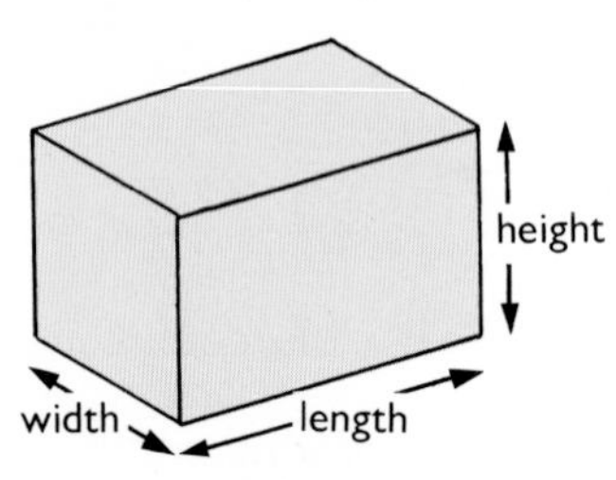

Volume of cuboid =
length × width × height

Prism:
constant cross-section

Volume of prism =
cross section × length

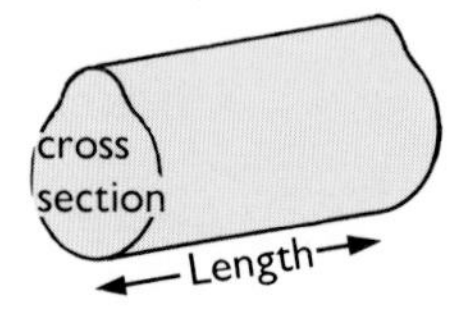

Examples:

Volume of *triangular prism* =
area of triangle × length

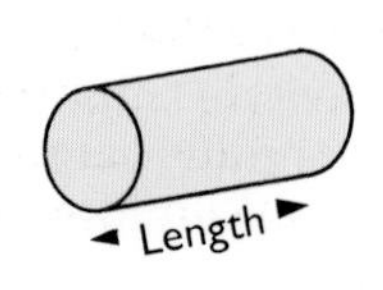

Volume of *cylinder* = area of circular end × length

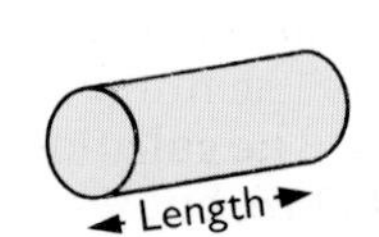

Area of curved surface of cylinder = circumference of circular end × length

Pyramid

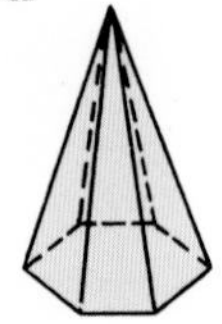

Volume of pyramid =
$\frac{1}{3}$ × area of base × height

Examples:

Volume of *tetrahedron* =

$\frac{1}{3}$ × area of triangular base × height

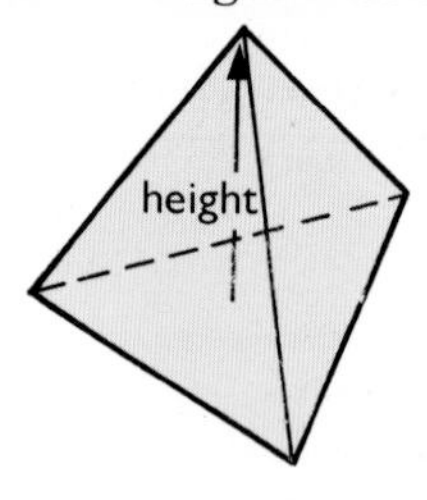

Volume of *cone*
$= \frac{1}{3}$ × area of circular base × height

Area of curved surface of cone $= \pi r l$ where $l^2 = r^2 + h^2$

Sphere

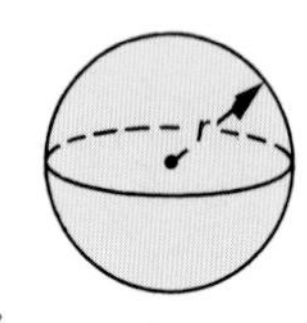

Volume of sphere $= \frac{4}{3} \pi r^3$

Surface area of sphere $= 4 \pi r^2$

Approximating

After doing a calculation involving measurements you should not normally give the answer more accurately than the *least* accurate measurement that was given.

For example, if you are finding the volume of a box with edges of length 2.4 m, 3.15 m and 4.3 m you multiply the numbers together on a calculator. The answer the calculator gives is 32.508. But two of the measurements given have *only 2 figures* in the number. So the answer you give should have *only* 2 *figures* in the number. So the answer you give is 33 m. (The 32 was rounded up to 33 because the next figure was 5 or more).

If the number is a large number you should not count the zeros at the end when working out the length of the number. The number 3400 has only 2 figures that count, not 4. The calculator gives the answer to 3400 × 3.27 as 11118, but a sensible approximation is 11000 (leave only 2 non-zero figures).

If the number is very small do not count the number of zeros at the beginning when working out how many figures are in the number. The number 0.00453 has 3 figures that count.

If the last figure is zero and is after the decimal point then you have to count it as one of the figures. 6.30 has 3 figures. The zero has been put on the end to show that the measurement is accurate to the nearest hundredth.

When giving sensible approximations you should also use your common sense. If you are working out how much someone should pay *don't* give the answer as £3.4527. Give it as £3.45. If you are giving the length of a rectangular field don't give it as 112.4 m. It would not have been measured that accurately and, in any case, fields are *not* exact rectangles. This length should probably be given as 110 m.

Sometimes you have to use your common sense and give an answer more accurately than the rule above implies. For example, if the question talks about a ladder 4 m long you should perhaps assume that it is 4.0 m long and give two figures in your answer.

If you are told that the area of a square is 5 cm^2 and are asked to find its length, you do this by finding the square root of 5. You might think it more appropriate to give your answer as 2.24 cm rather than as 2 cm. What you should not do is give your answer as 2.236067977 cm.

Thomas Nelson and Sons Ltd
Nelson House Mayfield Road
Walton-on-Thames Surrey
KT12 5PL UK

51 York Place
Edinburgh
EH1 3JD UK

Thomas Nelson (Hong Kong) Ltd
Toppan Building 10/F
22A Westlands Road
Quarry Bay Hong Kong

Thomas Nelson Australia
480 La Trobe Street
Melbourne Victoria 3000
Australia

Nelson Canada
1120 Birchmount Road
Scarborough Ontario
M1K 5G4 Canada

First published by Thomas Nelson and Sons Ltd 1991

ISBN 0-17-431145-1
NPN 9 8 7 6 5 4 3 2 1

Printed in Hong Kong.

ACKNOWLEDGEMENTS

The authors are grateful to the following authorities for permission to use questions from some of their examination papers in the Review Exercises.

London and East Anglian Group, Syllabus A	LEAG
Midland Examining Group	MEG
Nuffield*	MEG(Nuffield)
Northern Examining Association, Syllabus A	NEA[A]
Syllabus B*	NEA[B]
Joint GCE & CSE syllabus	Joint 16+
Associated Lancashire Schools Examining Board	
Joint Matriculation Board	
North Regional Examinations Board	
North West Regional Examinations Board	
Yorkshire and Humberside Regional Examinations Board	
Southern Examining Board	SEG
Alternative syllabus*	SEG[ALT]

The questions dated 1986 or 1987 are from Joint O Level/CSE examination papers; other questions are from GCSE examination papers.

The authors are grateful to all those who helped by trialling the material in this book. They value, in particular, the frequent and most helpful advice they received from Wendy Fisher, Linda Lord, Chris Miles, Sue Pope and Dave Short.

Thanks are due to the following for permission to reproduce photographs: Lydon Baker p. 1, 90, 223, 232, 229; British Rail p. 178; Black and Decker p. 255; J Allan Cash p. 56/57 X3; J Clark p. 247, 200, 179, 172; Neil Croft p. 163; Sally and Richard Greenhill p. 55; Holt Studios p. 233, 208; Paul Martin p. 231; Picture Bank p. 60; Chris Ridgers p. 5, 7 X 2, 12, 13 X 2, 55, 62 X2, 79, 162, 167 X4, 174, 178 X3, 179 X2, 237, 243, 197, 199, 200/201; Gareth Roberts p. 145; Susan Tebby p. 48; Tropix Photo Library p. 161 X2, 176, 160; Gary Woodley p. 193; Zephyr Picture Library p. 215.
The Publishers would like to thank The British Medical Association for permission to reproduce the two graphs on p. 208.